Soil Biology

Soil Biology

Edited by

A. BURGES

The New University of Ulster
Coleraine, Northern Ireland

and

F. RAW

Rothamsted Experimental Station
Harpenden, Hertfordshire, England

ACADEMIC PRESS · 1967

LONDON AND NEW YORK

ACADEMIC PRESS INC. (LONDON) LTD.
BERKELEY SQUARE HOUSE
BERKELEY SQUARE
LONDON, W.1

U.S. Edition published by
ACADEMIC PRESS INC.
111 FIFTH AVENUE
NEW YORK, NEW YORK 10003

Library of Congress Catalog Card Number: 66–30322

MADE AND PRINTED IN GREAT BRITAIN BY
WILLIAM CLOWES AND SONS, LIMITED, LONDON AND BECCLES

List of Contributors

*BURGES, A., *Hartley Botanical Laboratories, University of Liverpool, England* (pp. 1 and 479).

CLARK, F. E., *U.S. Department of Agriculture, Fort Collins, Colorado, U.S.A.* (p. 15).

HALE, W. G., *City of Liverpool College of Technology, Byron Street, Liverpool, England* (p. 397).

HEAL, O. W., *Natural Environment Research Council, The Nature Conservancy, Merlewood Research Station, Grange-over-Sands, Lancashire, England* (p. 149).

KÜSTER, E., *University College, Dublin, Ireland* (p. 111).

LUND, J. W. G., *Freshwater Biological Association, Ambleside, Westmorland, England* (p. 129).

NEWELL, P. F., *Westfield College, University of London, England* (p. 413).

NIELSEN, C. OVERGAARD, *Department of Zoology, Copenhagen University, Denmark* (p. 197).

O'CONNOR, F. B., *Department of Zoology, University College, London, England* (p. 213).

PARK, D., *Department of Botany, Queen's University, Belfast, Ireland* (p. 435).

PARKINSON, D., *Department of Biology, University of Waterloo, Waterloo, Ontario, Canada* (p. 449).

RAW, F., *Rothamsted Experimental Station, Harpenden, Hertfordshire, England* (p. 323).

SATCHELL, J. E., *Merlewood Research Station, Grange-over-Sands, Lancashire, England* (p. 259).

STOUT, J. D., *Soil Bureau, Department of Scientific and Industrial Research, Wellington, New Zealand* (p. 149).

WALKER, N., *Rothamsted Experimental Station, Harpenden, Hertfordshire, England* (p. 493).

WALLWORK, J. A., *Westfield College, University of London, England* (p. 363).

WARCUP, J. H., *Waite Agricultural Research Institute, Adelaide, South Australia* (p. 51).

*Present address : The New University of Ulster, Coleraine, Northern Ireland.

Foreword

One of the stimulating developments in soil biology in recent years has been the general recognition that the soil cannot be studied solely from a chemical, microbiological, botanical or zoological stand-point. The ever-changing pattern of processes going on in the soil is made up of elements from many disciplines, inextricably interwoven, which must be synthesized, not studied in isolation. Unless this is constantly borne in mind, the scientific understanding of the soil will cease to advance and will stagnate, just as many of the complex biological processes in the soil are inhibited if one essential component is missing.

The aim of this book is to bring together the microbiological, botanical and zoological aspects of soil biology in a way that provides information and ideas for the specialist in his own and related fields. To achieve this, leading specialists were invited to contribute critical reviews and assessments of their particular branches of soil biology, paying particular attention to functional aspects and biotic inter-relationships whenever possible. Because soil biology covers such wide and diverse fields of study it is not surprising that there are wide differences in the amount of space devoted to the different topics and organisms dealt with in this book. We believe that this reflects the present state of research interests, for there are many research workers in some fields and few in others, and topics studied in detail in some taxonomic groups have been neglected in others. If this very unevenness induces soil biologists to develop research in hitherto neglected fields, it will be an excellent thing.

The idea of producing this book originated with Mr J. B. Cragg, of the Nature Conservancy, Merlewood Research Station, Lancs., who began much of the early planning. When he found it necessary to cease taking part in active editorial work he first enlisted one of us (A. B.) to be responsible for the botanical and microbiological chapters and then asked the other (F. R.) to be responsible for the zoological chapters. We have pleasure in recording our indebtedness to Mr Cragg for his part in initiating the book, to the authors of the various chapters, and to the publishers for their efficiency and forbearance.

ALAN BURGES

November, 1966   FRANK RAW

Contents

9. LUMBRICIDAE

J. E. Satchell

10. ARTHROPODA (except ACARI and COLLEMBOLA)

F. Raw

11. ACARI

J. A. Wallwork

12. COLLEMBOLA

W. G. Hale

1*

The Soil System

ALAN BURGES

*Hartley Botanical Laboratories**
University of Liverpool, England

I. INTRODUCTION

Scientific studies of the soil have developed in very many ways over the last 100 years. In England much of the early work was associated with agricultural studies, and particularly with chemical problems. Questions of fertility were often considered to be solely a matter of how much potassium, nitrogen or phosphate was present in the soil. Quite early on in such studies it became clear that it was not sufficient just to know the result of chemical analyses of the soil, and thus to find out how much of a particular element might be there, but, also, that one had to estimate in some way or another how much of it was actually available for absorption by the plants. This led to an extension of the chemical analyses and to the introduction of biological testing to determine the availability levels of the essential nutrients.

Somewhat later, when people became interested in questions of soil structure, and particularly soil moisture, the physicists were brought into the picture. With the discovery that legume nodules were associated with nitrogen fixation, interest turned to some of the microbiological problems in the soil, and workers such as Winogradsky and Beijerinck studied many of the other processes associated with microbial growth in the soil. The transformations undergone by sulphur and by iron attracted particular interest. Such studies as these suggested that the micro-organisms might be playing a major part in the general turnover of key nutrients in the soil and that, therefore, soil microbiology was an essential background study for anyone interested in general problems of plant growth. Once biologists began to look at the soil carefully, it became clear that there were not only very large numbers of bacteria but fungi and actinomycetes were also numerous. Similarly, on the zoological side, it became apparent that animal activity was not confined to

* Present address: The New University of Ulster, Coleraine, Northern Ireland.

earthworms alone but that there were large populations of other soil animals, and the zoologists soon began to investigate both the species present and the part they played in soil processes. Unfortunately, for many years, soil chemistry, physics, microbiology and zoology tended to go their own way, and there were few attempts to bring together information from all these different disciplines. One of the great contributions of the late Sir John Russell during his tenure at Rothamsted was that he recognized clearly that the soil could not be studied solely as a chemical or as a biological entity, but that one had to obtain information from all the different branches of science to obtain a complete picture of the many interlocking processes going on in the soil.

If one is going to study the growth of organisms in the soil, one must have at least a general appreciation of both the structure and the properties of the soil which forms the framework within which the organisms live. All soils come either directly, or indirectly, from rocks which have weathered, and which during their weathering have undergone many changes. An examination of any rock shows that it is composed of a number of different minerals in very different proportions. In an igneous rock most of these minerals will be present in a crystalline form. When the rock is exposed to the weather a number of processes can take place; perhaps the simplest is the action of rain dissolving out water-soluble components. Where these represent a considerable portion of the rock, this may in itself be sufficient to cause the rock to fragment. Usually, however, there is very little readily water-soluble material in the parent rock and other processes cause the weathering. Physical forces can play an important part in the breaking up of many rocks, particularly where there are rapid changes in temperature, and the differential expansion and contraction of the outer layers of the rock leads to cracks developing and to fragmentation. Once cracks have developed, water can penetrate, and if temperatures drop below freezing, then the expansion of the water as it freezes can accelerate the cracking. Wind-blown particles can act as an abrasive and in this way assist in disintegration. Physical forces seem to be most active either at high altitudes or high latitudes where freezing temperatures are commonly experienced, or under desert regions where big variations in temperature are experienced between the day and night time. It was earlier thought that physical forces were by far the more important in the disintegration of rocks. More recently the emphasis has swung towards the chemical processes which take place during weathering. These changes lead to a disruption of the rock in two ways. Many of the chemical processes are associated with a change in volume, for instance, the oxidation or the hydration of a component leads to localized increase in volume, and this will have a physical disruptive effect on the rock. In other cases the hydration or oxidation may lead to one of the chemical components becoming soluble, and thus it is removed by the action of rain. Under tropical conditions many of these processes can proceed very rapidly, giving rise to soft rotten rocks so widespread in the moist tropics.

As weathering proceeds the rock is broken down to smaller and smaller particles until eventually a layer of soil is formed. An examination of soil shows that it is made up of particles which differ considerably in size. By convention these are divided as follows: fragments above 2 mm in diameter are regarded as gravel, those between 2 and 0·2 mm as coarse sand, from 0·2 to 0·02 mm as fine sand and from 0·02 down to 0·002 mm as silt. Particles smaller than 0·002 mm are classed as clay. With the use of appropriately-sized sieves the gravel, coarse and fine sand fractions can readily be separated from a dried soil. To separate the silt and clay fraction it is usual to suspend this material in water and to use the faster settling of the silt particles to separate the silt from the clay. Here again a somewhat arbitrary system based on empirical tests is used. By a combination of sieving and sedimentation, one can make a mechanical analysis of any given soil and express the proportion of the silt, clay or sand fractions either as a proportion by weight or, less commonly, by volume (Piper, 1944).

An examination of pieces of gravel shows that these are normally small remnants of the relatively unchanged parent rock; the sand fractions, on the other hand, usually represent grains of single mineral species. By far the commonest are grains of quartz which make up a large proportion of most rocks, and because of their relative resistance to further weathering tend to accumulate and form an even greater proportion of most well-weathered soils. The clay particles are less than 0·002 mm in diameter and are approaching the limit of resolution of the normal light microscope. It is therefore usually impossible to determine any structure in the clay particles under the light microscope. Chemical analyses show that clay differs very markedly from any of the parent minerals in the original rock. Many of the common rock minerals are essentially calcium, magnesium or potassium silicates, and these can be broken down to release the metal ions leaving primarily the silicate fraction behind, and this is converted into the secondary minerals, the clay minerals. Although clays are by far the most abundant of secondary minerals in the soil, there are a number of other secondary minerals which are formed during the weathering of the parent rock or during the subsequent changes which can take place during the formation of a soil profile. In particular, compounds of iron are frequently transported in the soil profile and can reappear lower down in the form of secondary minerals such as haematite. Even after a soil has been formed the weathering processes continue to bring some substances into solution and to form secondary minerals.

Normally as soon as weathering of the rocks begins, plants and animals of various kinds become associated with the weathering processes, and once any quantity of soil has been produced, plant cover of increasing complexity begins to appear. With the growth and subsequent death of living organisms, fresh organic matter is added to the soil and the various processes of decay begin, thus introducing a new system into the developing soil. The amount and the nature of the organic matter will of course be very largely determined by the organisms associated with the soil at this stage. As the fragments of the rock get smaller and smaller during the weathering, the interstices between the individual fragments also get smaller, so that water which may run away readily from the initial coarsely broken fragments begins to be held in the crevices between the smaller particles. Once the particles are of the size that we would normally regard as soil particles, appreciable amounts of water begin to be held in the small pore spaces. With the formation of the clay fraction, the water begins to be held not merely by capillarity, but by hydration forces associated with the colloids. The water held in the soil will, of course, contain various dissolved substances derived from the decomposing rocks and gases such as carbon dioxide and oxygen. The amounts will vary greatly, depending on the nature of the soil and the amount of rain which has fallen shortly before the examination is made. Except immediately following heavy rain, most soils do not have the whole of their pore spaces filled with moisture, the larger ones drain fairly readily and the space left behind is filled with gases. In a well-drained porous soil these approach fairly closely to air in their general composition.

II. COMPONENTS OF THE SOIL SYSTEM

From the foregoing discussion, it can be seen that one can separate the soil system into four major components: (A) the mineral fraction, (B) the organic matter, (C) the soil moisture, and (D) the soil atmosphere. While this is not the place to give a detailed account of each of these fractions, it is important that certain of their properties which have a direct bearing on the organisms growing in the soil should be examined.

A. THE MINERAL FRACTION

Mention has already been made of the conventional division of the mineral soil into gravel, coarse and fine sand, silt and clay fractions. The texture of the soil is clearly determined primarily by the relative proportions of the above fractions. In practice, the texture of the soil can be judged surprisingly accurately by rubbing some of the moist soil between the fingers and also observing whether there is sufficient clay to enable the soil to be moulded into a pellet. The extent to which the pellet can be deformed without it crumbling or breaking is also a useful guide.

The mineralogical nature of the soil particles is of extreme importance, particularly in relation to the fertility of the soil. In a strongly weathered and leached soil, quartz grains may form 90 to 95% of the sand fraction, whereas in a young soil derived from a base-rich rock the quartz may form only about 60%, and minerals such as plagioclase, augite and olivine make up most of the remainder (Leeper, 1964). It is the weathering of this fraction which provides a steady supply of some of the elements essential for plant growth.

Of the secondary minerals formed during the weathering processes the clay minerals are by far the most important. Many of the physical properties of the soil and much of its base exchange capacity is determined by the amount and the nature of the clay minerals present. The identification of clay minerals is a task for the expert. Occasionally, a soil may have its clay fraction composed mainly of a single clay mineral, but usually several minerals occur together. Often a rough idea of the type of minerals present can be obtained from the degree of swelling and shrinking a soil undergoes during wetting and drying and by estimating the base exchange capacity, but for accurate identification, X-ray crystallographic methods coupled with thermal conductivity measurements and electron microscopy are necessary.

The cation exchange capacity of a soil is primarily associated with negative charges on the surfaces of the clay particles, although the amorphous organic matter is also concerned. It might appear to be relatively simple to displace all the cations and then to saturate the exchange points with a simple base and thus measure the total exchange capacity. Similarly, by displacing the naturally occurring cations by adding excess ammonium acetate, one could obtain an estimate both of the cations present and the proportion of the sites occupied by bases and by hydrogen ions. Such measurements, however, give only a rough guide and the extent to which they represent arbitrary measurements is often not realized.

B. THE ORGANIC MATTER

The organic matter in the soil is exceedingly complex (Kononova, 1961). Almost all natural organic substances, sooner or later, fall into the soil. Their stay there may only be brief if they are readily decomposed by microorganisms, but if they are resistant, they may remain for many years. What a chemical analysis of soil reveals depends almost entirely on the degree of sensitivity of the analytical technique. Any plant or animal contains a very large number of chemical substances and these in turn become incorporated in the soil when the organism dies. Therefore, if the analyses are sufficiently sensitive, one should be able to detect practically all the materials recorded in living organisms. In practice, many of the substances decompose so rapidly that they have only a transient life and therefore exist in very small quantities within the soil. The major fractions of both plant and animal material, however, can remain for quite a while and thus form appreciable fractions of the total soil organic matter. Much of the organic matter which becomes incorporated into the soil falls either as plant or animal debris on the surface; it may decay there and the final products wash down in the soil, or it may be incorporated fairly early by the action of earthworms or other animals, and much of the decay occurs when the organic matter is well incorporated in the mineral soil. By convention we tend to regard plant material which still contains obvious structure as being distinct from the amorphous organic matter in the soil which is termed humus. This word, unfortunately, has been very much abused and it is impossible to define it with any precision. The term "amorphous" is also difficult to define when dealing with soil organic matter. For example, in typical mor soils, while the upper part of the organic debris clearly consists of leaves or twigs, there appears to be an amorphous black layer at the junction of the organic material and the mineral soil. Examination under a microscope, however, shows that this is far from being truly amorphous, and consists largely of faecal pellets of small animals containing very readily recognizable pieces of plant material.

The composition of the plant fragments changes continually. During the early stages of decay the water soluble materials, the starches and the proteins soon disappear. The decomposition of hemicelluloses and celluloses follows, leaving residues consisting largely of lignin and cuticularized cell walls. Few comparable studies of the decomposition of animal remains have been made. With many of the smaller animals, the soft protinaceous materials are rapidly decayed leaving chitinous exoskeletons. One characteristic of many acid soils is the number of exoskeletons of mites and other arthropods found at the junction of the litter and the mineral soil.

If attention is confined to the mineral soil, the total amount of organic matter varies considerably; in a good grassland chernozem, one may have as much as 10 to 12% dry weight of organic matter even after the roots have been removed. On the other hand an impoverished soil which has been cultivated for many years may contain less than 1%. A substantial fraction of the organic matter which can be regarded as truly amorphous falls into the group of substances which are classed as humic acids. It is difficult to obtain accurate estimates of what fraction of organic matter is present in any one group of compounds, but if we take humic acids in the widest sense these will frequently account for up to 80 or 90% of the total amorphous organic material. Simpler substances, such as amino acids, occur only in very small quantities, for instance the total amount of amino acids is of the order of about 0·1% of the total organic material. The simpler carbohydrates, such as glucose, similarly occur in very small quantities. This perhaps is readily understood when one remembers how easily these substances are attacked by microorganisms. Starches and pectins are not found in any great quantity, but the polysaccharides grouped under hemicelluloses can form a substantial fraction. The origin of these is very much a matter of debate. For a long time it was thought that the mucilaginous polysaccharides in soil were all the product of bacterial synthesis. There is, however, a certain amount of evidence to indicate that some at least of these substances may represent accumulations from higher plant debris which have resisted more rapid microbiological attack. Most analyses have revealed a certain amount of cellulose within the soil organic material; it is difficult to know whether this is occurring as amorphous cellulose, or whether it represents small shreds of tissue left from the decomposing plants that have not been fully disintegrated. The information regarding the occurrence of lignin is particularly unsatisfactory because of the difficulty involved in estimating it with any degree of accuracy. Many of the analyses which purport to show the presence of cellulose and lignin in soil depend on the old technique made popular by Waksman (1936), in which he used dilute acid hydrolysis to remove hemicelluloses followed by strong sulphuric acid to hydrolyse cellulose, and regarded the faction which resisted strong sulphuric acid digestion, and yet was clearly organic, as lignin. This type of analysis is reasonably satisfactory when dealing with fresh plant material, and it must be remembered that it was for this purpose that Waksman first introduced the analytical procedures. When, however, one is dealing with composted plant debris or with highly humified soil organic matter, then the use of acid digests become increasingly unsatisfactory, and the so-called lignin fraction which appears in many of the analyses is a combined estimate of what may be true lignin and may be any one of a number of resistant polymerized materials in the soil. Extraction with organic solvents such as ether or any of the other fat solvents usually reveals the presence of a small percentage of fats and waxes. It is usually assumed that these are residual materials from the decomposing animal or plant remains, and perhaps particularly from the cutin and suberin from the plant debris. Very little detailed work, however, has been done on these. Although a great many analyses have been made, there has been little attempt to get a full systematic analysis of any one particular soil. Usually the workers have been content to investigate the one or two groups of compounds in which they are specifically interested.

While many of the organic substances in soil can be regarded as residual it is clear that at least some of them are produced during the soil processes which are going on continually. The group of humic substances are typical products of such synthetic activities. Another class of compounds which are almost certainly formed in the soil are the very important organic phosphorus compounds, such as the inositol polyphosphates.

Quantitatively, the most important organic materials in the soil are those grouped under the term humic acids. Much of the earlier work on humic materials was associated with attempts to fractionate the dark-coloured organic material into well-characterized fractions which could then be subjected to normal chemical degradation and analysis. Of the very many proposed fractionations, that of Oden (1919) is the most used. If soil is treated with sodium hydroxide in the cold, it is found that a substantial proportion of the dark-coloured organic matter is brought into solution. There is also a residual fraction which can be partially removed by prolonged boiling in sodium hydroxide. The insoluble resistant fraction is frequently termed *humin*. The solution obtained from the initial extraction with sodium hydroxide is dark in colour, usually almost black, but does transmit a small amount of light at the red end of the spectrum. If the solution is acidified, a precipitate is obtained and some of the organic matter remains in the acidified solution. The fraction remaining in solution is termed *fulvic acid*. The precipitated material can be extracted with alcohol, yielding an alcohol-soluble fraction known as *hymatomelanic acid* and an insoluble fraction termed *humic acid*. These four fractions proposed by Oden have been accepted by the great majority of workers interested in soil organic matter. It was early realized, however, that these fractions almost certainly did not represent discrete organic species. As attempts are made to purify individual fractions, it is found that their solubilities change considerably, and many workers believe that the four distinct fractions differ primarily in terms of the size of the individual particles, which in turn affects their solubility. Small traces of metallic ions also have a profound influence on the solubilities. It is for this reason that there has been a tendency in recent years to use the term *humic acids* as covering the range of humic materials rather than restricting the name humic acid to the fraction insoluble in acid and alcohol.

For many years knowledge of the humic acids was very limited; it was generally agreed that they were highly polymerized substances and that their properties were due in part to their high molecular weight, so that colloidal solutions were obtained and with these the associated properties of colloids. Chemical investigation showed that the major reactive groups were carboxyls and phenolic hydroxyls. The high cation exchange capacity, associated with humic acids, was normally assigned to these carboxylic groups. Most humic acids on isolation contain a certain amount of nitrogen and at one time, mainly as the result of Waksman's work, it was thought that at least some humic acids were complexes of protein and lignin residues. The amount of nitrogen varies a great deal. In humic acids extracted from grassland soils one may find as much as 4 to 6% of nitrogen, although humic acids from highly leached soils such as podzols may contain less than 0·3% nitrogen. Prolonged acid hydrolysis will remove a considerable proportion of the nitrogen and an examination of the products of the hydrolysis shows the usual amino acids which one might expect from the hydrolysis of protein material (Kononova, 1961). Even after prolonged hydrolysis with acid, humic materials from grassland soils will still retain 1 or 2% of nitrogen. In contrast to this, humic acids obtained from highly acid soil and particularly from podzols may retain very little nitrogen at all. A typical humic acid from a podzol under *Pinus* may contain only 0·4% of nitrogen, and after prolonged acid hydrolysis this may be reduced to less than 0·2%. This would suggest that it is possible to form a typical humic acid without nitrogen being involved as a major component of the humic molecule.

In the early chemical investigations a great deal of time was spent in purifying the fractions and in carrying out elemental analyses of the different fractions. These studies were most unrewarding, and it became increasingly clear that one could not obtain a reproducible fraction with a repeatable analysis for the individual elements concerned. Most of the chemical studies have been restricted to the humic acid fraction in the narrow sense, that is, the fraction which is soluble in alkali but insoluble in acid and alcohol. Quite early on, it was assumed that this material was essentially aromatic in structure, but even yet there is no thoroughly satisfactory evidence to show that it is primarily aromatic in its constitution. The best yield so far would indicate that at least 30% of the material is aromatic and that the remainder probably is also primarily aromatic (Burges, Hurst and Walkden, 1964). Early attempts to characterize the individual fractions either by analytical information or more recently by chromatographic or electrophoretic studies were unsatisfactory; similarly, attempts at obtaining ultra-violet or infra-red spectra of the different fractions were most unsatisfactory in that humic acids from a wide range of sources gave very similar absorption patterns, and the spectra themselves revealed very little concerning the chemical structure of the fractions. More recently, chemical degradation using sodium amalgam has demonstrated convincingly that individual humic acids from different soils can be characterized by the phenols liberated. It has been possible to show that if the humic acid is degraded and the resulting phenols chromatographed, one can obtain "fingerprint patterns" for the humic acids from different sources (Burges, *et al.*, 1964).

An analysis of the phenolic fractions obtained on the degradation of different humic acids has led to the idea that during the formation of humic acids, phenolic fractions are oxidatively polymerized to form a polymeric complex, and that the phenols which go to form this complex polymer may be derived from lignin or from flavonoid compounds in the plant debris and perhaps from other sources as well. At the moment there is fairly convincing evidence to show that the type of lignin which might be expected from the vegetation cover can characterize the type of humic acid produced. Similarly, one can identify some of the flavonoid complexes. At the moment there is no convincing evidence that microbial synthesis plays any substantial contribution to the phenolic moieties of humic acid, although on ecological grounds, and as the result of experimental laboratory studies, it is possible that microbial synthesis can also contribute phenolic moieties to the polymer. As regards the lignin contribution, studies have shown that in the humic acid under a soft wood vegetation, such as *Pinus sylvestris*, one can find characteristically vanillic acid residues in the humic material. In contrast, under hard wood vegetation the underlying humic acid reveals the presence of syringic acid moieties. In a sample of humic acid extracted from soil under the moss *Bryum* in the Antarctic, no trace of any lignin components was found, the phenols being derived from flavonoid components. Where the vegetation changes over a small distance there is evidence to believe that the humic acid can likewise change; for example, in the studies at Delamere Forest, humic acid obtained from underneath a large area of bracken (*Pteridium*) showed on degradation a characteristic phenolic spot which was absent from humic acid obtained from soils where no bracken is at present growing. The studies carried out using the sodium amalgam degradation technique lend strong support to the view put forward by a number of workers (Flaig *et al.*, 1954) that humic acid is formed by the condensation of a large number of phenols and that there is probably no definable molecule which can specifically be called humic acid.

Such views as to the nature of humic acid would suggest that during the decomposition processes in the soil, phenolic fractions are released either from the decomposing lignin or from the flavonoid residues or from the metabolic activities of micro-organisms and that the phenolic fractions which come together are then polymerized. The proportions can vary from place to place, and perhaps from time to time. If free amino acids are present during the condensation, these may be incorporated into the polymeric complex, either loosely as amino acids, or perhaps as peptides or more tightly connected, perhaps even as structural units in the main framework of the polymer. It is probable that the individual polymeric units can grow in size as fresh phenolic units are condensed onto the outside. As the polymer grows in size so one could expect its solubility to change and one could thus offer a logical explanation of the different solubilities between the different fractions. If such views are correct, then we are faced with an extraordinarily difficult problem in trying to characterize the humic acid complexes. It is in fact even more complex than the pedologist has had to face in the chemistry of the clay minerals; here at least one has a lattice structure of a crystalline nature, and one can characterize the individual clays by their lattice structure. It would seem that in the humic acids one has no such crystalline pattern, although one may perhaps be able to characterize them at some future time by the proportions and distributions of the phenolic residues. It seems fairly clear at this stage that it is most unlikely that there is any definable molecule which can be termed humic acid and that attempts to put forward structural formulae in the way that Barton and Schnitzer (1963) have done is not productive and has very little relation to humic acid as it occurs in soil.

C. THE SOIL MOISTURE

Soil moisture is often regarded as belonging to three categories: (a) gravitational water which is moving through the soil under the influence of gravity, (b) ground water held below the water table and (c) held water which is retained in the soil after gravitational movement has ceased (Croney, 1952).

The amount of water in the soil with reasonably good drainage can vary greatly according to weather conditions. During exceptionally heavy rain, or if the soil is temporarily flooded, practically all the pores between the soil become almost filled with water. If the soil is then allowed to drain freely, much of the water runs away and the larger pores again become occupied by the soil atmosphere. After the initial drainage of the gravitational water has occurred, the soil moisture reaches a relatively stable condition in which the gravitational pull on the water is roughly balanced by the capillary and adsorption forces exerted by the interstices and colloidal materials in the soil. The moisture content under these conditions is said to be at *field capacity*. Because of the relative ease with which the field capacity can be obtained and measured, it is widely used as a measure of moisture levels in experimental work. As soils dry out and the moisture content falls well below the field capacity, plants have increasing difficulty in extracting water. Eventually a stage is reached where the plants can no longer remove water and the plants wilt permanently. The *permanent wilting point* of soil is a surprisingly constant value and differs only slightly for different plants. Examination of a wide range of soils showed that the amount of water expressed as a percentage of the dry weight of the soil at field capacity and at the permanent wilting point differs widely for different soils. It was clearly desirable therefore to know not only how much water was present but also to have some way of expressing the relative strength with which the water in the soil was held. To meet this need, Schofield (1935) introduced the pF scale. This scale expresses on a logarithmic basis the difference between the free energy of the moisture in the soil system and a free water surface. On this scale a soil at field capacity has a pF of 2, and permanent wilting point is about pF 4·2; oven-dry soils are at approximately pF 7. It is often more convenient to measure the force with which water is held in a soil by some means of suction measurement. This may be done with a simple vacuum pump or a greater force may be applied in a centrifuge. It is usual to express the suction in terms of the height of a column of water. Measurements of moisture tension using either the pF scale or the suction are readily interconverted over much of the range in which biologists are interested.

In practice, measurements of water tension in soils wetter than field capacity are most easily carried out by placing the soil in a container with a sintered glass base and connecting the base *via* a tube with a small reservoir of water to a vacuum pump. A manometer is fitted to the reservoir tube. When the soil first comes in contact with the water, the meniscus in the reservoir tube moves towards the soil. The pressure is then reduced till the movement ceases, and the pressure difference read from the manometer. The extent of the suction required is expressed in centimetres of water or converted to the pF scale.

The measurement of tensions between about pF 2 and pF 5 are usually made by using gypsum blocks containing two electrodes, and the electrical resistance between these is measured. When the blocks are buried in the soil the moisture in the block comes into equilibrium with that in the soil, and the resistance changes accordingly. The pF value corresponding to the measured resistance can be obtained from calibration charts provided by the makers of the gypsum blocks or by preparing calibrations with the aid of pressure-membrane apparatus. The measurement of pF values above 5 is usually carried out by equilibrating the soil against known vapour pressures maintained by salt solutions (Griffin, 1963). Since recent work has shown that considerable microbial activity can occur in soils drier than the permanent wilting point, it is important that the way in which any measure of the water relations has been made is clearly stated.

In recent years there has been considerable interest in the adsorption of organic materials (particularly antibiotics and proteins) onto soil particles and the effect this has on their availability to micro-organisms. The availability of these compounds is associated with the ability of free water to penetrate into the finer interstices of the soil. Schofield (1938) has given good reasons to show that the cohesive power of water is sufficiently high to allow water to exist as a liquid in spaces as narrow as 30 mμ, corresponding to only about 100 water molecules across.

Although the water may exist in the liquid form, it is important to remember that the physical conditions in such situations may differ considerably from those in the large bodies of water elsewhere in the soil. The density of the water and the ionic state of any dissolved materials will be considerably affected. For instance, the pH may differ by more than a unit from that of the bulk aqueous phase (McLaren, 1960).

D. THE SOIL ATMOSPHERE

The soil atmosphere is usually in a continual state of change, the composition at any one point or at any one time being the outcome of several processes which are going on continuously. The action of living organisms in the soil converts oxygen to carbon dioxide and, as the oxygen is utilized, fresh oxygen will diffuse down from the soil surface. The carbon dioxide formed will diffuse from the soil into the atmosphere; thus the relative proportions will depend on the ease of diffusion and on the rate of production of carbon dioxide. In a relatively dry soil, carbon dioxide seldom rises above 1%. If, however, the soil becomes wet and particularly if it becomes waterlogged, then, as the soil pores become filled with liquid, diffusion is impeded and the levels of carbon dioxide can rise rapidly and those of oxygen can fall. Following rain, one often gets a marked increase in microbiological activity, and concentration of carbon dioxide can then rise to 3 or 4%, or even as high as 10% for relatively short periods. The oxygen levels fall correspondingly as most soil organisms have a respiratory quotient of approximately 1. In waterlogged conditions, oxygen levels can fall very greatly indeed and may approach zero. Under such conditions the oxidation-reduction potential of the soil may lead to the ferric iron being converted to ferrous iron as in the characteristic gley phenomenon.

Not very much is known about the effect of the soil atmosphere on the different soil organisms. In the litter layers it is most unusual for the carbon dioxide levels to rise above about 0·5%. At these levels very few animals or micro-organisms seem to be affected. When the carbon dioxide rises to 3 or 4% one is approaching levels at which, under laboratory conditions, many fungi begin to show a falling off in growth rate, and there is evidence to show that fungi from the deeper layers of the soil are more tolerant to high carbon dioxide concentrations than the fungi which occur in the litter or in the surface layers (Burges and Fenton, 1953). Whether this ability to withstand higher carbon dioxide concentrations is a factor in the selection of the more deep-seated species has not been established, although such a view has been put forward.

It would seem from the work of Garrett (1956) that local concentrations of carbon dioxide are quite important in determining the activity of some parasitic fungi, so that soils which tend to accumulate carbon dioxide, either because of poor aeration or because of acidity, are less prone to certain root diseases than better aerated or alkaline soils. If the carbon dioxide rises to levels approaching 10%, then many plants begin to suffer, and correspondingly one finds marked changes in the soil microflora. The fluctuation in oxygen levels seems to have no important effect on soil organisms; even if the carbon dioxide rises to 10% and a corresponding fall occurs in the oxygen levels, most organisms do not seem to suffer severely from such oxygen deficits. It is only when oxygen levels fall below 5% that one begins to notice a marked falling-off in the activity of the soil organisms.

REFERENCES

Barton, D. N. R. and Schnitzer, M. (1963). *Nature, Lond.* **198**, 217.

Burges, N. A. and Fenton, E. (1953). *Trans. Br. mycol. Soc.* **36**, 104.

Burges, N. A., Hurst, H. M. and Walkden, B. (1964). *Géochim. cosmochim. Acta*, **28**, 1547.

Croney, D. (1952). *Géotechnique*, **3**, 1.

Flaig, W., Schultze, H., Küster, E. and Biergans, H. (1954). *Landbouwk. Tijdschr.* **66**, 392.

Garrett, S. D. (1956). "Biology of Root Infecting Fungi." Cambridge University Press, London.

Griffin, D. M. (1963). *Biol. Rev.* **38**, 141.

Kononova, M. M. (1961). "Soil Organic Matter." Oxford University Press, London.

Leeper, G. W. (1964). "Introduction to Soil Science." 4th Ed. Melbourne.

McLaren, A. D. (1960). *Enzymologia*, **21**, 256.

Oden, S. (1919). *Kolloidchem. Beih.* **11**, 75.

Piper, C. S. (1944). "Soil and Plant Analysis." University Press, Adelaide.

Schofield, R. K. (1935). *Trans. 3rd Int. Congr. Soil Sci., Oxford.* **2**, 37.

Waksman, S. A. (1936). "Humus." Williams & Wilkins Co., Baltimore.

Chapter 2

Bacteria in Soil

F. E. CLARK

U.S. Department of Agriculture
Fort Collins, Colorado, U.S.A.

I. INTRODUCTION

Bacteria are the smallest and the most numerous of the free-living micro-organisms in soil. Taken collectively, their spectrum of autotrophic and hetero-trophic capabilities is matched by none other of the major groups of the soil life. It belies their small size and comparatively simple morphology. Notwith-standing the abundance of bacteria in soil and extensive information about the activities of individual species in standardized environments, the role of bacteria in many soil processes is still poorly understood. Much also remains unknown concerning the forms of bacteria in soil and their ecological relation-ships within their micro-environments.

Commonly the soil bacteria are discussed according to their participations in the nitrogen and carbon cycles or in other cyclical transformations in soil. Discussions of them may also be undertaken on the basis of their morphology and taxonomy, their environmental tolerances, their spatial distribution in soil, and from the standpoint of their biotic relationships with other micro-organisms or with higher plants. Several of these approaches are used in subsequent chapters. It is the purpose of this chapter to consider the bacteria *en masse* in the soil, with little or no effort to spell out the many special problems posed by individual genera or species.

II. THE NUMBER OF BACTERIA IN SOIL

The number of bacteria in 1 g of soil ranges from 1 million or less to several billions.* That their population needs to be expressed within such extremes is in part due to the great differences in populations that do exist among and within soils. Somewhat more disconcerting is the fact that with existing methodology, the bacterial population cannot be determined with precision in any given soil sample. Estimation, not measurement, is accomplished.

Estimates are made culturally or by direct microscopic examination. The cultural method most commonly employed is the dilution plate technique. A primary assumption in this technique is that each viable bacterium in the soil suspension used as an inoculant develops into a visible colony during incubation. Any such assumption is highly idealistic. It is not possible to prepare any one combination of substrate ingredients and conditions of incubation that will permit the growth of all bacterial species. Even with the cultural conditions made as optimal as knowledge permits for a given species, not all viable cells of that species will invariably produce colonies. Due to differences in stored reserves and enzymatic activity, or in dormancy or senescence, the individual cells are not equally vigorous in initiating growth. There also are differences in their micro-environments within the cultural substrate, as for example, proximity or lack of proximity to other microbial cells.

That collectively these several factors can suppress colony formation by the majority of bacterial cells seeded into agar has been shown by Tchan (1952). A known number of cells was taken from a young, actively growing culture of Azotobacter and transplanted into glucose agar. As microscopic examination of the inoculant showed all cells to be actively motile, all the seeded cells were considered to be viable. The number of colonies subsequently developing represented only 25–33% of the number of bacterial cells known to have been seeded. If only one cell in three or four of a vigorously growing bacterium such as Azotobacter can successfully accomplish colony formation in a substrate designed especially for this organism, then it would indeed be surprising if more than one cell in ten, or even one in a hundred, of the wide assortment of bacteria in soil could initiate colony formation when seeded jointly on any single substrate under any given set of incubation conditions.

Soil bacterial populations as determined by cultural methods range from a few thousand cells per gram of soil to several hundred millions. Sand dunes, tundras, stony soils, and podsols usually contain comparatively low, and chernozems and other prairie soils, comparatively high bacterial populations. Commonly for arable soils cultural methods of examination reveal from

* One billion as used by the author equals 10^9.

5–50 million bacteria/g of soil. In rare instances bacterial populations as high as 500 million/g have been determined for field soil by cultural methods (Krasilnikov, 1958).

Even this value, however, hardly approaches the population estimates made by direct microscopical procedures. Strugger (1948), using fluorescent microscopy, observed from 2–9 billion viable cells/g. Taylor (1936), working with Rothamsted soils and using the dilution ratio method for direct counting, observed soil bacterial populations of approximately 3 billion/g. Direct counts were of the order of 10–50 times the magnitude of the agar plate counts made on the same samples. Jensen (1936) reported quite similar results for Australian soils. Direct counts were from 8–300 times higher than plate counts. The widest ratios between direct and cultural counts were found in soils receiving no recent additions of energy-rich material, such as green manure. Immediately following addition of an organic material to soil, the ratio between the two counts was narrowed very markedly. It frequently became less than 10 and at times approached unity.

Citations such as the preceding indicate that the soil bacterial population as determined by direct microscopy is usually of the order of 1–3 billion/g. In highly fertile soils and for short periods, the value may approach 10 billion. For purposes of discussion in some immediately following paragraphs, 2 billion cells/g will be taken as a representative value for the bacterial population of soil. Also, a representative bacterial cell in soil will be considered as spherical and to have a cell volume of 1 μ^3. These two generalizations permit making some estimates of the weight of bacteria in soil and of the extent to which bacteria occupy the available space in soil. The standard population estimate will also be used for considering the suitability of soil as a *milieu* for bacterial growth.

III. THE BACTERIAL BIOMASS AND ITS SPATIAL REQUIREMENT

On the basis of either a cell volume of 1 μ^3 and a cell density only slightly in excess of unity (1·04 according to Kendall, 1928) or on the common generalization that 1 trillion bacterial cells weigh 1 g (Pelczar and Reid, 1958), a direct count estimate of 2 billion bacterial cells/g of soil accounts for 0·2% of the soil weight. This amounts to 4,000 lb live weight of bacteria/acre 6 in. For many arable soils, the assumed bacterial population value, and therefore the live weight value per acre are probably over-estimates, but not markedly so. Most writers prefer to state a general range of values when speaking of the amount of bacterial tissue per acre. Alexander (1961) has stated the range as from 300–3,000 lb/acre-furrow slice; Russell (1950), as from 1,500–3,500 lb; and Krasilnikov (1944), as 600–1,200 lb for uncropped soils, to as high as 3,600–6,400 lb for soil cropped to legumes.

In most arable soils, the amount of living bacterial tissue per acre is commonly estimated to be somewhat less than that of the fungi, but to exceed that of the algae, protozoa, and nematodes combined. The matter of comparative weight, or biomass, in relation to population numbers merits emphasis. Although on a census basis the *Eubacteriales* may outnumber the *Actinomycetales* by a factor of 10, and the fungi by a factor of 100, the eubacterial biomass in many cultivated soils is about equal to that of the actinomycetes, and only about half that of the soil fungi.

To what extent do bacteria occupy the available space in soil? First, this can be calculated using the assumption that normally the bacteria exist in the water film in soil. For a soil containing 0·3 ml water/g, a bacterial population of 2 billion will occupy no more than 1·33% of the theoretically available space. This calculation is based on the fact that spheres, regardless of size other than the provision that they be of uniform size, when uniformly open or cubic-packed within a container, occupy approximately one-half the container volume. Accordingly, in 0·3 ml presumably there could occur 150 billion cells. If, however, the bacterial cells are sufficiently plastic that they pack solidly, then the estimated 1·33% occupancy figure becomes halved. Obviously also, if there were nothing to inhibit growth, the bacteria would continue to multiply until they packed the total porosity in soil. In such instance, there could occur something like 500 billion bacteria/g of soil, and the standard population postulated would occupy no more than 0·4% of the available space. Even this figure appears discordant with the statement a few lines above that 2 billion bacteria/g constitute only 0·2% of the soil weight. That the two values are not inharmonious becomes apparent when one considers that the space occupied by the mineral particles is not included when calculating the soil space available for occupancy by bacteria.

At first glance, an approximate 0·4 to 1·0% occupancy of available space suggests that the soil is not an especially suitable environment for bacteria. Accordingly, it becomes fitting to compare the bacterial density in soil to the populations that are encountered in various other environments. Rahn (1945) has recorded some population densities for soured milk and for fresh human feces, as well as for nutrient broth in which bacterial growth has been allowed to continue to a maximum population level. For all three environments, his estimates are of the order of 1 billion cells/g. This value is entirely comparable to the bacterial population in soil. Rahn's estimates are quite conservative, inasmuch as the writer has made estimates as high as 20 billion/g of decaying plant material as found in the field, and as high as 40 billion/g for fresh feces. Even higher values are on record, for example, 46 billion/g in decomposing green manure (Smith and Humfeld, 1930), and 100 billion/g in an infant's feces (Smith, 1961). Nevertheless, it still must be emphasized that on the basis of its contained population, the soil does appear to be an excellent environment for bacteria.

IV. RESPIRATORY ACTIVITY OF SOIL BACTERIA

Numbers alone, however, are no measure of microbial activity. It is possible that a high population present in an environment, particularly if the population estimate is based on direct microscopy, can be largely dormant or resting. Some assessment of the general activity level of the soil microbial population can be obtained by considering respiratory activity. This can be done conveniently in terms of carbon dioxide production.

According to Mooney and Winslow (1935), carbon dioxide production in glucose-peptone broth by *Salmonella pullorum* occurs at a rate of 1·14 mg/ billion cells per hour during the early logarithmic growth phase. At stationary maximum population, the rate was determined as 0·08 mg. Similar data were obtained by Walker and Winslow (1932) working with *Escherichia coli*. They reported 0·41 to 1·85 mg CO_2/billion cells per hour in the late logarithmic phase, and less than 0·02 mg at the close of the logarithmic phase. Actively multiplying bacterial cells therefore appear capable of producing many times their dry matter weight of CO_2 during 24 hours, whereas in stationary populations the production of CO_2 during 24 hours is approximately the equivalent of dry cell weight.

This latter estimate is in reasonable agreement with some observations on CO_2 production by micro-organisms in soil. Jensen (1936) noted production of up to 0·22 mg CO_2/billion bacteria in 24 hours, or roughly the equivalent of the bacterial dry weight. In general, however, the CO_2 production per billion bacteria during 24 hours amounted to about 0·1 mg. Miller and Schmidt (1961) measured 0·12 mg CO_2/billion bacteria per day in laboratory soil culture, and Goring and Clark (1952), 0·11 mg, from glucose-amended laboratory sand cultures.

As a first approximation, therefore, it appears plausible to accept Jensen's estimate of 0·1 mg CO_2/billion bacteria per day. This is equivalent to 0·004 mg on an hourly basis, a rate that is appreciably below those cited above for the stationary phase of *S. pullorum* and *E. coli*.

Rate of carbon dioxide production by field soil has been given by Alexander (1961) as 20 lb/acre per day; by Vine, Thompson and Hardy (1942) as 3 l/m² per day; and by Krasilnikov (1958) as 2 kg/hectare per hour. These values, if all reduced to a lb/acre per hour basis, become 0·83, 2·2, and 1·78, respectively. Their mean value is 1·6 lb CO_2/acre per hour.

On the basis of two separate premises stated above, namely, that there are 2 billion bacteria/g of soil, and that in soil, bacteria produce CO_2 at the rate of 0·004 mg/hour per billion, then the $1·8 \times 10^{15}$ bacteria in an acre-furrow slice should produce 7,200 g CO_2 in 1 hour. This quantity, 15·9 lb, appears entirely too high for any ready reconciliation with the 1·6 lb that has been revealed by some actual field measurements. How best can this discrepancy be resolved?

It appears reasonable and even obligatory to accept the field measurement of 1·6 lb/acre per hour for CO_2 production from soil. Insofar as production by the soil bacteria is concerned, the 1·6 lb must be several times too high, simply because the bacteria constitute only about one-fifth of the biomass in soil and therefore should be held responsible for only part of the total respiratory activity in soil. Accordingly, it appears necessary to challenge the proposition that there are 2 billion cells/g of soil that are producing CO_2 at the rate of 0·004 mg/billion bacteria per hour. Although some cells may be exhibiting this or some higher level of respiratory activity, the majority of them must be greatly enfeebled or resting cells, or spores, that are exhibiting an exceedingly low level of respiratory activity. Many of these probably would not be determined in the course of making plate count determinations of the soil population.

Acceptance of the possibility that appreciably less than 2 billion bacteria/g of soil are active helps to explain the wide disparity between plate count and direct count estimates of the bacterial population in soil. If, as documented above, the direct count exceeds the plate count by a factor of 50- to 300-fold, with the ratio below 10-fold only in freshly amended soils or in laboratory cultures of bacteria, then perhaps the plate count when used on soil does enumerate the viable and active bacteria somewhat more successfully than much of the raw data would indicate. The plate count appears more compatible with observed rate of CO_2 production by field soil than does the direct count. Bacterial plate counts of 50 million/g are commonly reported to occur in field soils. If this population respires at a rate of 0·004 mg CO_2/billion cells per hour, then in an acre-furrow slice it would produce CO_2 at the rate of 0·4 lb/hour. If one is willing to assume that the soil bacteria produce approximately one-fourth of the 1·6 lb/acre per hour produced by the total microbial population in soil, then this calculation of 0·4 lb/hour appears entirely reasonable.

Irrespective of any such subsidiary calculation, the discrepancy between the 15·9 lb calculated production and the measured 1·6 lb production makes it appear plausible that a major proportion of the possibly 2 billion bacteria in a gram of soil are in a resting or dormant condition, with their respiratory activity at a level appreciably below that of bacterial cells in broth cultures in the stationary phase of their growth cycle. In brief, population and respiratory data considered jointly indicate that soil permits the survival of a great many bacterial cells during periods in which they are not very active metabolically. It is probable that the resting vegetative cells of at least some soil organisms can attain levels of respiratory activity of the order of 0·0004 mg CO_2/billion cells per hour. At this level of activity, bacterial cells in the soil, even if present in such numbers as are suggested by direct microscopical counts, would make only a very minor contribution to the respiratory output field soil of 1·6 lb CO_2/acre per hour.

V. FACTORS LIMITING SOIL BACTERIAL ACTIVITY

If commonly in the soil, many of the bacteria are either inactive or else are showing only a very low level of activity, what are the factors that limit their activity? There is no quick and easy answer to this question. To do it justice, one becomes almost endlessly involved in innumerable interactions concerning many different soil factors variously affecting different bacteria. Any such approach conflicts with the initially announced objective of this discussion and will not be undertaken. Attention in the following paragraphs will be directed in quite general terms to limitations on bacterial activity imposed by the available food supply and by certain physical and biological factors in the environment. The physical factors given brief attention are those of moisture, aeration, reaction, and temperature.

The principal factor limiting bacterial growth in soil is scarcity of food, or lack of a suitable and available source of energy. Consequently, any addition of fresh energy material to soil almost invariably elicits an increase in bacterial activity. Many, if not most, bacteriologists believe that in the *in vitro* culture of single species of bacteria, the total yield of cells is proportional, over a wide range, to the amount of food available. The situation in soil in the presence of a mixed bacterial flora is probably analogous. Food supply is of paramount importance. The nature of an added energy material influences both the immediacy and the duration of the rise in activity, as well as the specificity of the responding flora.

Nutritionally, the great majority of the soil bacteria are heterotrophic, that is, they use organic compounds synthesized by autotrophic micro-organisms and higher plants both for their energy requirements and as the principal source of their cell carbon. In contrast, the autotrophic bacteria use carbon dioxide as a source of cell carbon and secure their energy by means of inorganic oxidations. Insofar as the nutrition of the heterotrophic bacteria is concerned, the amount of organic matter added to soil by autotrophic bacteria is negligible in comparison to that formed by the photosynthetic activity of higher plants. Although a tremendous tonnage of organic matter is produced yearly, the voracity of the heterotrophic organisms is such that in most soils the annual rate of decomposition balances out quite nicely with the annual rate of production of organic matter. Maintenance of this balance does not require that the soil organisms work at capacity throughout the year. Insofar as the soil bacteria are concerned, the supply of food materials in soil can be said to be perennially inadequate.

In instances where the supply of energy-yielding substrate is in itself adequate, it is possible that a short supply of one or more of the essential mineral nutrients or of necessary growth factors can be limiting for bacterial activity. A great deal of attention has been given to the requirements of bacteria for nitrogen, phosphorus, and other minerals in the course of decomposition of carbohydrates and of organic residues characterized by wide carbon/nitrogen ratios. With such materials, especially when used experimentally under favorable environmental conditions in the field or laboratory, dramatic stimulation of microbial activity can at times be achieved by using supplemental minerals. Data recently published by Stotzky and Norman (1961a, b) provide a good example. The respiratory output of carbon dioxide from a sandy soil treated with glucose only was doubled when nitrogen and phosphorus were used supplementarily. This rate in turn was quadrupled upon addition of sulfur.

A large number of essentially similar experiments could be cited. However, for most soils and with naturally occurring residues, similarly dramatic responses to supplemental minerals should not be expected to occur. In the work of Stotzky and Norman, the glucose amendment was free of sulfur, and the sandy soil to which the glucose was added in liberal quantity was itself relatively low in sulfur content. Most organic residues reaching field soils contain nitrogen and other minerals in sufficient quantity that supplies of these minerals should be non-limiting or but slightly limiting to bacterial activity. Nevertheless, with more extended study it may be found that limiting supplies of mineral nutrients or vitamins more often restrict decomposition processes in soil than is generally recognized.

Nitrogen is the mineral nutrient most in demand by bacteria in decomposition of carbonaceous residues. Most crop residues containing 1·5% or more of nitrogen need no additional nitrogen to meet the needs of the bacteria. For residues containing a lower level of nitrogen, the bacteria involved in the decomposition need extra nitrogen, particularly during the early stages of decomposition. Such extra nitrogen as is needed is usually available in the soil. Most arable soils in the course of a season produce from about 20 to about 100 lb of available nitrogen. The lower figure would be ample for the nitrogen demand during decomposition of 1 ton, and the latter figure for 5 tons, of straw or stover containing 0·5% nitrogen.

The quantity of residues returned annually to a soil is usually closely related to the nitrogen fertility of that soil. The residues from a poor soil are small and those from a fertile soil are large, and therefore less demand for soil nitrogen occurs in soils which are poor in nitrogen. It is difficult to find field conditions where the nitrogen content of the residues, when coupled with the available soil nitrogen, is not adequate to meet the nitrogen demands of the soil organisms carrying on the decomposition. Accordingly, it is but seldom that addition of nitrogen will accelerate residue decomposition in the field.

The fact that nitrogen is seldom limiting to the bacteria engaged in decomposition of residues does not mean that extreme nitrogen deficiency cannot occur in crop plants growing in soil well endowed with residues of wide carbon/nitrogen ratios. In the presence of the abundant energy material, the soil organisms may demand all the available soil nitrogen, and leave none for the growing crop. Nitrogen fertilization therefore is essential for the crop but not for the bacteria.

The addition of nitrogen to crop residues does not, as is sometimes assumed, result in the retention of any greater percentage of plant residues as soil organic matter. Nitrogen additions to soils over a number of years do often result in a higher level of soil organic matter than would otherwise exist, but this is due to the production of larger crops and more residues, and not to any higher rate of residue conversion to soil organic matter.

VI. DISTRIBUTIONAL PATTERNS OF BACTERIA IN SOILS

Bacteria are not uniformly distributed throughout the soil profile, nor even throughout a single soil horizon. With but few exceptions, their distribution in soil echoes the distribution of soil organic matter. In the soil profile, organic matter content is usually highest in the A horizon and of lesser quantity in the B and C horizons. A similar profile distribution of bacteria is commonly noted. Data compiled by Starc (1942) are cited in Table I. Essentially similar data have been obtained by various other workers in diverse localities.

There are, of course, many instances in which the standard profile pattern is subject to derangement. One such example is shown in Table II, wherein

TABLE I

Bacterial distribution according to depth in the soil profile (Starc, 1942)

Horizon	Depth (cm)	Aerobic bacteria	Anaerobic bacteria
		(millions/g)	
A_1	3– 8	7·8	1·95
A_2	20– 25	1·8	0·38
A_2–B_1	35– 40	0·47	0·10
B_1	65– 75	0·01	0·001
B_2	135–145	0·001	0·001

TABLE II

Organic matter and bacterial distribution according to depth in a chernozem soil profile (Timonin, 1935)

Horizon	Depth (cm)	Organic matter (%)	Aerobic bacteria	Anaerobic bacteria
			(millions/g)	
A_1	0– 6	8·04	49·2	1·0
A_2	6–12	3·18	131·8	1·0
B_1	12–28	2·41	158·3	10·0
B_2	28–48	1·76	45·3	1·0
C	48–80	0·80	6·0	0·001

the bacterial maximum does not occur at the same profile depth as does the maximum value for organic matter. In some instances, such non-conforming maxima can be due to droughty conditions at the soil surface. In others, the surface horizon may simply be too acid to permit profuse bacterial development. Failure of bacteria to develop in an A horizon containing abundant energy material does not mean that other units of the soil biota, such as fungi or insects, must also fail to flourish.

In soils in which plants are growing, the organic exudates and sloughings emanating from the root surfaces provide an abundant source of energy material, and there results a profuse development of micro-organisms on or near the root surface. This phenomenon is known as the rhizosphere response. Its study has intrigued many workers. The microbiology of the rhizosphere is

2+S.B.

discussed by Parkinson in a later chapter. The rhizosphere is mentioned here only to emphasize that plant roots have a profound influence on the occurrence and localization of soil bacteria. Data illustrative of the extent to which bacterial populations are increased in the immediate vicinity of plant roots are presented in Tables III and IV.

TABLE III

Influence of proximity to corn roots on abundance of bacteria
(Starkey, 1931)

Description of sample	Total bacteria	Types growing on mannite agar (millions/g)	Radiobacter types
Soil, 15 cm distant	14·2	7·6	0·02
Soil, 5–10 cm distant	25·4	14·0	0·18
Soil close to roots	122·0	91·4	3·22
Root surface material	1,315·6	523·2	14·12

TABLE IV

Influence of proximity to cotton roots on abundance of bacteria
(Clark, 1940)

Description of sample	Total bacteria	Hundred thousands/g of Dye-tolerant bacteria	Spores of Bacillus
Soil, 10–15 cm distant	52·6	7·4	17·0
Soil, 5–10 cm distant	47·9	9·0	18·0
Soil, 2·5–5 cm distant	45·6	7·7	17·0
Soil, 0·5–2·5 cm distant	54·7	15·0	10·0
Soil, 0–0·5 cm distant	129·9	91·3	13·7
Root surface scrapings	510·0	440·0	0·1

Additionally to local concentrations of bacteria in the rhizosphere, there can occur islands or foci of microbial activity in soil apart from plant roots. Such foci vary greatly in magnitude. At one extreme is the condition that prevails when a green manure crop is plowed down. In such instance a food supply measurable in tons per acre is layered into the soil. Such layers can contain many billions of bacteria per gram of plant material, while soil but a few centimeters distant, if free of contact with the added plant parts, shows only a few millions per gram (Smith and Humfeld, 1930). On a smaller scale, foci of bacterial activity develop when individual plants or portions of them fall onto or become incorporated into the soil. Following harvest of seed cotton from a field, the writer has observed that decaying cotton carpels in natural microclimates at the soil surface can support bacterial populations of 20 billion/g plant material.

Other foci of bacterial development are known to be associated with the fecal droppings of insects and with dead mesofaunal and microbial tissues. Microscopic examination of glass slides that have been buried in soil frequently reveals small threads or cylindrical masses of bacterial cells clustered about a disintegrating strand of fungus mycelium. Beyond this level of observation, there exists a relatively little explored area concerning the microdistribution of bacteria in soil. Alexander and Jackson (1954) observed that soil bacteria commonly occur in the film of colloidal material coating the mineral particles in soil. Jackson *et al.* (1947) have published electron micrographs showing small masses of bacteria closely surrounded by clay particles. Corroborative evidence that bacteria occur in small colonies in soil has been noted by Jones and Mollinson (1948). They observed that 77% of the bacteria in soil occurred in groups of several to many cells, while the remaining 23% occurred as single cells. Minderman (1956), on the other hand, examined soil sections and concluded that the majority of the bacterial cells observed therein occurred as single cells.

Some occurrence of solitary bacteria in soil is to be expected. Individual cells must be subject to some transport within the soil by the migratory activities of the soil micro- and mesofauna. A certain amount of self-tillage occurs in soil coincidentally to gross changes in soil moisture and temperature. Movement of gravitational water provides another possibility for bacterial transport in soil. According to Thornton and Gangulee (1926), motile bacteria propel themselves in the water films that exist in soil, and in so doing may achieve an effective migration rate of 1 in per day. Additionally to active motility, cell proliferation and elongation, particularly of filamentous bacteria, leads to some increase in the bacterial colonization of soil. This mechanism of extension through soil becomes more effective in the presence of filamentous fungi possessing rapid growth rates. Such hyphae serve as roadways along which the bacteria follow, dining upon them *en route*. Finally, bacteria may be transported long distances above soil by airborne dust, by man-made machines, and by the migratory activity of large animals.

These several dispersal mechanisms have in the aggregate widely seeded bacteria throughout the soils of the world. Consequently, only rarely need soil inoculation be practised. Indeed, the population naturally present in a given habitat is almost invariably the one best adapted to exploit the habitat, and introducing one or more additional species of bacteria simply by inoculation is usually wasted effort. Either naturally occurring or man-induced changes in the habitat, however, are quickly followed by changes in the qualitative nature of the soil flora, irrespective of whether or not inoculation is practised.

The cosmopolitan nature of the bacterial flora in soil attests to widespread distribution of the organisms involved, but it is uninformative as to the efficiency of the several dispersal mechanisms. The present-day distribution may have required thousands of years. Much more precise information is needed concerning the extent and rate at which bacteria can transport themselves or be transported within soil.

There is evidence that bacteria do not move freely into or through the soil water. Soil is well known for its capacity to entrap the bacteria which it receives in sewage effluents. In the course of nitrification experiments in a soil perfusion apparatus, Quastel and Scholefield (1951) observed that heavy populations of nitrifying bacteria became established on the soil particles while the perfusing liquid itself remained practically free of bacteria. The writer has observed that in a soil initially free of soybean rhizobia, uninoculated border or buffer rows intervening between inoculated (and nodulated) rows of soybeans remained uniformly free of nodulation throughout the growing season. This was surprising, inasmuch as at the time the soybeans were about 4 in high, the farm operator, faced with a heavy work schedule, turned in excessive heads of irrigation water and achieved a basin or flood irrigation, rather than a furrow irrigation along the rows. In the course of a single growing season, neither such flooding, nor any combination of dispersal mechanisms, sufficed to cause movement of rhizobia between nearly contiguous rhizospheres.

VII. MOISTURE REQUIREMENTS

The role of moisture in relation to microbial activity in soil has been studied extensively, possibly more so than has the influence of any other environmental factor. Notwithstanding such effort, there remain many gaps in knowledge concerning the soil water in terms of its interactions with other physical or biotic factors. Many of these gaps concern wet or extremely wet soils, in which the problem is really not one of moisture in itself, but of the severe restrictions imposed on aeration in wet soils.

Much of the earlier work on soil moisture in relation to bacterial activity is difficult to interpret. Moisture contents were expressed gravimetrically and without regard to the energy concept, in which soil moisture is expressed in terms of the physical force with which it is held in soil rather than in terms of actual percentage content. In some work, there was failure to insure a constant moisture content throughout an experimental period or to effect a uniform distribution of moisture throughout the experimental sample. In other work, data accumulated are informative only for the given experimental conditions. The rather widely quoted work of Bhaumik and Clark (1948), for example, is informative for soils maintained in a shallow layer of 12 mm and subjected to a rapidly moving air stream across the soil surface. What happens at the same moisture tensions in the field at a depth of 100 mm can hardly be extrapolated from such laboratory data.

The most satisfactory information on the moisture relationships of bacteria in soil is that which exists for the dry end of the moisture scale. Here the problem becomes simplified to definitions of the levels at which various bacteria can no longer hold water within their cells in amounts sufficient for their metabolism. At moisture tensions of 3 atmospheres or higher, bacterial activity in soil becomes reduced, and very markedly so at the 15 atmosphere, or permanent wilting percentage, moisture content. Inasmuch as bacteria differ in the extent to which they are active in droughty soil, not all bacterial transformations are uniformly curtailed during drying out of soil. Ammonification, for example, can proceed under more stringent drought than can nitrification. The latter, although it occurs slowly in soil at the permanent wilting percentage, does not occur in soil of lower moisture content. Ammonification has been observed to occur in soil with moisture content at one-half the wilting percentage (Robinson, 1957).

Degradation of organic residues can occur at moisture contents below that of the permanent wilting percentage. Bartholomew and Norman (1947) observed that the threshold moisture content for decomposition of many plant residues is approximately that of 80% relative humidity. Possibly the observed decompositions were initiated by fungi rather than by bacteria. From the practical standpoint, it must be emphasized that low moisture contents are generally limiting to microbial activity. As the moisture content drops to or below the wilting percentage, decomposition processes slow almost to a standstill. At 81% relative humidity, the rate of decomposition of oat straw was measured as less than 1% of that at the optimum moisture content (Table V).

It is probable that at least some soils, even when in an air-dry condition, permit a very low level of respiratory activity. Negligible but nevertheless measurable production of CO_2 has been observed by the writer for a soil containing 4·8% organic matter and holding 3% moisture following air-drying in the laboratory. The rate of CO_2 production was of the order of 0·0001 mg CO_2/g of air-dry soil per day. In the same study, several other soils containing approximately 1% organic matter and holding approximately 1% moisture in the air-dry state showed no measurable production of CO_2 during 2 weeks of incubation.

TABLE V

Carbon dioxide evolution from oat straw under differing moisture conditions (Bartholomew and Norman, 1947)

% Moisture in oat straw	Moisture tension (atmospheres)*	Relative humidity	CO_2 evolved/g of straw, mg in 144 hr
250		saturation	152
150		saturation	139
60		saturation	79
36	40	97·1%	40
24	113	92·0%	16
19	206	85·9%	4
16	289	80·8%	1

* Values in this column calculated by the writer; not shown in the initial publication.

There occurs a marked reduction in the number of bacteria in soil as it undergoes drying. Certain bacterial species are commonly believed more resistant to drying than are others, and that consequently, sporulating and other drought-resistant bacteria constitute the bulk of the remaining viable population. This point of view is an over-simplification. All of the soil bacteria are quite resistant to drying. Seldom are individual species entirely eliminated from soils that are stored in an air-dry condition. When such soils are re-wetted, such varied phenomena as nitrification, ammonification, non-symbiotic nitrogen fixation and sulfur oxidation almost invariably proceed without any soil reinoculation whatsoever being required. Calder (1957) noted that the nitrate productivity of dry soil stored for 3 years was almost unimpaired. Sen and Sen (1956) encountered two soils in which *Rhizobium japonicum* survived for 19 years during storage of the soils in an air-dry condition. The writer has noted survival of *Azotobacter* in soil stored air-dry in the laboratory for 30 years.

These citations should not lead the reader to assume that specific bacteria are never entirely eliminated from soil as it undergoes drying. Workers engaged in nitrification studies and making use of stored dry soil at times find that some soils, or possibly only a single replicate of several small lots taken from a larger gross lot, do fail to show nitrification when properly moistened and incubated. Occasionally rhizobia may also fail to withstand soil drying. In some field soils cropped to annual legumes, especially if such soils are poorly buffered and subjected to severe drought during the non-growing season, there may be insufficient carryover of viable rhizobia to effect nodulation of the newly planted crop. Consequently, inoculation of the legume seed with rhizobia must be undertaken annually at time of planting.

When a soil is dried rapidly, it is not uncommon to note that such widely differing subgroups as spores of aerobic bacilli, nitrifying bacteria, denitrifying bacteria, and aerogenic bacteria respond uniformly with decrease in the total count. The decrease in the viable count is not linked to unilateral survival of sporulating bacilli.

For many soils, the decrease in bacterial numbers during drying is more apparent than real, and hinges on some physical entrapment or clumping effect, rather than on any true lethality. If, following drying, special mechanical or chemical dispersing treatments are applied to the dry soils prior to making plate counts thereon, the viable counts in the several soils are then higher, with magnitude of the increase differing in different soils, than counts obtained on aliquots of the same dry soils not given dispersing treatment prior to plating. Differences in physical entrapment effects among soils during drying can be expected to occur. Such differences may help to explain why different soils show widely varying decreases in total counts during drying.

VIII. AERATION REQUIREMENT

Wet soils are unfavorable for most bacteria simply because filling up of pore space with water diminishes soil aeration. The restrictive factor is lack of oxygen and not the excess water in itself. At first glance it appears that soils with moisture content at or lower than field capacity could be expected to furnish oxygen to bacteria at a rate adequate to meet their biochemical oxygen demand. Seldom do field measurements of oxygen in the soil atmosphere reveal the presence of less than 10% oxygen; for most well-drained soils, the measurement usually is of the order of 20% (Russell, 1950). During wet periods and for heavy soils (Boynton and Compton, 1944; Vine *et al.*, 1942) or following heavy irrigation (Kemper and Ameniya, 1957), oxygen contents of 3% or below have been measured. These values represent oxygen contents measured in a large soil volume and may be an over-estimate of the oxygen content in some of the smaller and less accessible pores. The amount of oxygen present in a soil microsite at any given time is a function of the biochemical oxygen demand of soil organisms (and plant roots if present) and of the rate of oxygen movement into the soil atmosphere and into and through the water barriers in soil.

Movement of oxygen into the larger pores of the soil atmosphere occurs readily by gaseous diffusion. The oxygen pressure difference necessary to cause adequate movement through air-filled pores need equal only 1–4% oxygen. Bacteria in the soil, however, are surrounded by water films, and rate of oxygen diffusion through water is only about one ten-thousandth as fast as the rate through air. Consequently, water barriers to oxygen movement at times become limiting for bacterial respiration.

On a gross scale, such barriers can be established at the soil surface either by heavy rains or by irrigation practices. In the event that a water seal is thus established at the soil surface, the amount of oxygen in the soil atmosphere does not provide an inexhaustible reservoir for soil organisms. Its disappearance depends on the rate of oxygen use by soil organisms and plant roots and on the amount of oxygen initially entrapped. This amount is determined by the depth of the water table, the fraction of the soil volume occupied by air, and the initial oxygen content of the entrapped air. In many soils the entrapped oxygen is sufficient to supply the biochemical oxygen demand from several days to a week.

A much more difficult problem is that posed by the water barriers that occur in and around individual soil pores and bacteria and the extent to which these barriers can limit movement of oxygen to bacterial cells. One can be reasonably certain that these barriers are of little or no consequence at the moisture content of the permanent wilting percentage, inasmuch as at such content only soil pores having radii of 1 μ or less remain water-filled. With moisture content at field capacity, however, pores with radii as large as 3–4 μ become water-filled. Combinations of such pores, without intervening larger pores, may lead to conditions of inadequate aeration. Short of waterlogged conditions, however, it is difficult to postulate any idealized geometry on which to base calculations of rate of oxygen movement into and rates of consumption within soil micropores. Such calculations have been made for root segments surrounded by rhizosphere bacteria and soil-water barriers. Using experimentally measured rates of oxygen consumption and basing calculations on the logarithmic relation between diffusion coefficient and film thickness, Clark and Kemper (1966) concluded that critical oxygen levels could occur within the internal root cells when the water or water mucigel barrier immediately surrounding the root reaches thicknesses of 0·1–0·5 mm.

In many soils, it is highly probable that microsites of anaerobiosis occur in greater profusion in the plow layer than in the subsoil. Well-drained soils with droughty surfaces normally can be expected to be rather fully aerated throughout the entire profile. With either sufficient precipitation or irrigation to effect a temporary water seal at the soil surface, the plow layer loses its oxygen much more rapidly than does the deeper profile, simply because the greater number of micro-organisms, and thus the greater biochemical oxygen demand, occurs in the topsoil. In such instances, the subsoil is better aerated than is the topsoil.

The observed distribution of anaerobic bacilli throughout the soil profile suggests that oxygen-deficient sites must occur in the plow layer of field soils. The data in Table I show that anaerobic bacteria were found most numerous, both relatively and absolutely, in the upper profile. In the A_1 horizon, they constituted 25% of the total count for aerobic bacteria, and in the next three and successively deeper horizons, 21, 21, and 10%, respectively. Whether the anaerobes proliferate during the times when temporary water-seals develop at the soil surface or whether they proliferate on a more or less continuing basis within microsites whose oxygen is consumed by aerobic bacteria is not currently known.

It is well known that nitrates are produced in the plow layer of field soils and accumulate therein unless taken out by plants or by leaching. The oxygen level required for nitrification is distinctly higher than that tolerated by obligate anaerobes. That both nitrifying and anaerobic bacteria develop in the plow layer suggests either that microsites of aerobiosis and anaerobiosis exist contemporaneously, or else that some sites fluctuate between aerobiosis and anaerobiosis under changing soil conditions.

Workers attempting to define the optimum soil atmosphere for either microbial transformations or microbial species have commonly placed major if not sole emphasis on the factor of oxygen content. The fluctuations that occur in the carbon dioxide content are also deserving of attention. Either unusually high or low carbon dioxide concentrations in the soil atmosphere at times are limiting for bacterial activity. Much of the work determining tolerances of soil organisms to high concentrations of carbon dioxide has been with the soil fungi rather than with the soil bacteria. Studies on threshold and optimal levels of CO_2 more frequently have been concerned with a few pathogenic bacteria rather than with the soil bacteria. Some information, however, has been developed concerning the CO_2 requirements of the nitrifying bacteria.

In the course of numerous studies by various workers on nitrification in soil, it has been recognized that incubation of soil samples with too shallow a layer of soil or with too small a quantity of soil in the incubation container, or with too vigorous aeration of the incubating soil, adversely affects the rate of nitrification (Harmsen and van Schreven, 1955). Recent work indicates that the oxygen contents that exist under such differing conditions of incubation are not critical, but that build-up of soil carbon dioxide to a value above the normal atmospheric level is needed in order to secure an optimum rate of nitrification (Beard and Clark, 1962). Incubation techniques that favored rapid escape from soil of the respiratory carbon dioxide depressed rate of nitrification, and experimental removal of CO_2 from the soil atmosphere almost completely inhibited nitrification. These effects of CO_2 concentration could be observed at normal or near normal atmospheric oxygen levels. Oxygen itself became limiting only when its concentration by volume in the enclosed atmosphere fell to 10% or less. Nitrification rates in soils whose atmospheres contained concentrations of oxygen in the range of 10–20% by volume did not differ significantly. CO_2 content necessary for rapid nitrification fell within the range of 0·5–5·0% by volume.

Until more is known of the gaseous environment confronting the soil bacteria, one must be content with the generalization that soil moisture contents within the range of 50 – 80% of moisture-holding capacity appear compatible with good soil aeration. At least in soils of such wetness, there occurs a combination of moisture and aeration that favors the activities of most of the heterotrophic bacteria in soil.

IX. REACTION AND TEMPERATURE REQUIREMENTS

The reaction range commonly tolerated by soil bacteria is that between pH 4 and pH 10. The optimum within this range is slightly on the alkaline side of neutrality. Some bacteria are readily limited by acidity or alkalinity while others show wide tolerances to extremes in reaction. Such differences exist even within a single genus. *Azotobacter chroococcum*, for example, is widely distributed in neutral and alkaline soils but is not found in soils below about pH 6. *A. indicus*, in contrast, tolerates an acidity of pH 3. *Thiobacillus thiooxidans*, an autotroph capable of oxidizing elemental sulfur, tolerates an acidity of ph 0·6. It is reported to be the most acid tolerant of any living organism (Breed *et al.*, 1957).

As a group, the soil bacteria are less well adapted or less competitive for food supplies in distinctly acid soils than are the soil fungi. This is particularly evident in the microflora of forest and heath soils. In soils strongly acid in the surface profile, fungi are dominant, and even if the fungi are restricted experimentally by the addition of a fungicide, the pH alone suffices to restrict any vigorous colonization of the habitat by bacteria.

The optimum temperature range for soil bacteria is from about 25°–35°c. A great many grow quite well over the range of 10°–40°c. In the field, high soil temperatures are seldom if ever the primary factor limiting bacterial growth. Unusually high temperatures occur only at or near the surface in dry and barren soils. In such sites, lack of water is the primary factor limiting microbial growth. In moist tropical soils in which plants are growing, the soil temperature in the root zone is usually either optimal or suboptimal for

2*

bacteria. Some arable soils, if row-cropped, clean-tilled, and not shaded by the growing crop, at times slightly surpass the optimum temperature for soil bacteria. Temperatures of this magnitude may be harmful to plant roots and therefore of economic importance. Their occurrence is usually avoided by corrective or alternative methods of land management.

On a limited scale, temperatures above the optimum for bacteria occur in soils or waters under the influence of thermal hot springs or volcanic activity. Stored hay and grain, if not sufficiently dry to inhibit microbial activity, may yield sufficient heat during spoilage to be inimical to many species of bacteria and even to cause spontaneous combustion in the stored material itself. Small islands of plant residues in soils, or layers of such residues that are plowed under, show measurable but inconsequential microbial thermogenesis (Clark *et al.*, 1962). Such temperature elevations are very transitory and do not exceed about 1°C.

In other tropical soils, temperatures below the optimum range for bacteria occur seasonally, and at time of occurrence are limiting to bacterial activity. The principal effect of seasonally low soil temperatures is simply to postpone microbial activity until a later date. Such postponement may have great economic importance in a cold, wet spring insofar as nutrient availability to a growing crop is concerned.

An extensive literature on the influence of temperature on diverse microbial transformations in soil has been reviewed by Richards *et al.* (1952), and their discussion will not be duplicated here.

X. BIOTIC LIMITATIONS ON BACTERIAL ACTIVITY

Emphasis in the preceding paragraphs has been on the extent to which the available food supply and physical factors in the environment determine bacterial activity in soil. Discussion of these factors severally or jointly fails to tell the full story, inasmuch as soil micro-organisms themselves exhibit pronounced effects upon one another. In some instances the biotic relationships may be beneficial to one or more organisms, but more often than not, mixed colonization of a substrate leads to restricted development of one or more of the species involved. Norman (1947) has characterized the soil population as one nutritionally fiercely competitive within itself. The extent to which the antibiotic and inhibiting substances are limiting to microbial activity in soil is discussed by Park in a later chapter.

The proposition that many of the microbial species present in a soil at any given time are in a resting or dormant condition has been put forward above. The competitive or ecological significance of such resting cells must be quite analogous to that of ungerminated but viable seeds in a plant community. Furthermore, among the active microbial species in soil, food specializations make possible the co-existence of a large number of ecological niches within any given habitat. In the rhizoplane, for example, with its wide assortment of materials exuded or sloughed from the root, it is probable that many of the microbial species simultaneously present on the root surface are subsisting on different materials. The organisms occupy separate ecological niches and therefore are not in actual competition. Finally, any given substrate or microhabitat undergoes sequential changes with time, either because of fluctuations in the physical environment, or because of the activities of other micro-organisms. Such a substrate therefore presents a succession of ecological niches.

A simple illustration of one such succession can be seen in the nitrification cycle. Ammonia is oxidized to nitrite by the genus *Nitrosomonas*, and the nitrite to nitrate, by the genus *Nitrobacter*. Much more complex successions occur in the decomposition cycles of the organic residues that reach the soil. Many of these cycles have not yet been adequately studied. Recently, Kendrick and Burges (1962) have described the patterns of fungal specificity and succession that occur in decaying pine needles. Only by such studies, together with delimitation of the specific factors and mechanisms which enable one or another species to be found where it is found in soil, will the soil microbiologist be able to replace the redundancy in "this micro-organism is dominant in this microsite because it is the successful competitor" with a more meaningful conception of the role of competition in soil biology.

XI. PATTERNS IN MICROBIAL TRANSFORMATIONS

The many interactions of food supply with physical and biotic factors make each soil habitat, large or small, almost unique. At the same time, in the continual flux of microbial activity, some response patterns occur with such sufficient regularity that they are worthy of brief characterization. A few such response patterns are discussed in terms of CO_2 production, the parameter usually considered as the most informative concerning the course of organic matter decomposition in soil. When appropriate, some attention will be given to nitrification or other data. There is no implication that the few curves presented are all-inclusive for patterns of microbial activity, nor that any specific data, other than that given, will identify itself with any one curve. The rate curves shown, however, represent actual data taken from the literature, and are not constructed as idealized diagrams.

The principal food materials reaching the soil are plant and animal residues or excreta. These are almost continually added, and upon initial addition, contain soluble and easily available energy materials. The addition of such food materials to soil elicits therein the "microbial explosion" of which my former teacher Charles Thom so dearly loved to speak. Such explosions are characterized by a sudden onset of decomposition, the rise of the rate curve to a sharp peak within a day or so, and rapid subsidence of respiratory activity in the immediately following days, simply because the easily available food supply has been exhausted. Such decomposition curves are shown as the "A" curves in Figs 1 and 2.

Such data as are shown in Figs 1 and 2 represent total microbial respiratory

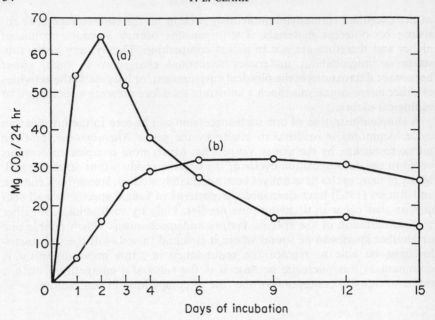

FIG. 1. Effect of two differing moisture tensions on the respiratory pattern in soil amended with 1% corn stover (Bhaumik and Clark, 1948).
(a) At 50 cm moisture tension; (b) at 0·0 cm moisture tension.

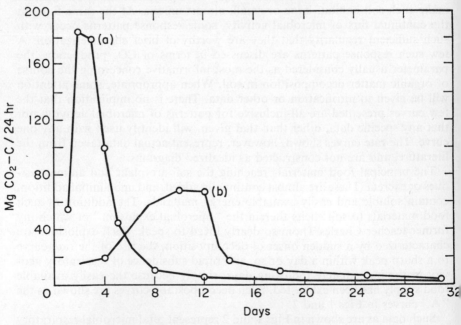

FIG. 2. Effect of additional nitrogen on the respiratory pattern in soil amended with 1% glucose (Stotzky and Norman, 1961).
(a) 1% glucose plus 0·15% nitrogen; (b) 1% glucose.

activity, and it is probable that much of the respiratory activity is by the soil fungi. However, it safely can be assumed that soil bacteria are also involved in the initial or explosive stage of decomposition of the added organic materials. Burges (1939) and Garrett (1956) have characterized the particular soil fungi involved in the early or rapid phase of decomposition as the "sugar fungi." Although their terminology might equally well be applied to the bacteria, the writer prefers not to speak of the "sugar bacteria." Nor for reasons to be discussed shortly does he concur in the designation of these rapidly responding bacteria as "zymogenous bacteria." Acceptance of the zymogenous and autochthonous classification of the soil bacteria as proposed by Winogradsky (1925) implies a rigidity of classification that does not exist. Bacteria that are zymogenous under one set of conditions may well be non-zymogenous under another set. It does, however, appear logical to speak of the explosive or peak activity that almost immediately follows the addition of fresh residues as the zymogenous response.

Under the influence of any one or more of a number of factors, the initial explosive activity or zymogenous response may be variously modified. Frequently, as some factor becomes limiting to decomposition, the ascending curve of respiratory activity breaks off to a horizontal plateau. With time, this limited activity accomplishes depletion of the food supply, and the respiratory curve drops off thereafter in much the same fashion as if the delaying factor had not intervened. Delayed or truncated patterns of zymogenous reponse are shown as the (b) curves in Figs 1 and 2. In Fig. 1, lack of adequate aeration due to excess moisture is the limiting factor; in Fig. 2, lack of essential mineral nutrient is responsible for the truncation.

Many organic residues that normally reach the soil contain, in addition to easily soluble and available components, others that are relatively resistant to decomposition. In plant residues, lignins and waxes commonly occur as such resistant material. They are responsible for the long-continued and relatively constant output of respiratory carbon dioxide following the transitory and explosive zymogenous response. The extent to which the water-soluble and non-water-soluble materials in corn stover contribute to the zymogenous and the residual patterns of response has been nicely demonstrated by Newman and Norman (1943). Their data are reproduced in Fig. 3. The water-extractables are responsible for the zymogenous peaks obtained on the first day, but after about 5 days their influence has been almost entirely dissipated, as shown by the coincidence of the respiratory curves for extracted and whole stover between the fifth and fourteenth days of incubation.

Some microbial transformations in soil show a lag pattern of response, or more descriptively, the growth curve pattern of response. This response is associated with the addition to a given soil of materials which are not commonly or frequently added thereto, or else if commonly added, only a few specialists in the soil population are capable of effecting their oxidation or hydrolysis. This pattern is characterized not only by a slow onset of microbial activity, corresponding to the lag phase of the well-known microbial growth curve for a population seeded into a fresh substrate, but also by the fact that this lag or slow onset can be greatly foreshortened by pretreatment or baiting of the soil with the specific material.

A representative lag curve is obtained when a material such as a chlorinated organic pesticide is first added to a soil. Its decomposition occurs slowly. A second addition made shortly following the first addition is decomposed within a much shorter interval of time. Such a small first addition as one part per million of 2,4-D in soil suffices to increase the rate of decomposition of a second dose.

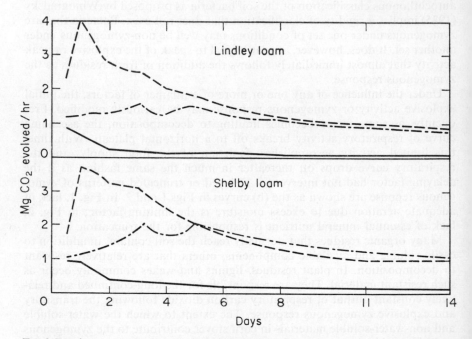

FIG. 3. Respiratory patterns in soils amended with extracted and whole corn stover (Newman and Norman, 1943).
Dashed line, soil and cornstalks; chain-dotted line, soil and water-extracted cornstalks; full line, soil alone.

A lag curve of response also is commonly observed when nitrifiable nitrogen is added to soil. A typical lag curve for nitrification in soil is shown in Fig. 4. The slow onset of nitrification is not due to any lack of nitrifiable nitrogen—indeed, the early part of the lag curve is entirely independent of the amount of nitrifiable nitrogen initially added.

The lag curve for nitrification in a laboratory soil perfusion apparatus is shown in Fig. 5. Additionally in this figure, there is shown the nitrification curve for ammonia added immediately following the completion of nitrification of a preceding addition.

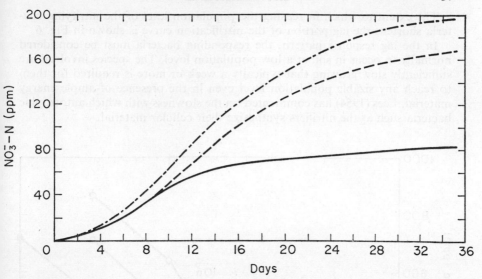

FIG. 4. Typical nitrification curves following additions of nitrifiable nitrogen to soil (Parker and Larson, 1962).
Chain dotted line, 150 ppm NH4—N; dashed line, 100 ppm NH4—N; full line, no nitrogen added.

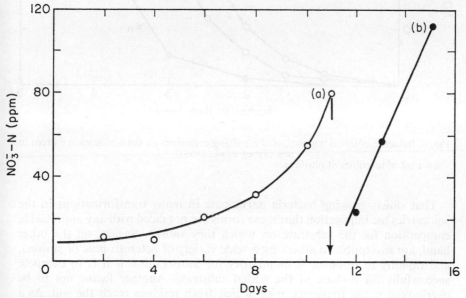

FIG. 5. Nitrification curves obtained during an initial and a second perfusion of soil with nitrifiable nitrogen (Quastel and Scholefield, 1951).
(a) Initial perfusion; (b) second perfusion of same soil.

The extent to which increasing the population level of the nitrifying bacteria shortens the lag portion of the nitrification curve is shown in Fig. 6.

In the lag response pattern, the responding bacteria must be considered normally to occur in soil at a low population level. The species involved are sufficiently slow growing that typically a week or more is required for them to reach any sizable population level even in the presence of ample energy material. Lees (1954) has commented on the slowness with which autotrophic bacteria such as the nitrifiers synthesize their cellular material.

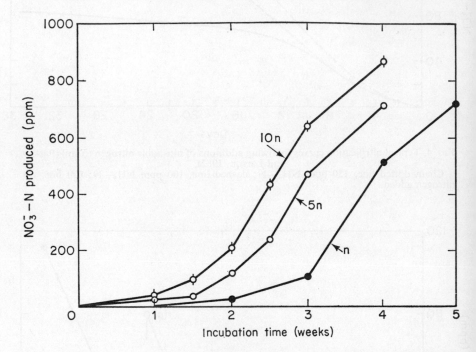

FIG. 6. Influence of initial population of nitrifying organisms on the nitrification pattern in soil (Sabey *et al.*, 1959).
n=1 ml of inoculum of nitrifiers.

That slowly-growing bacteria participate in many transformations in the soil carries the implication that these forms are not faced with any appreciable competition for the substrate on which they subsist. Sugars, on the other hand, are susceptible to attack by a wide variety of heterotrophic organisms, and rapidity of response is mandatory for an organism if it is to compete successfully for a share of the added substrate. Another factor not to be overlooked is the frequency with which fresh residues reach the soil. As a consequence of this continued baiting, a microflora capable of zymogenous response is ever present in the average topsoil.

XII. THE PRIMING EFFECT IN DECOMPOSITION OF SOIL HUMUS

A characteristic of the soil humus is the slowness with which it decomposes. Half or more of the carbon in fresh residues is lost as carbon dioxide within 2–6 months following addition of the residues to soil. Thereafter, the rate of decomposition slackens. The ultimate product, the soil humus, decomposes at a rate of approximately 2% per annum. This rate is subject to some acceleration. For example, decomposition of the soil humus is intensified by thorough drying of the soil followed by re-wetting.

A concept developed relatively recently in soil microbiology is that addition to soil of fresh organic residues such as green manures accelerates the rate of decomposition of the native soil humus. The influence of the added residues has variously been termed as a fanning of the bacterial fires or as a priming effect. Studies of this phenomenon involve the use of isotopically tagged fresh residues in order that the total quantity of carbon or nitrogen mineralized during the course of an experimental incubation can be identified as arising from either the added residues or the native soil organic matter.

It is difficult to explain why the presence of freshly added residues should accelerate the decomposition of the native soil humus. Although residue addition produces a measurable thermogenesis, the limited elevation of the soil temperature is much too inconsequential to affect rate of decomposition. Nor should the flood of carbon dioxide released during decomposition of the added residues be expected to act as a microbial stimulant. A high concentration of this gas might well be equally detrimental or beneficial. Garrett (1956) has suggested that the observed intensification of decomposition of resistant materials in the presence of fresh materials hinges upon the necessity for supplying initial growth energy to the microbes involved in order to enable them to attack the resistant materials. Another possible explanation of the priming effect has been suggested by Park (1956). In his opinion, humus decomposition slows almost to a standstill because there accumulates in soil a miscellany of antibiotic or inhibitory substances. Once developed, these materials depress the rate of decomposition to a level lower than that which would otherwise occur. Addition of fresh residues, however, counteracts this biostasis, and thereby accelerates decomposition of the native humus.

It is the writer's opinion that the priming effect is largely illusory. This implies no challenge of the accuracy of the isotope measurements for evolved carbon dioxide or mineralized nitrogen, but it does imply doubt as to whether these measurements should be accepted at face value.

The total metabolic activity within any soil represents a complex of mineralizations and immobilizations in which the soil organisms draw upon available carbon and nitrogen, tagged or untagged, for their cell needs. In an unamended soil, all re-immobilization must occur at the expense of non-tagged carbon or nitrogen. In the presence of fresh residues, there is some channeling of the residues-added carbon and nitrogen to the immobilization pool. The full significance of these interchanges is as yet unknown. Investigations such as that of Jansson (1960), in which an estimate was made of the active fraction of the soil humus by means of periodic additions of tagged glucose, should lead eventually to precise measurements of the interchanges between the soil and the added sources. Hauck and Bouldin (1961) have shown that dissimilar values for the nitrogen gas evolved from added nitrate in denitrification experiments are obtained according to whether or not one assumes dilution interchanges in soil of the original source material. Their work offers promise for a mathematical interpretation of the anomaly currently known as the priming effect.

XIII. SOME PROPOSED GROUPINGS OF THE SOIL BACTERIA

Any discussion of the bacterial flora of soil would be incomplete without some consideration of the approximate equilibrium among bacteria normally present in soil. What are the diverse types of bacteria in soil, and at about what frequency do some species of particular interest to the soil bacteriologist occur in soil?

Literally hundreds and possibly even thousands of bacterial species may be present in soil. It is not practical to discuss them individually. There are several ways in which the soil bacteria can be grouped together for convenience in discussion. Some groupings are too broad and too heterogenous to be informative—for example, the aerobic and anaerobic grouping with respect to oxygen tolerance, or the psychrophilic, mesophilic and thermophilic divisions based on temperatures at which growth occurs.

Within the past two decades, Canadian bacteriologists have made extensive use of a nutritional grouping of bacteria. The grouping initially proposed by Lochhead and Chase (1943) involved determination of growth responses of bacterial isolates on seven cultural media of increasing complexity. The types of cultural media required are shown in Table VI. Also shown therein are

TABLE VI

Growth requirements of soil bacteria (Lochhead and Thexton, 1947)

Nutritional group no.	Growth requirements	% Frequency in soil
1	Grow in basal mineral-salts medium plus energy energy	12·0
2	Require amino acids	6·8
3	Require growth factors	23·1
4	Require both amino acids and growth factors	16·2
5	Require yeast extract	16·2
6	Require soil extract	6·8
7	Require both yeast and soil extract	11·1

data by Lochhead and Thexton (1947) on the frequency of occurrence of soil bacteria in each nutritional category.

Later writers have criticized this classification and have proposed simplification. Taylor (1951) concluded that the nutritional groupings as proposed by Lochhead and associates yielded little information of value and did not allow bacterial groups to be distinguished with accuracy. Taylor proposed a modified scheme in which only five groupings were used. Later, Katznelson *et al.* (1956) made use of only the following three media: (a) basal medium consisting of inorganic salts and glucose; (b) this medium plus amino acids; and (c) the basal medium plus yeast and soil extracts. Gyllenberg (1957) made a different simplification; she used (a) basal medium; (b) basal medium plus amino acids; and (c) basal medium plus both amino acids and B vitamins.

At present there is no physiological grouping of the soil bacteria that will serve as a satisfactory substitute for their taxonomic grouping. Although it can be argued that the systematic identification of the wide assortment of bacteria in soil is not feasible for the individual worker, nevertheless the fact remains that in bacteriology, as in botany and zoology, the precision of the Linnaean system is needed in order that workers can effectively correlate their observations. Even though the individual worker cannot be expected to be proficient in making species identifications in more than a few genera, or indeed, to be interested in accomplishing identifications even in a single genus, nevertheless he should be able to recognize generic or some higher taxonomic category without too much difficulty.

Burges (1958) has noted that of approximately 1,600 species of bacteria and actinomycetes named in the sixth edition of *Bergey's Manual* (Breed *et al.*, 1948), approximately 250 species are listed as being typically soil-inhabiting forms. These were distributed among 50 genera. On the basis of these figures, slightly less than 16% of the named species are soil-inhabiting species. This percentage is probably an underestimate. Burges did not include in the soil flora isolates from muds and stagnant waters nor from decaying vegetation. Another qualifying factor is the extent to which taxonomic bacteriologists have been concerned with bacterial species pathogenic to man, animals, or plants, and with species encountered in the preparation and preservation of foods and in industrial fermentations. Intensive studies on bacteria in these categories have led to the naming of a great many species of non-soil origin. One can almost generalize that the "species splitters" have been in the ascendancy in the taxonomy of the plant and animal pathogens, and the "species lumpers," in soil bacteriology.

Using the seventh edition of *Bergey's Manual* (Breed, Murray and Smith, 1957), the writer has grouped the total number of bacterial genera listed as to whether or not they contain species of soil, or mud and pond water origin, or species occurring in association with plant debris in soil. Of a total of 190 genera, 97 genera, or 51%, contain species that broadly may be considered as soil bacteria. Surveys of this type have only limited value insofar as discussion on what actually occurs in the soil is concerned. If of 100 species listed as of soil origin, 99 collectively account for only a fractional percentage point of the bacterial population in soil, obviously the full story is not told simply by summarizing habitat information.

XIV. ZYMOGENOUS AND AUTOCHTHONOUS FLORAS

Winogradsky's (1925) concept of a zymogenous and an autochthonous flora is an extremely useful one in characterizing the soil population as consisting of an indigenous component carrying on a low but rather constant level of metabolic activity and at the same time providing for the recognition of the zymogenous bursts of activity that follow the addition of fresh food or energy materials to soil. Attempts to carry his grouping beyond this point, however, appear to render more disservice than service to soil bacteriology. Particularly does this seem to be the case when attempts are made to sort out and assign individual genera and species to one grouping or the other.

The definition of the autochthonous or indigenous bacteria as those always present in soil but not fluctuating much in numbers, and carrying on activities which require no nutrients or sources of energy other than those normally present in the soil, is quite uninformative. All soil bacteria normally require only those nutrients or sources of energy normally present in the soil at one time or another, and all soil bacteria fluctuate in numbers when given the appropriate conditions. Characterization of the zymogenous bacteria as those actively fermenting forms which require for their activity ingredients that are quickly exhausted at first sounds plausible. It sounds distinctly less so when one finds that assignments to this group include not only the rapidly growing saccharolytic and proteolytic bacteria in a broad and sweeping gesture, but also along with them the vegetative but not the sporulating stages of *Bacillus*, members of *Pseudomonas*, the nitrogen-fixing bacteria as a group regardless of whether they are symbiotic or nonsymbiotic or aerobic or anaerobic, the cellulose-destroying and the sulfur-oxidizing bacteria, and finally, such difficultly cultured, fastidious and relatively scarce autotrophs as the ammonia- and nitrite-oxidizing bacteria (Conn, 1948; Alexander, 1961).

Could one isolate two soil bacteriologists in separate cubicles, and assign one to study the autochthonous and the other to study the zymogenous flora of the soil, it would be surprising if given sufficient time either investigator omitted studying any appreciable segment of the total bacterial flora of soil. Indeed, microbiologists who have endorsed the zymogenous and autochthonous groupings of Winogradsky often make contrasting assignments of components of the soil flora. Conn (1948), for example, considered the nitrifiers and the sulfur-oxidizers as zymogenous, whereas Burges (1958) regards the nitrifying bacteria, and the autotropic bacteria generally, as true autochthonous forms. Both Winogradsky (1925) and Conn (1948) considered the small coccoid bacteria of soil that are now assigned to the genus (*Arthrobacter* as true autochthonous bacteria. Rovira (1956), however, who considers the rhizosphere flora as zymogenous, has assigned (Sperber and Rovira, 1959) most of the Gram-negative bacteria in the rhizosphere to the genus

Arthrobacter. Katznelson and Sirois (1961) consider *Arthrobacter* at times to constitute an important fraction of the rhizosphere flora, and Jagnow (1961) assigned the great majority of his rhizosphere isolates to this same genus.

For the most part, it appears that those bacteria whose specific and favorable environments have been defined are commonly listed in the literature as the zymogenous flora. Significantly, this listing now includes practically all of the better known species of soil bacteria. These lesser known species whose ecological environments have been less adequately defined constitute the bulk of the autochthonous flora.

Given the proper conditions, any bacterial species in soil will show zymogenous response. Within the genus *Bacillus*, for example, such well-known species as *B. cereus* and *B. subtilis* commonly are termed zymogenous. If one adds 1% sucrose to soil, there occurs a profuse development of these two species. If, however, 1% peptone is added to soil, *B. sphaericus* and other round-spored bacteria become dominant. In the rhizospheres of plants, there is preferential stimulation of such species as *B. polymyxa*, *B. circulans*, and *B. brevis* (Clark and Smith, 1950). Without turning to other genera for further examples, it can be stated that specificity of response almost invariably occurs following development of special environmental situations in soil. Perhaps one of the most widely known relationships in this category is the host-bacterial symbiont specificity that occurs in the rhizospheres of leguminous plants.

Rather than to consider the soil bacteria as divisible into an autochthonous and a zymogenous flora, and then to attempt to assign individual species or genera to one grouping or the other, the writer prefers to think of all bacteria whose normal and principal habitat is soil as indigenous or native. This flora at any one time is composed of two segments. One of these can be termed a resting, and the other, a responding flora. As the soil environment undergoes change, first one group and then another finds conditions which enable it to undergo a burst of activity, that is, to exhibit the zymogenous response as emphasized by Winogradsky.

XV. THE PREDOMINANT BACTERIA IN SOIL

There is extensive evidence that the bacteria most abundant in soil are small coccoid rods of variable morphology (Conn, 1928; Jensen, 1933; Topping, 1937; Taylor, 1938; Gibson, 1939; Lochhead, 1940; Clark, 1940). These bacteria produce small colonies on such agar media as are commonly employed for total bacterial counts on soil. Their pleomorphism is extreme. Both their Gram-staining and their cellular morphology vary with age of subculture and with the substrate on which the bacteria are grown. Cells from very young cultures are usually Gram-negative rods, with or without rudimentary branching. Cells from older colonies on favorable substrates almost always appear as Gram-positive cocci. Taxonomically, the majority of the globiforme bacteria in soil are placed in the genus *Arthrobacter*, in the family *Corynebacteriaceae* of the *Eubacteriales*. Those species which decompose cellulose are placed in the genus *Cellulomonas* within the same family (Breed *et al.*, 1957).

The soil corynebacteria usually constitute half or more of the total colonies encountered in the course of making plate count estimates of bacterial populations in soil. Taylor (1938) examined a wide variety of soils whose locations ranged from the rim of the Arctic Circle to southern Canada, and from the Atlantic to the Pacific coasts. Of 90 soils examined, globiforme bacteria were encountered in 89, and in these, constituted on the average about 65% of the total plate count populations determined. Numerous other workers dealing with arable soils of temperate regions have made essentially similar observations.

The extreme pleomorphism of the soil globiforme group makes extremely difficult the proper assignment to this group of the bacteria seen in direct microscopic examinations of soil. Burges (1958) has suggested division of the soil bacteria seen in direct microscopy into the following six groups:

1. small cocci about 0·5 μ in diameter;
2. short rods about 0·5 μ in diameter, 1 to 3 μ long;
3. short curved rods, the Vibrios;
4. long rods;
5. rods sometimes showing branching;
6. thin flexible rods with very thin walls, usually under 0·5 μ in diameter.

In this scheme, bacteria assigned to groups 1, 2, 4, and 5 could quite commonly be expected to be members of *Arthrobacter*, and occasionally, some of the asignments to groups 3 and 6. Similarly, in a morphological grouping made by Lochhead (1940) of the bacteria found in several soils in which plants were growing, the first five of the eight groups established (see Table VII) may well have been composed largely of the soil globiforme bacteria. These five groups constituted about 80% of the total number of bacteria examined.

XVI. OTHER BACTERIA ABUNDANT IN SOIL

Other bacteria abundantly present in soil are the sporulating bacilli and the actinomycetes. The latter commonly constitute at least 10% and at times as much as 70% of the total microbial count in soil. The actinomycetes are discussed by Kuster in a following chapter.

A cross-section of the census data available for soil bacteria shows the sporulating bacilli to constitute approximately 25% of the total number of bacteria culturally enumerated in soil. Mishustin (1956) has conducted population studies on a wide variety of soil types, ranging from tundra to desert. His data show that the bacterial spores constitute from 1 to 38% of the total bacterial count, with a mean percentage value of 24·2. Two of the tables that have been presented above show data on the occurrence of the genus *Bacillus* in soil. Table VII shows only approximately 10% of the total as sporeformers, but Lochhead's study was based on bacterial isolates from cropped soils, and it is well known that the rhizosphere does not preferentially stimulate the sporulating bacteria as a group. The relative abundance of *Bacillus* in rhizosphere and non-rhizosphere soil is shown in Table IV.

TABLE VII

Frequency of occurrence of morphological types of bacteria predominantly present in soil (Lochhead, 1940)

Morphological classification	% of bacteria in each class		
	Tobacco soil	Corn soil	Flax soil
Short rods, Gram-positive	23·3	23·1	7·7
Short rods, Gram-negative	13·3	26·9	15·4
Short rods, Gram-variable	11·7	5·8	7·7
Short rods, changing to cocci	13·3	7·7	1·9
Coccoid rods, Gram-positive	18·3	21·2	53·8
Cocci	1·7	0·0	7·7
Long, non-spore-forming rods	6·7	5·8	0
Spore-forming rods	10·0	9·6	5·8

Another group that is commonly present in soil is the mycobacteria. Censuswise their population density is less than that of the corynebacteria or the bacilli. It is difficult to place any precise estimate on their number, partly because of a paucity of published data, and partly because the more optimistic population estimates are by workers who have drawn wide boundary lines for this group of organisms.

XVII. WELL-KNOWN GENERA NOT ABUNDANTLY PRESENT IN SOIL

If one is to admit that the coryneforms account for as much as 65% of the bacterial flora exclusive of the actinomycetes in soil, and that the sporulating bacilli can account for another 25%, then collectively the *Pseudomonadacae*, *Nitrobacteriaceae*, *Rhizobiaceae*, *Azotobacteriaceae*, *Achromobacteriaceae*, and *Micrococcaceae* must account for no more than 10% of the total. On first thought, one would expect that by taking values for the occurrence of well-known genera within these families and summing up, the value so obtained would easily exceed 10%. Among the genera involved are *Agrobacterium*, *Azotobacter*, *Nitrosomonas*, *Nitrobacter*, *Rhizobium*, *Pseudomonas*, *Achromobacter*, and various others. Most of these have been studied intensively in relationship to specific transformations that they accomplish in soil or in their association with plants. With the notable exception of *Azotobacter*, the normal distribution in soil of many of these genera has not been studied intensively. Nevertheless, sufficient census data are available that some summing up can be accomplished.

Starkey (1931) enumerated *Agrobacterium radiobacter* in several soil samples collected from root-free soil. The average population of radiobacter encountered was 20,000/g of soil. The species accounted for no more than 0·1% of the total bacterial count determined on the same soil samples.

Azotobacter is usually present in soil at even lower population levels, and therefore constitutes an even more negligible fraction of the total count. Extensive data are available on the occurrence of *Azotobacter* in soil. Citation of a survey by Jensen (1950) on 264 Danish agricultural soils should suffice for purposes of this discussion. The following densities of *Azotobacter* were found:

Azotobacter per gram of soil	% of soils
0	46·2
100	26·9
100—1000	19·7
1000—10,000	6·1
10,000—100,000	1·1

The nitrifying bacteria also are commonly represented in soil by the thousands or ten thousands per gram. Only rarely are they to be found in excess of 100,000 per gram. *Nitrosomonas* and *Nitrobacter* together therefore can be expected to account for less than 1% of the soil population.

Holding (1960) has recently studied the abundance of Gram-negative bacteria in soil. He determined their frequency in the total bacterial population and, additionally, the frequency of occurrence of many individual genera. Some of his data are summarized in Table VIII.

TABLE VIII

Frequency of occurrence of Gram-negative bacteria in soil (Holding, 1960)

	% total microbial no. in		
	Plant-free soil	Rhizosphere soil	Soil with glucose added
Pseudomonas (all types)	5·53	13·6	12·4
Xanthomonas	0·28	1·2	
Chromobacterium	0·28	0·2	
Flavobacterium			1·0
Achromobacter	0·49	0·8	4·6
Cytophaga	0·42		
Agrobacterium		1·4	
Alcaligenes		1·0	2·0
All Gram-negative bacteria as a group	7·0	20·0	20·0

Holding's study reveals *Pseudomonas* as the only Gram-negative genus present in either rhizosphere or plant-free soil in excess of 5% of the total count. Clark (1940) has noted fluorescent bacteria, or *Pseudomonas* and *Xanthomonas* combined, to constitute from about 1 to 30% of the rhizosphere population of various plants.

The *Micrococcaceae* are rarely encountered in soil. Conn (1948) found the true cocci so rarely present that he doubted the few actually observed were of soil origin. Time and again, however, cultures were isolated from soil which seemed to be micrococci when first examined, but which on continued study were found to be the coccoid stages of *Arthrobacter*.

Recently, Stolp and Petzold (1962) have described some hitherto unrecognized obligately parasitic bacteria that possess lytic activity for bacteria of the genera *Pseudomonas* and *Xanthomonas*. That such parasitic or related types of bacteria may be encountered in the course of soil microscopy is suggested by recent observations of M. Fieldes.* He has observed spherical bodies or cells, about 0·25 µ in diameter and each bearing a single, heavy flagellum, in the course of examining electron-micrographs of carbon replicas of the surfaces of soil particles.

When considering the types of bacteria in any given soil, perhaps the safest course is always to expect the unexpected. Surveys that show the globiforme bacteria, the sporulating bacilli, or the fluorescent Gram-negative rods as the abundantly occurring bacterial flora in soil are summarizing generalities. Any or all of these types may be found only with difficulty in certain soils in which some combination of environmental conditions and type of energy material available may greatly favor relatively unknown or bizarre species. In such an event, bacteria commonly detected in soil only by special searching and enrichment procedure may become so numerous as to account for a major fraction of the bacterial biomass in soil.

* Personal communication, 1963.

REFERENCES

Alexander, F. E. S. and Jackson, R. M. (1954). *Nature, Lond.* **174**, 750–751.

Alexander, M. (1961). "Introduction to Soil Microbiology." John Wiley and Sons, Inc., New York.

Bartholomew, W. V. and Norman, A. G. (1947). *Soil Sci.* **11**, 270–279.

Beard, W. E. and Clark, F. E. (1962). *Agron. Abstr. 54th Ann. Meeting*, p. 23.

Bhaumik, H. D. and Clark, F. E. (1948). *Proc. Soil Sci. Soc. Am.* **12**, 234–238.

Boynton, D. and Compton, O. C. (1944). *Soil Sci.* **57**, 107–117.

Breed, R. S., Murray, E. G. D. and Hitchens, A. P. (1948). "Bergey's Manual of Det. Bact." 6th Ed. Williams and Wilkins, Baltimore.

Breed, R. S., Murray, E. G. D. and Smith, N. R. (1957). "Bergey's Manual of Det. Bact." 7th Ed. Williams and Wilkins, Baltimore.

Burges, A. (1939). *Broteria* **8**, 64–81.

Burges, A. (1958). "Micro-organisms in the Soil." Hutchinson and Co., Ltd., London.

Calder, E. A. (1957). *J. Soil Sci.* **8**, 60–72.

Clark, F. E. (1940). *Trans. Kans. Acad. Sci.* **43**, 75–84.

Clark, F. E., Jackson, R. D. and Gardner, H. R. (1962). *Proc. Soil Sci. Soc. Am.* **26**, 155–160.

Clark, F. E. and Kemper, W. D. (1966). *In*: "Irrigation of Agr. Lands. Monogr. Publ. Am. Soc. Agron." (R. A. Hagan, ed.), Madison, Wisconsin.

Clark, F. E. and Smith, D. H. (1950). *Proc. Soil Sci. Soc. Am.* **14**, 199–202.

Conn, H. J. (1928). *Bull. N.Y. St. agric. Exp. Stn.* 138.

Conn, H. J. (1948). *Bact. Rev.* **12**, 257–273.

Garrett, S. D. (1956). "Biology of the Root-infecting Fungi." Cambridge Univ. Press, London.

Gibson, T. (1939). Third International Congress of Microbiology (New York). Abstr. of Comm., pp. 304–305.

Goring, C. A. I. and Clark, F. E. (1952). *Proc. Soil Sci. Soc. Am.* **16**, 7–9.

Gyllenberg, H. G. (1957). *Can. J. Microbiol.* **3**, 131–134.

Harmsen, G. W. and van Schreven, D. A. (1955). *In* "Advances in Agronomy." (A. G. Norman, ed.), vol. 7, pp. 299–398. Academic Press Inc., New York.

Hauck, R. D. and Bouldin, D. R. (1961). *Nature, Lond.* **191**, 871–872.

Holding, A. J. (1960). *J. appl. Bact.* **23**, 515–525.

Jackson, M. L., Mackie, W. Z. and Pennington, R. P. (1947). *Proc. Soil Sci. Soc. Am.* **11**, 57–63.

Jagnow, G. (1961). *Nature, Lond.* **191**, 1220–1221.

Jansson, S. L. (1960). *7th Int. Congr. Soil Sci.* (*Madison*), **2**, pp. 635–642.

Jensen, H. L. (1933). *Proc. Linn. Soc. N.S.W.* **58**, 181–185.

Jensen, H. L. (1936). *Proc. Linn. Soc. N.S.W.* **61**, 27–55.

Jensen, H. L. (1950). *Int. Congr. Soil Sci.* vol. 1, 165–172. Amsterdam.

Jones, P. C. T. and Mollison, J. E. (1948). *J. gen. Microbiol.* **2**, 54–69.

Katznelson, H., Rouatt, J. W. and Payne, T. M. B. (1956). *6th Int. Congr. Soil Sci.* C, 151–156. Paris.

Katznelson, H. and Sirois, J. C. (1961). *Nature, Lond.* **191**, 1323–1324.

Kemper, W. D. and Ameniya, M. (1957). *Proc. Soil Sci. Soc. Am.* **21**, 657–660.

Kendall, A. I. (1928). "Bacteriology, General, Pathological and Intestinal." 3rd Ed. Lea and Febiger, Philadelphia.

Kendrick, W. B. and Burges, A. (1962). *Nova Hedwigia* **4**, 313–342.

Krasilnikov, N. A. (1944). *Microbiology* (*U.S.S.R.*) **13**, 144–146.

Krasilnikov, N. A. (1958). "Soil Micro-organisms and Higher Plants." Academy of Sciences USSR, Moscow.

Lees, H. (1954). *In* "Autotrophic Micro-organisms." (B. A. Fry and J. L. Peel, eds.) Cambridge University Press, London.

Lochhead, A. G. (1940). *Can. J. Res. C* **18**, 42–53.

Lochhead, A. G. and Chase, F. E. (1943). *Soil Sci.* **55**, 185–195.

Lochhead, A. G. and Thexton, R. H. (1947). *Can. J. Res. C* **25**, 20–26.

Miller, R. and Schmidt, E. L. (1961). *Agron. Abstr.* (*Ann. Meeting Am. Soc. Agron.*), **53**, 18.)

Minderman, G. (1956). *Pl. Soil* **8**, 42–48.

Mishustin, E. N. (1956). *Soils Fertil.*, **19**, 385–392.

Mooney, G. and Winslow, C. E. A. (1935). *J. Bact.* **30**, 427–440.

Newman, A. S. and Norman, A. G. (1943). *Soil Sci.* **55**, 377–391.

Norman, A. G. (1947). *Proc. Soil Sci. Soc. Am.* **11**, 9–15.

Park, D. (1956). *6th Int. Congr. Soil Sci.* C, 23–28. Paris.

Parker, D. T. and Larson, W. E. (1962). *Proc. Soil Sci. Soc. Am.* **26**, 238–242.

Pelczar, M. J., Jr., and Reid, R. D. (1958). "Microbiology." McGraw-Hill Book Co., Inc., New York.
Quastel, J. H. and Scholefield, P. G. (1951). *Bact. Rev.* 15, 1–53.
Rahn, O. (1945). "Microbes of Merit." J. Cattell Press, Lancaster, Pennsylvania.
Richards, S. J., Hagan, R. M. and McCalla, T. M. (1952). *In* "Soil Physical Conditions and Plant Growth" (Byron C. Shaw, ed.), pp. 303–480. Academic Press, Inc., New York.
Robinson, J. B. D. (1957). *J. agric. Sci. Cambridge* 49, 100–105.
Rovira, A. D. (1956). *Pl. Soil* 7, 178–208.
Russell, E. J. (1950). "Soil Conditions and Plant Growth." 8th Ed. Longmans, Green and Co., London.
Sabey, B. R., Frederick, L. R. and Bartholomew, W. V. (1959). *Proc. Soil Sci. Soc. Am.* 23, 462–465.
Sen, A. and Sen, A. N. (1956). *J. Indian Soc. Soil Sci.* 4, 215–220.
Smith, H. W. (1961). *Nature, Lond.* 191, 1151–1154.
Smith, N. R. and Humfeld, H. (1930). *J. agric. Res.* 41, 97–123.
Sperber, J. I. and Rovira, A. D. (1959). *J. appl. Bact.* 22, 85–95.
Starc, A. (1942). *Arch. Mikrobiol.* 12, 329–343.
Starkey, R. L. (1931). *Soil Sci.* 32, 367–393.
Stolp, H. and Petzold, H. (1962). *Phytopath. Z.* 44, 364–390.
Stotzky, G. and Norman, A. G. (1961a). *Arch. Mikrobiol.* 40, 341–369.
Stotzky, G. and Norman, A. G. (1961b). *Arch. Mikrobiol.* 40, 370–382.
Strugger, S. (1948). *Can. J. Res. C* 26, 188–193.
Taylor, C. B. (1936). *Proc. R. Soc. B*, 119, 269–295.
Taylor, C. B. (1938). *Soil Sci.* 46, 307–321.
Taylor, C. B. (1951). *Proc. Soc. appl. Bact.* 14, 101–111.
Tchan, Y. T. (1952). *Proc. Linn. Soc. N.S.W.* 77, 89–91.
Thornton, H. G. and Gangulee, N. (1926). *Proc. R. Soc. B.* 99, 428–450.
Timonin, M. I. (1935). *Can. J. Res. C* 13, 32–39.
Topping, L. E. (1937). *Zentbl. Bakt. ParasitKde*, Abt. II 97, 289–304.
Vine, H., Thompson, H. A. and Hardy, F. (1942). *Trop. Agric. Trin.* 19, 215–220.
Walker, H. H. and Winslow, C. E. A. (1932). *J. Bact.* 24, 209–241.
Winogradsky, S. (1925). *Annls. Inst. Pasteur, Paris* 39, 299–354.

Chapter 3

Fungi In Soil

J. H. WARCUP

Waite Agricultural Research Institute
Adelaide, South Australia

I. INTRODUCTION

Fifty years ago, Waksman (1916a) raised the question whether soil is the home of an indigenous mycoflora, or merely a resting place for fungal spores floating in the atmosphere. He and subsequent workers have indicated that many fungi grow and reproduce in soil; nevertheless soil is also undoubtedly a "sink" for a wide range of organisms from other habitats. As pointed out by Harley (1960), the term *soil fungi* has no precise meaning. It is applied to the heterogeneous collection of fungi which may be isolated from soil, or which have been observed to exist in some form in soil. With some fungi, the soil phase appears to be little more than a resting spore; other organisms appear confined to soil and complete their life cycle there. In a broad sense the organic layers on the surface of mineral soil are here included as part of the soil complex.

The range of fungi known to occur in soil is very wide, from chytrids to agarics, from saprophytes to root parasites, from parasites of amoebae to parasites of man. Interest in fungi occurring in soil has been great and Cooke (1958) considers that soil has probably been studied more extensively than any other natural habitat of fungi. This is partly because of the importance of fungi as plant pathogens, partly because of their importance in the decomposition of plant and animal residues, and partly through interest in mycorrhiza and the rhizosphere. Many workers have been interested in the ecology of fungi in soil; others have considered soil more as a reservoir for interesting or useful organisms in studies ranging from taxonomy to search for fungi producing antibiotics. This diversity of interest has meant that data on the ecology of fungi in soil are both scattered and in some respects surprisingly fragmentary. Chesters (1949) remarked that so far only a very indistinct picture has been obtained of the fungus at work.

Although knowledge of fungal fructifications occurring on soil is ancient, Adametz in 1886 is considered to have been the first person to isolate fungi from soil. A more detailed study was made by Oudemans and Koning (1902), who inoculated plates of wort agar or wort gelatin with aqueous suspensions, obtained by pulverizing in sterile water, fragments of organic matter extracted from soil. Forty-five species of fungi were identified. Further early studies were those of Hagem (1907, 1910) on the Mucorales in Norwegian soils; Lendner (1908), who studied Mucorales in Switzerland; Dale (1912, 1914), who isolated over 100 fungi from sandy, chalk, peat and black earth soils in England; Beckwith (1911), who investigated some "wheat-sick" soils of North Dakota; and Jensen (1912), who studied the fungal flora of several soils in the U.S.A. The majority of early investigations fall into one or more of three classes: purely systematic studies, physiological or biochemical research, and quantitative studies involving numerical estimates of the fungal flora of soils.

One of the first soilborne diseases to be ascribed to the activity of a parasitic fungus was stem canker of potatoes, which Kühn in 1858 showed to be due to infection by *Rhizoctonia solani*. Other early-ascribed diseases include wilt of potatoes, caused by *Verticillium albo-atrum*, clubroot of crucifers, caused by *Plasmodiophora brassicae*, "take-all" and foot rot of wheat, caused by *Ophiobolus graminis*, and root diseases of forest trees, caused by *Armillaria mellea* (Garrett, 1944). Early work was mainly concerned with elucidation of the cause of various root diseases, but later it was realized that the soil environment exercises a profound effect upon the development of most soilborne pathogens. It was also realized that the soil environment contains biological as well as chemical and physical factors, and that the development of a root disease might be affected not only by the parasite concerned but also by other organisms present. This led many plant pathologists to microbiological studies of soil for, as Garrett (1955) has said, "it is their saprophytic behaviour in the soil that is still the hidden phase in the life cycle of root-infecting fungi."

In 1885, Frank gave the name "mycorrhiza" to the composite fungus-root organ of the Cupuliferae. Associations between fungal hyphae and roots were described in other arborescent angiosperms, and mycorrhiza of the same type were found in many conifers, especially the Pinaceae. They are characterized by the presence of a complete sheath of fungal tissue which encloses the terminal rootlets of the root system. Further studies showed that the roots of many other plants, previously believed to be free from fungal infection, were also colonized by hyphae. In these no external fungal sheath was found, but the mycelium penetrated and ramified through the cortex. Two types of mycorrhiza were therefore recognized: ectotrophic mycorrhiza having an external fungal sheath, and endotrophic mycorrhiza lacking a sheath. The mycorrhizal condition is found in some members of all higher plant phyla; it appears at least as usual amongst seed plants as the uninfected state (Harley, 1959). The majority of the fungi which form ectotrophic mycorrhiza belong to the Basidiomycetes; endotrophic mycorrhiza do not represent a single group, and a variety of fungi, including Phycomycetes, are represented.

In 1904 Hiltner described how the surface of roots was colonized by bacteria and he coined the term rhizosphere for the soil volume immediately influenced by the roots. Since Starkey (1929) reviewed what was then known of the influence of higher plants on soil micro-organisms, the microflora of the rhizosphere has been the subject of much investigation. The rhizosphere has been shown to be a zone of stimulation of many organisms, particularly certain groups of bacteria, the stimulation being due to release of nutrients by the plant as root exudates or as moribund root cells. Many fungi, including saprophytes, plant parasites and mycorrhizal fungi, occur on root surfaces and in the rhizosphere (Garrett, 1956).

Much of the work on fungal floras of the soil has been essentially floristic, but more recently there has been emphasis on the ecology of fungi in soil, on the habitats of individual species and the parts they play in the biochemical processes that take place in soil. The general picture of fungi in soil which seems to be emerging from many recent studies is one of organisms consisting mainly of resting structures in a mosaic of micro-habitats, often making little mycelial growth but bursting into activity when some event brings fresh nutrient to resting cells able to exploit it. Root growth, litter accumulation and the activity of the soil fauna play important parts in producing such events. Much detail is, however, lacking. Further, so little is known about some fungi in soil that we cannot be sure that we are not looking at merely half of the picture.

II. METHODS OF STUDY

The methods that have been used to study fungi in soil are considered in detail for, as with any branch of science, it is a truism to say that knowledge is governed by the techniques available and progress is intimately linked with the development of new approaches and methods. Thus evaluation of present knowledge on fungi in soil is largely dependent on understanding the techniques by which the information has been obtained.

Compared with some other fungal habitats, soil has proved difficult to study. This is a consequence of the multitude of organisms that occur in soil, of the complexities of fungal life cycles, together with the difficulties inherent in investigating soil because of its opacity, its heterogeneous nature and its complex structure.

Fungi may occur in soil as mycelium, as fructifications or as a variety of inactive spores. As has recently been re-emphasized (Garrett, 1955; Harley and Waid, 1955) one of the first requirements for an ecological study of soil organisms is that the methods must distinguish between organisms which are vegetatively active and playing a part in the soil processes and those which exist in a dormant or inactive form as spores and other propagules. Many of the methods that have been used, in fact, do not give this information (Warcup, 1960). In attempts to overcome these problems, a wide range of methods, both microscopic and cultural, have been used to study fungi in soil (Durbin, 1961).

In general there have been two different approaches to the study of fungi in soil. The first is by microscopic examination either of soil or of substrates or materials, such as glass or nylon, after they have been placed in soil; the second is by isolation of organisms, either directly or by cultural techniques. Each approach has both advantages and disadvantages.

A. DIRECT OBSERVATION METHODS

Kubiena (1938) approached the problem directly by observing fungi actually growing in the soil, using a microscope equipped with a normal incidence illuminator. His observations were necessarily confined to naturally or artificially exposed soil surfaces but yielded information not previously obtained by other methods, While other investigators have used direct observation (Chesters, 1948) this approach has been rather neglected. Surfaces need not always be examined in the field, but freshly exposed surfaces of soil blocks may be examined in the laboratory (Warcup, 1957).

1. Soil sections

Several workers have prepared sections of soil. Kubiena (1938) used a thermolabile plastic material to prepare sections of soil, but his method has not been followed extensively. Haarløv and Weis-Fogh (1953, 1955) impregnated soil with agar for sectioning. An undisturbed sample of soil was soaked in a hot, 2% aqueous solution of agar, cooled, hardened in alcohol and sectioned as thinly as the largest mineral particles would allow. From sandy soils good serial sections of 750 μ thickness were obtained while organic soils were cut at 100 μ. Alexander and Jackson (1955) adapted standard geological techniques for sectioning rock to prepare sections of soils. The method involves impregnation with a synthetic resin and final preparation of sections by cutting, grinding and polishing. Sections about 100 μ thick can easily be obtained. Hepple and Burges (1956) and Burges and Nicholas (1961) used a similar method but with different resins, and obtained sections 50–60 μ in thickness. Minderman (1956) froze soil to −10°C and infiltrated it with gelatin which was then fixed in formalin. The sample was then treated with hydrofluoric acid to dissolve sand grains before preparing sections. Sections as thin as 7·5–10 μ were obtained.

These methods are of use in studying micro-organisms in their natural relationships to soil structure, although the methods which involve desiccation before embedding have been criticized (Harrløv and Weis-Fogh, 1955) because desiccation changes the texture of those soil layers in which most of the organic activity is concentrated.

2. Soil staining

Conn (1918) seems to have been the first to stain soil suspensions. He prepared an infusion of soil (1:9) in dilute gelatin (0·015%) and spread 0·1 ml of this across a slide, staining it with rose bengal; erythrosin (Cholodny, 1930) may be used instead. A more recent staining procedure is that of Jones and Mollison (1948), who suspended soil in melted and cooled 1·5% agar. A drop of the agar suspension is placed on a haemocytometer and a coverslip quickly added. The film obtained is floated off on sterile water, placed on a microscope slide, allowed to dry, then stained with phenolic aniline blue and made into a permanent mount. Hyphae were measured as total length per g of soil.

Staining methods allow organisms to be seen and counted, but their relation to soil structure is, in general, lost. It should perhaps be noted that the Jones and Mollison technique tends to neglect the heavier soil particles with which many organisms are associated.

3. Slide or burial techniques

A different approach, but still predominantly observational, is that of the burial methods such as Rossi-Cholodny slides. Rossi (1928) pressed a clean microscope slide against a freshly exposed soil surface so that soil particles and microbial colonies adhered to the slide. After removal and staining, the soil impression slide depicted micro-organisms as they actually occurred in the soil at that time. He also buried slides in soil for different periods. This latter method was perfected by Cholodny (1930) who first brought it to the attention of most workers and it has become known as the Rossi-Cholodny or contact-slide method. It has become the most widely used *in situ* method.

Demeter and Mossel (1933) used the method to detect changes in the population of a field soil and it was used in the laboratory by Conn (1932), who considered it satisfactory to demonstrate a change in the microflora of soil from fungi or actinomycetes to bacteria. Eaton and King (1934) employed the method to ascertain the time of the year at which growth of *Phymatotrichum omnivorum* occurred. Jensen (1934, 1935) adapted the method for quantitative study by estimating the frequency of fungal hyphae in 500 randomized microscopic fields. Starkey (1938) studied the occurrence of micro-organisms in relation to plant roots by letting the roots grow against buried slides. Blair (1945) used the method to study the growth of *Rhizoctonia solani* through soil in the laboratory.

It should be noted that there is an essential difference between soil impression slides and Rossi-Cholodny slides. The former indicate fungal occurrence

3+S.B.

at the time of examining a soil, the latter provide a substrate for fungal growth after the soil has been disturbed. There is strong circumstantial evidence that fungal growth on buried slides may be influenced by the disturbance of the soil in burying the slides. Sewell (1959b), noting the frequency of species of *Mortierella* on Rossi-Cholodny slides, remarks that "either by reduction of the soil fungistatic factor or by effecting changes in local soil conditions, or both, the immersion in soil of solid inert objects might produce a physical 'rhizosphere' within which certain fungi normally quiescent or sparsely growing are stimulated to vigorous growth and consequently are isolated so frequently by direct methods as to misrepresent their real occurrence." Brown (1958a) used impression slides similar to those of Rossi, but smeared the slides with nitro-cellulose thinned to a suitable consistency with amyl acetate to aid retention of soil on the slide.

Instead of glass slides, Waid and Woodman (1957) buried nylon mesh in soil. After periods of burial up to several months the gauze was removed and fungal activity estimated by counting the number of hyphae per mesh.

4. Observation boxes

Another observational method is the use of an observation box (Dean, 1929; Linford, 1942; Sewell, 1959c; Parkinson, 1957). Slides, coverslips, etc., can be incorporated into the side of a box containing soil in which plants may be growing, permitting microscopic examination at a high magnification under reflected light.

While microscopic methods give information on the location and form of fungi in soil, all direct observation methods suffer from the fact that the majority of the mycelia seen in soil or on slides are without fructifications and hence cannot be identified. Since the number of different fungi found in any soil is large, this is a serious handicap and it is probable that the tedium of examining slides, together with the difficulty of identifying the fungi present, have discouraged the use of direct observation methods.

B. ISOLATION METHODS

Most workers who have studied fungi in soil have used isolation methods because these, in general, allow identification of the organisms obtained. It seems probable, also, that well-prepared isolation plates, such as soil dilution plates, have direct aesthetic appeal. Most isolation techniques, however, are indirect methods and it is difficult to tell whether the fungi growing on the plates arise from active mycelia or from inactive spores. This affords a marked contrast with direct observation methods, a contrast that has been epitomized by Garrett (1952): "with the plate count one identifies what one cannot see (i.e. *in situ*), whereas with the direct method one sees what one cannot identify." Recognition of these difficulties has led to much work on isolation techniques in relation to the study of active mycelia in soil. While isolation methods have recently been discussed (Warcup, 1960), they are treated in some detail here since understanding of the type of information obtained by different methods is essential for an understanding of soil mycology.

1. The soil dilution plate method

The classical and most widely used isolation method is the soil dilution plate method (Waksman, 1927; Garrett, 1951; Warcup, 1960). The method consists of shaking a known amount of soil in sterile water, then obtaining a progressive series of dilutions. From one or more of the dilutions, 1 ml samples are placed in Petri dishes and dispersed with melted but cooled agar. The effect of these various operations on the degree of variability in estimated numbers has been studied extensively (Brierley, Jewson and Brierley, 1927; Bisby, James and Timonin, 1933; James and Sutherland, 1939; Waksman, 1944; Montégut, 1960).

Since there are normally more bacteria than fungi in soil it is necessary to suppress them on isolation plates. To reduce the growth of bacteria and Actinomycetes on soil dilution plates, Waksman (1922) and Jensen (1931) adjusted the medium with sulphuric acid to about pH 4·0; other acids, lactic, boric, and phosphoric, have also been used. Acid, however, is known to depress or prevent the growth of some fungi (Thornton, 1956a). Smith and Dawson (1944) proposed the use of rose bengal at a concentration of 1 : 15,000 as a bacteriostatic agent, which Dawson and Dawson (1946) found to produce no fungistatic effect other than a reduction of colony size; Martin (1950) recommended the use of a peptone-dextrose agar containing 1 : 30,000 rose bengal and 30 μg/ml streptomycin or 2 μg/ml aureomycin (chlortetracycline). Pugh (1958) and Warcup (1960) recorded, however, that rose bengal inhibited the growth of some mycelia. Pady, Kramer and Pathak (1960) noted suppression of fungi on media containing rose bengal if exposed to bright light. The effect of light in depressing growth or killing fungi on certain media has also been noted by Weinhold and Hendrix (1962), Nash and Snyder (1962) and Kerr (1963). While antibiotics used either singly or in combination (Dulany, Larsen and Stapley, 1955) are more satisfactory than acidification for suppression of bacteria, the growth of some fungi may also be suppressed by antibacterial antibiotics. For instance, Hine (1962) reported that whereas *Pythium aphanidermatum* and *P. ultimum* grew in the presence of 100 ppm of streptomycin, *P. arrhenomanes*, *P. graminicolum* and *P. mamillatum* were inhibited by much lower concentrations; Schmitthenner (1962) found that chloromycetin even at 5 mg/l partially inhibited *Pythium* spp.; streptomycin is also inhibitory to certain isolates of *Phytophthora* (Eckert and Tsao, 1962).

Several chemicals, including sodium deoxycholate, oxgall, sodium propionate, pentachloronitrobenzene (PCNB), or rose bengal, have been used to retard fungal colony growth and thus minimize the degree of interference between developing colonies on isolation plates (Papavizas and Davey, 1959b; 1961a). Paharia and Kommedahl (1956) reported that distributing 1 ml of soil solution over the solidified agar surface 2–3 days after the plates were poured gave more colonies than incorporating the soil dilution at the time of pouring the plates, especially in the presence of streptomycin and rose bengal. James (1959) found that soil extract agar and Martin's agar with soil extract were superior to Martin's without soil extract. Soil extract, however, is not always superior (Johnson and Manka, 1961); the difference may be due to differences in the soil extracts used by different workers. Miller (1956) showed that potato dextrose agar and "V-8 juice" agar contain copper in amounts sufficient to be toxic to some fungi, particularly Phycomycetes.

By the soil dilution plate method, the number of colonies/g oven-dry soil may be obtained, also species may be isolated for compiling species lists. It was early realized that the "number" of fungi in soil has little meaning since during the manipulations a single hypha may break into fragments each of which would count as one while a single cluster of spores might be counted as thousands. Further, the method has always been considered to be highly selective, particularly for species that spore abundantly, since many fungi known to occur in soil are rarely isolated on soil dilution plates (Brierley, 1923; Chesters, 1949). Direct evidence for this view has recently been obtained (Warcup, 1955b, 1957). Dilution plates after a short incubation were searched for young fungal colonies, each of which was removed in a small block of agar for direct examination. After the nature of the propagule had been determined, the colony was transferred to fresh medium to permit growth and identification. In this way the majority of colonies developing on dilution plates prepared from samples of wheat-field soil were found to have arisen from spores. Comparative studies showed that not only did dilution studies neglect a large number of fungi but that many of these were present in soil as hyphae.

Warcup (1960) concluded that the dilution plate method is of little value in estimating the activity of fungi in soil. This view has been questioned by Griffiths and Siddiqi (1961), who consider that while a single quantitative estimate from dilution plates is of very restricted value, this is not necessarily true of a succession of estimates made at relatively frequent intervals, for here it is possible to detect changes in populations of spores. They suggest that the spore population may be regarded as a barometer of fungal activity and, just as with an ordinary barometer, it is change in value rather than absolute value which is of interest. This viewpoint has merit but it should always be borne in mind that change in spore number may occur without mycelial activity. For instance, decay of roots or fragmentation of debris may increase spore number without fungal growth. Further, while it is undoubtedly correct to hold the view that even if soil contains a large number of inert conidia these must have resulted from previous mycelial activity, yet this is of little help in elucidating the dynamics of soil populations.

While there has been much criticism of the soil dilution plate method, it has been of great value and, if due regard is paid to its known limitations, it is a most useful means of investigating certain aspects of soil mycology.

2. The soil plate method

In this method (Warcup, 1950, 1960) a small quantity of soil is dispersed throughout a thin layer of agar medium in the isolation plate. The method was devised after it was observed that in the preparation of dilution plates many fungi are discarded with the residue; it also dispenses with the preparation of water blanks. To prepare soil plates from soils with a high number of colonies/g, Johnson and Manka (1961) diluted the soil with sterile sand.

While incorporation of soil particles with agar should allow hyphae present to grow, recent data (Warcup, 1957) suggest that this may not be so. Colonization of the agar is dependent upon fungal growth rate, and usually the number of fast-growing organisms present as spores in a soil is sufficient to mask growth from viable hyphae. In any case, without further evidence, it is impossible to tell which fungi on a soil plate may have developed from hyphae.

In a comparison of soil dilution and soil plates, Warcup (1957) concluded that both methods give essentially the same picture of the fungal flora of the soil, though soil plates tend to favour faster-growing species present in soil in relatively low number. The chief advantage of soil plates is their ease of preparation. Since they incorporate all the soil, soil plates in conjunction with selective media or other selective isolation procedures may be of more use than soil dilution plates. Park (1961a) has used soil plates incubated in an atmosphere of CO_2 to isolate *Fusarium oxysporum* from populations of less than 10 units/g soil.

3. The direct inoculation and the soil desiccation methods

These methods, more of historical than of practical significance, were both devised to try to answer the question of what fungi are present in soil as mycelia. In the direct inoculation method, Waksman (1916a) transferred lumps of soil, about 1 cm in diameter, on to sterile plates of Czapek's solution agar. After incubation at 22°c for 24 hours, hyphal tips were removed. Waksman remarked: "the organisms thus isolated are believed to come from the mycelium that is actually found in the soil. The period allowed for incubation was not long enough for spores to germinate and produce such a mass of mycelium." Saitô (1955a) and Warcup (1960) found, however, that while Mucorales were isolated from soil lumps, direct microscopic examination of lumps failed to reveal phycomycetous hyphae, thus suggesting that the mycelia developing were derived from spores.

McLennan (1928) suggested that a possible method for discriminating between fungal mycelium and spores in soil might be drying the soil over calcium chloride in a desiccator. Her experiments showed that mycelium was killed by this treatment whereas spores were not. Eastwood (1952) with fungi in pure culture and Warcup (1960) with natural soil found that besides its effect on mycelium, desiccation over calcium chloride caused a marked loss of viability of spores.

4. The immersion techniques

Several general techniques have been devised in which a substrate for fungal growth is placed in soil.

The earliest is the Rossi-Cholodny slide technique; a few workers (Chesters and Thornton, 1956) have attempted isolation from fungal hyphae growing on such slides. Gams (1959) used nylon strips and isolated fungi by placing the strips on agar media. Tribe (1957a, 1960a, 1961) buried pieces of Cellophane attached to coverslips in soil. After different periods of time and at different stages of decomposition of the Cellophane the coverslips were removed and examined microscopically. Fungi may also be isolated, care being taken that growth occurs from hyphae in the Cellophane and not from attached soil particles. Lens tissue paper has been used in a similar way (Griffiths and Jones, 1963).

Immersion tubes (Chesters, 1940, 1948) and screened immersion plates (Thornton, 1952, 1956a, 1958) resemble each other in that both attempt the isolation of mycelium from soil and both introduce an agar medium into natural soil. Immersion tubes consist of glass tubes, with 4–6 spirally arranged invaginated capillaries, filled with a nutrient agar. A soil core is removed in the field and an immersion tube inserted in its place. After 7–14 days it is removed, and fungi isolated from it by removing a core the length of the tube which is then cut into portions which are plated out. Mueller and Durrell (1957) and MacWithey (1957) have described modifications of Chesters' immersion tubes. Screened immersion plates consist of a distilled water agar-coated glass slide carried in a "Perspex" box with a lid containing 10 spaced holes for entry of fungi. After a suitable period of burial in soil, the plates are removed, examined and fungal growth transferred to potato-dextrose agar. Further immersion techniques have been reported by La Touche (1948), Sewell (1956), Wood and Wilcoxson (1960) and Andersen and Huber (1962).

Chesters and Thornton (1956) compared the fungi isolated from a forest soil by immersion tubes and by screened immersion plates. Discussing the results, they remark that colonization of immersion tubes depends on the ability of individuals to compete successfully with other members of the soil population for entry through capillary orifices (Chesters, 1948; Nicot and Chevaugeon, 1949). Also, once established, the fungi must be capable of growing into the depths of the medium far enough to be isolated in the agar core. Sewell (1959b) noted that fast-growing fungi once established may colonize the bulk of the agar in the tube, and therefore be recorded with a high frequency of isolation. Brown (1958b) recorded that *Trichoderma viride*, by its vigorous growth on the agar film, often excluded the entry of other species into Sewell soil traps.

While it is considered that immersion techniques isolate active mycelium from soil, and the isolation of *Rhizoctonia* and *Armillaria* (Chesters, 1948) and *Rhizoctonia*, *Papulaspora* and other non-sporing mycelia (Thornton, 1956b, 1960) substantiate this, it must be pointed out that there is an element of doubt about sporing fungi isolated, since Dobbs and Hinson (1953, 1960) found that spores may germinate in water that condenses on glass surfaces buried in soil. There is also the possibility that mites and other small soil animals may carry spores on to the buried agar (Warcup, 1960; Dobbs and Hinson, 1960).

5. Soil partition methods

Several methods have been devised for fractionating or partitioning soil, usually into particles of various sizes (Chesters, 1948; Parkinson and Williams, 1961), or sometimes of a particular type (Warcup, 1955a; Levisohn, 1955; Ohms, 1957; Boosalis and Scharen, 1959). Most methods have used sieves of varying sizes, but sedimentation, centrifuging and impaction have also been used; the aim of most techniques has been the removal of fungal spores and fine soil particles and the examination of other units in soil.

Warcup (1955a) reported a simple method for isolating hyphae from soil; essentially the method depends on the fact that when a soil suspension is prepared, many of the fungal hyphae remain with the heavier soil particles of the residue. Removal of the fine suspended matter from the residue also permits visual examination of the latter for hyphae, which may then be removed and grown on agar media. Soils high in organic matter may be more difficult to examine than soils with a high proportion of fine particles. The location of and examination of hyphae on the isolation plates, though tedious, is essential since hyphae may have small humus particles or occasionally spores along their surfaces and growth may originate from these attached particles. However, with suitable precautions one may be sure that growth is from a hypha and no other fungal unit.

In a study of the fungal flora of a wheat-field by dilution plates and by hyphal isolation, Warcup (1957) found that a high proportion of the fungi obtained by hyphal isolation were rare or absent from dilution plates. In contrast to dilution plates, where the most abundant fungi obtained were species of *Penicillium*, *Rhizopus*, *Mucor*, *Cladosporium*, and *Fusarium*, hyphal isolation gave many fungi which remained sterile in culture. Some have since been found to be Discomycetes or Basidiomycetes. While hyphal isolation records many of the fungi present as mycelium in soil, it gives no information on fungi present as mycelium on, or in, residues, large fragments of organic matter, or roots.

Sclerotia may also be obtained from soil by examination of the heavier soil particles following sedimentation or sieving (Warcup, 1959).

Following sieving and comminution of plant debris obtained from soil, Boosalis and Scharen (1959) found by microscopic examination that *Aphanomyces euteiches* may overwinter as oospores embedded in dead plant tissue. They also isolated *Rhizoctonia solani* by plating out similarly treated debris. Levisohn (1955) isolated *Boletus* from soil by picking out rhizomorphs, surface sterilizing them in 0·1% HCl, then plating them on agar media; surface sterilization is not always necessary (Warcup, 1959).

Ohms (1957) obtained large numbers of vesicles of a phycomycetous endophyte by sieving soil and then separating the vesicles from accompanying particles by centrifuging in tubes containing sugar-water mixtures of different densities. Ledingham and Chinn (1955) used a flotation method to recover spores of *Helminthosporium sativum* from soil. Soil mixed with a small amount of mineral oil is shaken up with water; the emulsion which collects on the surface of the water contains most (80–90%) of the spores of *H. sativum*.

The method is suitable also for other fungi with spores with hydrophobic surfaces. Parkinson and Williams (1961) have used a series of washing boxes to fractionate soil into particles of various sizes.

A radically different method for obtaining soil particles of particular size is through use of the Andersen sampler (Buxton and Kendrick, 1963). Weighed amounts of lightly pulverized soil were drawn through a perforated aluminium disk and impacted on agar media, the soil being dispersed uniformly into 400 equal-sized units per dish. Buxton and Kendrick found that this method gave more reproducible counts of *Pythium* and *Fusarium* than did soil dilution plates.

6. Isolation from roots and debris

Since roots and larger pieces of debris constitute major substrates for fungi in soil, any investigation into fungal occurrence and activity in soil needs to consider the growth of fungi on and in these substrates. Roots have long been examined for fungi, particularly for root-disease organisms, mycorrhizal fungi or in connection with rhizosphere studies; larger pieces of debris in soil can be examined in a similar way. Rhizosphere studies have mainly been made by dilution techniques so that little information on activity of fungi is obtainable from them (Harley and Waid, 1955). Pathological investigations have often been made by plating out suitable pieces from the edges of lesions following some sterilization procedure. In some cases, and particularly with fine roots, surface sterilization may kill all organisms in the root, so washing techniques have been used (Simmonds, 1930).

Washing techniques have been used by many workers for the study of fungi particularly on root surfaces (Kurbis, 1937; Simmonds and Ledingham, 1937; Robertson, 1954; Stenton, 1958; Parkinson and Kendrick, 1960). Harley and Waid (1955), in a study of the fungi on roots and decaying petioles in soil, gave the material serial washings in sterile water and by plating out portions of the wash water checked how effectively fungal units were removed. They noted that populations growing on agar from unwashed surfaces are different from those obtained from washed surfaces, because in the former sporing Hyphomycetes are greatly over-estimated, whilst Phycomycetes and more particularly slow-growing non-sporing mycelia are under-represented. The difficulties in removing fungal spores from roots and other surfaces in soil have often not been fully appreciated (Stenton, 1958).

A further difficulty in isolating from roots or other larger fragments is that on plating out such material on agar usually only the faster-growing species survive, overgrowing any other fungi. Stover (1953b) macerated banana roots in a Waring Blender, and reported a greater range of fungi by this technique than from plating root segments. For examining small individual roots, Warcup (1959, 1960) used a root-fragmentation method and isolated many slower-growing non-sporing fungi, including Basidiomycetes, from the roots of pasture plants. Fragmentation of some roots, however, may reduce the number of colonies obtained, owing to release of toxic materials (Clarke and Parkinson, 1960).

With some fungi, including plant pathogens, it may be more advantageous to keep roots or debris in a moist chamber than to plate out on agar (Taubenhaus and Ezekiel, 1930; Keyworth, 1951; Butler, 1953).

Wilhelm (1956) used a different approach for examining fungi occurring on roots. He surface-sterilized roots, often whole root systems, with mercuric chloride, and buried them for 2–4 weeks in sterilized moist sand. Roots were then examined for resting or reproductive structures of various fungi; these were isolated for further study.

7. Selective methods

A range of selective methods has been used to isolate fungi from soil. Selective methods are especially valuable when the organisms are present in soil in low numbers.

A method especially profitable with species of *Pythium* and other watermoulds is to isolate from hemp seed floating in water covering the soil sample. Papavizas and Davey (1959a) have used stem pieces of mature Buckwheat (*Fagopyrum esculentum*) for isolation of *Rhizoctonia solani* from soil; Baker (1953) used rose stick baits for *Chalaropsis thielavioides*. Many workers have used straw burial techniques such as that devised by Sadasivan (1939) to isolate fungi from soil. Yarwood (1946) isolated *Thielaviopsis basicola* with carrot disks; to prevent bacterial rot, soaking the disks in 0·05% streptomycin has been recommended (Maloy and Alexander, 1958). Lloyd and Lockwood (1962) have cautioned, however, that carrots bought in plastic bags in the U.S.A. may themselves be contaminated with *Chalaropsis thielavioides* and *Thielaviopsis*. Campbell (1949) inoculated apples with soil for isolation of *Phytophthora cinnamomi*; Newhook (1959) found that better results were obtained if the soil to be tested was soaked for two days before being inserted into the apples. Pineapple leaves have also been used for *P. cinnamomi* (Anderson, 1951) and lemons for *P. parasitica* and *P. citrophthora* (Klotz and Fawcett, 1939). Cellophane, boiled grass leaves, pine pollen, shrimp chitin, insect wings, hair, and cast snakeskin have been used as bait for soil chytrids (Sparrow, 1957); hair has also been used for dermatophytes (Vanbreuseghem, 1952; Griffin, 1960) and other fungi. Dermatophytes have also been isolated by the mouse-injection method (Emmons, 1951). Many workers have used hosts as selective media for isolation of soil-borne pathogens; hosts are often the only means of showing the presence in soil of pathogens of aerial parts of plants. Maloy and Alexander (1958) have also used hosts as selective media for a "most probable number" method for the estimation of populations of plant pathogens in soil.

8. Selective media

In general, mycologists have had less success than bacteriologists in their search for selective media, though they have well realized how much easier isolation would be by use of selective media. Recently, however, with the spate of antibiotics and antifungal agents being produced commercially, the

3*

possibilities of obtaining good selective media have become much more promising. Vaartaja (1960) screened a range of fungicidal materials in agar culture and found that many had a selective action on 10 species of fungi representing different fungal groups. He considered that this selectivity might be utilized in isolating fungi; for instance the polyene group of antibiotics are tolerated by *Pythium* and *Phytophthora* but not by most other organisms; limited tests suggested that *Phytophthora cactorum* can be separated from the usually faster-growing *Pythium* through its better tolerance of tannins; compound B22555 (Dexon) was highly specific against Pythiaceae.

Eckert and Tsao (1962) have used pimaricin for isolating *Phytophthora* and *Pythium* from root tissues; on media incorporating pimaricin no fungi other than *Pythium* and *Phytophthora* were obtained. Singh and Mitchell (1961) used both PCNB and pimaricin for making a selective enumeration of *Pythium* in soil platings. Since pimaricin rapidly deteriorates at high temperatures and in the presence of moisture and sunlight, it should be used immediately after the suspension is prepared. Schmitthenner (1962) has used endomycin for Pythiaceae because it is more stable than pimaricin. Singh and Mitchell also stress the need for caution in selecting media to be used with inhibitors since PCNB and pimaricin adversely affected *Pythium* when used in media containing oxgall.

Russell (1956) reported a medium using *o*-phenyl phenol for selective isolation of Basidiomycetes from wood pulp and from air in pulp mills; in my experience this medium is not successful for isolating Basidiomycetes from soil. Parmeter and Hood (1961) have used autoclaved culture filtrates of *Fusarium solani* f. *phaseoli* incorporated in agar as a medium to isolate that strain from soil. Isolates developed their characteristic pigment and sporulated well but competing fungi, including *F. oxysporum*, were restricted on the culture-filtrate medium. Martinson and Baker (1962) found that exudates from radish combined with media significantly increased the isolation of *Rhizoctonia solani*.

If good selective media become available, it may be necessary to reconsider present isolation procedures; it may no longer be necessary to fragment tissues to isolate slow-growing fungi; it may be simple to demonstrate a low number of units of a fungus in soil. Caution, however, will be necessary to make sure that no form (mycelium, resting structures, or spores) of a fungus is inhibited by the selective substances used.

III. THE FUNGI OCCURRING IN SOIL

Although floristic lists of soil fungi have been compiled since the end of the last century, it is of interest that we are still unable to give an adequate picture of the fungal flora of a soil. This is because most of our knowledge of the fungi present in soil has been derived from studies using the soil dilution plate method, and because many fungi do not sporulate readily on agar media.

A wide range of soils under many different types of vegetation and from many different geographical areas has been examined for fungi. A partial list of such investigations includes: fungi from coniferous forest soils (Morrow, 1932; Ellis, 1940; Kendrick, 1958), deciduous forest soils (Tresner, Backus and Curtis, 1954; Krzemieniewska and Badura, 1954; Witkamp, 1960; Christensen, Whittingham and Novak, 1962), heath soils (McLennan and Ducker, 1954; Sewell, 1959d), peat soils (Stenton, 1953; Moore, 1954), grassland soils (Warcup, 1951a; Orpurt and Curtis, 1957; Apinis, 1958), recently glaciated soils (Cooke and Lawrence, 1959), desert soils (Nicot, 1960; Durrell and Shields, 1960), tropical soils (Farrow, 1954), mangrove swamps (Swart, 1958), sand dunes (Webley, Eastwood and Gimingham, 1952; Saitô, 1955b; Brown, 1958b), salt marshes and mudflats (Bayliss Elliot, 1930; Saitô, 1952; Pugh, 1960), and cultivated soils (Nicot, 1953; Miller, Giddens and Foster, 1957; Guillemat and Montégut, 1957; Warcup, 1957; Joffe, 1963).

Early studies by the soil dilution plate method in various countries showed that certain genera of fungi were commonly found in soil; this observation led Waksman (1916b, 1917) to postulate that there is a cosmopolitan fungal flora of the soil. Waksman studied the fungi occurring in 25 soils from North America and Hawaii and collated his results with those obtained by investigators in different parts of Europe. Since *Aspergillus, Mucor, Penicillium* and *Trichoderma* were found in all investigations, Waksman concluded that these organisms, associated with several of the following, *Zygorrhynchus, Cladosporium, Alternaria, Rhizopus, Fusarium, Verticillium, Cephalosporium, Acrostalagmus, Scopulariopsis, Botrytis,* some sterile mycelium, and some yeasts, made up the fungal flora of a soil. Species of these genera are still prominent in lists of soil fungi today (Gilman, 1957). Burges (1958) has pointed out that this apparent uniformity of the soil flora may be largely an artifact, based partly on uniformity in the method of isolation, and partly on the fact that the genera quoted all have fairly characteristic sporing structures that allow easy identification at least to genus, whereas isolates which are difficult to identify are seldom included in lists of soil fungi. It also ignores what is known of the distribution of fructifications of the larger Ascomycetes and Basidiomycetes. Populations of these fungi may be different for a forest, a meadow or a heath; one of the most obvious specializations in habitat is that of coniferous forests in contrast with dicotyledonous (Corner, 1950).

The soil dilution plate method has been used to obtain the "number" of fungi in soil and also to study the diversity of the soil flora. It was early realized that many fungi known to fruit on soil did not occur on soil dilution plates. Brierley (1923) remarked "that of the multitudes of Basidiomycetes growing in wood and meadow not one should have been recorded is indeed startling. It was at first thought that many imperfect fungi might be conidial stages of Basidiomycetes, but much search at Rothamsted has, up to the present, failed to reveal clamp connections in the hyphae." Bisby, Timonin and James (1935) point out that there are records of some 670 species of Basidiomycetes in Manitoba, the large majority of which grow "on the ground," yet these fungi were virtually absent from their isolations from soil.

While it is known that most larger Ascomycetes and Basidiomycetes do not sporulate readily, if at all, on agar media, dilution studies usually fail to reveal non-sporing mycelia which could represent these fungi. Chesters (1949) emphasized that while a great deal of labour has been expended on the estimation of numbers and species of fungi in soil it must be understood that these labours have been successful only in part. He considered, that, quite apart from the higher Basidiomycetes, such frequent inhabitants of the soil as species of *Pythium*, species of *Mortierella* and a galaxy of the darker Hyphomycetes are seldom, if ever, reflected in their true relationships in dilution plate studies.

The species recorded by Gilman (1957) provide an interesting commentary on present knowledge of the fungi isolated from soil. Gilman lists over 690 fungi in 170 genera as having been isolated from soil; however, 10 genera, *Penicillium, Fusarium, Mucor, Aspergillus, Achlya, Mortierella, Pythium, Chaetomium, Saprolegnia* and *Monosporium*, account for more than half the species isolated. Gilman lists 80 Ascomycetes, 2 Mycelia Sterilia, and no Basidiomycetes. Burges (1958) commented that, while it would be unjustifiable to place great importance on any particular one of these figures, nevertheless they reflect quite fairly the general picture of soil fungi as determined by the dilution plate method. With the reservation that Gilman's book is a compilation, this is probably so apart from the species of watermoulds, *Achlya, Saprolegnia*, etc., most of which were not isolated by the soil dilution plate method. Some workers are of the opinion that soil mycologists must accept such genera as *Mortierella, Penicillium* and *Aspergillus* as dominant and active members of the soil population; most workers, however, find it difficult to reconcile the lists of fungi isolated by the dilution plate method with many of their general observations of fungal activity in soil, and also with the diverse range of organisms obtained by selective techniques.

Robertson (1954) and Harley and Waid (1955) showed that on many living mycorrhizal root systems cleansed of fungal spores by prolonged washing, there occurred many non-sporing mycelia which were not obtained when unwashed root surfaces or dilutions of washings from root surfaces were cultured. Similar mycelial forms had been encountered by many earlier workers on mycorrhiza. Since such non-sporing mycelia were not known from soil or litter fragments, Harley and Waid suggested that they might perhaps belong to the group of "root-inhabiting" fungi which had been distinguished from the actively saprophytic and rapidly-growing "soil-inhabiting" fungi by Garrett (1951).

Warcup (1955a, 1957) investigated the occurrence and activity of fungi in a wheat-field soil by plating techniques and by direct isolation. He found that a high proportion of the fungi obtained by hyphal isolation were non-sporing species which were rare or absent from soil dilution or soil plates. *Rhizoctonia solani, Rhizoctonia* spp. and 9 Basidiomycetes were among the 68 non-sporing fungi obtained by hyphal isolation. Thornton (1956b, 1960) found that *Rhizoctonia* occurred in natural grassland soils and formed a high proportion of his isolates on screened immersion plates. Papavizas and Davey

(1962) also isolated many clones of *R. solani* existing saprophytically in soil. Sewell (1959b) and Parkinson and Kendrick (1960) have noted many dark non-sporing mycelia in soil and litter; Saitô (1956), Warcup (1959) and Witkamp (1960) have provided evidence that Basidiomycetes are active in certain horizons of undisturbed and cultivated soils. Listing the fungi isolated from soils in Israel, Rayss and Borut (1958) comment that "many forms of sterile mycelia belonging to the genera *Rhizoctonia*, *Sclerotium* and others have been isolated by us from different soils without being definitely identified." Evidence is strong that non-sporing fungi have been obtained more frequently by plating techniques than published lists would suggest, but are not included in such lists because they are difficult to identify and because they are found only occasionally and are not usually among the "abundant" fungi. It is also interesting to recall that the fungi seen on Rossi-Cholodny slides are usually sterile. While it is often considered that this may be because conditions favourable for growth need not be suitable for sporulation, it may well be that many of these mycelia, if isolated, would prove to be non-sporing on agar media. The data show that non-sporing fungi are common though not necessarily present in high "number," that they may be isolated from soil, from root surfaces and other microhabitats. Some have clamp connections and may be placed as Basidiomycetes, but the identity of the majority is not known. Another neglected aspect is that both non-sporing *and conidial* fungi may represent imperfect states of Ascomycetes.

Investigation into the identity of non-sporing mycelia obtained from Urrbrae loam at the Waite Institute, Adelaide, is being undertaken, and some progress has been made, particularly with Basidiomycetes and Discomycetes (Warcup and Talbot, 1962, 1963). While the identity of many of the fungi isolated from this soil is not yet known, it may be of interest to list the genera (Table I) which have been obtained from *one* soil. All were obtained from any of two adjacent wheatfields and a sown permanent pasture, all on the same soil type. The fungi were investigated by direct observation, by isolation of hyphae, rhizomorphs, sclerotia or fructifications from soil, by examination of living and dead roots, decomposing residues and other substrates, besides soil dilution plates and soil plates; no special baiting techniques were used.

While a wide range of genera has been obtained, the number of sterile mycelia as yet unidentified is perhaps surprising (Warcup and Talbot, 1962). It should be remembered, however, that not all mycelial isolates may represent different species of fungi. Mycelial isolates are grouped on cultural and hyphal characters into "types." Since it is easier to combine records if two cultural types are found to represent different strains of the same fungus than to disentangle records where more than one fungus is accidently placed under one type, cultures showing some differences are usually kept as distinct types. Sometimes when fructifications are subsequently obtained, different types are found to be the same species; nevertheless, experience suggests that the majority of the mycelial types represent different species of fungi. On the other hand some cases are known where fungi differing widely taxonomically have indistinguishable mycelia. It is noteworthy that of 29 identified

TABLE I

List of genera of fungi obtained from Urrbrae loam

Phycomycetes	
†Chytridiales	‡*Rhizophydium*; ‡polycentric chytrids, 2 spp.
Saprolegniales	‡*Aphanomyces*; *Thraustotheca*
Peronosporales	*Pythium*, 4 spp.
Mucorales	*Absidia*, 3 spp; *Actinomucor*; *Circinella*, 2 spp.; *Coemansia*; *Cunninghamella*; *Gongronella*; *Helicostylum*; *Mortierella*, 5 spp.; *Mucor*, 3 spp.; *Piptocephalis*; *Rhizopus*, 2 spp.; *Syncephalis*, 2 spp.
Entomophthorales	*Conidiobolus*; *Entomophthora*
Ascomycetes	
Eurotiales	*Anixiopsis*; *Arachniotus*; *Aspergillus*, 2 spp.; *Auxarthron*; *Emericellopsis*; *Pseudoarachniotus*; *Spiromastix*
Chaetomiales	*Chaetomium*, 3 spp.
Helotiales	‡*Sclerotinia*
Pezizales	‡*Humarina*; ‡*Anthracobia*; ‡*Ascophanus*
Pleosporales	‡*Ophiobolus*; *Pleospora*
Xylariales	‡Xylariaceae, 2 spp.
Basidiomycetes	
Tremellales	‡*Sebacina*, 2 spp.
Agaricales	‡*Agrocybe*; ‡*Coprinus*; ‡*Leptoglossum*; ‡*Leucocoprinus*; ‡*Marasmiellus*; ‡*Marasmius*; ‡*Omphalina*
Polyporales	‡*Athelia*; ‡*Coniophora*; ‡*Coriolus*; ‡*Corticium*; ‡*Cristella*, 2 spp.; ‡*Hyphodontia*; ‡*Oliveonia*; ‡*Peniophora*, 3 spp.; *Pistillaria*; ‡*Physalacria*; ‡*Sistotrema*, 2 spp.; ‡*Thanatephorus*; ‡*Tomentella*; ‡*Waitea*
Nidulariales	‡*Cyathus*; ‡*Sphaerobolus*
Fungi Imperfecti	
Sphaeropsidales	*Ascochyta*; *Dinemasporium*; *Haplosporella*; *Phoma*, 7 spp.
Moniliales	*Acremoniella*; *Acremonium*; *Alternaria*, 3 spp.; *Aspergillus*, 7 spp.; *Beauveria*; *Botryotrichum*; *Botrytis*; *Brachysporiella*; *Cephalosporium*; *Cladosporium*; ‡*Costantinella*; *Curvularia*; *Cylindrocarpon*, 2 spp.; *Dactylella*, 2 spp.; *Dendryphion*; *Eladia*; *Epicoccum*; *Fusarium*, 4 spp.; *Geotrichum*; *Gliocladium*, 2 spp.; *Gliomastix*; *Gonytrichum*; ‡*Helicodendron*; ‡*Helicomyces*; ‡*Helicosporium*; *Helminthosporium*; *Humicola*; *Metarrhizium*; *Myrothecium*; *Oidiodendron*; *Oospora*; *Paecilomyces*; *Papularia*; *Penicillium*, 16 spp.; ‡*Phialophora*; ‡*Phymatotrichum*; *Pithomyces*; *Podosporiella*; *Pullularia*; *Stachybotrys*; *Stemphylium*; *Stysanus*; *Trichoderma*; *Verticillium*
Melanconiales	*Pestalotia*
Mycelia Sterilia	approx. ‡160 cultures

† Classification after Martin in Ainsworth (1961).
‡ Non-sporing on agar media.

Basidiomycetes 11 lack clamp connections. Besides the fungi listed in Table I, vesicular-arbuscular endophytes are common in roots and in soil, *Olpidium brassicae* has been noted in roots, and a fungus which forms small plate-like sclerotia is common in soil; none of these have been obtained in culture.

Selective methods have shown that other groups of fungi, chytrids (Willoughby, 1961), water-moulds (Harvey, 1925), fungi which attack nematodes, protozoa and amoebae (Drechsler, 1941; Duddington, 1955, 1957), plant pathogens (Garrett, 1956), animal and human pathogens (Ajello, 1956; de Vries, 1962), and mycorrhizal fungi (Harley, 1959), may be isolated from soil or plant roots. Other groups such as *Endogone, Tuber*, and the hypogeous Gasteromycetes (Hawker, 1954, 1955a) occur in soil, although, as far as I am aware, they have not yet been isolated apart from their fruit-bodies. Considering also the diversity of habitat of many terrestrial Basidiomycetes and Ascomycetes as shown by occurrence of their fructifications in restricted localities or in association with particular plants, the opinion of Brierley (Brierley, Jewson and Brierley, 1927), that the number and kinds of fungi in soil is legion and that there are perhaps few fungi capable of existing saprophytically which may not sooner or later be cultured from soil, seems very apposite.

How many of the fungi isolated from soil are capable of carrying out their whole life cycle in soil is not known; in fact, life cycles of comparatively few "soil fungi" are known in detail. Burges (1958) for instance, has pointed out that many of the Ascomycetes recorded from soil seem to be more closely connected with dung and animal droppings than with the mineral soil. Besides Ascomycetes such as *Fimetaria* and *Sporormia*, this is probably also true of Phycomycetes such as *Basidiobolus* (Griffin, 1960), *Pilaira*, and members of the Kickxellaceae. While the evidence suggests that these fungi are predominantly dung inhabitants and that they are found in soil as long-lived spores, we do not possess sufficient data to know whether or not they are also capable of growth in certain habitats in soil. It is of interest that some ubiquitous soil fungi such as certain species of *Aspergillus* and *Penicillium* have been found sporing, not in mineral soil, but on the remains of soil animals (Warcup, 1957; Sewell, 1959b).

A. FUNGAL STRUCTURES IN SOIL

The species of fungi that live in soil are, like other fungi, remarkable for their diversity of form and, being a heterogenous group drawn from different families and orders, vary immensely in size and in the complexity of their life cycles. The vegetative thallus is typically filamentous but may be unicellular. Some species are able to survive throughout the year as mycelium in soil and have no known reproductive structures; others form the complex sporophores of the larger Ascomycetes and Basidiomycetes. Information on the fungal structures that occur in soil has been gained from microscopic examination of soil itself, of soil-contact slides and of washed debris or plant roots. Study of the form of fungi in soil has, however, been a rather neglected field.

1. Hyphae

Most workers have noted fungal hyphae in soil since Frank first noted their abundance in forest litter in 1885. They occur on the surface of mineral particles, traverse soil pores and other spaces and occur on, and in, roots and organic debris. Some hyphae are full of cytoplasm, possess growing tips, stain deeply and are alive and active; others lack contents, do not stain appreciably, are collapsed or shrivelled and are dead. Where hyphae are very fine or possess thick dark-coloured walls, or stain with difficulty, or are of very irregular shape, it may be difficult to decide whether they are alive or dead (Warcup, 1957). Owing to close contact with irregular particles, hyphae in soil, unlike those developing on agar media, are often more or less irregular in shape and size (Saitô, 1955a). Portions of hyphae traversing air spaces may differ in appearance from those parts in close contact with mineral particles. Hyphae in root hairs and plant cells may swell to fill the cavity in which they occur, or become greatly constricted in passing from cell to cell; oidium-like hyphal systems are not uncommon in roots (Hildebrand and Koch, 1936; Nicolson, 1959). Hyphae on particles or on surfaces may be compacted into plates of sheath-like tissue, the extreme of this hyphal form being the hyphal sheaths of ectotrophic fungi on mycorrhizal roots.

Many types of hyphae occur in soil: non-septate phycomycetous hyphae; fine or wide, hyaline or dark-coloured, septate hyphae; hyaline or coloured hyphae with clamp connections. Burges and Nicholas (1961), studying hyphal occurrence in soil sections, divided the hyphae found in a humus-podzol under pine into 6 groups. They consider that with further experience it would be possible to make a more critical division into hyphal groups.

Among phycomycetous hyphae there is considerable range in size and form. Hyphae of *Pythium* and *Mortierella* are often fine, about 2 μ in diameter, but hyphae of some members of the Saprolegniacae such as *Thraustotheca clavata* growing on the surface of buried leaves may be 20–30 μ in diameter. In many Phycomycetes, dense cytoplasm occurs only near hyphal tips; further back the cytoplasm is often vacuolate or the hyphae appear empty.

A type of phycomycetous hypha that is widespread in soil is that of the vesicular-arbuscular endophytes (Peyronel, 1924; Butler, 1939; Gerdemann, 1955; Mosse, 1959; Nicolson, 1959). These are coarse, generally aseptate hyphae with highly characteristic unilateral, angular projections and thick (up to 4 μ), yellowish walls. Such hyphae may carry large terminal vesicles, which are not separated from the hyphae by septa (Butler, 1939; Nicolson, 1959). Besides the thick-walled hyphae there may be a system of thin-walled, often septate hyphae which arise as lateral branches, often from the angular projections of the coarse hyphae (Mosse, 1959; Nicolson, 1959).

Among septate hyphae, a type that is common in soil is the "rhizoctonia-like" hypha (Thornton, 1956b, 1960; Warcup, 1957; Tribe, 1960a). These hyphae are thin to relatively wide (5–20 μ in diameter), and bear characteristically constricted side branches at a wide angle from the parent hypha. A septum occurs near the constriction. Their colour may vary from hyaline to dark brown or black, the coloured hyphae usually possessing thickened walls. Many fungi with this type of hypha have been classified in the genus *Rhizoctonia*. *R. solani*, the pathogen, with its innumerable strains, is the best-known member of the group but many other Rhizoctonias have been isolated from soil. Some species are known to be Basidiomycetes; however, rhizoctonia-like mycelial states are known for some Ascomycetes such as *Morchella* and *Anthracobia*, and for Hyphomycetes such as *Phymatotrichum* so that this mycelial growth form has wide taxonomic limits. Durbin, Davis and Baker (1955) record that mycelium of *Helminthosporium cactorum* in cacti may be confused with that of *R. solani*, and McKeen (1952) considered that *Phialophora radicicola* may have been confused with *R. solani* because of the branching, septation and brown colour of old hyphae. Examination of septal pores may help to differentiate Basidiomycetes from other fungi with rhizoctonia-like hyphae (Bracker and Butler, 1963).

Many other types of septate hyphae occur in soil but there are comparatively few data on these forms, and even fewer on form in relation to identity. Some Basidiomycete hyphae are notable not only for possession of clamp connections but also for the crystals that encrust them.

It is difficult to decide how many of the hyphae present in a soil are viable. Warcup (1957) found that, on average, 23% of the hyphae washed from a wheat-field soil were viable. This value rose to 75% soon after crop residues were ploughed in and fell to 3–15% during the dry summer. When the soil dried out well below wilting point most hyphae were killed, but a few, including single hyphae besides mycelial strands, survived. In the same soil, but under an old pasture, percentage viability was always lower, ranging from 1–25%. Evidence suggests that in some natural uncultivated soils percentage viability may appear to be even lower. Here, however, even more than in agricultural soil, one has the added complication of hyphae that are viable but do not grow readily on the isolation medium. Other sources of viable mycelia are roots and residues in soil but these habitats are not investigated by the hyphal isolation method. Studies in the old pasture, for instance, showed that although there were comparatively few viable hyphae present in the soil, there was considerable viable mycelium on and in both living and dead roots.

Very little is known of the functional life of an individual hypha in soil, but it is generally considered that hyphae are short-lived through being attacked by other organisms (Waksman, 1927; Starkey, 1938; Russell, 1961; Tribe, 1957a). Sewell (1959b) has commented on the evanescent nature of most hyphae on Rossi-Cholodny slides which had been immersed in a heath soil for only 7 days; it is probable, however, that he was dealing with a restricted part of the mycelial population, since some slower-growing species would not have colonized buried slides in that period. Warcup (1957, 1960) found that some hyphae remained viable in dry soil for over 12 months, but commented that little was known of their ability to survive in moist soil. He found that many hyaline hyphae, both phycomycetous and septate, appeared short-lived in moist soil and soon lost their cell contents when not actively growing, but his data suggested that some dark-brown or black hyphae might be relatively long-lived. Many of the latter may be "resting hyphae." Tracey

(1956) and Witkamp (1960) recorded that dark hyphae appear to persist in soil longer than hyaline hyphae. Other fungi which may have relatively long-lived hyphae in soil include the vesicular-arbuscular endophytes and some Basidiomycetes. Waid and Woodman found that on nylon mesh left in a woodland soil for 410 days a high proportion of the hyphae present were pigmented or had clamps (Waid, 1960). Hyphae in residues appear longer-lived than those on mineral particles or traversing air spaces in soil (Jones and Mollison, 1948; Boosalis and Scharen, 1959).

2. Rhizomorphs

Rhizomorphs or mycelial strands may be common in soil and typically occur when a mycelium is growing over a surface or through a medium having a negligible content of free nutrients. Strands are not usually formed by mycelia growing within substrates. They are formed by some Ascomycetes and Hyphomycetes but are best developed among the Basidiomycetes. Rhizomorphs and mycelial strands are often conspicuous features of the litter and uppermost layers of woodland and forest soils (Mikola, 1956; Thornton et al., 1956; Saitô, 1956; Witkamp, 1960), but also occur in culti-vated soils (Warcup, 1959).

Garrett (1951, 1954, 1956) has rejected the earlier explanation that rhizo-morphs are primarily a protection against desiccation since, so far as they have been investigated, they are not tolerant of severe drying. For instance the strands of Phymatotrichum omnivorum (Texas cotton root-rot fungus) are quickly killed by drying (King et al., 1931). Further, rhizomorphs are common in soils where drought is no problem. Data suggest, however, that the rhizo-morphs of different fungi vary in their ability to withstand drying. Many mycelial strands in wheat-field soil at Adelaide remain viable over the summer dry period when soil moisture may be below wilting point for several months (Warcup, 1959). Whether individual hyphae of these strand-forming Basidio-mycetes are equally drought-resistant is not known.

3. Vesicles

Although reported by few investigators, vesicles, most of which represent extra-matrical spores of phycomycetous endophytes, are widespread in soil (Gerdemann and Nicolson, 1963). Since vesicles do not germinate on agar media and are present in comparatively low number they are not recorded by plating techniques and other methods must be used to show their presence in soil. They are usually obtained by partition methods, flotation, wet sieving, decanting, etc., thus they have been noted by nematologists (Triffitt, 1935), who commonly use such methods.

Vesicles are spherical, cylindrical or irregularly globose in shape, vary in diameter from 100–800 µ, usually have thick walls, contain many oil globules, and are light yellow to black when mature. Vesicles may occasionally contain other thin-walled, spherical spores; the nature of these internal spores is not known. Recently Gerdemann and Nicolson (1963) have recorded six different types of vesicles or spores from Scottish soils and have shown that some types produce endophytic mycorrhiza. At least one other type of spore occurs in Urrbrae loam, hence it is probable that others will also be found.

4. Chlamydospores

Chlamydospores are essentially vegetative resting spores with a thickened, often dark-coloured wall. They are typically formed as swollen cells in vegetative hyphae, but may also occur in sporangiophores or in conidia. Chlamydospores of water-moulds are sometimes developed from vegetative cells but are commonly formed from unfertilized oogonia (Hawker, 1957a). In particular species chlamydospores are induced by: a high concentration of sugar (*Mucor*); a reduction in available food (*Saprolegnia*); a low C—N ratio (*Fusarium oxysporum*; Carlile, 1956); by heat treatment (*Fusarium*; Roistacher, Baker and Bald, 1957); by the presence of antagonistic bacteria (*Fusarium*; Venkat Ram, 1952; unknown mycelia; Waid and Woodman, 1957); and in unsterilized soil (*Fusarium*; Nash, Christou and Snyder, 1961; *Mycosphaerella*; Carter and Moller, 1961).

Chlamydospores are generally considered to be formed by relatively few fungi (Hawker, 1957a), but are prominent in many fungi occurring in soil (Park, 1954; Dobbs and Hinson, 1960; Waid, 1960), and are probably formed more commonly than is usually realized. They occur in all major groups of fungi but are best known in the Mortierellaceae, the Mucoraceae, the Saprolegniaceae and the Hyphomycetes, including *Fusarium*, *Cylindrocarpon*, *Trichoderma*, *Botryotrichum* and *Humicola*. They may be formed in the Boletaceae (Pantidou, 1961) and in other Basidiomycetes. Chlamydospores are common in soil but comparatively little is known about them. They may be formed in soil as in *Mucor ramannianus* (Hepple, 1958) or in, or on, plant tissues as in *Fusarium* (Nash *et al.*, 1961; Christou and Snyder, 1962), or *Thielaviopsis* (Christou, 1962a). On decay of the tissue the chlamydospores are released in the soil embedded in small humus particles where, without staining, they are not easily detected by microscopic examination.

5. Sclerotia

Sclerotia consist of closely interwoven hyphae which often lose their original form so that individual cells become globose or tightly compacted. In some sclerotia the outer layer, or layers, may form a thick rind of pseudosclerenchyma often with brown or black walls; others are more or less uniform in structure throughout. Sclerotia vary in size from structures less than 50 μ in diameter (Boosalis and Scharen, 1959) to large sclerotia such as those of the Australian fungus *Polyporus mylittae* which may be 20–30 cm in length (Burges, 1958). *Polyporus tuberaster* in Canada (Vanterpool and Macrae, 1951) and *Poria cocos* in the U.S.A. (Weber, 1929) also form large sclerotia. Sclerotia may germinate directly by formation of hyphae or, as in *Sclerotinia*, *Typhula*, *Polyporus* and *Poria*, give rise to complex sporophores. Sclerotia may be formed in soil itself, on the external parts of plants as with *Rhizoctonia solani* on potato tubers, or they may occur inside plant tissues as with *Sclerotinia sclerotiorum* on Compositae and Cruciferae and *R. solani* on bean (Christou, 1962b). Much of our information on sclerotia in soil has come from study of soilborne plant parasites many of which, including *Helicobasidium, Rhizoctonia, Sclerotium, Phymatotrichum* and species of the Sclerotiniaceae, form sclerotia (Garrett, 1956).

Reserve foods, including oils and glycogen, are accumulated in sclerotia so that these structures are well adapted for surviving adverse conditions. Many sclerotia can survive long periods in soil. Gadd and Bertus (1928) found *Rhizoctonia* to survive 6 years in dry storage; Ezekiel (1940) reported that 8% of the sclerotia of *Phymatotrichum omnivorum* were still viable after 7 years in moist soil, and Coley-Smith (1959) found that a high proportion of the sclerotia of *Sclerotium cepivorum* (white rot of onions) survived 4 years in undisturbed soil in the field. Garrett (1956), who considers that sclerotia and rhizomorphs are homologous structures, thinks that the protection afforded to sclerotia by thick-walled outer layers does not imply that their primary function is survival of desiccation but that this merely supplements their function of storing food. Hawker (1957b) considers that perhaps both resistance to drought and provision of food reserves are equally important for survival. Drought, however, is not the only significant factor operating against survival of a fungus in soil; protection against other organisms is also important. Ferguson (1953) has shown that nutrient-rich, viable sclerotia are rarely colonized by other soil organisms whereas those killed or injured by various soil treatments are rapidly decomposed. He found that in *Sclerotinia sclerotiorum* the protective mechanism was independent of the thickened rind since both intact and halved sclerotia generally remained free of other organisms.

Studies at Adelaide have shown that some 30 fungi isolated from Urrbrae loam form sclerotia, and a considerable number of these have been isolated from sclerotia from soil in the field. It is interesting that some fungi isolated from sclerotia washed from soil only form indefinite sclerotium-like masses on agar media. Sclerotia have been found in species of *Aspergillus, Penicillium, Botrytis, Cephalosporium,* and *Rhizoctonia* and other non-sporing mycelia, *Leptoglossum,* and in the Basidiomycetes *Coprinus, Leucocoprinus, Omphalina, Cristella, Sistotrema* and *Waitea* (Warcup and Talbot, 1962).

6. Spores

Fungi produce a wide variety of spores, moreover many species may produce more than one type of spore. Asexual spores (zoospores, non-motile sporangiospores and conidia) are considered to be primarily organs of dispersal (Hawker, 1957b). Their ability to survive unfavourable conditions is limited, but they are often better equipped for survival than is some mycelium. Even naked zoospores of the Saprolegniaceae may rapidly encyst and develop thick walls. Conidia usually have denser cytoplasm than have hyphae and vacuoles are usually absent, factors which aid resistance to unfavourable conditions.

In several groups, as with the oospores of the Oomycetes and the zygospores of the Zygomycetes, the sexual spores are thick-walled resting spores. In Ascomycetes and Basidiomycetes the sexual process results in the formation of characteristic ascospores or basidiospores; these may be resistant spores in some species. Many ascospores, including those of *Byssochlamys*, *Neurospora*, *Aspergillus*, coprophilous Ascomycetes, and the species that fruit on burnt ground, are resistant to heat. Ascospores of truffles and the ecologically similar *Elaphomyces* are so resistant to external changes that they have not been germinated in artificial culture (Hawker, 1954, 1955a). Basidiospores of some Hymenomycetes may survive for several years under dry conditions (Cochrane, 1960), also certain hypogeous Gasteromycetes have resistant spores, but there are comparatively few data for this group.

Many investigators have recorded fungal spores in soil; they have been seen in soil films (Jones and Mollison, 1948), on Rossi-Cholodny slides (Jensen, 1934; Starkey, 1938), on stained soil plates (Warcup, 1951a; Stenton, 1953), in oil-water suspensions of soil (Ledingham and Chinn, 1955), and in soil suspensions (Dobbs and Hinson, 1960). Warcup (1955b, 1957) investigated the unit of origin of colonies developing on dilution plates prepared from wheat-field soil and found that at least 54–82% of the colonies on the plates grew from spores. This means that in this soil there are of the order of $75–150 \times 10^3$ viable spores/g oven dry soil; one sample gave $1 \cdot 5 \times 10^6$ viable spores/g oven dry soil. These figures may be low since it is known that not all spores in soil enter the suspension. A few float on the surface, others are attached to, or embedded in, the heavier soil particles of the residue; further, individual fragments, either in the suspension or in the residue, may contain more than one spore. Spores observed include sporangiospores, ascospores, conidia and chlamydospores. Data suggest that not all soils may contain such high numbers of fungal spores. Dobbs and Hinson (1960) comment that many spores obtained from an A_2 horizon under beech had angular shapes and were difficult to distinguish from mineral particles even after they had been stained. Many spores in wheat-field soil were also angular, the majority of these appearing to be chlamydospores.

Little is known of the longevity of spores in soil; it is probable, however, that there is great variation in survival of different spores, either of the same fungus or of different fungi. Chinn (1953) and Park (1955, 1956a), who added spores to soil, noted that, even with the addition of decomposable organic materials, most of these spores decomposed rapidly, and those which germinated were either destroyed by the activities of soil organisms or produced chlamydospores. Other reports, however, suggest that spores may survive for long periods in soil. Caldwell (1958) found that a few conidia and many chlamydospores of *Trichoderma viride* survived for over 1 year in garden soil, and Chinn and Ledingham (1958) found that conidia of *Helminthosporium sativum* survived 12–22 months in soil in the field.

While asexual spores are considered primarily organs of dispersal, it is likely that in general dispersal in soil is on a limited scale compared with the possibilities available in aerial habitats. Even so this dispersal may be no less important in the biology of the organisms concerned. Widespread root attack by *Phytophthora* or *Aphanomyces* following mass dispersal of zoospores under wet conditions may indicate dispersal approaching the scale possible in some aerial habitats, but presupposes a number of substrates suitable for colonization being available at the same time. As emphasized by Garrett (1955), however, fungal habitats in soil are often separated in time as well as in space, and under these conditions survival may be more important than dispersal. Perhaps the comments that Fennell (1960) made in discussing methods of preservation of fungal cultures are pertinent here: "it is perhaps noteworthy that certain genera, *Aspergillus*, *Fusarium*, *Mucor*, and *Rhizopus*, have been preserved by all the techniques considered here. Their ability to survive under a variety of conditions is undoubtedly a measure of their inherent resistance and an explanation of their ubiquity." Species of these genera are common in soil.

Dobbs and Hinson (1953) and other workers (Chinn, 1953; Hessayon, 1953; Jackson, 1958) have reported a widespread mycostatic (Dobbs, Hinson and Bywater, 1960) or fungistatic factor that inhibits germination of fungal spores buried in soil, although such spores may germinate when placed in distilled water. It is possible that the reaction of spores to this factor prevents wastage from germination in the absence of organic matter suitable for supporting growth (Waid, 1960).

Sexual spores of fungi may occur in soil; many of these are resting spores and are capable of surviving long periods. Legge (1952) found that oospores of *Phytophthora cactorum* and *P. megasperma* survived in soil for over a year. *Phytophthora fragariae* may survive in soil at least 13 years (Hickman, 1958). The resting spore of *Synchytrium endobioticum* set free in the soil by decay of infected potato tubers may remain viable for as long as 10 years (Muskett, 1960). Comparatively little is known about the presence or survival of ascospores in soil, and even less on basidiospores.

It is evident that many points of interest on the occurrence and the role of fungal spores in soil still await elucidation.

7. Fructifications

Fructifications vary in size and complexity from simple, scarcely differentiated conidiophores to the complex sporophores of the larger Ascomycetes and Basidiomycetes. The factors inducing the formation of these widely different types of reproductive structures are likely to differ greatly and may be very distinct from those favouring maximum production of mycelium (Cochrane, 1960).

While some large complex fructifications are hypogeous (Endogonaceae, Tuberales and many Gasteromycetes), most occur at the soil surface. Fructifications of agarics, and other large fungi are common in woodlands and pastures; much less is known of their occurrence in agricultural soils. In wheat-field soil resupinate Basidiomycetes may fruit beneath clods (Warcup and Talbot, 1962), but this habitat should probably be considered as an extension of the soil surface. Many fungi have fructifications of a size that could be formed within soil, in the larger cavities, if not within the finer pores. Dobbs and Hinson (1960) consider that many moulds are able to spore in soil cavities of the order of 200 μ in diameter. A point on which we lack adequate information, however, is the relative importance of sporulation within soil compared with that on the soil surface.

While fructifications have been noted in soil pores (Kubiena, 1938; Warcup, 1957), on Rossi-Cholodny slides (Starkey, 1938; Sewell, 1959b), and on roots and other structures in soil (Tribe, 1957a; Waid, 1960), many workers have commented upon the apparent scarcity of fungal fructifications to be found in soil. In general, studies of soil show copious spores and some hyphae but very few fructifications are seen. Yet the high number of spores would indicate that sporulation must be relatively common unless spores have a considerable life in soil. There are probably several diverse reasons for this apparent lack of fructifications: some are ephemeral; others are so like hyphae that unless spores were present the fructifications would remain undetected. While fructifications usually develop after periods of active growth, growth of a fungus may occur in soil without conditions being suitable for sporulation. This is common in fungi with complex sporophores, but may also occur in moulds. Warcup (1957) showed that many fungi, while present throughout the year, have restricted periods of growth and sporulation in soil. Unless soil is examined at the appropriate time, fructifications of these fungi are not observed.

Another reason for this apparent lack of fructifications in soil may be that examination of the soil surface has been neglected. Many fungi are known to fruit at the soil surface, often on residues, but this area, particularly in agricultural soils, has not been thoroughly explored as a site for fungal fructifications. In arable soil the surface is highly complex with both exposed and protected surfaces. In studies of wheat-field soil (Warcup, unpublished data) many fungi have been found fruiting at the soil surface, particularly but not always on the protected under surface of clods. Fructifications obtained include those of species of *Mortierella*, *Mucor*, *Rhizopus*, *Absidia*, *Cephalosporium*, *Fusarium*, *Trichoderma*, *Penicillium*, *Helicomyces*, *Helicosporium*, *Phymatotrichum*, and Basidiomycetes such as *Thanatephorus*, *Sistotrema*, *Oliveonia* and *Sebacina*. Some fructifications are associated with plant residues but others have no obvious connection. The presence of these fructifications at the soil surface raises many interesting questions on the fate of the spores produced, and on possible spore dispersal by wind, rain or members of the soil fauna, but the answers to these questions are still unknown. At least in the case of *Helminthosporium sativum*, spores formed on residues at the soil surface are known to enter the soil and to survive for long periods (Chinn and Ledingham, 1958).

Fructifications also occur in the wheat-field soil itself, being most frequent in the complex of worm tunnels in the upper 1–3 in of soil. After ploughing and seeding, the loose surface of the soil becomes flattened and compacted during heavy rain. Following ploughing, worm action, mainly by *Eisenia rosea* and *Allolobophora caliginosa*, produces a series of horizontal and vertical tunnels in the upper layer of the soil where the worms feed on plant residues; these tunnels may remain in the soil until it is ploughed again. Fungal sporulation is often noted in these tunnels, sometimes on the remains of soil animals that use them, sometimes on residues, sometimes on mineral particles. It is interesting that sporulation on buried residues is often confined to those portions which abut on tunnels or other large cavities in the soil. Fungi noted sporulating on buried straws include species of *Dinemasporium*, *Chaetomium*, *Myrothecium*, *Periconia*, *Trichoderma*, *Gonytrichum* and *Brachysporiella*.

Kubiena (1938) made some interesting observations on the fungi fruiting in soil pores and found that, in general, there was a reduction in the size of fruiting structures with decrease in pore size. He also noted that the dimensions of fruiting structures in soil were smaller than those recorded for the same fungi grown in culture; this, however, could be an effect of low nutrient level in soil. In wheat-field soil, an interesting case of effect of pore size was seen with *Rhizopus*. Sporangiophores formed in larger cavities were normal and straight whereas those occurring in smaller cavities were coiled and spring-like (Warcup, 1957).

Some fructifications are embedded in organic particles; this may explain their apparent absence when soil is examined microscopically. Many oogonia (Warcup, 1952; Boosalis and Scharen, 1959), sporangia of chytrids (Willoughby, 1961), and vesicles of endophytes (Nicolson, 1961) are embedded in humus particles, either following breakdown of plant tissue or through being surrounded by a considerable accumulation of bacterial cells and small mineral particles (Barton, 1958), so that their presence would not be suspected without staining or allowing germination.

The fate of spores from fructifications formed in the soil is not known, or whether such fruiting constitutes a major source of supply of spores to the "soil spora."

B. SUBSTRATES FOR GROWTH OF FUNGI IN SOIL

Information on occurrence of fungi "in the soil" is very imprecise, and it has been emphasized that fungal occurrence should be considered in relation to specific substrates or microhabitats rather than to the complex, soil itself (Chesters, 1949, 1960; Garrett, 1951; Harley and Waid, 1955). All fungi are dependent upon organic materials for growth, and since much of the organic matter in soil occurs as discrete units, varying from small humus particles to tree roots, data on occurrence and growth on or in such substrates will further our understanding of fungal life in soil. Fungi may also be able to use humified organic matter, but knowledge of their ability to do so *in situ* is lacking.

While the importance of specific substrates for fungal growth has become recognized, there have been major problems concerned with their study, with determining what organisms are present on a substrate, with the difficulty of differentiating between dormant and active portions of a fungus or of different fungi, and with measuring, in some sense, the "activity" of fungi on natural substrates. Further, there is usually difficulty in interpretation owing to the complexity of natural substrates, particularly in relation to the small size of the microhabitats that may be inhabited by individual fungal colonies (Griffin, 1960; Burges, 1963). As Stanier (1953) has emphasized, a "single cellulose fibre provides a specialized environment with its own characteristic microflora, yet may occupy a volume of not more than a cubic millimetre." While this is true for many moulds, it should be borne in mind that some Basidiomycetes, such as *Marasmius oreades*, may migrate through soil, occupy a considerable volume, and decompose many different substrates; there are probably many gradations between these two extremes.

Since a substrate is changed by supporting the development of micro-organisms, it may be expected in the course of time to provide a succession of microhabitats. Garrett (1955) has stressed that a succession of micro-organisms does not improve but rather depletes the capacity of a habitat to support further plant life, so that the end point of such a succession is not a persisting climax, as with higher plants, but zero. Some microbiologists have questioned the occurrence of an ordered succession of organisms on a microhabitat within soil because it is technically difficult to demonstrate, but there is evidence that succession of fungi may occur on certain roots (Waid, 1960) and on litter. With simpler substrates, Tribe (1960a) has shown an interesting succession of fungi and other organisms on Cellophane, and Griffin (1960) has recorded fungal succession on hair in contact with soil. Their work shows that while a given substrate in soil may have a characteristic fungal flora and succession, these may vary within wide limits. Apart from physical and environmental factors which may influence succession, the species composition of different soils as providers of fungal inoculum is highly important.

Garrett (1955) remarked that a new picture of the distribution of many soil micro-organisms is slowly emerging. "We may imagine the soil as a three-dimensional pattern of substrates, each of which passes in turn through the successive phases of colonization, exploitation and exhaustion. Sites of former substrates, now exhausted, are marked by the resting cells of organisms that had colonized them, at least for as long as the resting cells survive." Although fungi may grow away from a colonized site, Garrett considers that many form resting cells upon the substrate rather than growing out as mycelium through the soil. Certainly it is possible for fresh substrates to come to a resting fungus in soil, for instance, by growth of roots or by movement of members of the soil fauna.

Since substrates for fungal growth consist of living or dead, fresh or partly decomposed plant or animal tissues on or in soil, the number of possible substrates and microhabitats present in different soils, under different vegetations and in different climatic zones is legion. There is much incidental information on fungal occurrence on different substrates and on the ability of fungi to decompose various materials, particularly under laboratory conditions, but as yet only a few substrates in soil have been studied in any detail. Also the value of such studies is very dependent on the methods used and particularly on the amount of microscopic examination carried out during the investigation. Study of a substrate by dilution techniques alone is likely to record predominantly the dormant organisms from its surface rather than the fungi inhabiting it (Harley and Waid, 1955; Stenton, 1958). This account of substrates in soil is far from exhaustive but outlines some major groups of substrates, also some of the problems associated with their study.

1. Litter

Chesters (1960) has pointed out that while the organic matter of natural soils reaches its maximum value on and in the surface layers, most mycologists interested in soil-inhabiting fungi neglect the surface litter "in favour of that apparently entrancing and most elusive quantity—the soil." He has emphasized both the importance of surface litter in the economy of natural soils and that little is known of the fungal flora of this layer.

Much work has been carried out on forest litter, particularly in relation to the formation of mull and mor, but comparatively few detailed studies have been made of the fungi of various litter horizons or their relation to decomposition *in situ*. Litter layers, from the surface downwards, are often designated as the litter (L), the fermentation (F), and the humification (H) layers (Hesselman, 1926).

Saitô (1956, 1957, 1958, 1960) studied microbiological decomposition, both by direct observation and by plating methods, in the L and F layers of beech litter. The L layer consisted of freshly fallen leaves and brown leaves only slightly subject to microbial attack; surface leaves were liable to dry out rapidly and thoroughly. In the F layer, where the moisture content remained more constant, many leaves turned yellow following attack by Basidiomycete mycelia associated with a vigorous growth of bacteria. Infected leaves first became much thinner without losing their structure, then mouldy from overgrowth of Basidiomycete mycelia; later, growth of other organisms was seen and leaves gradually became transformed into amorphous debris. Not all leaves in the same layer became infected by Basidiomycetes, furthermore decomposition did not always take place uniformly throughout a leaf. Four Basidiomycetes, including two species of *Collybia* and a *Mycena* fruited on the experimental area.

As is usual in such investigations, plating techniques failed to record Basidiomycetes, but showed that a few species of *Penicillium*, *Absidia*, *Mucor ramannianus* and *Trichoderma viride* were widespread throughout the litter horizons. Saitô found that in yellow, Basidiomycete-infected leaves there was a marked disappearance of lignin followed by a rise in the quantity of water-soluble substances. He considered that the filamentous moulds recorded by plating were active on the water-soluble substances initially present in the leaves and on these materials liberated later during lignin decomposition. Basidiomycete mycelia in the decomposing leaves were finally broken down by bacteria.

Leaf litter of conifers, with its strong mor-forming tendencies and with an accumulated bulk of material at different stages of decay, has been investigated on many occasions. The studies on decomposition of litter of *Pinus sylvestris* in Delamere Forest, Cheshire (Kendrick, 1958, 1959; Parkinson and Kendrick, 1960; Kendrick and Burges, 1962) are noteworthy in illustrating the different pictures of fungal occurrence obtained by different methods of investigation, in showing how important it is that microbiological sampling be undertaken in relation to the characteristic horizons of soil or litter, and in pointing out the importance of knowledge of the time sequence of the events being studied.

Kendrick found that soil plates and soil dilution plates indicated a population of heavily-sporing moniliaceous fungi such as species of *Penicillium* and *Trichoderma viride* in the litter. Using a modification of the Harley and Waid serial washing technique to remove surface propagules from decomposing needles before plating out, he obtained *Trimmatostroma*, *Pullularia*, *Fusicoccum* and *Desmazierella*, besides species of *Penicillium* and *T. viride*. This result contrasts markedly with that obtained from unwashed needles. Kendrick remarked that *Desmazierella acicola*, perhaps the most important internal colonizer of the needles, was not isolated on dilution plates. Direct microscopic observation revealed that even isolation from washed debris failed to give a full picture of the fungal population, since needles of the L layer were often seen to be colonized by the parasitic *Lophodermium pinastri* (pine needle cast) which persisted and fruited in the litter but did not grow in culture. Furthermore two previously undescribed dematiaceous hyphomycetes, *Helicoma monospora* and *Sympodiella acicola*, and Basidiomycete mycelia were seen in the F layer, but were not isolated from washed debris.

Microscopic examination of the H layer also showed large numbers of dematiaceous hyphal fragments, an observation previously made by Romell (1935). These fragments invariably failed to grow by hyphal isolation which suggested that they might have been produced, at least in part, in the overlying layers. It was found that many of the hyphal fragments consisted primarily of empty pieces of conidiophores of *Desmazierella acicola* from the L layer. These had been attacked by oribatid mites and many of the hyphal fragments were originally enclosed in faecal pellets deposited in the H or A_1 horizon. Later these pellets had disintegrated and released the empty conidiophore fragments (Kendrick and Burges 1962).

Summarizing the results obtained by various methods, Kendrick and Burges (1962) suggest the following sequence of decomposition of needles of *Pinus sylvestris* at Delamere. In spring about 40% of living needles on a tree become infected by *Lophodermium pinastri*, a parasitic Ascomycete, which produces no obvious symptoms at this stage. Other fungi present but without visible symptoms include *Coniosporium* sp., *Pullularia pullulans* and *Fusicoccum bacillare*. The latter two appear to attack needles which are senescent and which generally die and become brown while still attached to the tree. At this stage 80% of these needles are infected with *Pullularia* and 90% with *Fusicoccum*.

These brown needles fall to the ground in late August or in early September, and become part of the L layer of litter, in which they spend some 6 months.

During this time the pycnidia of *Fusicoccum bacillare* and the hysterothecia of *Lophodermium pinastri* are produced, providing the inoculum whereby further living needles on the tree become infected. Meanwhile many of the needles on the ground are invaded by *Desmazierella acicola*, a discomycete, which was recorded only in its *Verticicladium* conidial state. Six to eight months after they had fallen, *Verticicladium* was recorded from 70–100% of the needles.

The next stage of the succession, represented spatially by the F_1 layer, takes about 2 years. During this phase colonization proceeds along two distinct lines. *Desmazierella acicola* attacks the interior of needles where it lays down zones of black pigment and each summer produces numerous conidiophores through stomata. Meanwhile the exterior of the needle, now surrounded by a much more humid atmosphere than that found in the surface litter, is colonized by the Hyphomycetes, *Sympodiella acicola* and *Helicoma monospora*. These fungi produce appressed networks of fine dematiaceous hyphae, and later enormous numbers of small darkly pigmented conidiophores are formed. External and internal colonizers combine to bring about the darkening in colour which is such a characteristic feature of the F_1 layer.

After about 2 years in the F_1 layer, the character of the needles changes once more. They become tightly compressed and generally break up into fragments. Those fragments which have been attacked by fungi are gradually penetrated by members of the soil fauna which are the dominant organisms of this phase. Mites, Collembola, enchytraeid worms and others remove the innumerable conidiophores of *Helicoma* and *Sympodiella* while mite instars eat their way through the interior of the needles, eventually bringing about complete comminution. Those fragments which have escaped extensive internal attack by fungi accumulate in the F_2 layer. *Trichoderma viride* and one or more species of *Penicillium* occur on most of these but these fungi are usually present only as a high spore potential.

The needle fragments are slowly attacked by Basidiomycetes and a sterile dematiaceous form over a period of about 7 years. Eventually the meiofauna complete their physical reduction also, and the remains enter the H or humus layer. Here biological activity seems to be at a very low level.

The studies of Witkamp (1960) on decomposition of oak litter emphasize the role of Basidiomycetes in litter breakdown, also the importance of members of the soil fauna in the comminution and decomposition of litter. Witkamp and Van der Drift (1961) have also considered breakdown of oak litter in relation to environmental factors and to time.

2. Roots

Roots provide a major habitat or series of habitats for fungi living in soil, but discussion of roots lies outside the scope of this contribution except to note that they provide the main source of plant residues in some soils.

3. Plant residues

It is well known that addition of plant residues to soil greatly stimulates the fungal population. There have been, however, few detailed studies of fungal decomposition of such added material. The ability of root-infecting fungi to survive in or to colonize residues has attracted much attention (Garrett, 1956) but usually without detailed study of other organisms present or of the course of decomposition. Martin, Anderson and Goates (1942) added a considerable amount of plant residues to soil and traced the rise in activity of fungi and the disappearance of constituents of the residues. During the first period Phycomycetes, including *Mucor* and *Rhizopus*, increased in number, and sugar and starch were rapidly decomposed. Then followed a rise of *Pencillium* and *Aspergillus*, coupled with a loss of cellulose and hemicellulose, and lastly a rise of other fungi coupled with decomposition of lignified material. This study, however, was made by the soil dilution plate technique, which would have failed to record any non-sporing mycelia decomposing the added residues.

More recently several workers have studied a later stage of decomposition of residues and have washed debris particles from soil and studied their fungal populations. Most data show that different fungi are recorded from washed than from unwashed particles, there being, in general, a decrease in the frequency of isolation of heavily-sporing forms (Parkinson and Kendrick, 1960). This observation has been considered to support the contention that many of the isolates obtained from washed substrates are from mycelium. It is noticeable, however, that many of the fungi obtained are organisms known to produce resting spores, oospores, sclerotia or chlamydospores, in decomposing tissues; they include *Aphanomyces* and *Rhizoctonia* (Boosalis and Scharen, 1959), *Fusarium*, *Pythium* and *Cylindrocarpon* (Parkinson and Kendrick, 1960; Parkinson and Williams, 1961; Nash *et al.*, 1961). Much more information is necessary before we can be sure that these fungi are active in decomposition of debris particles in soil.

The studies of Tribe (1957a, 1960a, b, c) on the organisms colonizing Cellophane film are of interest, although this is not a natural substrate. Cellophane is a pure regenerated cellulose and its advantages are its simplicity as a substrate and its transparency, which renders it excellent for microscopic examination. Tribe has shown that relatively few fungi in a soil are capable of attacking cellulose film, and that many of these are species which are not recorded in dilution plate studies. The fungi attacking Cellophane differed markedly from soil to soil. In England some alkaline soils gave *Botryotrichum piluliferum* (*Chaetomium piluliferum*; Daniels, 1961), *Chaetomium*, *Humicola grisea*, chytrids and occasionally *Stachybotrys*. *Stysanus* was common in a chalk soil and *Oidiodendron* in an acid soil. A brown forest soil in Canada yielded *Rhizoctonia*, *Humicola*, *Botryotrichum* and chytrids. Some fungi grew on the surface of the film; others including species of *Humicola* and *Botryotrichum*, were notable for their "rooting branches" in the thickness of the Cellophane.

4. Seeds

While much is known of the fungi which are seed-borne, comparatively little attention has been paid to germinating seed as a substrate for the growth of fungi in soil. Seed may liberate sugars, amino acids and other substances during germination; further, all reserve foods may not be utilized by the developing germling. Warcup (1957) found that *Rhizopus* often grew on germinating wheat seed after emergence of the shoot above ground. Although *Alternaria*, *Stemphylium* and *Cladosporium* were common on wheat seed they were not observed to grow extensively on seed planted in the field. *Fusarium*, in part seed-borne, *Penicillium*, *Rhizopus* and occasionally *Thraustotheca clavata* often grew extensively and the dark synnemata of *Podosporiella verticillata* which may be seed-borne (Wallace, 1959) were also occasionally found (Warcup, unpublished data). The latter fungus was more frequent on seed of weed grasses than on wheat. Detached pieces of synnemata are also not uncommon among the heavier soil particles concentrated for hyphal isolation.

5. Animal substrates

Apart from the group of predacious fungi which attack nematodes, protozoa and amoebae, very little attention has been paid to animal tissues or residues as substrates for fungi in soil. This is perhaps surprising, particularly with groups such as mites and collembola, which may occur in soil in high number; similarly cast insect exuviae often occur in sufficient number to provide adequate material for study of organisms able to use this source of chitin in soil. There have been incidental observations, particularly of species of *Aspergillus* and *Penicillium* fruiting on dead soil animals (Warcup, 1957; Sewell, 1959b), but as far as I am aware, no systematic study of the occurrence and growth of fungi on members of the soil fauna, apart from nematodes, has been made. Insect parasites, such as *Entomophthora* (Miller *et al.*, 1957; Griffin, 1960) and *Beauveria bassiana*, have been isolated from soil itself, and the latter was of frequent occurrence in certain profiles (Sewell, 1959a; Brown, 1958b). Little is known, however, of the biology of these fungi in soil; similarly little is known of the life of the species of *Cordyceps* that infect soil-inhabiting insects.

The predacious fungi form a well-marked ecological group, united by their habit of capturing and consuming minute animals. Taxonomically they fall into two groups: the Zoopagales, belonging to the Zygomycetes; and the predacious Hyphomycetes, a diverse group in the Moniliales. Two general forms of predacious activity may also be recognized in members of both taxonomic groups. The endozoic forms such as *Endocochlus* and *Harposporium* pass the whole of their vegetative state within the bodies of their hosts, which they usually attack by means of sticky spores. The second group consists of active predators such as *Stylopage* and *Arthrobotrys*, which capture living animals on their mycelia. The best-known predacious fungi are the nematode-trapping Hyphomycetes with their remarkable array of specialized trapping devices, sticky knobs, nets, non-constricting and constricting rings. Knowledge of these fungi has been particularly due to the studies of Drechsler, who isolated many predacious fungi from leaf mould. They are also widely distributed in soil, although there is little direct evidence of their activity in this habitat since most observations on predacious fungi have been made from agar cultures. Capstick, Twinn and Waid (1957) showed, however, that a small proportion of free-living nematodes isolated directly from forest litter were infected with various predacious fungi thus confirming that these organisms are active in a natural habitat. Cooke (1962), using a direct method of observation, has studied the behaviour of nematode-trapping fungi during decomposition of organic matter in soil in the laboratory.

Fungi also attack nematode eggs. Van de Laan (1956) investigated the fungi which attack eggs and kill the larvae within the cysts of *Heterodera rostochiensis*. Certain fungi, including *Phialophora heteroderae*, *Monotospora daleae*, *Phoma tuberosa* and *Colletotrichum atramentarium* were found repeatedly in or on cysts. The latter two fungi also occur on potato. Cysts from Jersey in the Channel Islands contained *Penicillium vermiculatum* and *Pseudoeurotium ovalis*. Ellis and Hesseltine (1962) have recorded that *Rhopalomyces* is parasitic on nemotode eggs. *Fusarium* and *Cephalosporium* may be parasitic (Lýsek, 1963) on eggs of parasitic roundworms (*Ascaris* sp.).

Griffin (1960) studied the colonization of hair by fungi in soil in the laboratory. Although hair had previously been widely used as a bait for keratinolytic fungi, no previous study of its general colonization had been made. Besides keratin, hair contains traces of many other substances (Bolliger and Gross, 1952). Griffin found that many fungi sporulated on the surface of hair so that direct observations could be used as a check on isolation data. Initial colonizers were often Fusaria, certain Penicillia, and various members of the Mucorales; these were overlapped or followed by a second group including *Chaetomium cochlioides*, *Gliocladium roseum*, *Humicola* species and certain other Penicillia; the final group comprised keratinolytic fungi such as *Keratinomyces ajelloi* and *Microsporum gypseum*. Griffin remarked that while the broad outlines of the general succession were clear, the fate of individual colonies as they were succeeded was uncertain. Many sporulated profusely as they passed their peak of activity and then survived as dormant spores, the hyphae remaining at least initially as empty tubes. In others, however, much of the protoplasm of the colony was probably destroyed by direct parasitism of a succeeding fungus.

Griffin also commented that the existence of keratinolytic fungi in the great variety of soils which have now been examined by various workers raises a problem of great interest, for it seems scarcely possible that the accession of keratin in normal soils should be sufficient to support an almost ubiquitous keratinolytic flora, even allowing for very prolonged periods of dormancy. Pugh and Mathison (1962) found keratinophilic fungi to be common in some salt marsh and sand dune soils, particularly from sites where there was a natural deposition of keratinous substrates such as rabbit fur and bird feathers. Mathison also suggested that keratinophilic fungi compete successfully with other fungi on a wide range of protein substrates, particularly fibrous proteins which are normally fairly resistant to digestion by proteolytic enzymes. Watling (1963) has found keratinophilic fungi to be present in dung of birds of prey.

6. *Fungal structures*

Fungal structures themselves may provide substrates for other fungi. A number of soil fungi appear capable of parasitizing other fungi. Fructifications of agarics are frequently attacked by fungi including Mucorales, Fungi Imperfecti and other agarics. Below ground, *Scleroderma* may be infected with *Boletus parasiticus*; the ascomycete *Elaphomyces* may be parasitized by *Cordyceps*. Hawker (1955b) recorded how *Sepedonium chrysospermum* occurred on fruit bodies of *Melanogaster* and *Rhizopogon* and extended and sporulated profusely in the soil some centimetres from the host. *Syncephalis* may parasitize *Mortierella* particularly where the host is growing abundantly (Warcup, 1952).

The behaviour of *Trichoderma viride* as a parasite of other soil fungi has attracted much attention (Rishbeth, 1950; Aytoun, 1953; Boosalis, 1956; Campbell, 1956) since its original discovery by Weindling (1932). A *Papulospora* (Warren, 1948) and *Penicillium vermiculatum* (Boosalis, 1956,) have been recorded as parasites of *Rhizoctonia solani*; *R. solani*, itself, has been recorded as parasitic on several Phycomycetes (Butler, 1957). Campbell (1947) isolated *Coniothyrium minitans* from sclerotia of *Sclerotinia trifoliorum* and showed that it was capable of killing sclerotia. Tribe (1957b) showed that *C. minitans* was of frequent occurrence in East Anglia and that spores of the parasite may persist ungerminated for at least a year in disintegrated sclerotia in soil; so far the fungus has only been found in connection with sclerotia.

Fungi may also take part in decomposition of dead fungal structures, although little information is available. Since some fungi possess chitinases it is probable that they may decompose chitin-containing hyphae. Although the occurrence in soil of organisms which decompose chitin has been studied (Veldkamp, 1955; Witkamp, 1960; Y. Lingappa and Lockwood, 1961), little is known of the ability of these organisms to utilize either fungal or insect chitin in soil.

IV. FACTORS AFFECTING GROWTH OF FUNGI IN SOIL

Chesters (1949) commented that, while much information has been collected on fungi in soil, so far only a very indistinct picture of the fungus at work has been obtained. Much of the difficulty in such study centres around the question of having adequate methods for distinguishing between active and resting structures of fungi in soil. In several investigations such difficulties have been overcome, at least in part, by combinations of microscopic examination and isolation procedures. While many points still await elucidation, it is perhaps now possible to sketch some outlines of fungal life in soil.

A. FUNGAL PROPAGULES IN SOIL

Much work has indicated that soil contains a large number of inactive units of fungi; these include "resting hyphae," chlamydospores, sclerotia, sporangiospores and conidia, oospores, ascospores and probably, though there is little information on this point, basidiospores. The number of resting units varies markedly with the soil, with its past history and with the kinds of organisms present. In Urrbrae loam, some Basidiomycetes such as *Waitea circinata* are present as 1–10 sclerotia per 500 g of soil, others such as *Omphalina* may reach concentrations as high as 20–25 sclerotia per g in some areas; at the other end of the scale certain Penicillia are present relatively uniformly in the surface layers as $1-4 \times 10^4$ spores per g of oven-dry soil.

It is now considered that, in general, the "soil spora" (the population of chlamydospores, sporangiospores, ascospores and conidia) provides the bulk of the propagules in soil suspensions and hence on soil dilution plates, that they are common on the surface of roots and other particles in soil and represent the majority of the units obtained in rhizosphere studies (Harley and Waid, 1955). While we know of the existence of the soil spora, many facts concerning the formation, occurrence and longevity of its members are not yet known.

1. *Mycostasis*

Since the sporangiospores and conidia of many fungi occurring in soil are able to germinate in distilled water, the presence of large numbers of ungerminated spores in soil may appear anomalous. Dobbs and Hinson (1953), however, reported widespread inhibition of fungal spores in the organic layers of most soils. Failure of spores to germinate when in contact with soil has been observed in many soils in different parts of the world (Chinn, 1953; Hessayon, 1953; Park, 1955; Chinn and Ledingham, 1957; Jackson, 1957, 1958a, b; Dobbs *et al.*, 1960).

Dobbs and Hinson used cellulose film to demonstrate inhibition of spore germination in soil, the most sensitive test being the "closed" film test where spores of the fungus are placed inside folded film pressed between two lumps of soil (Dobbs *et al.*, 1960). Free margins of the fold act as controls. Other tests for inhibition are based on the use of agar; Jeffreys and Hemming (1953) placed agar slabs directly on the soil profile; Chinn (1953) coated a slide with spores in very weak agar; Molin (1957) and Jackson (1958a) have used agar disks. More recently, Lingappa and Lockwood (1963) have placed spores directly on a compacted soil surface. After time for germination spores are recovered in a collodion film.

Dobbs and Hinson (1953) found that germination of *Penicillium frequentans* spores in contact with fresh moist surface soils was totally inhibited. Inhibition decreased with depth and appeared to coexist broadly with the region of biological activity in soil. No fungus whose spores germinate readily in distilled water was found to be unaffected. Inhibition is removed by severe heating or by desiccation, and is masked by adding glucose above a threshold quantity which varies widely from soil to soil, also by any other treatment liable to release nutrients by killing soil organisms, by organic solvents (ether, acetone) and by mixing soil with activated charcoal. Inhibition usually returns after the glucose or other nutrient has been removed from the soil.

4+S.B.

Neither the nature of the inhibitor nor whether it is a complex rather than a single substance is known. Dobbs *et al.* (1960) consider that it might be an anti-metabolite. Brian (1960) thought that there were still too many uncertainties concerning mycostasis to know whether it is a positive effect. Park (1960, 1961b) has compared mycostasis with the staling of fungal cultures on media. Lingappa and Lockwood (1961) consider that the indirect techniques used to demonstrate fungistasis do not reveal the presence of fungistatic substances in soil, but provide a substrate for growth of micro-organisms which produce antibiotic substances thus making the assay medium fungistatic. Since fungal spores do not germinate in soil it is considered that nutrients diffusing from spores stimulate a microflora around them with resultant inhibition of their germination. Dobbs and Carter (1963) consider that there is so far no evidence that soil mycostasis is occasioned, to any large degree, by the proliferation of inhibitory organisms on the actual spore surface, but there is some evidence that fresh spores may stimulate the growth of such organisms in their vicinity, with the production of diffusible inhibitors in the soil solution. Griffin (1962) and Lockwood and Lingappa (1963) found that both antagonistic and non-antagonistic micro-organisms induced an observable fungistatic effect in non-amended autoclaved soil. They consider that the fungistatic effect of natural soil may result in part from the general saprophytic activities of the soil microflora.

Some soils possess inhibiting factors whose properties differ from mycostasis (Dobbs *et al.*, 1960). Jeffreys and Hemming (1953) detected traces of antibiotic activity in soil, their observations suggesting discontinuous "islands" of inhibition rather than a widespread "sea" of inhibition. Lingappa and Lockwood (1962) found that certain lignin-like substances isolated from soil were fungistatic.

Apart from observations on hyphal growth of some Basidiomycetes (Molin, 1957; Dobbs *et al.*, 1960), there is little information on the effect of mycostasis on other fungal structures in soil. Certainly many sclerotia remain ungerminated in soil but whether they are affected by mycostasis is not known. Coley-Smith (1960) showed that sclerotia from 6-week-old cultures of *Sclerotium cepivorum* would germinate only if the rind had been artificially damaged by abrasion. When unabraded sclerotia were buried in the field for a month or longer, however, some became capable of germination. Germination of sclerotia which produce fructifications may be highly seasonal, as in *Sclerotinia camelliae*, but not in others such as *Sclerotinia sclerotiorum* and *Sclerotinia fuckeliana*.

2. *Spore dormancy*

The significance of dormancy in relation to fungi occurring in soil is not known. Many Phycomycetes form thick-walled resting spores that do not germinate until after a period of maturation; at least part of this apparent resting period represents time required for cytological processes. With some resting sporangia, the thickness of the wall is one of the decisive factors in germination; resting sporangia grown under conditions inducing a thin wall germinate without a rest period (Cochrane, 1958). Ascospores of many Ascomycetes, particularly but not exclusively coprophilous species, exhibit a pronounced dormancy which is often broken by brief exposure to heat; Warcup and Baker (1963) found that certain soils contain large numbers of ascospores which do not germinate on agar unless the soil has been heat-treated. In culture oospores of *Phytophthora cactorum* exhibit dormancy (Blackwell, 1943), but Legge (1952) showed that its oospores buried in soil may germinate after a week or may survive ungerminated for at least a year. In decomposing roots containing copious oospores of *Pythium* I have noted that the fungus was isolated only from chlamydospores present in the material. Whether these oospores were dormant was not tested.

B. SPORE GERMINATION

While some sclerotia are nutritionally independent, there is increasing evidence that spores and resting structures of fungi in soil germinate only when stimulated by an external source of nutrients. In some cases this occurs in response to a specific substance, in other cases the response is more general. Known sources of nutrients are seeds, roots and decomposing plant and animal residues. Germination also depends on suitable pH, carbon dioxide concentration, temperature, oxygen and water supply and absence of inhibitors (Cochrane, 1958).

Exudates from plant roots have been shown to stimulate germination of fungal propagules in soil; much of the work has been done with root parasites, but stimulation of saprophytic fungi by roots has also been demonstrated. Germination of spores of *Plasmodiophora brassicae* is stimulated by host and non-host roots (Macfarlane, 1952); *Spongospora subterranea* is stimulated by roots of the host family Solanaceae (White, 1954); banana roots stimulate germination of spores of *Fusarium exysporum* f. *cubense* in soil extracts (Stover, 1958); oospore germination of *Aphanomyces euteiches* is stimulated by roots of peas, soyabean and sweet corn, but significantly greater numbers germinate near peas than near the non-host plants (Scharen, 1960; Cunningham and Hagedorn, 1962); oospore germination of *Pythium mamillatum* is stimulated by exudates from turnip seedlings (Barton, 1957); chlamydospores of *Fusarium solani* f. *phaseoli* germinate most consistently close to germinating bean seed and root tips (Schroth and Snyder, 1961) but germination also occurs near non-susceptible plants (Schroth and Hendrix, 1962). Coley-Smith (1960) found that in the presence of host roots the sclerotia of *Sclerotium cepivorum* (white rot of onion) were strongly stimulated to germinate, there being little or no germination in the presence of non-hosts or in soil alone. Germination was greatest in the root tip region and was independent of contact between roots and sclerotia, occurring over a distance up to 1 cm from the roots. Tichelaar (1961) recorded that root exudates of *Gladiolus* also stimulate germination of sclerotia of *S. cepivorum*. Jackson (1957, 1960) found that conidia of *Gliocladium roseum*, *Fusarium* sp. and *Paecilomyces marquandii* on glass slides buried beneath peas germinated in the immediate vicinity (1–2 mm) of the young roots but not elsewhere, except that some

Fusarium conidia distant from the roots germinated to form chlamydospores. Germ tubes of *G. roseum* and *Fusarium* showed strong tropic growth towards the roots.

There are several records of fungal germination being stimulated by addition of residues to soil. Mitchell, Hooton and Clark (1941) found that organic matter stimulated germination of sclerotia of *Phymatotrichum omnivorum* in the absence of living host roots. Chinn, Ledingham, Sallans and Simmonds (1953) found that the addition of soyabean meal to soil stimulated germination of conidia of *Helminthosporium sativum* present in soil. Further studies showed that wheat-germ bran, oil meals, molasses or green plant tissue were very effective, but that refined flour and commercial sugar were only slightly so, and that dead wheat roots and straw gave no spore germination (Chinn and Ledingham, 1957). Toussoun and Patrick (1962) found that chlamydospores of *Fusarium solani* f. *phaseoli* germinated around decomposing residues of barley, broccoli and beans, and when water extracts of these residues were added to soil.

Factors affecting the germination of spores of the larger Ascomycetes and Basidiomycetes are unknown. Spores of some of these fungi have proved difficult to germinate in culture, but some germinate more readily in the presence of tissues from sporophores. Germination of spores of *Agaricus campestris* has been found to be stimulated by an olefin, 2–3 dimethyl-1-pentane (McTeague, Hutchinson and Reed, 1959).

C. HYPHAL GROWTH

Following germination, fungal growth is dependent upon a suitable substrate or a continuing supply of nutrients, otherwise lysis of germ tubes takes place or the fungus forms a resting structure such as a chlamydospore, and ceases further growth. Continuing growth also depends upon a suitable physical environment.

In general, fungal growth is affected by both high and low temperatures. Various reports (Lebeau and Cormack, 1956; Lebeau and Logsdon, 1958) that fungi can cause damage to snow-covered plants are evidence that certain species grow at low temperatures. The distribution of *Phymatotrichum omnivorum*, however, is limited by low winter soil temperature in conjunction with soil type (Peltier, 1937; Ezekiel, 1945). Waid (1960) reported that mycelial activity on buried nylon gauze was less in winter, when temperature was low, than in summer. Similarly, *Trichoderma viride* is not active in soil at low temperatures (Rishbeth, 1950; Griffiths and Siddiqi, 1961). At high temperatures, so long as water is not limiting, some fungal growth may occur, since many soils contain thermotolerant fungi such as certain species of *Chaetomium* and *Aspergillus fumigatus*.

When the water content of a soil either falls below the wilting point or becomes sufficiently great to impede soil aeration there is great reduction in the active growth of fungal hyphae. Warcup (1957) found negligible activity in an Australian wheat-field soil during the summer dry period when soil moisture fell markedly below wilting point (30–50% r.h.). While many fungi have been found in waterlogged or periodically inundated sites (Boswell and Sheldon, 1951; Stenton, 1953; Pugh, 1960), there is little information on mycelial activity in such soils.

In his admirable review on soil moisture and the ecology of soil fungi, Griffin (1963) considers that it is probable that nearly all fungi are able to exert the necessary force to absorb water and to grow unimpeded by reduced hydraulic conductivity of the soil throughout the suction range pF 0–4·2 and even in drier soils. In soils drier than permanent wilting point, however, ability will be likely to differ from one species to another, probably leading to ecological diversification. Griffin considers that except below permanent wilting point it seems unlikely that the actual volume of water in soil, taken as a factor in itself, has any effect on fungal ecology. While factors such as moisture content, soil texture and structure have a profound influence on fungal activity, it seems that aeration is, in fact, the effective agent.

Fungi are commonly considered to be strictly aerobic and this opinion is basically correct; however, many are able to grow at low oxygen tensions. This ability to grow at reduced oxygen tension is probably important in growth in a subterranean environment. However, although the concentration of oxygen in the soil atmosphere is normally about 20%, great reductions can occur in waterlogged or compacted soils and in water films adjacent to respiring tissues, owing to the extremely low solubility and rate of diffusion of oxygen in water. Greenwood (1961) has shown that in a clay loam, no oxygen at all was present at the centre of water-saturated crumbs of more than 3 mm radius, even when the intercrumb space was air-filled. Griffin (1963) remarks that the presence of such crumbs must be fairly common even in well-drained soils and these anaerobic pockets must act as fungal inhibitors as well as providing niches for anaerobic bacteria. Thus oxygen deficiency probably causes a restriction in fungal activities not only in water-saturated soils, where Scott and Evans (1955) have shown that oxygen rapidly disappears, but also in apparently well-aerated soils where individual crumbs are water-saturated. In the former case fungal activity is probably inhibited, whereas in the latter case hyphae will be able to ramify in the air-filled pores but their depth of penetration into the anaerobic centres of crumbs will depend, amongst other factors, on the rate of transfer of oxygen along the length of the hypha.

That carbon dioxide concentration can effect fungal activity is suggested by several workers. Burges and Fenton (1953) studied the effect of carbon dioxide and oxygen on the growth in culture of several fungi isolated from various horizons of a soil. Their results show that fungi abundant near the surface were intolerant of carbon dioxide whereas those abundant in subsurface horizons could tolerate concentrations as high as 10%. Durbin (1959) studying clones of *Rhizoctonia solani*, found that those clones isolated from an aerial environment were less tolerant of carbon dioxide than isolates from subterranean habitats while clones from the soil surface were intermediate in tolerance. Papavizas and Davey (1961b) found that accumulation of carbon dioxide in the immediate neighbourhood of buried substrates reduced or prevented growth of *Rhizoctonia* into them. Garrett (1937) had earlier suggested that absorption of carbon dioxide by alkaline soils was the factor which increased the growth of *Ophiobolus graminis* in them. All who have investigated the direct effect of carbon dioxide on fungal growth have shown that, although there is considerable variation from species to species, in general the concentration needed to produce appreciable reduction in linear growth rate is of the order of 10–20%. There are indications, however, that change in linear growth rate may be an insensitive measure of the effect of carbon dioxide; for instance, Burges and Fenton (1953) showed that growth as measured by increase in mycelial weight may be markedly reduced at much lower concentrations of the gas. While the volume of carbon dioxide reported from bulk samples of soil atmospheres is usually between 0·2 and 2%, higher values, 10% or more, have been recorded in soil at depth, or after rain or waterlogging (Russell, 1961).

Soil pH affects the availability of plant nutrients but whether this is important for fungi in soil is not known. Some fungi can tolerate a wide range of soil pH, others are restricted to either acid or alkaline environments (Warcup, 1951a; Brown, 1958b). Cowley and Wittingham (1961) have suggested that tannins may be one of the factors influencing distribution of certain species of fungi in soil. They noted that tannin exerted a pronounced inhibiting effect on microfungi from prairie soils, whereas it had no adverse effects on a majority of the species either prominent in forest soils or common to both.

D. FUNGAL GROWTH PATTERNS IN SOIL

The question of hyphal growth in soil is a complex problem on which our information is very fragmentary. For instance, it is apparent that there is great diversity in growth patterns of fungi in soil; in particular the life of mycelia of many Ascomycetes and Basidiomycetes that form complex fructifications seems to be very different from that of the sporing moulds. Growth rates of the former are often slower and hyphae appear to function for a much longer period; but even between members of each group there is considerable variation. Warcup (1957, 1959) found that in soil some moulds such as *Rhizopus*, *Mortierella* and *Penicillium* have a short life span (3–4 days) from spore germination to formation of spores, whereas some Basidiomycetes may be present in soil as mycelium for several years without forming fructifications. While these Basidiomycete mycelia are perennial, there is little information on the longevity of individual hyphae. It is of interest that Schütte (1956) found that hyphae of moulds such as *Aspergillus* and *Penicillium* were unable to translocate whereas hyphae of the Phycomycetes and Basidiomycetes tested were able to do so.

1. Moulds

Direct examination indicates that different fungi exploit soil and soil habitats in different ways. For instance, Phycomycetes such as *Pythium* and

Mortierella appear to have short-lived mycelium in soil. One can often see phycomycetous hyphae with densely cytoplasmic tips, but a short distance back the cytoplasm becomes vacuolate, and still further back the hyphae appear empty. On the other hand phycomycetous endophytes possess hyphae that ramify from humus particle to humus particle and appear relatively long-lived and resistant to decomposition. With other Phycomycetes such as *Phytophthora* there is doubt whether free growth in soil occurs (Hickman, 1958). Oospores occur in soil, often being embedded in plant residues; germination takes place by the formation of germ tubes which quickly give rise to sporangia (Legge, 1952); the zoospores are attracted to plant roots (Zentmyer, 1961).

Some parasitic Fusaria have also been shown to have limited free growth in soil. The studies of Snyder and co-workers on *Fusarium solani* f. *phaseoli* are of interest; there have been few comparably detailed studies on the biology of saprophytic fungi in soil. *F. solani* f. *phaseoli* is a cortical root- and stem-rotting fungus pathogenic to bean, which it normally attacks by multiple infections of roots and hypocotyl (Toussoun, Nash and Snyder, 1960). Direct examination showed that the fungus exists in soil as thick-walled chlamydospores many of which are embedded in plant debris or particles of organic matter. When macroconidia are added to unsterilized field soil they form chlamydospores either directly or at the end of a short germ tube. Chlamydospores are also formed abundantly at the surface or in the outer cortex of lesions when infected plants die (Nash *et al.*, 1961). Macroconidia are formed at the soil surface in the presence of light (Christou and Snyder, 1962). Although chlamydospores will germinate in water, they were rarely observed to germinate in unsterilized soil, even when the soil was saturated with water (Toussoun and Snyder, 1961). They germinated, however, when in close proximity to germinating bean seed and root tips. Mature roots had little effect on chlamydospore germination and growth when tested in soil. Exudation of amino acids and sugars was most abundant from germinating bean seeds and root tips, and only traces of exudate were detected from mature roots unless they were dried or injured. Solutions of aspartic acid, asparagine, glucose and sucrose stimulated germination and growth of chlamydospores when tested *in vitro*. All these materials were identified as constituents of bean exudate (Schroth and Snyder, 1961). Chlamydospores also germinate near seed of several non-hosts (Schroth and Hendrix, 1962) and around decomposing residues of barley and broccoli, and when water extracts of these residues are added to soil (Toussoun and Patrick, 1962). Data suggest that growth of *F. solani* f. *phaseoli* in soil is limited to the rhizosphere of bean plants, various non-hosts and other temporary supplies of nutrients.

While saprophytic species of *Fusarium* may possibly grow more extensively in soil, it is probable that many features in the growth cycle of *F. solani* f. *phaseoli* apply also to these species. It is known that most *Fusarium* units in soil are chlamydospores (Warcup, 1955b; Nash *et al.*, 1961); *Fusarium* is common in the root zone of various plants (Simmonds and Ledingham, 1937; Waid, 1957, 1960; Parkinson and Chesters, 1958; Peterson, 1958);

macroconidia are often formed on plant residues at the soil surface; conidia or hyphae of many Fusaria added to soil form chlamydospores (Jackson, 1960; Newcombe, 1960); *Fusarium* is often isolated abundantly from debris particles in soil (Parkinson and Kendrick, 1960; Parkinson and Williams, 1961).

It is possible that *Cylindrocarpon radicicola*, which is common on root surfaces (Peterson, 1958; Parkinson and Clarke, 1961; Papavizas and Davey, 1961c; Kubíková, 1963), forms chlamydospores, and is abundant in organic fragments (Parkinson and Williams, 1961), may have a similar life cycle in soil to *Fusarium*. *C. radicicola* is also known, however, to grow on the surface of nematode eggs (van der Laan, 1956).

There is evidence that many other fungi, including species of *Penicillium* and *Aspergillus*, do not normally grow extensively through soil. Sewell (1959b), investigating fungi in a *Calluna*-heath soil, observed Penicillia on few soil slides but in each case these fungi were confined to specific substrates, frequently animal remains, from which there was negligible mycelial spread but considerable sporulation. Discussing growth patterns of fungi in soil, Burges (1960) outlined the *Penicillium* pattern as follows: "A small piece of substrate is densely colonized by the fungus. Spore production occurs heavily over the surface of the substrate, and there is no extension of the mycelium into the surrounding soil." Sewell's observations substantiate this, but other data suggest that not all Penicillia may have the same growth pattern. For instance, *P. vermiculatum* is recorded as a parasite on fungal hyphae in soil (Boosalis, 1956). In Urrbrae loam some Penicillia grow and sporulate on dead soil animals, much as outlined by Sewell; others have been noted on insect exuviae where growth and reproduction are very sparse; others have been noted on the surface of living roots, where once again growth was very sparse and where conidial heads were depauperate compared with those produced by the fungi on isolation in culture; on the other hand, *Penicillium urticae* occasionally flourishes on pieces of root and other substrates in soil and may grow out and sporulate abundantly a cm or so from the substrate. Burges (1963) quotes *Desmazierella* sp. as an example of a fungus occurring in a very restricted habitat, the inside of a pine needle.

With many fungi found in soil, such as coprophilous species, entomogenous fungi, and human and animal pathogens, there is little information available concerning possible growth in soil. Macroconidia of several dermatophytes have been isolated from soil and since these spores are not produced in infected hosts, their presence in soil suggests that they were formed there by the fungus (McDonough *et al.*, 1961). Likewise there is little information on yeasts in soil (Miller and Webb, 1954).

While they are laboratory, not field studies, the observations of Tribe (1957a, 1960a, b, c, 1961) on the decomposition of Cellophane film in soil are of considerable interest. Tribe found that the primary colonizers of buried film were fungi. Chytrids were frequent early colonists but filamentous fungi appeared at the same time. After a short period (2–6 weeks) bacteria developed profusely around the mycelium and over the Cellophane; bacteria were not usually prominent before fungal growth occurred. The bacteria invariably supported a population of nematodes and sometimes patches of amoebae. Nematodes were often parasitized by predaceous fungi which appeared to be the only fungi capable of developing over the bacterial debris. If no larger members of the soil fauna appeared, colonized film persisted in this condition for several months. Frequently, however, the microbial tissue and cellulose were consumed by soil animals. In acid sand and litter, mites were the predominant organisms; in neutral to alkaline soils Collembola and enchytraeid worms were found. Enchytraeid worms were often seen in the soil from the time of burial of the cellulose film, but did not attack it until it was partly replaced by microbial tissue. Mites and Collembola produced well-defined faecal pellets which contained microbial cells; enchytraeid worms mixed the residues with a large proportion of soil and their excreta were difficult to recognize. Decomposition of mite faeces appeared to be very slow. Went (1959) also found that after Cellophane had been attacked by fungi, mites and springtails would start to eat it.

Different pieces of film varied greatly in the time taken to decompose, even in one soil, and the rate of decomposition was greatly influenced by the organisms present. In the absence of fungi capable of attacking the Cellophane, bacterial growth was slight. Keynan, Henis and Keller (1961) have found that cellulose-decomposing bacteria such as *Cellvibrio* are unable to utilize Cellophane film. Because of the restricted development of their rhizoids chytrids were not of great importance in decomposition unless present in large number. Rooting fungi were more active, but a *Rhizoctonia* was able to reduce film to a mushy condition in 2–3 weeks. Further decomposition was dependent on soil animals consuming the film, the combination that decomposed the cellulose most thoroughly being *Rhizoctonia* and enchytraeid worms. In some soils certain pieces of Cellophane remained untouched for weeks, by which time others were virtually destroyed by *Rhizoctonia* or rooting fungi. Presumably none of these occurred near the untouched pieces and other fungi in contact with them were unable to use this substrate.

Tribe (1961) studied both colonization of cellulose film and its influence on the mineral nitrogen status of the soil. He found that under the conditions of incubation provided, mineral nitrogen in the soil was immobilized within 2 weeks of burial of the film but after 16 weeks nitrate began to be released. There was a general succession of fungi, bacteria, and protozoa, especially thecate amoebae, on the cellulose. He suggested that mineral nitrogen was taken up by soil organisms until a mature population had developed approximately 16 weeks after burial of the film. Thereafter nitrogen was slowly released from the population, which was declining as the cellulose substrate became progressively exhausted. He considered that nitrogenous excretion by the protozoa and autolysis of microbial cells were the biological mechanisms of nitrogen release.

2. Basidiomycetes and large Ascomycetes

As with moulds and other fungi with a relatively short mycelial life in soil, Basidiomycetes and Ascomycetes with longer-lived mycelia have many

4*

different growth patterns in soil. These groups, however, have been less extensively studied. Burges (1960) gave the Basidiomycete pattern as: "The fungus colonizes the substrate with a long-lived mycelium and then migrates to other substrates or to a position where it will produce fruit-bodies by means of rhizomorphs or well-developed mycelial strands." The size that such a rhizomorph system may attain is indicated by Grainger (1962), who found by excavation that the length of rhizomorphs from a fructification of *Phallus impudicus* was 55·5 ft. This is probably a general picture of many Basidiomycetes, but other growth cycles are known. A species of *Omphalina* in Urrbrae loam oversummers as sclerotia which are produced abundantly in the late spring (Warcup and Talbot, 1962). In the autumn when the soil again becomes moist the fungus returns to the mycelial condition by germination of some of the sclerotia; only once in the last 7 years have fructifications of this fungus been seen. Several other Basidiomycetes in this soil form sclerotia and may be present in the resting condition for much of the year; their growth cycle has marked resemblances to that of some moulds.

Basidiomycetes that occur in forest litter and soil are considered, in general, to belong to three groups: these are the ectotrophic mycorrhizal fungi which as a group seem incapable of lignin decomposition and only a few are able to break down cellulose; those which produce white rots in wood, causing a break down of cellulose and lignin; and those which produce brown rots in wood, attacking cellulose and hardly affecting lignin (Harley, 1959). It will be noted that these are physiological groups; there is little available information on the ecology of these organisms in soil. Many Basidiomycetes, and particularly mycorrhizal species, are slow-growing and sensitive to competition on agar media, making them difficult to isolate from soil, root tissues or other habitats. Further, it is difficult to identify unknown cultures which may be obtained since data on how to obtain fructifications of Basidiomycetes are scanty.

Melin (1925) showed that several mycorrhizal fungi made their greatest growth in culture upon glucose; more complex carbohydrates were not useful as carbon sources. These results have been generally confirmed (How, 1940; Mikola, 1948), although Norkrans (1949) showed a wider range of utilization of carbohydrates by mycorrhizal species of *Tricholoma*, *T. fumosum* being able to use cellulose to a significant extent. Most mycorrhizal fungi are also characterized by being dependent in culture on the presence of vitamins or growth-factors. Unidentified stimulating substances have also been found naturally: in secretions of germinating pine seeds (Melin, 1925); newly-fallen litter (Melin, 1946); and in root secretions (Melin, 1954; Melin and Das, 1954). The question whether most mycorrhizal fungi are virtually confined to the root zone of host plants or whether they may make appreciable free growth in soil has not been resolved.

Fairy rings are common in woodlands, grasslands and lawns and are the result of activity of soil-inhabiting fungi, mainly Basidiomycetes. Shantz and Piemeisel (1917) classified fairy ring fungi into three types according to their effect on grassland: Type 1, those that kill or damage the grass; Type 2, those which stimulate the grass only; Type 3, those having no effect on the grass but producing fructifications in rings. Type 1 rings have a well-defined mycelial zone in the soil, from which the fungus is usually easily isolated (Warcup, 1951b). They often show three rings in grass; an inner-zone where the grass is stimulated, a middle zone where the grass may be dead, and an outer zone where the grass is stimulated. Fructifications of the fungus are produced in the bare zone, or at the junction of the bare and outer zones, and may not be formed every year. The bare zone appears due to accumulation of mycelium in such large quantities that the soil becomes water-repellent (Shantz and Piemeisel, 1917; Bayliss Elliot, 1926; Warcup, 1951b) causing the grass to become "droughted out" under appropriate conditions. Mycelium of fairy rings grows outwards with a yearly increase of some 3–18 inches depending on the fungus and environmental conditions (Smith, 1957). Fairy rings are often visible on aerial photographs and large rings have been calculated to be several hundred years old (Ramsbottom, 1953). Warcup (1951b) showed that the mycelial zones of several Type 1 rings contain a restricted population of microfungi, both fewer species and fewer colonies as compared with uninvaded soil. Ascomycetes, including *Arachniotus*, *Chaetomium*, *Gymnoascus* and *Penicillium*, have been isolated more frequently from mycelial zones than from normal soil; it is possible that these fungi were present as resistant ascospores.

E. SPORULATION

1. Development of fructifications

Very little is known of the factors, internal or external, inducing reproduction in fungi, but it is probable that the conditions necessary for formation of the complex fructifications of Ascomycetes and Basidiomycetes are different from those for moulds. The principal factors involved in cessation of fungal growth are likely to be exhaustion of carbon or nitrogen supply, but undoubtedly many other factors are also concerned. Data show that in many cases growth may cease without sporulation, hyphae either "resting," forming hyphal segments or chlamydospores, or dying. Some fructifications, particularly oospores, are formed in plant tissue, others may occur in larger cavities in mineral soil, or on plant roots, or on plant or animal residues. Sporulation is common at the soil surface, on residues or in the litter layer.

Some fungi require light for sporulation; this varies from an absolute requirement for initiation or maturation of fructifications, to a quantitative response such as an increase in the number of sporophores upon illumination. Light is an absolute requirement for the formation of many different reproductive organs, including sporophores of Basidiomycetes, apothecia, perithecia, pycnidia, sporangia and conidia (Cochrane, 1958). On the other hand light is known to depress growth or sporulation of other fungi. The effect of light on sporulation of fungi occurring in soil has not been studied in any detail, but it is known that *Trichoderma viride* produces no or very few conidia in continuous darkness, whereas in light it sporulates profusely (Barnett and Lilly, 1953; Miller and Reid, 1961), and that in *Fusarium* light brings about macrospore formation (Snyder and Hansen, 1941; Carlile, 1956; Reid, 1958).

Fructifications of larger fungi are often seasonal and many, though by no means all, fruit in autumn. According to Grainger (1946) and Wilkins and Harris (1946), autumn is the only season when soil temperature, moisture conditions and nitrogen supply are simultaneously adequate for formation of fruiting bodies. Hora (1959) has carried out some interesting experiments on the influence of various fertilizers on the number of Basidiomycete fructifications developing in Scots pine litter. He found that ammonium but not nitrate fertilizer increased sporophore number; lime decreased sporulation of most fungi but vastly increased the number of *Omphalia maura*, normally a very rare fungus in the area. In a few cases the requirements for fruiting have been investigated. Remsberg (1940) noted that sclerotia of *Typhula* normally germinated to give fructifications in wet cold weather in autumn and spring. She found that if sclerotia were refrigerated at 0–3° c with ultraviolet light for 2 hours daily they fruited in 2–4 weeks. Many members of the Sclerotiniaceae also require a rest period at 0° c before fructifications are obtained (Groves and Elliott, 1961). In a study of hypogeous fungi, Hawker (1954) noted the effect of contact stimuli by the frequency with which the fructifications of some species developed in contact with hard objects such as the edge of paths, clay hardpans, etc.

2. Spore dispersal

One of the surprising features of soil fungal studies, especially when using dilution plating techniques, is the wide dispersal of the population within a soil. Dobbs and Hinson (1960) and Burges (1960) have examined the distribution of fungal units in clods of soil. Small samples taken at 1 cm intervals on freshly exposed surfaces of clods were examined for their fungal populations. In each case the more common fungi were widely and relatively evenly distributed in the clods, and there appeared few "high counts" where sporulation might be considered to have taken place. Discussing their results, Dobbs and Hinson suggest that local accumulation of spores from sporulation must be very ephemeral, that spores seem to be subjected to a continual local mixing which gives every soil crumb a relatively uniform species composition. They consider that this mixing is carried out by members of the soil fauna. While soil dilution and soil plate data from Urrbrae loam mainly substantiate the results of Dobbs and Hinson, some of the less abundant fungi do occur in pockets where numbers are much larger than elsewhere. Similarly sclerotia, which are too large to be carried by most members of the soil fauna, often occur in areas of high or low density. Wensley and McKeen (1963) have found *Fusarium oxysporum* f. *melonis* in soil in loci of high or low concentration, the high loci being probably related to sites of infected plants in previous crops. Dick (1962) has also presented evidence that the distribution of the Saprolegniaceae within defined areas in soil is grouped and that the distribution patterns thus recognizable are relatively constant over periods of many months at least.

Another factor of possible importance in mixing spores in soil is water movement. Hirst (1959) has commented that rain-scrubbing seems an ideal method of deposition for air-dispersed soil fungi. Burges (1950) studied the movement of spores through a sand column. He found that spores which had mucilaginous wettable coats may wash down readily, whereas spores with non-wetting coats remained at the surface. Dobbs and Hinson (1960) point out that with fungi from agar culture, wet spores pass through sand and dry spores are retained, but when a soil suspension is used no such differentiation occurs. Since Penicillia were numerous in the effluent, this would suggest that their conidia had lost their unwettable coat. Hepple (1960) studied the movement by water of spores through sand and certain horizons. She found that although such movement is possible under experimental conditions, its occurrence in the field is unlikely except over short distances. As Griffin (1963) points out, however, water movement of spores in natural soils is likely to occur where cracks, root channels, etc., are present. Movement and mixing, though not to great depths, also occurs when heavy rain breaks up soil clods in ploughed fields.

F. DESTRUCTION OF FUNGAL STRUCTURES

The processes of fungal growth and sporulation in soil have been examined; the other side of the balance sheet, the ways in which fungal structures are degraded, must also be considered.

Lysis of young mycelia has been observed on many occasions (Chinn, 1953; Novogrudsky, 1948; Park, 1955; Stevenson, 1956; Tribe, 1957a; Saitô, 1960). Such lysis may be a result of purely internal metabolic changes (autolysis), as a result of contact with enzymes of other organisms, or as a result of exposure to toxic materials. Autolysis is usually a consequence of nutrient deficiency, but may also occur if utilization of energy sources is prevented by oxygen lack or through accumulation of by-products which are toxic to the organism producing them (Brian, 1960). Many toxic materials, including some antibiotics, will cause lysis.

Park (1961a) studied the growth in pure culture of 20 moulds, including Phycomycetes, Ascomycetes and Fungi Imperfecti. He found that in older cultures there was much hyphal lysis and all fungi had one or more types of resting structure in the cultures. Further study revealed that *Armillaria*, *Merulius* and *Xylaria*, fungi with bulky sporophores, did not show extensive lysis, had no resistant resting structures and maintained an intact hyphal network. *Pellicularia subcoronata*, a Basidiomycete without a complex sporophore, showed extensive lysis, however. This work shows that, at least in culture, autolysis is common in fungi.

1. Lysis

There is ample evidence that lysis may be caused by other organisms. Novogrudsky (1948) found that certain bacteria characteristically settled on fungal hyphae, forming a bacterial sheath; lysis of the hyphae usually followed. Similar concentrations of bacteria around hyphae had been noted earlier (Cholodny, 1930; Conn, 1932). Starkey (1938) noted that while such bacterial-fungal associations were common, they were not seen with certain brown mycelium present in soil. Kovoor (1954) noted that severity of bactial attack on hyphae of *Rhizoctonia bataticola* depended on the moisture content of the soil and was much more severe at high moisture levels. Park (1956a) isolated a bacterium, *Bacillus macerans*, which would actively lyse fungi *in vitro*. Stevenson (1956) found that some *Streptomyces* could lyse *Helminthosporium sativum* in mixed culture in soil, and Lockwood (1959) recorded *Streptomyces* as a cause of natural fungitoxicity in soil. Mitchell and Alexander (1961a, b) found that the mycolytic bacteria, *Bacillus cereus*, *B. megaterium*, and a *Pseudomonas*, had high chitinase activity. They also found that addition of chitin to soil increased the number of chitin-decomposing organisms, particularly Actinomycetes, and markedly reduced the severity of root-rot of bean caused by *Fusarium solani* f. *phaseoli*. Further work showed that *B. cereus* and the *Pseudomonas* sp. digested living and dead *Fusarium* mycelium as well as cell wall preparations (Mitchell and Alexander, 1963).

Many fungal spores in soil germinate when residues are added, and evidence suggests that young germ tubes are particularly susceptible to lysis (Chinn and Ledingham, 1961). Brian (1960) considers that lysis under these conditions can probably be attributed to competition and antagonism by other organisms.

The question of antibiotics in soil has been extensively studied and direct evidence for their production has been difficult to obtain (Brian, 1957). Evidence for their production in localized environments such as fragments of plant material, seed coats or in the rhizosphere is gradually accumulating. Wright (1956a, b) buried wheat straws inoculated with *Trichoderma viride* in natural soil and after recovering them, she demonstrated the production of gliotoxin. Similar tests with viable spores of various fungi demonstrated the production of frequentin, gladiolic acid and gliotoxin. While specific antibiotics were not demonstrated, Witkamp (1960) found that powdered twigs naturally infected with *Trichoderma viride* added to agar markedly reduced the bacterial flora of soil-dilution plates. He also showed that mycelial strands of Basidiomycetes collected from oak litter inhibited *Bacillus subtilis* on agar media.

2. Parasitism

A number of soil fungi appear capable of parasitizing other fungi. Some are known parasites such as *Piptocephalis* and *Syncephalis* on members of the Mucorales; others belong to genera where parasitism would not be expected. Very little is known of the role of parasitic fungi on other fungi in soil. Boosalis (1956), in studies in natural soil, showed that *Penicillium vermiculatum* greatly reduced the viability of host hyphae of *Rhizoctonia solani*.

3. Predation

Members of the soil fauna feed on fungal structures in soil. In addition to nematodes and mites, thecamoebae, snails, slugs, some myriapods, Collembola, and certain beetles are all fungus eaters (Kuhnelt, 1961). The data of Tribe (1957, 1960a, b) give a good picture of some members of the soil fauna in relation to the fungi decomposing Cellophane film in soil. Sewell (1959c) working with plants in soil boxes, observed that *Verticillium* spore heads and distal parts of conidiophores were commonly eaten by Collembola and soil mites. Hooper (1962) found that *Aphelenchus avenae* almost completely destroyed mushroom mycelium in compost; this nematode occurs commonly in soil. Some preferences between mycelia of different fungi as food for soil animals have been noted. Winston (1956) found that few soil animals fed on the mycelium of *Armillaria mellea* compared with some other Basidiomycete mycelia. Jacot (1939) noted that *Lophodermium piceae* formed conspicuous black hyphal walls across fallen spruce needles through which feeding soil animals did not penetrate. Soil insects may affect fungi in further ways. Timonin (1961a, b) has shown that the volatile odoriferous material from the scent glands of the plant bug, *Scaptocoris talpa*, is fungistatic or fungicidal.

Witkamp (1960) has carried out a series of interesting experiments on the effects of members of the soil fauna on soil fungi. He estimated the amount of mycelium of *Mortierella pusilla* var. *isabellina* consumed by the springtail *Onychiurus armatus* and by 7 different species of Oribatid mites. Under favourable conditions one springtail consumed 6 m of hyphae a day; the consumption per day per mite was 0·8 m in summer and 0·2 in winter. Direct observation showed the presence of fungal spores adhering to the bristles of oribatid mites. Mites and springtails collected from oak litter and placed on agar transferred fungi which grew on the media; the fungi disseminated belonged predominantly to the genera *Penicillium*, *Mucor* and *Alternaria*. Slugs from fruiting bodies of Basidiomycetes also spread propagules of Fungi Imperfecti; similar observations were made by Talbot (1952). Each of a number of droppings of mites and springtails, sown on agar, gave rise to fungal colonies. On examination under the microscope, these droppings always appeared to contain fragments of mycelium, and in many cases spores were also observed. Poole (1957) showed that fungi may remain viable after passing through the gut of Collembola.

Adverse physical conditions may also kill fungi in soil. Drying causes death of both hyphae and spores (Warcup, 1957) and many fungal fructifications are very susceptible to drying. Flooding kills many, but not all, fungal structures in soil (Moore, 1949; Stover, 1953a).

V. CONCLUSIONS

Although it is possible to sketch outlines, it is evident that there are major gaps in our knowledge of the occurrence and growth of fungi in soil. New techniques will undoubtedly aid acquisition of fresh data, but it must be pointed out that there are many points of information which would greatly aid our conception of fungal biology in soil which are capable of elucidation by present techniques. It is hoped that the time has come when a "species list" will not appear sufficient reward for study of organisms in soil; there are too many other interesting aspects waiting to be investigated.

REFERENCES

Ainsworth, G. C. (1961). "Ainsworth & Bisby's Dictionary of the Fungi." Commonwealth Mycological Institute, Kew, Surrey.
Ajello, L. (1956). *Science*, **123**, 876–879.
Alexander, F. E. S. and Jackson, R. M. (1955). *In* "Soil Zoology." (D. K. McE. Kevan, ed.), pp. 433–440. Butterworth, London.
Andersen, A. L. and Huber, D. (1962). *Phytopathology*, **52**, 1.
Anderson, E. J. (1951). *Phytopathology*, **41**, 187–189.
Apinis, A. E. (1958). *Angew. Pflsoziol.* **15**, 83–90.
Aytoun, R. S. C. (1953). *Trans. Proc. bot. Soc. Edinb.* **36**, 99–114.
Baker, K. F. (1953). *Plant Dis. Reptr.* **37**, 430–433.
Barnett, H. L. and Lilly, V. G. (1953). *Proc. W. Va. Acad. Sci.* **24**, 60–64.
Barton, R. (1957). *Nature, Lond.* **180**, 613–614.
Barton, R. (1958). *Trans. Br. mycol. Soc.* **41**, 207–222.
Bayliss, Elliott, J. S. (1926). *Ann. appl. Biol.* **13**, 277–288.
Bayliss Elliott, J. S. (1930). *Ann. appl. Biol.* **17**, 284–305.
Beckwith, T. D. (1911). *Phytopathology*, **1**, 169–176.
Bisby, G. R., James, N. and Timonin, M. I. (1933). *Can. J. Res. C*, **8**, 253–275.
Bisby, G. R., Timonin, M. I. and James, N. (1935). *Can. J. Res. C*, **13**, 47–65.
Blackwell, E. (1943). *Trans. Br. mycol. Soc.* **26**, 71–89.
Blair, I. D. (1945). *N.Z. J. Sci. Technol.* (Sec. A) **26**, 258–271.
Bolliger, A. and Gross, R. (1952). *Aust. J. exp. Biol. med. Sci.* **30**, 399–408.
Boosalis, M. G. (1956). *Phytopathology*, **46**, 473–478.
Boosalis, M. G. and Scharen, A. L. (1959). *Phytopathology*, **49**, 192–198.
Boswell, J. G. and Sheldon, J. (1951). *New Phytol.* **50**, 172–178.
Bracker, C. E. and Butler, E. E. (1963). *Mycologia*, **55**, 35–58.
Brian, P. W. (1957). *In 7th Symp. Soc. gen. Microbiol.* pp. 168–188. Cambridge University Press, London.
Brian, P. W. (1960). *In* "The Ecology of Soil Fungi." (D. Parkinson and J. S. Waid, eds.), pp. 115–129. Liverpool University Press.
Brierley, W. B. (1923). *In* "The Micro-organisms of the Soil." (Sir John Russell, ed.), pp. 118–146. Longmans, Green and Co., London.
Brierley, W. B., Jewson, S. T. and Brierley, M. (1927). *1st Int. Congr. Soil Sci.* **3**, 48–71.
Brown, J. C. (1958a). *Trans. Br. mycol. Soc.* **41**, 81–88.
Brown, J. C. (1958b). *J. Ecol.* **46**, 641–664.
Burges, A. (1950). *Trans. Br. mycol. Soc.* **33**, 142–147.
Burges, A. (1958). "Micro-organisms in the Soil." Hutchinson, London.
Burges, A. (1960). *In* "The Ecology of Soil Fungi." (D. Parkinson and J. S. Waid, eds.), pp. 185–191. Liverpool University Press.
Burges, A. (1963). *Trans. Br. mycol. Soc.* **46**, 1–14.
Burges, A. and Fenton, E. (1953). *Trans. Br. mycol. Soc.* **36**, 104–108.
Burges, A. and Nicholas, D. P. (1961). *Soil Sci.* **92**, 25–29.
Butler, E. E. (1957). *Mycologia*, **49**, 354–373.

Butler, E. J. (1939). *Trans. Br. mycol. Soc.* **22**, 274–301.
Butler, F. C. (1953). *Ann. appl. Biol.* **40**, 284–311.
Buxton, E. W. and Kendrick, J. B. (1963). *Ann. appl. Biol.* **51**, 215–221.
Caldwell, R. (1958). *Nature, Lond.* **181**, 1144–1145.
Campbell, W. A. (1947). *Mycologia*, **39**, 190–195.
Campbell, W. A. (1949). *Plant. Dis. Reptr.* **33**, 134–135.
Campbell, W. P. (1956). *Can. J. Bot.* **34**, 865–874.
Capstick, C. K., Twinn, D. C. and Waid, J. S. (1957). *Nematologica*, **2**, 193–201.
Carlile, M. J. (1956). *J. gen. Microbiol.* **14**, 643–654.
Carter, M. V. and Moller, W. J. (1961). *Aust. J. agric. Res.* **12**, 878–888.
Chesters, C. G. C. (1940). *Trans. Br. mycol. Soc.* **24**, 352–355.
Chesters, C. G. C. (1948). *Trans. Br. mycol. Soc.* **30**, 100–117.
Chesters, C. G. C. (1949). *Trans. Br. mycol. Soc.* **32**, 197–216.
Chesters, C. G. C. (1960). *In* "The Ecology of Soil Fungi." (D. Parkinson and J. S. Waid, eds.), pp. 223–238. Liverpool University Press.
Chesters, C. G. C. and Thornton, R. H. (1956). *Trans. Br. mycol. Soc.* **39**, 301–313.
Chinn, S. H. F. (1953). *Can. J. Bot.* **31**, 718–724.
Chinn, S. H. F. and Ledingham, R. J. (1957). *Can. J. Bot.* **35**, 697–701.
Chinn, S. H. F. and Ledingham, R. J. (1958). *Can. J. Bot.* **36**, 289–295.
Chinn, S. H. F. and Ledingham, R. J. (1961). *Can. J. Bot.* **39**, 739–748.
Chinn, S. H. F., Ledingham, R. J., Sallans, B. J. and Simmonds, P. M. (1953). *Phytopathology*, **43**, 701.
Cholodny, N. (1930). *Arch. Mikrobiol.* **1**, 620–652.
Christensen, M., Whittingham, W. F. and Novak, R. O. (1962). *Mycologia*, **54**, 374–388.
Christou, T. (1962a). *Phytopathology*, **52**, 194–198.
Christou, T. (1962b). *Phytopathology*, **52**, 381–389.
Christou, T. and Snyder, W. C. (1962). *Phytopathology*, **52**, 219–226.
Clarke, J. H. and Parkinson, D. (1960). *Nature, Lond.* **188**, 166–167.
Cochrane, V. W. (1958). "Physiology of Fungi." John Wiley and Sons, New York.
Cochrane, V. W. (1960). *In* "Plant Pathology." (J. G. Horsfall and A. E. Dimond, eds.), vol. II, pp. 169–202. Academic Press, New York.
Coley-Smith, J. R. (1959). *Ann. appl. Biol.* **47**, 511–518.
Coley-Smith, J. R. (1960). *Ann. appl. Biol.* **48**, 8–18.
Conn, H. J. (1918). *Tech. Bull. N.Y. St. agric. Exp. Stn*, **64**, 1–20.
Conn, H. J. (1932). *Tech. Bull. N.Y. St. agric. Exp. Stn*, **204**, 3–31.
Cooke, R. C. (1962). *Trans. Br. mycol. Soc.* **45**, 314–320.
Cooke, W. B. (1958). *Bot. Rev.* **24**, 341–429.
Cooke, W. B. and Lawrence, D. B. (1959). *J. Ecol.* **47**, 529–549.
Corner, E. J. H. (1950). *Ann. Bot. Mem. No.* 1, Oxford.
Cowley, G. T. and Whittingham, W. F. (1961). *Mycologia*, **53**, 539–542.
Cunningham, J. L. and Hagedorn, D. J. (1962). *Phytopathology*, **52**, 616–618.
Dale, E. (1912). *Ann. Mycol.* **10**, 452–477.
Dale, E. (1914). *Ann. Mycol.* **12**, 33–62.
Daniels, J. (1961). *Trans. Br. mycol. Soc.* **44**, 79–86.
Dawson, V. T. and Dawson, R. C. (1946). *Proc. Soil Sci. Am.* **11**, 268–269.
Dean, A. L. (1929). *Phytopathology*, **19**, 407–412.
Demeter, K. J. and Mossel, H. (1933). *Zbl. Bakt.* (11) **88**, 384–393.
Vries, G. A. de. (1962). *Antonie van Leeuwenhoek*, **28**, 121–133.
Dick, M. W. (1962). *J. Ecol.* **50**, 119–127.

Dobbs, C. G. and Carter, N. C. C. (1963). Report on Forest Research for 1962, pp. 103–112. H.M.S.O. London.

Dobbs, C. G. and Hinson, W. H. (1953). *Nature, Lond.* **172**, 197–199.

Dobbs, C. G. and Hinson, W. H. (1960). In "The Ecology of Soil Fungi." (D. Parkinson and J. S. Waid, eds.), pp. 33–42. Liverpool University Press.

Dobbs, C. G., Hinson, W. H. and Bywater, J. (1960). In "The Ecology of Soil Fungi." (D. Parkinson and J. S. Waid, eds.), pp. 130–147. Liverpool University Press.

Drechsler, C. (1941). *Biol. Rev.* **16**, 265–290.

Duddington, C. L. (1955). *Bot. Rev.* **21**, 377–439.

Duddington, C. L. (1957). "The Friendly Fungi." Faber and Faber, London.

Dulaney, E. L., Larsen, A. H. and Stapley, E. O. (1955). *Mycologia*, **47**, 420–422.

Durbin, R. D. (1959). *Am. J. Bot.* **46**, 22–25.

Durbin, R. D. (1961). *Bot. Rev.* **27**, 522–560.

Durbin, R. D., Davis, L. H. and Baker, K. F. (1955). *Phytopathology*, **45**, 509–512.

Durrell, L. W. and Shields, L. M. (1960). *Mycologia*, **52**, 636–641.

Eastwood, D. J. (1952). *Trans. Br. mycol. Soc.* **35**, 215–220.

Eaton, E. D. and King, C. J. (1934). *J. agric. Res.* **49**, 1109–1113.

Eckert, J. W. and Tsao, P. H. (1962). *Phytopathology*, **52**, 771–777.

Ellis, J. J. and Hesseltine, C. W. (1962). *Nature, Lond.* **193**, 699–700.

Ellis, M. (1940). *Trans. Br. mycol. Soc.* **24**, 87–97.

Emmons, C. W. (1951). *J. Bact.* **62**, 685–690.

Ezekiel, W. N. (1940). *Rep. Tex. agric. Exp. Stn*, **1939**, 84–86.

Ezekiel, W. N. (1945). *Phytopathology*, **35**, 296–301.

Farrow, W. M. (1954). *Mycologia*, **46**, 632–646.

Fennell, D. I. (1960). *Bot. Rev.* **26**, 79–141.

Ferguson, J. (1953). *Phytopathology*, **43**, 471.

Gadd, C. H. and Bertus, L. S. (1928). *Ann. R. bot. Gdns Peradeniya*, **11**, 27–49.

Gams, W. (1959). *Sydowia*, **13**, 87–94.

Garrett, S. D. (1937). *Ann. appl. Biol.* **24**, 747–751.

Garrett, S. D. (1944). "Root Disease Fungi." Chronica Botanica, Waltham, Mass., U.S.A. (*Annales Cryptogamici et Phytopathologici*, Vol. 1).

Garrett, S. D. (1944). *Chronica bot.*

Garrett, S. D. (1951). *New Phytol.* **50**, 149–166.

Garrett, S. D. (1952). *Sci. Progr. Lond.* **159**, 436–450.

Garrett, S. D. (1954). *Trans. Br. mycol. Soc.* **37**, 51–57.

Garrett, S. D. (1955). *Trans. Br. mycol. Soc.* **38**, 1–9.

Garrett, S. D. (1956). "Biology of Root-infecting Fungi." Cambridge University Press, London.

Gerdemann, J. W. (1955). *Mycologia*, **47**, 619–632.

Gerdemann, J. W. and Nicolson, T. H. (1963). *Trans. Br. mycol. Soc.* **46**, 235–244.

Gilman, J. C. (1957). "A Manual of Soil Fungi." Iowa State College Press, Ames, Iowa.

Grainger, J. (1946). *Trans. Br. mycol. Soc.* **29**, 52–63.

Grainger, J. (1962). *Trans. Br. mycol. Soc.* **45**, 147–155.

Greenwood, D. J. (1961). *Pl. Soil*, **14**, 360–376.

Griffin, D. M. (1960). *Trans. Br. mycol. Soc.* **43**, 583–596.

Griffin, D. M. (1963). *Biol. Rev.* **38**, 141–166.

Griffin, G. J. (1962). *Phytopathology*, **52**, 90–91.

Griffiths, E. and Jones, D. (1963). *Trans. Br. mycol. Soc.* **46**, 285–294.

Griffiths, E. and Siddiqi, M. A. (1961). *Trans. Br. mycol. Soc.* **44**, 343–353.
Groves, J. W. and Elliott, M. E. (1961). *Can. J. Bot.* **39**, 215–231.
Guillemat, J. and Montégut, J. (1957). *Annls. Épiphyt.* **8**, 185–207.
Haarløv, N. and Weis-Fogh, T. (1953). *Oikos,* **4**, 44–57.
Haarløv, N. and Weis-Fogh, T. (1955). *In* "Soil Zoology." (D. K. McE. Kevan, ed.), pp. 429–432. Butterworth, London.
Hagem, O. (1907). *Math. naturw. Klasse Bd,* **7**, 1–50.
Hagem, O. (1910). *Annls. mycol.* **8**, 265–286.
Harley, J. L. (1959). "The Biology of Mycorrhiza." Leonard Hill, London.
Harley, J. L. (1960). *In* "The Ecology of Soil Fungi." (D. Parkinson and J. S. Waid, eds.), pp. 265–276. Liverpool University Press.
Harley, J. L. and Waid, J. S. (1955). *Trans. Br. mycol. Soc.* **38**, 104–118.
Harvey, J. V. (1925). *J. Elisha Mitchell scient. Soc.* **41**, 151–164.
Hawker, L. E. (1954). *Phil. Trans. R. Soc. B,* **237**, 429–546.
Hawker, L. E. (1955a). *Biol. Rev.* **30**, 127–158.
Hawker, L. E. (1955b). *Trans. Br. mycol. Soc.* **38**, 73–77.
Hawker, L. E. (1957a). "The Physiology of Reproduction in Fungi." Cambridge University Press, London.
Hawker, L. E. (1957b). *In* "Microbial Ecology." *7th Symp. Soc. gen. Microbiol.,* pp. 238–258. Cambridge University Press, London.
Hepple, S. (1958). *Mucor ramannianus* in a podsolized soil. Ph.D. thesis, University of Liverpool.
Hepple, S. (1960). *Trans. Br. mycol. Soc.* **43**, 73–79.
Hepple, S. and Burges, A. (1956). *Nature, Lond.* **177**, 1186.
Hessayon, D. G. (1953). *Soil Sci.* **75**, 395–404.
Hesselman, H. (1926). *Medd. Skogsförsöksanst Stockh.* **22**, 169–552.
Hickman, C. J. (1958). *Trans. Br. mycol. Soc.* **41**, 1–13.
Hildebrand, A. A. and Koch, L. W. (1936). *Can. J. Res. C,* **14**, 11–26.
Hine, R. B. (1962). *Phytopathology,* **52**, 736.
Hirst, J. M. (1959). *In* "Plant Pathology: Problems and Progress 1908–1958." (C. S. Holton, ed.), pp. 529–538. University of Wisconsin Press, Madison.
Hooper, D. J. (1962). *Nature, Lond.* **193**, 496–497.
Hora, F. B. (1959). *Trans. Br. mycol. Soc.* **42**, 1–14.
How, J. E. (1940). *Ann. Bot., N.S.* **4**, 135–150.
Jackson, R. M. (1957). *Nature, Lond.* **180**, 96–97.
Jackson, R. M. (1958a). *J. gen. Microbiol.* **18**, 248–258.
Jackson, R. M. (1958b). *J. gen. Microbiol.* **19**, 390–401..
Jackson, R. M. (1960). *In* "The Ecology of Soil Fungi." (D. Parkinson and J. S. Waid, eds.), pp. 168–176. Liverpool University Press.
Jacot, A. P. (1939). *J. For.* **37**, 858–860.
James, N. (1959). *Can. J. Microbiol.* **5**, 431–439.
James, N. and Sutherland, M. L. (1939). *Can. J. Res. C,* **17**, 97–108.
Jefferys, E. G. and Hemming, H. G. (1953). *Nature, Lond.* **172**, 872–873.
Jensen, C. N. (1912). *Bull. N.Y. (Cornell) agric. Exp. Stn,* **315**, 415–501.
Jensen, H. L. (1931). *Soil Sci.* **31**, 123–158.
Jensen, H. L. (1934). *Proc. Linn. Soc. N.S.W.* **59**, 200–211.
Jensen, H. L. (1935). *Proc. Linn. Soc. N.S.W.* **60**, 145–154.
Joffe, A. Z. (1963). *Mycologia,* **55**, 271–282.
Johnson, L. F. and Manka, K. (1961). *Soil Sci.* **92**, 79–84.
Jones, P. C. T. and Mollinson, J. E. (1948). *J. gen. Microbiol.* **2**, 54–69.

Kendrick, W. B. (1958). *Nature, Lond.* **181**, 432.
Kendrick, W. B. (1959). *Can. J. Bot.* **37**, 907–912.
Kendrick, W. B. and Burges, A. (1962). *Nova Hedwigia*, **4**, 313–342.
Kerr, A. (1963). *Aust. J. biol. Sci.* **16**, 55–69.
Keynan, A., Henis, Y. and Keller, P. (1961). *Nature, Lond.* **191**, 307.
Keyworth, W. G. (1951). *Trans. Br. mycol. Soc.* **34**, 291–292.
King, C. J., Loomis, H. F. and Hope, C. (1931). *J. agric. Res.* **42**, 827–840.
Klotz, L. J. and Fawcett, H. S. (1939). *Phytopathology*, **29**, 290–291.
Kovoor, A. T. A. (1954). *J. Madras Univ.* B, **24**, 47–52.
Krzemieniewska, H. and Badura, L. (1954). *Acta Soc. Bot. Polon.* **23**, 727–781.
Kubiena, W. L. (1938). "Micropedology." Collegiate Press, Inc., Iowa.
Kubíková, J. (1963). *Trans. Br. mycol. Soc.* **46**, 107–114.
Kurbis, W. P. (1937). *Flora, Jena*, **131**, 129–175.
Kuhnelt, W. (1961). "Soil Biology." Faber and Faber, London.
La Touche, C. J. (1948). *Trans. Br. mycol. Soc.* **31**, 281–284.
Lebeau, J. B. and Cormack, M. W. (1956). *Phytopathology*, **46**, 298.
Lebeau, J. B. and Logsdon, C. E. (1958). *Phytopathology*, **48**, 148–150.
Ledingham, R. J. and Chinn, S. H. F. (1955). *Can. J. Bot.* **33**, 298–303.
Legge, B. J. (1952). *Nature, Lond.* **169**, 759–760.
Lendner, A. (1908). *Beitr. Kryptogflora Schweiz*, **3**, 1–180.
Levisohn, I. (1955). *Nature, Lond.* **176**, 519.
Linford, M. B. (1942). *Soil Sci.* **53**, 93–103.
Lingappa, B. T. and Lockwood, J. L. *J. gen. Microbiol.* **26**, 473–485.
Lingappa, B. T. and Lockwood, J. L. (1962). *Phytopathology*, **52**, 295–299.
Lingappa, B. T. and Lockwood, J. L. (1963). *Phytopathology*, **53**, 529–531.
Lingappa, Y. and Lockwood, J. L. (1961). *Nature, Lond.* **189**, 158–159.
Lloyd, A. B. and Lockwood, J. L. (1962). *Phytopathology*, **52**, 1314–1315.
Lockwood, J. L. (1959). *Phytopathology*, **49**, 327–331.
Lockwood, J. L. and Lingappa, B. T. (1963). *Phytopathology*, **53**, 917–920.
Lýsek, H. (1963). *Nature, Lond.* **199**, 925.
McDonough, E. S., Ajello, L., Austermann, R. J., Balows, A., McClellan, J. T. and Brinkman, S. (1961). *Am. J. Hyg.* **73**, 75–83.
MacFarlane, I. (1952). *Ann. appl. Biol.* **39**, 239–256.
McKeen, W. E. (1952). *Can. J. Bot.* **30**, 344–347.
McLennan, E. (1928). *Ann. appl. Biol.* **15**, 95–109.
McLennan, E. I. and Ducker, S. C. (1954). *Aust. J. Bot.* **2**, 220–245.
McTeague, D. M., Hutchinson, S. A. and Reed, R. I. (1959). *Nature, Lond.* **183**, 1736.
MacWithey, H. S. (1957). *Rept 36th A. Conv. NWest. Ass. Hortic., Entomols Pl. Pathol.* pp. 5–6.
Maloy, O. C., and Alexander, M. (1958). *Phytopathology*, **48**, 126–128.
Martin, J. P. (1950). *Soil Sci.* **69**, 215–232.
Martin, T. L., Anderson, D. A. and Goates, R. (1942). *Soil Sci.* **54**, 297–302.
Martinson, C. and Baker, R. (1962). *Phytopathology*, **52**, 619–621.
Melin, E. (1925). "Untersuchungen über die Bedeutung der Baummykorrhiza," pp. 1–152. G. Fischer, Jena.
Melin, E. (1946). *Symb. bot. Upsal.* **8**, 1–116.
Melin, E. (1954). *Svensk bot. Tidskr.* **48**, 86–94.
Melin, E. and Das, V. S. R. (1954). *Physiologia Pl.* **7**, 851–858.
Mikola, P. (1948). *Commn. Inst. For. Fenn.* **36**, 1–104.

Mikola, P. (1956). *Commn. Inst. For. Fenn.* **48**, 5–22.
Miller, P. M. (1956). *Phytopathology*, **46**, 526.
Miller, J. H., Giddens, J. E. and Foster, A. A. (1957). *Mycologia*, **49**, 779–808.
Miller, J. J. and Reid, J. (1961). *Can. J. Bot.* **39**, 259–262.
Miller, J. J. and Webb, N. S. (1954). *Soil Sci.* **77**, 197–204.
Minderman, G. (1956). *Pl. Soil* **8**, 42–48.
Mitchell, R. B., Hooton, D. R. and Clark, F. E. (1941). *J. agric. Res.* **63**, 535–547.
Mitchell, R. and Alexander, M. (1961a). *Nature, Lond.* **190**, 109–110.
Mitchell, R. and Alexander, M. (1961b). *Plant Dis. Reptr.* **45**, 487–490.
Mitchell, R. and Alexander, M. (1963). *Can. J. Microbiol.* **9**, 169–177.
Molin, N. (1957). *Medd. Skogsförsöksanst. Stockh.* **47**, 1–36.
Montégut, J. (1960). *In* "The Ecology of Soil Fungi." (D. Parkinson and J. S. Waid, eds.), pp. 43–52. Liverpool University Press.
Moore, J. J. (1954). *Scient. Proc. R. Dubl. Soc.* **26**, 379–395.
Moore, W. D. (1949). *Phytopathology*, **39**, 920–927.
Morrow, M. B. (1932). *Mycologia*, **24**, 398–402.
Mosse, B. (1959). *Trans. Br. mycol. Soc.* **42**, 439–448.
Mueller, K. E. and Durrell, L. W. (1957). *Phytopathology*, **47**, 243.
Muskett, A. E. (1960). *In* "Plant Pathology." (J. G. Horsfall and A. E. Dimond, eds.), vol. III, pp. 58–96. Academic Press, New York.
Nash, S. M. and Snyder, W. C. (1962). *Phytopathology*, **52**, 567–572.
Nash, S. M., Christou, T. and Snyder, W. C. (1961). *Phytopathology*, **51**, 308–312.
Newcombe, M. (1960). *Trans. Br. mycol. Soc.* **43**, 51–59.
Newhook, F. J. (1959). *N.Z. Jl. agric. Res.* **2**, 808–843.
Nicolson, T. H. (1959). *Trans. Br. mycol. Soc.* **42**, 421–438.
Nicot, J. (1953). *Rev. Mycol.* **18** (*suppl. colon* 2), 88–93.
Nicot, J. (1960). *In* "The Ecology of Soil Fungi." (D. Parkinson and J. S. Waid, eds.), pp. 94–97. Liverpool University Press.
Nicot, J. and Chevaugeon, J. (1949). *Bull. Mus. Hist. nat. Paris* **31**, 384–392.
Norkrans, B. (1949). *Svensk bot. Tidskr.* **43**, 485–490.
Novogrudsky, D. M. (1948). *Mikrobiologiya*, **17**, 28–35.
Ohms, R. E. (1957). *Phytopathology*, **47**, 751–752.
Orpurt, P. A. and Curtis, J. T. (1957). *Ecology*, **38**, 628–637.
Oudemans, C. A. J. A. and Koning, C. J. (1902). *Archs. néerl. Sci. Série 2*, **7**, 286–298.
Pady, S. M., Kramer, C. L. and Pathak, V. K. (1960). *Mycologia*, **52**, 347–350.
Paharia, K. D. and Kommedahl, T. (1956). *Plant. Dis. Reptr.* **40**, 1029–1031.
Pantidou, M. E. (1961). *Can. J. Bot.* **39**, 1149–1162.
Papavizas, G. C. and Davey, C. B. (1959a). *Plant. Dis. Reptr.* **43**, 404–410.
Papavizas, G. C. and Davey, C. B. (1959b). *Soil Sci.* **88**, 112–117.
Papavizas, G. C. and Davey, C. B. (1961a). *Phytopathology*, **51**, 92–96.
Papavizas, G. C. and Davey, C. B. (1961b). *Phytopathology*, **61**, 693–699.
Papavizas, G. C. and Davey, C. B. (1961c). *Pl. Soil* **14**, 215–236.
Papavizas, G. C. and Davey, C. B. (1962). *Phytopathology*, **52**, 834–840.
Park, D. (1954). *Nature, Lond.* **173**, 454–455.
Park, D. (1955). *Trans. Br. mycol. Soc.* **38**, 130–142.
Park, D. (1956a). *Trans. Br. mycol. Soc.* **39**, 239–259.
Park, D. (1956b). *6th Int. Congr. Soil Sci.* **3**, 23–28.
Park, D. (1960). *In* "The Ecology of Soil Fungi." (D. Parkinson and J. S. Waid, eds.), pp. 148–159. Liverpool University Press.

Park, D. (1961a). *Trans. Br. mycol. Soc.* **44**, 119–122.
Park, D. (1961b). *Trans. Br. mycol. Soc.* **44**, 377–390.
Parkinson, D. (1957). *Pedologie*, **7**, *no. spéc.* (*Symp. Meth. Et. Microbiol. Sol*), 146–154.
Parkinson, D. and Chesters, C. G. C. (1958). *Nature, Lond.* **181**, 1746–1747.
Parkinson, D. and Clarke, J. H. (1961). *Pl. Soil*, **13**, 384–390.
Parkinson, D. and Kendrick, W. B. (1960). In "The Ecology of Soil Fungi." (D. Parkinson and J. S. Waid, eds.), pp. 22–28. Liverpool University Press.
Parkinson, D. and Williams, S. T. (1961). *Pl. Soil*, **13**, 347–355.
Parmeter, J. R. and Hood, J. R. (1961). *Phytopathology*, **51**, 164–168.
Peltier, G. L. (1937). *Phytopathology*, **27**, 145–158.
Peterson, E. A. (1958). *Can. J. Microbiol.* **4**, 257–265.
Peyronel, B. (1924). *Boll. Staz. Patol. veg. Roma*, **5**, 73–75.
Poole, T. B. (1957). Report on Forest Research for 1956, pp. 109–111. H.M.S.O. London.
Pugh, G. J. F. (1958). *Trans. Br. mycol. Soc.* **41**, 185–195.
Pugh, G. J. F. (1960). In "The Ecology of Soil Fungi." (D. Parkinson and J. S. Waid, eds.), pp. 202–208. Liverpool University Press.
Pugh, G. J. F. and Mathison, G. E. (1962). *Trans. Br. mycol. Soc.* **45**, 567–572.
Ramsbottom, J. (1953). "Mushrooms and Toadstools." Collins, London.
Rayss, T. and Borut, S. (1958). *Mycopath. Mycol. appl.* **10**, 142–174.
Reid, J. (1958). *Can. J. Bot.* **36**, 507–537.
Remsburg, R. E. (1940). *Mycologia*, **32**, 52–96.
Rishbeth, J. (1950). *Ann. Bot. N.S.* **14**, 365–383.
Robertson, N. F. (1954). *New Phytol.* **53**, 253–283.
Roistacher, C. N., Baker, K. F. and Bald, J. G. (1957). *Hilgardia*, **26**, 659–684.
Romell, L. G. (1935). *Mem. Cornell Univ. agric. Exp. Stn*, **170**, 1–28.
Rossi, G. M. (1928). *Italia agric.* **4**.
Russell, E. W. (1961). "Soil Conditions and Plant Growth." (9th Edition) Longmans, Green and Co. London.
Russell, P. (1956). *Nature, Lond.* **177**, 1038–1039.
Sadasivan, T. S. (1939). *Ann. appl. Biol.* **26**, 497–508.
Saitô, T. (1952). *Ecol. Rev. Japan*, **13**, 111–119.
Saitô, T. (1955a). *Ecol. Rev. Japan*, **14**, 69–74.
Saitô, T. (1955b). *Sci. Rep. Tôhoku Univ. 4th Ser.* **21**, 145–151.
Saitô, T. (1956). *Ecol. Rev. Japan*, **14**, 141–147.
Saitô, T. (1957). *Ecol. Rev. Japan*, **14**, 209–216.
Saitô, T. (1958). *Sci. Rep. Tôhoku Univ. 4th Ser.* **24**, 73–79.
Saitô, T. (1960). *Sci. Rep. Tôhoku Univ. 4th Ser.* **26**, 125–131.
Scharen, A. L. (1960). *Phytopathology*, **50**, 274–277.
Schmitthenner, A. F. (1962). *Phytopathology*, **52**, 1133–1138.
Schroth, M. N. and Hendrix, F. F. (1962). *Phytopathology*, **52**, 906–909.
Schroth, M. N. and Snyder, W. C. (1961). *Phytopathology*, **51**, 389–393.
Schütte, K. H. (1956). *New Phytol.* **55**, 164–182.
Scott, A. D. and Evans, D. D. (1955). *Proc. Soil Sci. Soc. Am.* **19**, 7–12.
Sewell, G. W. F. (1956). *Nature, Lond.* **177**, 708.
Sewell, G. W. F. (1959a). *Trans. Br. mycol. Soc.* **42**, 343–353.
Sewell, G. W. F. (1959b). *Trans. Br. mycol. Soc.* **42**, 354–369.
Sewell, G. W. F. (1959c). *Trans. Br. mycol. Soc.* **42**, 312–321.

Sewell, G. W. F. (1959d). *New. Phytol.* **58**, 5–15.
Shantz, H. L. and Piemeisel, R. L. (1917). *J. agric. Res.* **11**, 191–245.
Simmonds, P. M. (1930). *Phytopathology*, **20**, 911–913.
Simmonds, P. M. and Ledingham, R. J. (1937). *Scient. Agric.* **18**, 49–59.
Singh, R. S. and Mitchell, J. E. (1961). *Phytopathology*, **51**, 440–444.
Smith, J. D. (1957). *J. Sports Turf Res. Inst.* **9**, 324–352.
Smith, N. R. and Dawson, V. T. (1944). *Soil Sci.* **58**, 467–471.
Snyder, W. C. and Hansen, H. N. (1941). *Mycologia*, **33**, 580–591.
Sparrow, F. K. (1957). *Trans. Br. mycol. Soc.* **40**, 523–535.
Stanier, R. Y. (1953). *In* "Adaptation in Micro-organisms." *3rd Symp. Soc. gen. Microbiol.* Cambridge University Press, London.
Starkey, R. L. (1929). *Soil Sci.* **27**, 319–334.
Starkey, R. L. (1938). *Soil Sci.* **45**, 207–249.
Stenton, H. (1953). *Trans. Br. mycol. Soc.* **36**, 304–314.
Stenton, H. (1958). *Trans. Br. mycol. Soc.* **41**, 74–80.
Stevenson, I. L. (1956). *J. gen. Microbiol.* **15**, 372–380.
Stover, R. H. (1953a). *Can. J. Bot.* **31**, 693–697.
Stover, R. H. (1953b). *Nature, Lond.* **172**, 465.
Stover, R. H. (1958). *Can. J. Bot.* **36**, 439–453.
Swart, H. J. (1958). *Acta bot. neerland.* **7**, 741–768.
Talbot, P. H. B. (1952). *Trans. Br. mycol. Soc.* **35**, 123–128.
Taubenhaus, J. J. and Ezekiel, W. N. (1930). *Phytopathology*, **20**, 761–785.
Thornton, R. H. (1952). *Research, Lond.* **5**, 190–191.
Thornton, R. H. (1956a). *Trans. Br. mycol. Soc.* **39**, 485–494.
Thornton, R. H. (1956b). *Nature, Lond.* **177**, 230–231.
Thornton, R. H. (1958). *Nature, Lond.* **182**, 1690.
Thornton, R. H. (1960). *In* "The Ecology of Soil Fungi." (D. Parkinson and J. S. Waid, eds.), pp. 84–91. Liverpool University Press.
Thornton, R. H., Cowie, J. D. and McDonald, D. C. (1956). *Nature, Lond.* **177**, 231–232.
Tichelaar, G. M. (1961). *Tijdschr. PlZiekt.* **67**, 290–295.
Timonin, M. I. (1961a). *Pl. Soil*, **14**, 323–334.
Timonin, M. I. (1961b). *Can. J. Bot.* **39**, 695–703.
Toussoun, T. A., Nash, S. M. and Snyder, W. C. *Phytopathology*, **50**, 137–140.
Toussoun, T. A. and Patrick, Z. A. (1962). *Phytopathology*, **52**, 30.
Toussoun, T. A. and Snyder, W. C. (1961). *Phytopathology*, **51**, 620–623.
Tracey, M. V. (1956). *Rep. Rothamsted exp. Stn.* 1955, pp. 87–88.
Tresner, H. D., Backus, M. P. and Curtis, J. T. (1954). *Mycologia*, **46**, 314–333.
Tribe, H. T. (1957a). *7th Symp. Soc. gen. Microbiol.* 287–298. Cambridge University Press, London.
Tribe, H. T. (1957b). *Trans. Br. mycol. Soc.* **40**, 489–499.
Tribe, H. T. (1960a). *Can. J. Microbiol.* **6**, 309–316.
Tribe, H. T. (1960b). *Can. J. Microbiol.* **6**, 317–323.
Tribe, H. T. (1960c). *In* "The Ecology of Soil Fungi." (D. Parkinson and J. S. Waid, eds.), pp. 246–256. Liverpool University Press.
Tribe, H. T. (1961). *Soil Sci.* **92**, 61–77.
Triffitt, M. J. (1935). *J. Helminth.* **13**, 59–66.
Vaartaja, O. (1960). *Phytopathology*, **50**, 870–873.
Vanbreuseghem, R. (1952). *Annls, Soc. belge Méd. trop.* **32**, 173–178.
van der Laan, P. A. (1956). *Tijdschr. PlZiekt.* **62**, 305–321.

Vanterpool, T. C. and Macrae, R. (1951). *Can. J. Bot.* **29**, 147–157.
Veldkamp, H. (1955). *Meded. LandbouwHoogesch. Wageningen,* **55**, 127–174.
Venkat Ram, C. S. (1952). *Nature, Lond.* **170**, 889.
Waid, J. S. (1957). *Trans. Br. mycol. Soc.* **40**, 391–406.
Waid, J. S. (1960). *In* "The Ecology of Soil Fungi." (D. Parkinson and J. S. Waid, eds.), pp. 55–75. Liverpool University Press.
Waid, J. S. and Woodman, M. J. (1957). *Pedologie,* **7**, no. spéc. (*Symp. Méth. Et. Microbiol. Sol*), pp. 155–158.
Waksman, S. A. (1916a). *Science,* N.S. **44**, 320–322.
Waksman, S. A. (1916b). *Soil Sci.* **2**, 103–155.
Waksman, S. A. (1917). *Soil Sci.* **3**, 565–589.
Waksman, S. A. (1922). *J. Bact.* **7**, 339–341.
Waksman, S. A. (1927). "Principles of Soil Microbiology." Baillière, Tindall and Cox, London.
Waksman, S. A. (1944). *Soil Sci.* **58**, 89–114.
Wallace, H. A. H. (1959). *Can. J. Bot.* **37**, 509–515.
Warcup, J. H. (1950) *Nature, Lond.* **166**, 117.
Warcup, J. H. (1951a). *Trans. Br. mycol. Soc.* **34**, 376–399.
Warcup, J. H. (1951b). *Ann. Bot. N.S.* **15**, 305–317.
Warcup, J. H. (1952). *Trans. Br. mycol. Soc.* **35**, 248–262.
Warcup, J. H. (1955a). *Nature, Lond.* **175**, 953.
Warcup, J. H. (1955b). *Trans. Br. mycol. Soc.* **38**, 298–301.
Warcup, J. H. (1957). *Trans. Br. mycol. Soc.* **40**, 237–262.
Warcup, J. H. (1959). *Trans. Br. mycol. Soc.* **42**, 45–52.
Warcup, J. H. (1960). *In* "The Ecology of Soil Fungi." (D. Parkinson and J. S. Waid, eds.), pp. 3–21. Liverpool University Press.
Warcup, J. H. and Baker, K. F. (1963). *Nature, Lond.* **197**, 1317–1318.
Warcup, J. H. and Talbot, P. H. B. (1962). *Trans. Br. mycol. Soc.* **45**, 495–518.
Warcup, J. H. and Talbot, P. H. B. (1963). *Trans. Br. mycol. Soc.* **46** (4).
Warren, J. R. (1948). *Mycologia,* **40**, 391–401.
Watling, R. (1963). *Trans. Br. mycol. Soc.* **46**, 81–90.
Weber, G. F. (1929). *Mycologia,* **21**, 113–130.
Webley, D. M., Eastwood, D. J. and Gimingham, C. H. (1952). *J. Ecol.* **40**, 168–178.
Weindling, R. (1932). *Phytopathology,* **22**, 837–845.
Weinhold, A. R. and Hendrix, F. F. (1962). *Phytopathology,* **52**, 32.
Wensley, R. N. and McKeen, C. D. (1963). *Can. J. Microbiol.* **9**, 237–249.
Went, J. C. (1959). *Acta bot. neerl.* **8**, 490–491.
White, N. H. (1954). *Aust. J. Sci.* **17**, 18–19.
Wilhelm, S. (1956). *Phytopathology,* **46**, 293–295.
Wilkins, W. H. and Harris, G. C. M. (1946). *Ann. appl. Biol.* **33**, 179–188.
Willoughby, L. G. (1961). *Trans. Br. mycol. Soc.* **44**, 305–332.
Winston, P. W. (1956). *Ecology,* **37**, 120–132.
Witkamp, M. (1960). *Meded. Inst. toegep. biol. Onderz. Nat.* **46**, 1–51.
Witkamp, M. and van der Drift, J. (1961). *Pl. Soil,* **15**, 295–311.
Wood, F. A. and Wilcoxson, R. D. (1960). *Plant Dis. Reptr.* **44**, 594.
Wright, J. M. (1956a). *Ann. appl. Biol.* **44**, 461–466.
Wright, J. M. (1956b). *Ann. appl. Biol.* **44**, 561–566.
Yarwood, C. E. (1946). *Mycologia,* **38**, 346–348.
Zentmyer, G. A. (1961). *Science,* **133**, 1595–1596.

Chapter 4

The Actinomycetes

E. KÜSTER

University College, Dublin, Ireland

I. GENERAL INTRODUCTION

The Actinomycetes are in general a group of micro-organisms important not so much for their frequent occurrence in nature as for their particular physiological properties. This importance entitles us to describe the Actinomycetes in a little more detail and separately from the other bacterial groups.

A. TYPE OF ORGANISMS

In earlier times the Actinomycetes were designated as fungi because of their morphological appearance and the development like fungi of true mycelium. Therefore they were at first called "ray fungi." However, recent exhaustive studies give support to the opinion that the Actinomycetes are more closely related to bacteria than to fungi. In the sizes of their cells and spores, and in the absence of aerial mycelia they correspond to bacteria; they possess nucleoids like bacteria (see also Hagedorn, 1955; Petras, 1959). Chitin or cellulose compounds, characteristic of the cell walls of true fungi, do not occur in Actinomycetes (Avery and Blank, 1954). Their cell walls are polymers of sugars, amino sugars, and a few amino acids (Cummins and Harris, 1958) like those of Gram-positive bacteria. The sensitivity of the Actinomycetes to phages and antibiotics also places them with the bacteria. Because of these and other facts the Actinomycetes have to be designated as bacteria and it is recommended that the International Code of Nomenclature of Bacteria and Viruses (1958) should be used in classifying them.

TABLE I

Families and genera of the Actinomycetales

Vegetative mycelium	Family / Genus	Aerial mycelium	Spore characteristics
Vegetative mycelium fragmenting into bacillary elements	Actinomycetaceae		
	Actinomyces		
	Nocardia		
	Micropolyspora		
	Dermatophilaceae		
	Dermatophilus		
Vegetative mycelium not fragmenting into bacillary elements	Streptomycetaceae		
	Micromonospora	aerial mycelium absent	single spores on vegetative mycelium only
	Thermoactinomyces		single spores on vegetable and aerial mycelium
	Thermomonospora		single spores on aerial mycelium only
	Microbispora	aerial mycelium present	pairs of spores on aerial mycelium only
	Streptomyces		chains of spores on aerial mycelium only
	Actinoplanaceae		
	Microellobosporia	aerial mycelium present	non-motile sporangiospores in club-shaped sporangia
	Streptosporangium		non-motile sporangiospores in spherical sporangia
	Spirillospora		motile sporangiospores in spherical sporangia
	Actinoplanes		motile sporangiospores in spherical sporangia
	Ampullariella	aerial mycelium absent	motile sporangiospores in cylindrical sporangia
	Amorphosporangium		non-motile sporangiospores in irregularly-shaped sporangia

1. Systematics

The order Actinomycetales comprises four families with a number of genera (Table I). Several other genera have been proposed in the last few years, but are not fully recognized (*Jensenia, Pseudonocardia, Polysepta, Promicromonospora, Thermopolyspora, Streptoverticillium, Chainia, Actinosporangium, Thermoactinopolyspora*). The division into genera is based mainly upon morphological characters such as fragmentation of the hyphae, formation of aerial mycelium, and manner of spore formation (singly, in chains, or in sporangia). Other methods have been recently elaborated and employed in order to facilitate and improve the classification of form-genera of Actinomycetes. Valuable results have been obtained by the examination of the cell-wall composition (Becker, Lechevalier and Lechevalier, 1965; Yamaguchi, 1965). Spectrophotometric (Arai, Kuroda and Koyama, 1963) and serological (Kwapinski, 1964) methods have also been used.

2. Variation and genetics

The Actinomycetes are known as particularly variable organisms. This extreme variability renders classification and taxonomical work difficult. Morphological variations as well as cultural and physiological ones are widespread among the Actinomycetes. The appearance of colony sectoring is very frequent. This means a variant present in the colony forms a type of mycelium, aerial or vegetative, which differs from that of the majority of the colony. This can result from a loss of the ability to form aerial mycelium or the formation of sterile aerial mycelium only. Other characteristic variations are changes in pigmentation, antibiotic production, pathogenicity, etc. The nature and composition of media, the age and type of the culture used as inoculum, and the presence of other organisms or of antagonistic or promoting substances formed by them are important factors in the phenomenon of variation. Some variations are only temporary and can be reversed to the original form. It has been observed that a loss of pigmentation and antibiotic production could be restored after a transfer of the "degenerated" culture to soil agar or another medium which is more natural in its composition than most of the synthetic media.

There are many types of genetical changes, some of which, e.g. mutations, have also been found and examined intensely in Actinomycetes. The parent strain and the mutant are sometimes so different in their morphological and/or physiological behaviour that the mutant has been named as a new species (e.g. Horvath, Marton and Oroszlan, 1954). Mutagenic agents such as irradiation or chemicals have also been applied to Actinomycetes. In particular, research of this kind has been carried out in order to obtain strains with a higher antibiotic activity.

Bacterial genetics as applied to Actinomycetes has been a wide field of study in recent times. Several cases of genetic recombination with Streptomycetes have been reported. These are intraspecific (Sermonti and Spada-Sermonti, 1956; Alikhanian and Mindlin, 1957; Saito, 1958; Hopwood,

1959; Bradley and Anderson, 1960; Alikhanian and Borisova, 1961) as well as interspecific (Horvath, 1962; Alacevic, 1963). In spite of these studies the results obtained are still deficient and the explanations offered still too contradictory to permit final general conclusions about sexual reproduction.

3. Actinophages

Actinophages are submicroscopic, filtrable, virus-like organisms. They attack the living cells of Actinomycetes, multiply inside the host-cells and cause a complete lysis of them, similar to the way in which bacteriophages act. They can also act as mutagenic agents (Alikhanian and Iljina, 1957). They consist of a spherical or polygonal head with a thin tail attached (Mach, 1958).

The phage is adsorbed in such a manner that the tail-like appendix is in contact with the host-cell. Actinophages occur abundantly in soil, particularly in compost and soils rich in organic matter. It is a simple procedure to observe the presence of actinophages and to isolate them (Newbould and Garrard, 1954; Welsch, Minon and Schönfeld, 1955). The phenomenon of lysogeny also occurs with Actinomycetes (Rautenstein, 1957; Welsch, 1958). The actinophages differ greatly in their host range; they are either polyvalent, lysing strains of different species, or monovalent, attacking only strains of one species (Weindling, Tresner and Backus, 1961; Kutzner, 1961). Bradley, Anderson and Jones (1961) suggest the use of polyvalent actinophages in identifying genera or species-groups, but not for classification.

4. Taxonomy

The taxonomy of Actinomycetes and particularly of Streptomycetes is a very complicated and unsatisfactory problem. One of the main reasons for it is the above-mentioned great variability of these kinds of organisms. Constant characters have to be chosen to provide an exact description of the species, independently of their phylogenetic importance. There have been many attempts to provide keys for a species classification. The works of Krassilnikov (1949), Baldacci, Spalla and Grein (1954), Gause et al. (1957), Ettlinger, Corbaz and Hütter (1958), and Waksman (1961) are the most important and the most frequently used ones. Kutzner (1956), Pridham, Hesseltine and Benedict (1958), Shinobu (1958) and others contributed valuable suggestions. The morphology of the sporophores, the shape of the spores, the colour of the aerial and vegetative mycelium, and the melanin reaction are the main characters which are suitable for a first division into groups, series, and the like. The introduction of the infrageneric taxa "series" and "groups" facilitates the taxonomical work on these organisms. The further separation into species needs more and specific physiological tests.

B. Morphology

1. Colony

The Actinomycetes, in particular the Streptomycetes, are characterized by a typical colony growth. A colony of Actinomycetes is not an accumulation of many single and uniform cells such as is the case with bacteria; it is rather a mass of branching filaments. A colony grown on a solid medium is composed of what has been termed vegetative and aerial mycelium. In the absence of aerial mycelium the surface of the colony is glossy or matt. Strains of the genus *Streptomyces* form an extensive mycelium growing into the medium so that it firmly adheres to the solid substrate and is taken off with a wire loop as a whole unit. On the other hand, colonies formed by the *Nocardia* type tend to break up into hyphae of varying lengths, which are less tenacious of the substrate, are of a mealy consistency and have a tendency to crumble. If aerial mycelium develops, the surface acquires a powdery or cottony appearance. The structure, shape, size, and colour of the colony vary widely with changes in cultural conditions. Colonies of many Streptomycetes exhibit a characteristic earth-like odour. Acetic acid, acetaldehyde, ethanol, isobutanol, and isobutylacetate have recently been identified as the major aroma-producing substances (Gaines and Collins, 1963). Even hydrogen sulphide is believed to contribute to the earthy-odour complex (Collins and Gaines, 1964).

2. Vegetative mycelium

The vegetative or substrate mycelium consists of non-septate long hyphae. Some hyphae are straight and of a considerable length of more than 600 μ, whilst others are much shorter, branched, and curved. The branching is typically monopodial. The vegetative mycelium fragments into bacillary or coccoid elements in the case of Actinomycetaceae and Dermatophilaceae, but not with the Streptomycetaceae. The vegetative mycelium can be stained in the ordinary way. Generally, the Actinomycetes are Gram-positive; some are acid-fast, particularly in the genus *Nocardia*. The cytoplasm of the hyphal cells is at first homogenous and becomes vacuolated at advanced and older stages of development. Fat and volutin granules may be found in the vacuoles (Prokofeva-Belgovskaja and Kats, 1960). The vegetative mycelium is often characteristically coloured, cream, yellow, orange, red, green, brown, or black. If water-soluble, the pigments are secreted into the medium.

3. Aerial mycelium

The aerial mycelium, if present, is much more characteristic in its structure and shape than the vegetative mycelium. This applies in particular to *Streptomyces*. The aerial mycelium rises from the substrate mycelium and may cover the whole colony so that it becomes cottony or powdery in appearance. The aerial mycelium can be fertile or sterile. Sterile mycelium sometimes occurs as white spots on cultures with normally grey fertile aerial mycelium and is also called "secondary aerial mycelium" (Kutzner, 1956). Sterile hyphae are generally thin and show no increase in their diameter, whereas sporogenous hyphae are in the beginning thinner than the hyphae from which they derive, but later at the final state of development they increase in thickness.

The fertile aerial mycelium consists of sporophores which are arranged on sterile filaments. The *Streptomyces* sporophores can be long or short, straight or more or less curved. The short hyphae give a powdery colony surface while a cottony surface derives from long hyphae. There are all intermediates between straight and spirally curved structures. The sporophores can grow straight or flexuous, or they show open or closed spirals. The sporophores may also be arranged in a verticillate form in some *Streptomyces* species.

The specific structure of the aerial mycelium is constant and characteristic for each *Streptomyces* species under standardized conditions, so that it is used as a good criterion for taxonomic work. Schemes of this kind have been composed recently by Pridham *et al.* (1958), Ettlinger *et al.* (1958), Shinobu (1958), Nomi (1960) and others.

Another character of the *Streptomyces* aerial mycelium is its pigmentation, which ranges from white or grey to yellow, orange, rose, lavender, blue, and green. So-called "Colour Wheels" introduced by Tresner and Backus (1963) facilitate the often confusing determination of the colour. When sporogenous hyphae are clumped together they appear like the coremia of fungi. This particular phenomenon can be observed under specific cultural conditions with some *Streptomyces* species (Giolitti, 1960; Grein and Spalla, 1962).

4. Spores

Spores originate at the tips of the sporogenous hyphae. They are formed by fragmentation or segmentation. In the fragmentation process the cytoplasm breaks away from the cell wall and separates into more or less uniform units. These are later liberated by the splitting of the cell wall. This manner of sporulation is characteristic of the genus *Streptomyces*. In the segmentation process new cross walls are formed so that the hyphae break up into small segments. *Nocardia* shows this manner of sporulation. With *Micromonospora* conidia are formed as single spores at the end of straight and short branches. The spores are arranged singly, in pairs, or in chains of different length. Motile, flagellated sporangiospores occur with some genera of Actinoplanaceae (Table I). The spores are spherical, oval, or cylindrical reproductive bodies. In electron microscope studies it has been demonstrated (Küster, 1953; Flaig, Küster and Beutelspacher, 1955; Baldacci and Grein, 1955; and others) that the surface structure of *Streptomyces* spores is smooth or rough (spiny, hairy, or warty). The spore surface is characteristic for each species, and is also used as a taxonomical criterion (Ettlinger *et al.*, 1958; Preobrashenskaja, Sveshnikova and Maksimova, 1959; Tresner, Davies and Backus, 1961). In some strains a dependence on the appearance of spiny spores upon the composition of the medium was reported (Flaig *et al.*, 1955; also Lechevalier and Tikhonenko, 1960; Mordaskij and Kudrina, 1961). Recent observation of an outer layer of sporogenic hyphae of *Streptomyces* (Hopwood and Glauert, 1961) and of a sporangium containing short chains of spores with *Microellobosporium* (Rancourt and Lechevalier, 1963) led to the suggestion that sporangia which more or less break up and disappear during the development of spores may occur more commonly than hitherto assumed.

C. PHYSIOLOGY

1. Carbon-metabolism

The Actinomycetes utilize a wide range of organic compounds. Besides the usual good carbon sources such as sugars, starch, hemicelluloses, proteins, and numerous other substances, compounds which are generally not so easily decomposed can also be attacked by some Actinomycetes. Some of these substances will be considered later in so far as they are concerned with soil organic matter and its decomposition (p. 120). The best carbon sources are glucose, maltose, dextrin, starch, glycerol, and proteins.

The utilization by the Streptomyces species of some carbohydrates is so specific that this specificity can be employed for species differentiation (Pridham and Gottlieb, 1948). Several acids are formed under particular fermentation conditions. *Nocardia* species show some peculiarities in so far as they oxidize various unusual carbon compounds, e.g. long-chain fatty acids and hydrocarbons (Raymond, 1961; Nolof, 1962; Seeler, 1962). Hirsch (1960) described some *Nocardia* and *Streptomyces* species as oligo-carbophilic organisms which are able to assimilate CO_2, utilizing traces of volatile C-compounds in air. The organism isolated from sewage and described by Ware and Painter (1955) as a strictly autotrophic Actinomycete which is able to utilize cyanide as a C- and N-source seems to be a *Nocardia*. The oxidation of benzene is a further peculiarity of *Nocardia* (Haccius and Helfrich, 1958), as also is the utilization of some aromatic compounds (Villanueva, 1960). An oxidation and conversion of steroids by Nocardiae and Streptomycetes have also been reported (Perlman, 1953; Spalla, Amici and Bianchi, 1961).

2. Nitrogen-metabolism

As mineral nitrogen, ammonium salts are generally preferred to nitrates. Nitrite and carbamates (Schatz *et al.*, 1954) are also used by some species. Nitrification as well as nitrate reduction occur with certain *Streptomyces* (Kawato and Shinobu, 1960, 1961; Hirsch, Overrein and Alexander, 1961). Proteins, peptones, and certain amino acids are the best nitrogen sources for Actinomycetes. *Streptomyces* generally possess a stronger proteolytic activity than *Nocardia*, from which it can be completely absent. Some amino acids are utilized and deaminated by *Streptomyces* (Gottlieb and Ciferri, 1956). The accumulation of ammonia after deamination shows that the amino acids are used as a source of carbon rather than of nitrogen. The same happens with proteins and peptones (Waksman, 1959, p. 124). The effect of various amino acids on the tyrosinase activity of Streptomycetes has been studied by Küster (1958). Amino acids, e.g. methionine, or vitamins, e.g. biotin, are in some cases needed as essential growth factors, in particular for thermophilic species (Webley, 1958; Tendler, 1959). *Streptomyces* growing on synthetic media are also able to synthesize and to secrete free amino acids into the medium before a strong autolysis appears (Pfennig, 1956). Some *Nocardia* are capable of utilizing heterocyclic N-compounds as nitrogen sources as well as sources of carbon and energy (Küster, 1952; Batt and Woods, 1961).

3. Mineral elements

Like other micro-organisms the Actinomycetes need a nutrient medium which is well-balanced with regard to its mineral composition. A sufficient proportion of K, Mg, Zn, Fe, Cu, and Ca is generally necessary for the growth and metabolism of Actinomycetes. But this may vary according to the required effect. Extensive studies have been carried out on the influence of elements on the production of various antibiotics. Cobalt favours the sporulation of *Streptomyces* (Hickey and Tresner, 1952). Combinations of micro-elements are often more effective than single additions, and these can also be replaced by soil extracts or their ashes (Spicher, 1955). Webley (1960) reported marked morphological changes in *Nocardia* which have been caused by a deficiency in manganese.

4. Vitamins, pigments, antibiotics

Actinomycetes produce many vitamins, pigments, and antibiotics, in some cases to such a great extent that their ability is industrially employed. This is true of vitamin B_{12} and a series of antibiotics. Vitamin B_{12} is mainly formed by *Strept. griseus*, *Strept. olivaceus*, and *Strept. aureofaciens* (Darken, 1953). In the latter case it is a by-product of the aureomycin fermentation and is applied to animal nutrition. Vitamins of the B-complex, such as thiamine (Herrick and Alexopoulos, 1942, Harington, 1960) and riboflavin (Protiva, 1956) are produced by a number of Actinomycetes.

A great variety of pigments are formed by Actinomycetes. The pigmentation of the vegetative and aerial mycelia has been mentioned before (see p. 116). The pigments differ in their solubility in water and organic solvents, in their behaviour as indicators for changes in reaction, and in their chemical structure. N-free and N-containing pigments have been found. Carotenoids and quinones belong to the first group, whereas prodigiosin-like pigments and phenoxazone derivatives are heterocyclic N-compounds. The function and role of pigments in the life and metabolism of Actinomycetes are not yet clearly known. Some pigments, especially those with quinonoid structure, can be considered as humic acid precursors (see p. 122), whilst others exhibit a more or less strong antibiotic effect. A very large number of antibiotics formed by Actinomycetes is known. The Streptomycetes belong to the most important and best studied antibiotic-producers. Many antibiotics such as streptomycin, aureomycin, neomycin and others are industrially manufactured on a large scale and usefully applied in medicine. As well as the genus *Streptomyces*, some species of *Nocardia*, *Micromonospora*, and *Thermoactinomyces* also form antibiotic substances. There are many cases where the same antibiotic is formed by several organisms; on the other hand one species is sometimes capable of producing more than one antibiotic. The antibiotic substances are mostly bound to the mycelium and its cell wall.

D. ECOLOGY

Actinomycetes are widely distributed in nature, having been found in soil, water, in living tissues of men and animals, and in the atmosphere. In general, but with exceptions, we can state that most of the Actinomycetes are soil organisms. Strains of *Streptomyces*, *Micromonospora*, and *Actinoplanes* have also been occasionally observed living in fresh and salt water. Many members of the Actinomycetaceae are pathogens causing human and animal diseases.

Most Actinomycetes are aerobic, except those of the genus *Actinomyces* which are anaerobic or micro-aerophilic and are the cause of actinomycosis in men and cattle. Soil Actinomycetes which act as plant pathogens will be mentioned later (see p. 122). The majority of Actinomycetes are mesophilic but several thermophilic species occur in *Streptomyces*. *Thermoactinomyces* and *Thermomonospora* consist of thermophilic forms only. The spores of *Streptomyces* are not alone in exhibiting a strong resistance to heat and dryness, as Jagnow (1957) has reported that in some cases non-sporulated mycelium also does this.

Many Streptomycetes are distinguished by a high salt tolerance (Stapp, 1953; Szabo *et al.*, 1959). Except for a few species, e.g. *Strept. acidophilus*, Streptomycetes grow best on alkaline media and primarily occur on substrates with a slightly alkaline reaction. Some species of *Streptomyces* show a marked sensitivity to acid, e.g. *Strept. caeruleus* (Taber, 1960).

II. ACTINOMYCETES AS SOIL ORGANISMS

A. OCCURRENCE IN SOIL

The numbers of *Streptomyces* spp. in the soil vary widely, absolutely as well as relatively. Depth, moisture content, soil reaction, soil type, and soil vegetation influence the occurrence and growth of *Streptomyces* in soil at least to the same extent as with other micro-organisms. The methods used in counting and the manner of preparation of the soil samples are also important. Skinner (1951) found that a continued shaking of the soil sample effects a breaking of hyphae and consequently an increase in the number of colonies. *Streptomyces* colonies found on soil plates originate from mycelial fragments rather than from spores.

The proportion of *Streptomyces* in the total number of micro-organisms ranges between 10 and 70%. The absolute numbers of Actinomycetes decreases with the depth of soil, but they increase in proportion to the bacteria by from 10 to 65% (Waksman, 1959, p. 31). Also the number of different species in deeper layers is much reduced. Szabo *et al.* (1958, 1959) confirmed this observation and found that sterile types dominate in deeper layers (B-horizon), while sporulating types more frequently occur in the A-horizon. They explain this by the better aeration and dryness of the upper layers in comparison with the wet B-horizon. Streptomycetes which were isolated from deep layers at low temperatures are quite sensitive towards higher

5+s.b.

temperatures (Marton, 1962). This indicates a close ecophysiological relationship between the micro-organisms and their habitat. Decreasing moisture and increasing temperature stimulate the growth of soil Streptomycetes. The low incidence or near absence of *Streptomyces* in acid peat is caused not only by its acidity but also by the poor aeration (Waksman and Purvis, 1932). The frequent occurrence of *Streptomyces* in saline soils (Szik soils in Hungary, Szabo *et al.*, 1959; Marsh soils) and sea water (Grein and Meyers, 1958) may be due to their high salt tolerance. The enormous influence of added lime on development has been shown by Jensen (1930). Cultivation of soil which usually creates better aeration often results in a higher number of Streptomycetes.

In comparison with cultivated soil the percentage of *Streptomyces* is higher in grassland because it is richer in plant roots. Kutzner (1956) reported a considerable number of chromogenous, i.e. peptone-browning strains in grassland. This fact may probably also be related to the so-called soil fertility, as Singh (1937) found earlier when comparing manured and unmanured soils. The frequency of antibiotic-producing strains is also particularly high in grassland and fallow land (Lindner and Wallhäusser, 1955; Chun, 1956; Craveri *et al.*, 1960; and others). Kutzner (1956) calculated an "antibiotic index" for a soil sample and obtained the highest one from grassland. However, this cannot be generalized, because the search has only been intense for antibiotic-producing strains, and resulted in the conclusion that this attribute occurs very frequently with *Streptomyces* and is not limited to a certain soil type. It may be interesting to note that antagonistic *Streptomyces* isolated from a soil rich in organic matter lose their antibiotic properties under laboratory conditions and storage, more readily than those from poor soils (Valyi-Nagy, Hernadi and Jeney, 1961). Our own experience confirms that an alkaline, dry, loamy soil rich in organic matter (roots, manure, etc.) is the best natural habitat for *Streptomyces*, and that this is true for *Streptomyces* in general as well as for specialized strains (antagonists, etc.).

Thermophilic Actinomycetes occur primarily in manure, compost (Waksman, Umbreit and Cordon, 1939; Henssen, 1957), and mouldy hay (Corbaz, Gregory and Lacey, 1963), but also in nearly all kinds of soil (Kosmachev, 1956; Craveri and Pagani, 1962; Küster and Locci, 1963). The geographical distribution of *Streptomyces* is world wide. Their occurrence is not limited to any particular climate, although they are more abundant in the warmer zones. *Streptomyces* have been found even under the most extreme conditions in deserts.

B. ACTIVITY IN SOIL

1. Decomposition and transformation of organic matter

There are many carbon- and/or nitrogen-containing substances which occur in soil as residues from plants and animals and which are usually classed as soil organic matter. Some of these are attacked and decomposed to a great extent by Actinomycetes, under natural conditions in the soil.

Water-soluble carbohydrates are the most readily attacked, then the hemi-celluloses, and finally the celluloses. The ability to decompose cellulose and other polysaccharides is wide-spread among Actinomycetes. *Streptomyces* spp. are very active in the decomposition of hemicelluloses (Waksman and Diehm, 1931), particularly of mannans and xylans, probably by means of the extracellular enzyme xylanase (Sørensen, 1957). The formation of pectinase by *Streptomyces* has recently been recorded by Bilimoria and Bhat (1961). Other enzymes which are formed by *Nocardia* cause a degradation of lamina-rin and alginates in seaweeds (Chesters, Apinis and Turner, 1956). Even agar can be decomposed by *Streptomyces* and *Nocardia* (Stanier, 1942). Although these latter substances do not appear as soil organic matter, it is of interest to mention them to give an idea of the large range of carbon com-pounds present in nature which can be utilized by Actinomycetes. Cellulolytic enzymes have not yet been demonstrated in *Streptomyces* and *Nocardia*, although these organisms play an important role in the decomposition of cellulose in soil. Under appropriate conditions thermophilic Actinomycetes exhibit a strong cellulolytic activity (Henssen, 1957). Anaerobic cellulose-decomposers, e.g. *Micromonospora propionici*, belonging to the Actinomycetes have also been found (Hungate, 1946). Among the cellulose-decomposing Actinomycetes isolated from forest litter some *Streptosporangium* have been identified (van Brummelen and Went, 1957).

A peculiarity of *Actinoplanes* is its ability to attack and decompose keratin (Gaertner, 1955). A highly active keratinase has been prepared from *Strept. fradiae* (Noval and Nickerson, 1959; Kuchaeva *et al.*, 1963). A great increase in the number of Streptomycetes after the addition of keratin-containing material such as hoof and horn to peat compost has been recently observed by the author. Little is known about the decomposition of lignin by Actinomycetes. Waksman (1959, p. 247) supposes an ability to attack lignins, but satisfactory evidence such as is available for fungi has not yet been obtained. *Streptomyces* spp. (Jagnow, 1957; Kolb, 1957) and to a greater extent *Nocardia* spp. (Müller, 1950) can use oxalic acid as a carbon and energy source. These organisms may play an important role in the detoxification of the Ca-oxalate of plant residues under natural conditions.

Chitin is another organic compound which can be utilized as a carbon and nitrogen source by many Actinomycetes by means of the enzyme chitinase (Reynolds, 1954; Horikoshi and Iida, 1959). The number of chitin-decomposing *Streptomyces* is lower in forest soils than in other soil types probably because of the lack of arthropods in these (Jagnow, 1957). Urea is used as a nitrogen source by many Streptomycetes (Stapp and Spicher, 1954) and an active urease has been found in the mycelium of *Strept. griseus* (Simon, 1955).

There are contradictory reports on nitrogen fixation by Actinomycetes but the introduction of the tracer technique with ^{15}N should clarify this problem. It seems unlikely that fixation of atmospheric nitrogen will occur to any great extent. Recently Metcalfe and Brown (1957) described two *Nocardia* species isolated from grassland which are able to fix nitrogen at a rate of up to 12 mg N/g of decomposed cellulose. The breakdown of plant residues by micro-organisms, especially by Actinomycetes, is an important step in the carbon and nitrogen cycles in nature. The organically fixed nitrogen is more or less mineralized by microbial activity, but the carbon compounds are partially transformed into humic acids which are very important for soil fertility. Even in this process of humic acid formation the soil Actinomycetes play a unique role. This is true not only in soil, but also particularly in manure and composts in which these transforming processes take place at higher temperatures and by the activity of thermophilic Actinomycetes (Henssen, 1957). As is well known, the first reactions which lead to humic acids are induced by micro-organisms. The break down of high-molecular plant components and the formation of humic acid precursors are the main function of micro-organisms in the origin of humic acids; whereas the further reactions which result in the formation of highly polymerized humic acids are chemical ones. After autolysis, many *Streptomyces* spp. form dark brown substances which exhibit chemical and physical properties very similar to those of humic acids extracted from soil (Flaig *et al.*, 1952, Bremner, Flaig and Küster, 1955). The Streptomycetes are therefore good objects for studying humic acid formation. It was demonstrated that micro-organisms in general and *Streptomyces* spp. in particular only produce humus-like substances when they are able to form quinonoid metabolic products by means of phenolases (Küster, 1955). How far these processes are important for humic acid formation in nature may be illustrated by the following consideration: the ability of chromogenous Streptomycetes to brown peptone-containing media depends on the presence and activity of phenolases (Küster, 1958), and the numbers of chromogenous Streptomycetes are relatively high in grassland soils (Kutzner, 1956) which are known to be rich in humus and of high fertility. Humic acids are considered as substances quite resistant to chemical and microbial attack. However, some micro-organisms, mainly *Nocardia* spp., are capable of decomposing humic acids, probably because of their ability to utilize heterocyclic N-compounds (Küster, 1950, 1952).

2. Plant pathogenicity

In spite of the many different species of Actinomycetes present in soil, only a very few act as plant pathogens. The most important plant disease caused by an Actinomycete is potato scab. Hoffmann (1958) found that *Strept. scabies* is the sole pathogen of this disease, whereas various other species previously reported as parasitic forms of scab are saprophytic accompanying organisms only. The previously supposed relationship between the tyrosinase reaction (brown ring test) and the ability to cause potato scab could not be confirmed by genetic studies, which proved that tyrosinase is not associated with the virulence of *Strept. scabies* (Gregory and Vaisey, 1956). Another plant disease caused by an Actinomycete (*Strept. ipomoea*) is the sweet potato pox or soft rot (Stapp, 1956). It was believed that *Strept. alni* infected the roots of the alder bush (*Alnus glutinosa*) and formed nodules on them (von Plotho, 1941), but recent studies have shown that *Strept. alni* is not responsible for this phenomenon (Pommer, 1959).

3. Antibiosis

(a) *Formation of antibiotics.* Many *Streptomyces* spp. isolated from soil are capable of producing antibiotics of medical and industrial importance under artificial and optimal conditions in the laboratory in large amounts. Formation of antibiotics in soil occurs, if at all, to a very slight extent and is limited to small zones surrounding the antibiotic-producing colony. The restricted formation and appearance of antibiotics in soil is due to poor nutritional conditions in the soil, strong competition by other organisms, and inactivation by microbial activity and physical-chemical reactions. A partial or complete sterilization of soil favours the growth and antibiotic production of certain strains. Likewise, an addition of organic matter stimulates the production of antibiotics, as reported by Grossbard (1952) with fungi. The amounts of antibiotics formed and present in soil are mostly too small to be detected, but they can exert localized inhibitory effects. This has been successfully proved with actinomycin (*Strept. antibioticus*) (Stevenson, 1956) and chloromycetin (*Strept. venezuelae*) (Gottlieb and Siminoff, 1952). In spite of their low productivity antibiotic-producing Streptomycetes can play a role in natural soil fungitoxicity (Lockwood, 1959). Attempts to control pathogenic fungi by inoculating the soil with very heavy infections of *Streptomyces* which are known to form antibiotics active against the pathogen have met with only limited and temporary success (Mach, 1956; Rehm, 1959).

Besides the antibiotic effects the beneficial ones which are exerted by Streptomycetes on other soil organisms should also be briefly mentioned. Katznelson and Henderson (1962) recently isolated *Streptomyces* spp. from plant roots and found that they attracted nematodes, probably due to their metabolic products and not by serving as food for the worm.

(b) *Inactivation of antibiotics.* If antibiotics are produced in or added to soil they are very easily inactivated. Some organisms of the original soil microflora decompose antibiotics by means of specific enzymes or by using them as a carbon and/or nitrogen-source (Abd-el-Malek, Monib and Hazem, 1961). Clay minerals adsorb antibiotics and inactivate them. Basic and amphoteric antibiotics, such as tetracyclines and streptomycin, are readily adsorbed, while acidic and neutral ones, such as penicillin and actidione, are only slightly inactivated and are more effective and stable in soil (Martin and Gottlieb, 1952; Gottlieb, Siminoff and Martin, 1952; Krüger, 1961). Most antibiotics cause flocculation of soil colloids which is generally correlated with adsorption.

4. Microbial equilibrium

Any soil which is a natural habitat for micro-organisms possesses its own microflora which is well-balanced and typical. This microbial equilibrium depends on all the factors which characterize the particular soil. By the

cultivation of a crop, for example, this equilibrium is disturbed and the Streptomycetes decrease in number, as has been shown with barley (Rehm, 1960).
Each artificial change only causes a temporary change in the microflora. After
a relatively short time this change is compensated for and the original equilibrium is restored. A single application of organic or inorganic fertilizers
favours all types of micro-organisms, useful as well as undesirable ones. The
addition of antibiotics to prevent plant diseases is also ineffective after a short
time because of the above-mentioned factors of inactivation. The importance
of an inoculation with antibiotic-producing organisms is limited to a very
small area of efficiency. Considering all these factors, we come to the conclusion that a high range of soil fertility and health can be obtained and
maintained by factors such as fertilization, cultivation, and vegetation which
create a desired microflora, of which the Actinomycetes are not the least
important because of their favourable physiological properties.

REFERENCES

Abd-el-Malek, Y., Monib, M. and Hazem, A. (1961). *Nature, Lond.* **189**, 775–776.
Alacevic, M. (1963). *Nature, Lond.* **197**, 1323.
Alikhanian, S. L. and Borisova, L. N. (1961). *J. gen. Microbiol.* **26**, 19–28.
Alikhanian, S. L. and Iljina, T. S. (1957). *Nature, Lond.* **179**, 784.
Alikhanian, S. L. and Mindlin, S. Z. (1957). *Nature, Lond.* **180**, 1208–1209.
Arai, T., Kuroda, S. and Koyama, Y. (1963). *J. gen. appl. Microbiol, Tokyo.* **9**,
　119–136.
Avery, R. J. and Blank, F. (1954). *Can. J. Microbiol.* **1**, 140–143.
Baldacci, E. and Grein, A. (1955). *G. Microbiol.* **1**, 28–34.
Baldacci, E., Spalla, C. and Grein, A. (1954). *Arch. Mikrobiol.* **20**, 347–357.
Batt, R. D. and Woods, D. D. (1961). *J. gen. Microbiol.* **24**, 207–224.
Becker, B., Lechevalier, M. P. and Lechevalier, H. A. (1965). *Appl. Microbiol.* **13**,
　236–243.
Bilimoria, M. H. and Bhat, J. V. (1961). *J. Sci. Technol., Cawnpore,* **43**, 16–25.
Bradley, S. G. and Anderson, D. L. (1960). *J. gen. Microbiol.* **23**, 231–241.
Bradley, S. G., Anderson, D. L. and Jones, L. A. (1961). *Devs. ind. Microbiol.* **2**,
　223–237.
Bremner, J. M., Flaig, W. and Küster, E. (1955). *Z. PflErnähr. Düng. Bodenk.*
　71, 58–63.
Brummelen, J. van and Went, J. C. (1957). *Antonie van Leeuwenhoek,* **23**, 385–392.
Chesters, C. G. C., Apinis, A. and Turner, M. (1956). *Proc. Linn. Soc. Lond.* **166**,
　87–97.
Chun, D. (1956). *Antibiotics Chemother.* **6**, 324–329.
Collins, R. P. and Gaines, H. D. (1964). *Appl. Microbiol.* **12**, 335–336.
Corbaz, R., Gregory, P. H. and Lacey, M. E. (1963). *J. gen. Microbiol.* **32**, 449–456.
Craveri, R., Lugli, A. M., Sgarzi, B. and Giolitti, G. (1960). *Antibiotics Chemother.*
　10, 306–311.
Craveri, R. and Pagani, H. (1962). *Ann. Microbiol.* **12**, 115–130.
Cummins, C. S. and Harris, H. (1958). *J. gen. Microbiol.* **18**, 173–189.
Darken, M. A. (1953). *Bot. Rev.* **19**, 99–130.
Ettlinger, L., Corbaz, R. and Hütter, R. (1958). *Arch. Mikrobiol.* **31**, 326–358.

Flaig, W., Küster, E., Segler-Holzweissig, G. and Beutelspacher, H. (1952). Z. PflErnähr. Düng. Bodenk. 57, 42–51.
Flaig, W., Küster, E. and Beutelspacher, H. (1955). Zentbl. Bakt. ParasitKde II, 108, 376–382.
Gaertner, A. (1955). Arch. Mikrobiol. 23, 28–37.
Gaines, H. D. and Collins, R. P. (1963). Lloydia, 26, 247–253.
Gause, G. F., Preobrashenskaja, T. P., Kudrina, E. S., Blinow, N. O., Riabova, I. D. and Sveshnikova, M. A. (1957). "Problems pertaining to the classification of actinomycetes-antagonists." Moscow. German translation: (1958) "Zur Klassifizierung der Aktinomyceten." Jena (G. Fischer).
Giolitti, G. (1960). J. gen. Microbiol. 23, 83–86.
Gottlieb, D. and Ciferri, O. (1956). Mycologia, 48, 253–263.
Gottlieb, D. and Siminoff, P. (1952). Phytopathology, 42, 91–97.
Gottlieb, D., Siminoff, P. and Martin, M. M. (1952). Phytopathology, 42, 493–496.
Gregory, K. F. and Vaisey, E. B. (1956). Can. J. Microbiol. 2, 65–71.
Grein, A. and Meyers, S. P. (1958). J. Bact. 76, 457–463.
Grein, A. and Spalla, C. (1962). G. Microbiol. 10, 175–184.
Grossbard, E. (1952). J. gen. Microbiol. 6, 295–310.
Haccius, B. and Helfrich, O. (1958). Arch. Mikrobiol. 28, 394–403.
Hagedorn, H. (1955). Zentbl. Bakt. ParasitKde II, 108, 353–375.
Harington, J. S. (1960). Nature, Lond. 188, 1027–1028.
Henssen, A. (1957). Arch. Mikrobiol. 27, 63–81.
Herrick, J. A. and Alexopoulos, J. (1942). Bull. Torrey bot. Club, 69, 569–572.
Herrick, J. A. and Alexopoulos, J. (1943). Bull. Torrey bot. Club, 70, 369–371.
Hickey, R. J. and Tresner, H. D. (1952). J. Bact. 64, 891–892.
Hirsch, P. (1960). Arch. Mikrobiol. 35, 391–414.
Hirsch, P., Overrein, L. and Alexander, M. (1961). J. Bact. 82, 442–448.
Hoffmann, G. M. (1958). Phytopath. Z. 34, 1–56.
Hopwood, D. A. (1959). Ann. N.Y. Acad. Sci. 81, 887–898.
Hopwood, D. A. and Glauert, A. M. (1961). J. gen. Microbiol. 26, 325–330.
Horikoshi, K. and Iida, S. (1959). Nature, Lond. 183, 186–187.
Horvath, J. (1962). Acta microbiol. hung. 9, 189–195.
Horvath, J., Marton, M. and Oroszlan, I. (1954). Acta microbiol. hung. 2, 21–37.
Hungate, R. E. (1946). J. Bact. 51, 51–56.
Jagnow, G. (1957). Arch. Mikrobiol. 26, 175–191.
Jensen, H. L. (1930). Soil Sci. 30, 59–77.
Katznelson, H. and Henderson, V. E. (1962). Can. J. Microbiol. 8, 875–882.
Kawato, M. and Shinobu, R. (1960, 1961). Mem. Osaka Univ. Nat. Sci. 9, 54–62, 10, 211–217.
Kolb, E. (1957). Naturwissenschaften, 44, 12.
Kosmachev, A. E. (1956). Mikrobiologiya, 25, 546–552.
Krassilnikov, N. A. (1949). "Guide to the identification of bacteria and actinomycetes." Moscow (Akad. Nauk. Sci. SSSR). German translation: (1959) "Diagnostik der Bakterien und Aktinomyceten." Jena (G. Fischer).
Krüger, W. (1961). S.A. J. agric. Sci. 4, 171–183.
Kuchaeva, A. G., Taptykova, S. D., Gesheva, R. L. and Krassilnikov, N. A. (1963). Dokl. Akad. Nauk SSSR, 148, 1400–1402.
Küster, E. (1950). Arch. Mikrobiol. 15, 1–12.
Küster, E. (1952). Zentbl. Bakt. Parasitkde I. Orig. 158, 350–356.
Küster, E. (1953). 6th Int. Congr. Microbiol. 1, 114–116.

Küster, E. (1955). Z. PflErnåhr. Düng. Bodenk. 69, 137–142.
Küster, E. (1958). Zentbl. Bakt. ParasitKde. II, 111, 227–234.
Küster, E. and Locci, R. (1963). Arch. Mikrobiol. 45, 188–197.
Kutzner, H. J. (1956). Beitrag zur Systematik und Ökologie der Gattung Streptomyces Waksm. et Henr., Diss. Hohenheim.
Kutzner, H. J. (1961). Path. Microbiol. 24, 170–191.
Kwapinski, J. B. (1964). J. Bact. 87, 1234–1237.
Lechevalier, H. A. and Tikhonenko, A. S. (1960). Mikrobiologiya, 29, 43–50.
Lindner, F. and Wallhäusser, K. H. (1955). Arch. Mikrobiol. 22, 219–234.
Lockwood, J. L. (1959). Phytopathology, 49, 327–331.
Mach, F. (1956). Zentbl. Bakt. ParasitKde II, 110, 1–25.
Mach, F. (1958). Zentbl. Bakt. ParasitKde II, 111, 553–561.
Martin, M. M. and Gottlieb, D. (1952). Phytopathology, 42, 294–296.
Marton, M. (1962). Z. PflErnåhr. Düng. Bodenk. 96, 105–114.
Metcalfe, G. and Brown, M. E. (1957). J. gen. Microbiol. 17, 567–572.
Mordaskij, M. Y. and Kudrina, E. S. (1961). Mikrobiologiya, 30, 86–90.
Müller, H. (1950). Arch. Mikrobiol. 15, 137–148.
Newbould, F. H. S. and Garrard, E. H. (1954). Can. J. Bot. 32, 386–391.
Nolof, G. (1962). Arch. Mikrobiol. 44, 278–297.
Nomi, R. (1960). J. Antibiot., Tokyo, 13, 236–247.
Noval, J. J. and Nickerson, W. J. (1959). J. Bact. 77, 251–263.
Perlman, D. (1953). Bot. Rev. 19, 46–97.
Petras, E. (1959). Arch. Mikrobiol. 34, 379–392.
Pfennig, N. (1956). Arch. Mikrobiol. 25, 109–136.
Plotho, O. von (1941). Arch. Mikrobiol. 12, 1–18.
Pommer, E. H. (1959). Ber. dt. bot. Ges. 72, 138–150.
Preobrashenskaja, T. P., Sveshnikova, M. A. and Maksimova, T. S. (1959). Mikrobiologiya, 28, 623–627.
Pridham, T. G. and Gottlieb, D. (1948). J. Bact. 56, 107–114.
Pridham, T. G., Hesseltine, C. W. and Benedict, R. G. (1958). Appl. Microbiol. 6, 52–79.
Prokofeva-Belgovskaja, A. A. and Kats, L. N. (1960). Mikrobiologiya, 29, 826–833.
Protiva, J. (1956). Čslká Biol. 5, 57–60.
Rancourt, M. and Lechevalier, H. A. (1963). J. gen. Microbiol. 31, 495–498.
Rautenstein, J. I. (1957). Mikrobiologiya, 26, 573–579.
Raymond, R. L. (1961). Devs. Ind. Microbiol. 2, 23–32.
Rehm, H. J. (1959). Zentbl. Bakt. ParasitKde II, 112, 388–395.
Rehm, H. J. (1960). Zentbl. Bakt. ParasitKde II, 113, 219–233.
Reynolds, D. M. (1954). J. gen. Microbiol. 11, 150–159.
Saito, H. (1958). Can. J. Microbiol. 4, 571–580.
Schatz, A., Isenberg, H. D., Angrist, A. A. and Schatz, V. (1954). J. Bact. 68, 1–4.
Seeler, G. (1962). Arch. Mikrobiol. 43, 213–233.
Sermonti, G. and Spada-Sermonti, I. (1956). J. gen. Microbiol. 15, 609–616.
Shinobu, R. (1958). Mem. Osaka Univ. Nat. Sci. 7, 1–76.
Simon, S. (1955). Acta microbiol. hung. 3, 53–65.
Singh, J. (1937). Ann. appl. Biol. 24, 154–158.
Skinner, F. A. (1951). J. gen. Microbiol. 5, 159–166.
Sørensen, H. (1957). Acta agric. scand. Suppl. 1.
Spalla, C., Amici, A. M. and Bianchi, M. L. (1961). G. Microbiol. 9, 249–254.
Spicher, G. (1955). Zentbl. Bakt. ParasitKde. II, 108, 577–587.

Stanier, R. Y. (1942). *J. Bact.* **44**, 555–570.
Stapp, C. (1953). *Zentbl. Bakt. ParasitKde II*, **107**, 129–150.
Stapp, C. (1956). *In* "Sorauer Handbuch der Pflanzenkrankheiten." Vol. II, 491–548.
Stapp, C. and Spicher, G. (1954). *Zentbl. Bakt. ParasitKde II*, **108**, 19–34.
Stevenson, J. L. (1956). *J. gen. Microbiol.* **15**, 372–380.
Szabo, I., Marton, M. and Szabolcs, I. (1958). *Agrokém. Talajt.* **7**, 163–175.
Szabo, I., Marton, M., Szabolcs, I. and Varga, L. (1959). *Acta agron. hung.* **9**, 9–39.
Taber, W. A. (1960). *Can. J. Microbiol.* **6**, 503–514.
Tendler, M. D. (1959). *Bull. Torrey. bot. Club*, **86**, 17–30.
Tresner, H. D. and Backus, E. J. (1963). *Appl. Microbiol.* **11**, 335–338.
Tresner, H. D., Davies, M. C. and Backus, E. J. (1961). *J. Bact.* **81**, 70–80.
Valyi-Nagy, T., Hernadi, F. and Jeney, A. (1961). *Acta Biol. hung.* **12**, 69–82.
Villanueva, R. J. (1960). *Microbiol. esp.* **13**, 387–391.
Waksman, S. A. (1959). "The Actinomycetes." Vol. I. Baillière, Tindall & Cox, London.
Waksman, S. A. (1961). "The Actinomycetes." Vol. II. Baillière, Tindall & Cox, London.
Waksman, S. A. and Diehm, R. A. (1931). *Soil Sci.* **32**, 97–117.
Waksman, S. A. and Purvis, E. R. (1932). *Soil Sci.* **34**, 95–109.
Waksman, S. A., Umbreit, W. W. and Cordon, T. C. (1939). *Soil Sci.* **47**, 37–61.
Ware, G. C. and Painter, H. A. (1955). *Nature, Lond.* **175**, 900.
Webley, D. M. (1958). *J. gen. Microbiol.* **19**, 402–406.
Webley, D. M. (1960). *J. gen. Microbiol.* **23**, 87–92.
Weindling, R., Tresner, H. D. and Backus, E. J. (1961). *Nature, Lond.* **189**, 603.
Welsch, M. (1958). *Bull. Res. Coun. Israel*, **7**, 141–154.
Welsch, M., Minon, P. and Schönfeld, J. K. (1955). *Experientia*, **11**, 24–25.
Yamaguchi, T. (1965). *J. Bact.* **89**, 444–453.

Chapter 5

Soil Algae

J. W. G. LUND

Freshwater Biological Association
Ambleside, England

I. ABUNDANCE IN AND ON SOIL

Algae are found in soils everywhere (for recent reviews see Lund, 1962, Shields and Durrell, 1964). Satisfactory methods for estimating rates of production (productivity) have not been devised. Populations (production) are estimated by three main methods (Bristol Roach, 1927a; Petersen, 1935; Lund, 1945–46; Brendemühl, 1949; Tchan, 1952, 1953, 1959; Tchan and Bunt, 1954; Shtina, 1956b; Vaidya, 1964). First, by direct observation, sometimes with the aid of fluorescence microscopy. Second, by dilution cultures. A known amount of soil is placed in a liquid or on solid medium, usually agar; by repetition of this process smaller and smaller amounts of soil can be sampled and the number of algae appearing in each dilution later estimated. Third, by extracting the chlorophyll with acetone or methanol and measuring it spectrophotometrically. The variability of the estimates of maximum numbers or biomass of algae in Table I may be related partly to the different methods of estimation and partly to seasonal variations in abundance. Though the estimation of biomass may be a "very superficial calculation" (Potul'nitskiĭ, 1962) Russian work suggests that the amount of organic matter produced by algae can be very considerable and that their importance in soil processes has been underestimated (Table II); see also Shtina, 1964a, b.

Algae are usually most abundant at or close to the surface but may also be found in the lower horizons of the soil (Fig. 1). Sometimes the largest population is found a few centimetres below the surface (Bristol Roach, 1927a; John, 1942; Flint, 1958) where there will be insufficient light for photosynthesis (Sauberer and Härtl, 1959; Durrell and Shields, 1961). It may be,

TABLE I

Maximum number of algal cells found in diverse types of soil from various parts of the world

Cells/g × 10⁻³	Depth in cm	Notes	Type of land or soil	Country	Reference
800	0–0·4	B.D.*	virgin, sandy	Australia	Tchan (1953)
462	0	B.D.	garden	Denmark	Petersen (1935)
3,000	0	B.D.	garden	Denmark	Petersen (1935)
40	0	B.D.	pasture	Denmark	Petersen (1935)
10	0	B.D.	arable	Denmark	Petersen (1935)
20	0	B.D.	acid heath	Denmark	Petersen (1935)
10	0	B.D.	forest	Denmark	Petersen (1935)
149	0	B.D.	grazing	Denmark	Petersen (1935)
106	0–2·5	B.C.	manured	England	Bristol Roach (1927a)
130	0–2·5	B.C.	manured	England	Bristol Roach (1927a)
37	0–2·5	B.C.	unmanured	England	Bristol Roach (1927a)
333	0	B.D.	virgin, bird dung	Greenland	Petersen (1935)
793	?	?	forest	Hungary	Féher (1933)
510	3	B.C.	cultivated	Italy	Florenzano et al. (1963)
548	0	A.C.	limed	U.S.A.	Stokes (1940)
800	?0–5	?B.C.	arid	U.S.A.	Martin (1940)
329	?0–5	B.D.	virgin, ploughed	U.S.S.R.	Shtina (1954)
229	?	B.D.	fertilized	U.S.S.R.	Shtina (1954)
188	0–5	B.D.	grassland	U.S.S.R.	Shtina (1954)
28	?	B.D.	virgin, tundra	U.S.S.R.	Shtina (1964)
94	?	B.D.	solod	U.S.S.R.	Shtina (1959)
155	0–10	B.D.	fallow sod-podsol	U.S.S.R.	Shtina (1957)

* A, air-dried soil; B, soil not dried; C, estimation by dilution cultures; D, by direct observation. In the Danish and Greenland soils the number of cells per cm³ is given.

therefore, that these aggregations are produced by the action of rain on superficial growths, but there is still some uncertainty about the amount of growth possible in the dark under natural conditions. Féher (1948) found nearly 700 species at 15 to 20 cms below the surface of soils from many parts of the world. He says that this is the depth "where can be found the highest intensity of soil life." However, many of the algae are aquatic and, without confirmation, his data are open to considerable doubt. Rain and earthworms are believed to be the chief agents in the vertical transport of algae (Petersen, 1935; Tchan and Whitehouse, 1953). Many soil algae are able to return to the surface if they are not buried too deeply. Nearly all the diatoms and Cyanophyta are motile forms, and many Chlorophyta and Xanthophyta produce zoospores, especially when they are wetted after a dry period. Among pigmented flagellates, the commonest are species of *Chlamydomonas* and *Euglena*. Though motility may be of biological advantage over small distances and in relation to the microclimate, distribution over greater distances seems to be in wind-borne dust (Bock, 1963; Brown, Larson and Bold, 1964; Schlichting, 1964).

TABLE II

Abundance of algae in certain virgin soils and in four cultivated chernozems of the U.S.S.R.

Virgin soils*	Cells/g × 10^{-3}	Biomass (kg/ha)
Sod podsol	10–208	40–300
Podsol	5– 30	7– 20
Boggy podsol	6– 50	10– 45
Peaty-boggy	5– 80	20– 80
Alluvial meadow	52–300	80–450
West-Siberian chernozem	48	16
Dark chestnut	2,150	187
Solonetz-meadow, deep columnar	988	515
Solonetz-steppe, deep columnar	392	74
Solonetz-crusty, nutty	5,146	429
Cultivated chernozem		
Under red oats	755–2,161	194–494
gooseberries	588–1,702	134–436
strawberries	181–1,578	55–525
Vegetable garden	390–2,043	98–546

* In the virgin soils average abundance from the surface to 10 cm depth, except for the chestnut and solonetz soils where the depth range is 0–2 cm. In the cultivated chernozems under different crops the Cyanophyta and Chlorophyta were counted together and all the figures shown were obtained from samples 5 cm below the surface.
Data from Shtina, 1959a and Potul'nitskiĭ, 1962; for later data on number of cells present see Shtina, 1960, 1964a.

Such evidence as is available about their periodicity shows that the same species may be found throughout the year and from one year to another (Lund, 1945–46, 1947; Shtina, 1959b; Forest, Willson and England, 1959; Potul'nitskiĭ, 1962). In temperate lands they are least numerous in winter and multiply spasmodically at other times in relation to the weather conditions and to the growth of higher plants (e.g. in deciduous woodlands). In arid or tropical regions rainfall seems to be the major factor determining their periodicity.

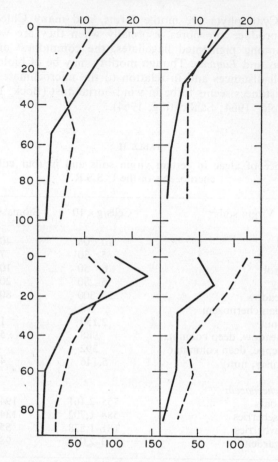

FIG. 1. Vertical distribution of algae in ploughed sod-podsol soils.
(a) 19 November, 1950; (b) 28 May, 1952; (c) 10 July, 1952; (d) 11 August, 1953.
————, cells; — — — —, species/g soil. Vertical axis, depth (cm). Horizontal axes, upper
number of species $\times 10^{-3}$; lower, number of cells. Redrawn from Figs 5 to 8 of Shtina,
1959b.

II. EFFECTS OF PHYSICAL ENVIRONMENT

Soil algae and associated moss protonemata form the only microbial soil
community dependent on light for its development. It is true that there is
evidence for some growth within the soil but, as will be seen, this is only of
limited extent. They are therefore exposed to the severe and often rapid
changes in the physical conditions at the air-soil interface. It is, however,
difficult to separate the effects of moisture, light and temperature on them in
nature, though most of them are so cosmopolitan that their powers of resistance to adverse physical conditions must be considerable.

A. MOISTURE

In air-dried soil, live algae have been found after many years (Bristol, 1919; Becquerel, 1942; Lipman, 1941; cf. also Petersen, 1935). Nevertheless they rarely produce large populations except on damp soil (Stokes, 1940a; Brendemühl, 1949, re diatoms). This may be true even of arid areas where they depend on short, wet periods. However, waterlogging has been found to be unfavourable (Tchan and Whitehouse, 1953), perhaps because the experiments did not last long enough. If the soil does not become anaerobic, prolonged saturation permits new communities to appear. These, in my experience, are either typical of ephemeral aquatic habitats or transitional between those of soil and water. In some semi-deserts, such as the takӯrs of Russia (Bolӯshev and Evdokimova, 1944; Bolӯshev, 1952; Gollerbakh, Novichkova and Sdobnikova, 1956; Sdobnikova, 1958), there is an alternation of freezing conditions in winter, while in spring the thaw and the flood water from the mountains produce semi-aquatic or, in hollows and beds of streams, truly aquatic conditions. Finally, in summer it is extremely hot and dry. During spring the waterlogged soil is inhabited by vast growths of Cyanophyta, the dominant forms being species common to soil and water. In addition many other soil algae, especially Chlorophyta, are present.

Cells may die when dried in air but remain alive when immersed in soil which contains very little water and, superficially, appears to be dry (Petit, 1877; Bristol Roach, 1927a; Petersen, 1935; Evans, 1958, 1959). Diatoms as a whole seem to be the least resistant, but the data are somewhat contradictory. Nitzschia palea (Kütz.) W.Sm. grown in liquid culture died when dried in air (Denffer, 1949) but remained alive in soil which contained little water or was dried in air for 70 to 98 years (Bristol, 1919; Becquerel, 1942). It may be that different forms were investigated, but there is also no doubt that the conditions prevailing before drying and the rate at which this takes place affect the viability of cells (Petit, 1877; Lange, 1953; Füchtbauer, 1957a, b). One of the reasons for the prevalence of Cyanophyta in arid areas is their ability to withstand very wet and very dry conditions (e.g. Fay and Fogg, 1962) and rapid changes from the one to the other. In dry periods they often exist as mats or crusts and when heavy rain or floods come these rapidly imbibe water, expand and are not easily displaced.

B. TEMPERATURE

The effects of fluctuations in temperature, like those in moisture, depend partly on the previous history of the cells and the rapidity with which it rises (e.g. Glade, 1914) or falls (e.g. Höfler, 1951). Some algae can live at temperatures equal to or beyond any to which they will be exposed in nature (Glade, 1914; Kärcher, 1931; Becquerel, 1936; Booth, 1946; Kingsbury, 1956; Trainor, 1962; Trainor and McLean, 1964). Drought may be the cause of death at high or low temperatures for the rate of freezing is important in relation to loss of water (Höfler, 1951). Despite the very low temperatures, algae are common or abundant in alpine, arctic and antarctic areas (Kosheleva and Novichkova, 1958; Dorogostaĭskaya, 1959; Roĭzin, 1960; Dr E. Flint, Sir V. Fuchs and Dr W. H. Holdgate, personal communications). However, in more temperate lands it seems that cold is probably one of the main reasons for the reduction in algal numbers in winter (Lund, 1947; Shtina, 1959b). It does not follow that the cells die; it could be that the rate of loss (e.g. from rainfall) becomes relatively greater because the rate of growth of the algae has decreased. The abundance of algae in hot climates is referred to several times in this chapter. While about 50° c is near or above the maximum temperature of the surface of the soil in temperate regions (Geiger, 1950), 70° c or higher is known for arid or tropical areas; for example 75° c on takȳrs with algae (Sdobnikova, 1958). The highest recorded temperature on takȳrs is above 87°c (Kovda, Bazilevich and Rodin, 1956). Under such conditions the moisture content of the soil may fall to 1 to 2% and in winter the ground is frozen, the lowest temperature recorded for the surface soil being −11·5°c (Kovda et al., 1956). Despite such a severe climate not only are Cyanophyta very abundant over a great area but about 150 spp. of algae have been recorded (Gollerbakh et al., 1956). Similar data, apart from low winter temperatures, are recorded for Death Valley, California, U.S.A., where the air temperature reaches 57°c and that of the ground 88°c. Annual rainfall averages about 4 cm and the evaporation power of the environment is equal to a surface loss of about 370 cm (Durrell, 1962).

III. EFFECTS OF CHEMICAL ENVIRONMENT

A. pH AND IONIC BALANCE

More has been written about the range of pH tolerated or favoured by soil algae than any other chemical factor (Shelhorn, 1936; Gollerbakh, 1936; John, 1942; Lund, 1945–46, 1947; Zauer, 1956; Shtina, 1959b). The ease with which pH can be measured, but not always in such a manner that the true soil value is found, has led perhaps to over-emphasis on this factor. Most species can grow on soil which is neither very acid nor very alkaline (e.g. pH 5·5 to 8·5). The widest diversities of species are found on neutral to moderately alkaline soils. Such soils are usually productive but large crops, composed of a few species, may be found elsewhere. On highly acid soil Chlorophyta often predominate and on the more alkaline ones, including those which are saline or arid, Cyanophyta are usually prominent. A few species seem to be calciphobes, notably *Euglena mutabilis* Schmitz, which is common on peat and may flourish at pH 1 to 3 (Lackey, 1938; Prát, 1955; Fott, 1956; U.K. National Coal Board, in litt.).

pH is so bound up with other factors, notably the calcium carbonate content of the soil, that it is difficult to know how far it determines the flora. An example of the effect of the ratio of mono- to divalent cations is provided by *Monodus subterraneus* Boye Pet., which grows well up to pH 8 to 9, provided this ratio is high (Miller and Fogg, 1957). Algae must often be exposed to rapid changes of salinity in relation to the drying and wetting of the surface of the soil. Many are also found on saline soils and in salt marshes. The addition of solid inorganic fertilizers produces rapid growth, especially of green algae, and several species are resistant to or are stimulated by the addition of seawater or sodium chloride (e.g. Gistl, 1932; Pringsheim and Pringsheim, 1956; Allen, 1956; Rieth, 1962a; Fay and Fogg, 1962).

B. INORGANIC NUTRIENTS

Most of the information about the nutrition of soil algae concerns compounds of carbon, nitrogen and phosphorus. Probably much information is concealed in the vast literature on the physiology of *Chlorella*. Unfortunately the natural habitats of most *Chlorellae* in culture are not known.

It might seem that silicon would never be lacking for the amounts are high compared to those of freshwaters in which shortages of this element have been demonstrated. Further, the algae often live apposed to more or less siliceous particles, and so where the concentration may be expected to be highest and new supplies most rapidly produced. However, the decomposition of siliceous minerals by diatoms (see Hutchinson, 1957) may be a reflection of the adjustment of the equilibrium between mineral silicates, silica in solution and diatom silica; rather than the solution of mineral silica by the excretion of special compounds. The weak silicification of some soil diatoms may be inherent or related to other factors, for they are often accompanied by heavily silicified forms (Hustedt, 1942). I have never found a population solely composed of weakly silicified species. Nevertheless the detailed study of *Navicula pelliculosa* (Bréb.) Hilse shows that silicon can affect the formation of the wall and the rate of growth, while its uptake may be affected by other substances (Lewin, 1954, 1955a, b, 1957). Therefore the amount of silicon in the soil solution may be important for diatoms as it is for rice and other grasses.

The importance of calcium is clear from the discussion of pH. Its effect is more evident in the quality of the flora than in its richness, because calcareous soils are so often relatively rich in nitrates and phosphates (e.g. Lund, 1945–46, 1947). There is little information about potassium. When grasses, clover and Cyanophyta were grown in pots, the last flourished in all those devoid of the Angiosperms. When grown with the Angiosperms, Cyanophyta only flourished when fertilizers were added. A mixture of phosphorus and potassium was specially effective and ammonium nitrate ineffective. Addition of potassium has less effect than that of phosphorus (Knapp and Lieth, 1952; Schwabe, 1963).

The effects of phosphorus and nitrogen are often considered together. Lund (1945–46, 1947) found that soils relatively rich in phosphates and nitrates were also the richest in algae. Shtina (1959b) added phosphate to soil but did not find it had marked effects on the diatoms. She says, however, that it may be that her experimental plots contained sufficient phosphorus before fertilization. Green algae may abound on soil poor in nitrates and phosphates, but they are also stimulated by inorganic nitrogeneous fertilizers. Some of them grow well on acid soil but one reason why Knapp and Lieth (1952) found NH_4NO_3 so ineffective in their experiments with Cyanophyta may be increased acidity of the soil, ammonia being preferentially utilized (cf. Syrett, 1954). Phosphate added to rice fields increases the crop of Cyanophyta (Singh, 1961). It should be said here that the common assumption that the algae of rice fields are soil algae, that is terrestrial algae, is not necessarily true. Some are wholly aquatic, others are common to soil and water. The development of the soil community will be affected by the degree of flooding of the fields. This can vary in relation to local practice or the developmental stage of the crop.

A few algae seem to be nitrophilous (Petersen, 1928; Knebel, 1935; Barkman, 1958). The best known example is *Prasiola crispa* Menegh. Enormous growths are found where birds abound, for example in Penguin rookeries. Samples from the soil around Puffin (*Fratercula arctica*) burrows on the Farne Islands, England, when dried, contained 8·9% of nitrogen, a very high figure for a Green alga in nature. It is not known whether both inorganic and organic nitrogen are used, but some Cyanophyta can use the latter and hydrolyse proteins (Allen, 1952). *Porphyridium purpureum* (Bory) Drew and Ross (*P. cruentum* (S. F. Gray) Hansg. and including *P. marinum* Kylin) also seems to be nitrophilous though a high phosphorus content in the soil may also be important (Rieth, 1961, 1962a, b; Rieth and Sagromsky, 1964).

Several Cyanophyta which are common on soil can fix nitrogen. The abundance and often dominance of Blue-green algae on tropical and subtropical soils (Esmarch, 1911; Duvigneaud and Symoens, 1949; Mitra, 1951; Singh, 1961; Durrell, 1964; personal observations on East African soils collected by Drs J. F. and I. Talling) which are so often deficient in nitrogen, may be related in part to this ability. There is abundant evidence that they do fix nitrogen under natural conditions, especially in arid soils (Fletcher and Martin, 1948; Shields, Mitchell and Drouet, 1957; Cameron, 1960; Cameron and Fuller, 1960; Singh, 1961; Shields and Durrell, 1964; Shtina, 1965; Tret'yakova, 1965). The fixation of nitrogen by Cyanophyta in rice fields has received much attention (see Singh, 1961, for a review up to 1959 and for original data). Other temporarily inundated areas may also benefit from the growth of Blue-green algae (e.g. Saubert and Grobbelaar, 1962). Both Japanese and Indian agriculturalists add fertilizers (notably phosphates, sometimes with molybdenum) and, if necessary, also lime to raise the pH. It is considered that under these conditions Blue-green algae are an effective substitute for nitrogenous fertilizers such as ammonium sulphate and, if the soil is poor, far superior to them (Subrahmanyan, Relwani and Manna, 1964a, b). Watanabe (1960) has grown mass cultures of *Tolypothrix* and then inoculated rice-fields with the alga (Watanabe *et al.*, 1959). The alga exerted a marked and long-lasting effect on the growth of the rice (Watanabe, Nishigaki and Konishi, 1951). The influence of the algae is not confined to the wetter periods of cultivation. Their cellular nitrogen is soon released after death by bacterial action, ammonia being the chief end product (Fedorov,

1952; Watanabe and Kiyohara, 1960). However, Sulaiman (1944) says that there is a loss of nitrogen when dried algae from a rice field decompose *in situ*. On the other hand part of the nitrogen they fix will be available to the rice while they are alive in the form of extracellular products (Fogg, 1960). After two months, in experiments with rice in a medium lacking added nitrogen, plants in containers with a nitrogen-fixing *Anabaena* had 10 times the dry weight and contained 20 times as much nitrogen as those to which no alga had been added (Allen, 1956). Cameron and Fuller (1960) found that from none to over half of the nitrogen fixed by species from soil was present in culture media. Algae are not always beneficial to rice, for young plants may be harmed if algal mats and scums are too abundant (Bunt, 1961). Rice plants may increase the growth of the algae, and a similar effect is obtained in their absence by aerating with carbon dioxide (De and Sulaiman, 1950).

Although these investigations mainly cover algae growing on waterlogged or underwater soils, the results may well indicate what happens in ordinary soil. Singh (1961) finds that considerable fixation occurs in India in fields of sugarcane and maize, on fallow land and in grassland. However, doubt has also been expressed about the contribution made by Cyanophyta to the nitrogen economy of soil (Stokes, 1940b). Cyanophyta are only abundant on neutral or alkaline temperate soils and these are usually richer in nitrates than acid ones. If ammonia or nitrates are present, fixation of nitrogen may be depressed (De, 1939; Fogg, 1960). In the laboratory, Blue-green algae commonly become more predominant the longer the soil is kept moist and free of plant-cover (Drewes, 1928; John, 1942; Lund, 1947). The reason for this is unknown. Fogg (1960, in discussion, cf. Lund, 1947) suggests that the available nitrogen in the algal mats may be exhausted and that free nitrogen will diffuse in more rapidly than combined nitrogen so that fixation is occurring in these algal strata. Drewes (1928) found that Cyanophyta become dominant early in an enriched soil if phosphorus but not nitrogen has been added to it but much later if salts of both elements are supplied originally. Even in some semi-arid regions where Cyanophyta cover considerable areas, the amount of nitrogen fixed may be so small that it cannot be detected on a yearly basis using the Kjeldahl technique for its estimation (Tchan and Beadle, 1955). However, the algae concerned may be different from those forming crusts in the arid regions referred to earlier. The algae are found mainly beneath translucent pebbles and stones. These "Fensterpflanzen" (Vogel, 1955) have been observed in Australia, Egypt, Sudan, South Africa and the U.S.A. (Williams, 1943; Tchan and Beadle, 1955; Vogel, 1955; Durrell, 1962). Samples collected for me from East Africa by Dr J. F. Talling were dominated by Chroococcaclae, a family not known to contain any nitrogen-fixing species. The algae grow on the parts of the stones at or below the surface of the soil and will be protected from extremes of light and temperature. It may be that conservation of moisture is the main advantage of life under translucent stones. Moisture is often only available as dew which will condense on the stones during the night.

It is not known whether deficiencies of trace elements known to affect

Angiosperms in nature also influence the growth of algae. The range of essential elements for soil algae may well be the same or very similar to that needed by algae elsewhere judging from Eyster's (1958, 1959, 1964) work on *Nostoc muscorum* Ag. ex Born. et Flah. and Wiessner's (1962) review. Molybdenum is concerned in nitrogen fixation (Fogg, 1960, in discussion; Singh, 1961) and has been added to soil from rice-fields containing algae. In the light, with the addition of phosphorus, more nitrogen was fixed than with phosphorus alone. In the dark algae were absent and nitrogen fixation was insignificant, indeed in two cases nitrogen was lost from the soil (De and Mandal, 1956).

C. ORGANIC MATTER—HETEROTROPHY

Many soil algae can grow in the dark if suitable organic compounds are present, notably glucose, which, however, will be rapidly utilized by most soil microbes. Some species can only grow in the light (obligate phototrophs, Fogg, 1953; Parker, Bold and Deason, 1960; Parker, 1961). It is not surprising that the pioneer studies of Bristol Roach (1926, 1927a, b, c, 1928) led to the view that the frequent occurrence of algae within the soil probably was the result of the active multiplication of cells within it. Later workers (Petersen, 1935; De and Sulaiman, 1950; Stokes, 1940a; Tchan and Whitehouse, 1953) came to the opposite conclusion, for they could not detect any significant increase in algal numbers in soil kept in the dark even when glucose was added. It is significant that in the desert areas referred to earlier, the algal communities are only found under translucent pebbles. Nevertheless recent experiments (Parker and Bold, 1961; Parker, 1961) suggest that facultative heterotrophy can be of ecological importance. If suitable bacteria or actinomycetes are present some of the algae will grow in the dark, though, as will be seen, the interrelationships are complex and vary markedly from alga to alga. The largest increase found in soil and water cultures was sixteenfold in 14 months. This is equivalent to only 4 cell divisions or the production of one or two autosporangia in over a year. As other algae would not grow in the dark, it is not surprising that workers have failed to detect any increases in the populations as a whole. The rate of growth of many such small algae in the light can be equivalent to about one cell division per day, so that an increase equal to that in about 60 weeks in the dark could be produced in less than one week in the light. Facultative heterotrophy, therefore, seems to be of biological value in maintaining populations buried in the soil but is of little importance in production as a whole. As Schwabe (1963) says, there is indirect support for this view in that macroscopic strata of Blue-green algae are only found on the surface. This is equally true of discolorations by Green algae and Xanthophyceae. Heterotrophy may explain the records of comparatively large populations in the rhizosphere (Shtina, 1954, 1961; Hadfield, 1960; Gonsalves and Yalavigi, 1960), though it remains to be seen whether algae are relatively easily washed into the soil down the passages made by roots and to what extent such populations differ from those at a distance from roots (cf. Troĭtskaya, 1961) and are composed of facultative heterotrophs.

Fresh dung seems to be inimical (Stokes, 1940a; Shtina, 1963; personal observations) probably because of the vast growth of other micro-organisms and the exclusion of light. Later, as in sewage lagoons, very large populations may arise (cf. Shtina, 1959b, 1963, and personal observations).

IV. INTERRELATIONS WITH OTHER ORGANISMS

A. Micro-Organisms

The interrelations between algae and other soil organisms are little known. Grazing has scarcely been studied (Nielsen, 1949; Bunt, 1954; Schwabe, 1960a; Kühnelt, 1961) and nothing is recorded about parasites. The discussion on heterotrophy has shown that bacteria and actinomycetes may permit algae to grow in the dark, but these interrelationships are affected by the type of soil. There is still controversy over the effect of algae on *Azotobacter* and the relative importance of this bacterial genus and Cyanophyta in the fixation of nitrogen in many soils. Early workers believed that soil algae, even if they did not fix nitrogen themselves, stimulated the growth of *Azotobacter*. The discovery that many Cyanophyta fix nitrogen, that marked increases in the nitrogen in algal and lichen associations arise in the absence of *Azotobacter*, and that live or dead growths of other algae do not seem to assist this or other nitrogen-fixing bacteria, caused a change of view (e.g. Drewes, 1928; Clark, 1936; De, 1939; Stokes, 1940a; Martin, 1940; Sulaiman, 1944; Russell, 1950; Cameron and Fuller, 1960). However, some modern authors find that algae do stimulate *Azotobacter* or that algae and bacteria together may fix more nitrogen than either do alone (Szolnoki, 1951; Fedorov, 1952; Shtina, 1959b, 1961; Bjälfve, 1962; Shtina and Yung, 1963, Fedorov (1952) points out that if moist, pure sand is exposed to the light the nitrogen content increases, while in the dark it does not, and that this increase is accompanied by a visible greening of the surface. Parker and Turner (1961) and Bjälfve (1962) produced good experimental evidence against an interaction between some algae and *Azotobacter*. The nitrogen fixed in the latter's mixed culture was almost exactly the sum of the increases when *Nostoc calcicola* Bréb. and *Azotobacter* were grown separately. However, in dual cultures with some other bacteria more nitrogen was fixed than when *Nostoc* grew alone. In the case of *Rhizobium* spp. and *Nostoc* the fixation might be expected to be by the latter, but a curious feature of the cultures was the appearance of bacteroid forms similar to those in nitrogen-fixing nodules of Leguminosae. In earlier work Clark (1936) did not find any fixation of nitrogen in cultures containing the Green alga *Chlorella* and *Rhizobium*. A number of interactions between algae and fungi or bacteria have been described from observations on natural populations and laboratory experiments. Fletcher and Martin (1948) found that if crusts from the Arizona desert were kept moist for more than a week, the algae degenerated and fungi took their place. Cribb's (1955) and Litvinov's (1956) descriptions of pale spots or rings in crusts of Blue-green algae are similar, though they were unaware of each other's work. The fungi concerned are Ascomycetes and an imperfect species, *Stemphylium algophagum* Litv. Other species of

Stemphylium are known to be stages of an Ascomycete (Ainsworth, 1961). The algae grow rapidly when rain follows drought. The later appearance of the fungus may be related to the reduced vigour of the alga after it has utilized nutrients in its vicinity, because Parker and Bold (1961), in different circumstances, found that the destruction of a *Phormidium* by a Basidiomycete in mixed culture could be prevented by enriching the medium with certain

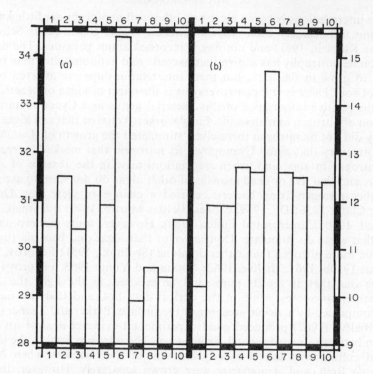

FIG. 2. Influence of *Azotobacter* and algae on the growth of oats.
Left-hand columns (a) weight of plants; right-hand columns (b) weight of grain. Each result the mean of four pot experiments. Horizontal axis; 1, control soil; 2, *Azotobacter* added to the soil and 3, to the oat seeds; 4 to 10, additions to soil: 4, *Azotobacter* on peat enriched with algae; 5, *Azotobacter* and Cyanophyta; 6, *Azotobacter* and Chlorophyta (mainly *Chlorella terricola* Gollerb.); 7, *Azotobacter* and filtrate from culture of Cyanophyta; 8, *Azotobacter* and filtrate from culture of Chlorophyta; 9, Cyanophyta; 10, Chlorophyta. Vertical axes, weight (g); right hand, plants; left hand, grain. (Based on Table 4 of Shtina and Yung, 1963.)

nitrogen compounds. Lack of available nitrogen by itself was not the cause of the death of the alga. The mechanisms involved in these interrelationships are not understood. A bacterium increased the growth of a coccoid Green Alga because of its ability to decompose organic nitrogen compounds (Parker and Bold, 1961). From 143 dual cultures, all involving at least one alga, a variety of results were obtained ranging from neither partner affecting the other to each partner inhibiting the other. The majority of the heterotrophic organisms, Protozoa excluded, stimulated the algal partner (Parker and Turner, 1961). In some cases the growth of a fungus may depend on the presence of sufficient algal cells in its vicinity. For example, several soil fungi needing thiamin or its components could obtain them in a culture medium which did not contain them originally. Such a mixture of an alga and a fungus generally grew together without either inhibiting the other. In a few cases the alga was killed sooner or later, apparently by the exclusion of light when the fungus grew over it (Gaümann and Jaag, 1950).

B. HIGHER PLANTS

Inhibition is well known, but it is difficult to discover its ecological importance in nature. The same is often true of stimulation of one organism by another. In experiments with Angiosperms and Cyanophyta, the effect of the former on the latter is ascribed to inhibition (Knapp and Lieth, 1952) but the data are not very satisfactory. Piercy (1917) found that *Chlorohormidium flaccidum* (A. Br.) Fott only grew extensively in grassland in wet periods after drought had killed the grass and before a new sward was formed. Apart from those discussed, there are several other accounts of algae inhibiting or stimulating one another, Angiosperms, or other micro-organisms (Drewes, 1928; Flint, 1947; Bolyshev, 1952; Harder and Oppermann, 1953; Wolters, 1960; Jacob, 1954a, b, 1961). The germination of seeds may be unaffected or stimulated or inhibited by algae (Shtina, 1954, 1956a; Troïtskaya 1961; Novichkova, 1955). Shtina (1954, 1956a, 1959b, 1961) finds no evidence that roots of Angiosperms are inhibited by soil algae, but algal extracts may stimulate their development. The roots of some plants, but not those of conifers, may stimulate algal growth. She also found that algal extracts retarded the growth of some phytopathogenic fungi. Engle and McMurtrey (1940) found that algae protected tobacco roots, but it is not clear that they would do so in nature, when they would have no illumination. Enhanced growth of algae in the rhizosphere has been observed (Katznelson, 1946; Shtina, 1959b; Hadfield, 1960; Gonsalves and Yalavigi, 1960; Cullimore and Woodbine, 1963) but Katznelson (1961) and Troïtskaya (1961) could not detect any such effect. More data are needed, including information about the surface flora and soil treatment, before any general conclusions can be drawn from these divergent results.

V. EFFECTS ON SOIL

The data concerning rice-fields, cited previously, show that dead or live algae may act as fertilizers. In arid zones, algae may be important sources of organic matter (e.g. humus, Ponomareva, 1956; concerning nitrogen, see p. 136 and Shields and Durrell, 1964). It remains to be shown that in non-arid zones they are equally important. The abundance of algae on soils which are also fertile in relation to other plants has lead to their use for bio-assay

(Tchan, 1959; Tchan *et al.*, 1961). They may be considered more suitable for this purpose than the heterotrophs used because they are photosynthetic plants. Green algae, moreover, are in general similar in physiology and biochemistry to higher plants—indeed some taxonomists would include all "green" plants in one phylum. Other soil algae, notably diatoms and Cyanophyta, differ so markedly from Chlorophyta and in all groups there is such ecological and physiological diversity that a variety of techniques for bio-assay might be elaborated.

In man-made "deserts" or "dust bowls" algal crusts may bind soil particles together (e.g. Schwabe, 1960a, b; Durrell and Shields, 1961; Bond and Harris, 1964) and so prevent erosion and permit re-colonization by Angiosperms (Booth, 1941). There is, however, evidence for an alternative view, namely that algae are of little value in soil conservation, simply occupying spaces between or around the sparse vegetation. The crusts in the Arizona desert are said to interfere with infiltration of water into the soil (Fuller, Cameron and Raica, 1960) or to improve infiltration (Fletcher and Martin, 1948). They interfere with infiltration on takȳrs but also reduce the rate of water loss from the soil below them (Gollerbakh *et al.*, 1956). In Arizona, crust formation reduces soil erosion except in storms, when the crust delays the penetration of water and so increases erosion (Cameron, 1964). The classic story of the role of algae in the re-colonization of Krakatoa (Treub, 1888) is also disputed (Backer, 1929). Similarly the predominance of soil algae on rocks and thin soils in high-mountain arctic "deserts" (Roǐzin, 1960) and their ability to "rot" rock does not necessarily mean that they are as effective in the breakdown of rock as are frost, sunshine, wind and rain.

The study of soil algae lags behind that of many other micro-organisms. The most extensive investigations have been carried out in Russia and, in relation to waterlogged or underwater soils of rice fields, in India and Japan. We need, among other things, methods for determining productivity, detailed observations on seasonal periodicity and more laboratory experiments which, so far as is possible, are so devised that the results are likely to be relevant to practical problems.

REFERENCES

Ainsworth, G. C. (1961). "Ainsworth and Bisby's Dictionary of the Fungi," 5th ed. Commonwealth Mycological Institute, England.
Allen, M. B. (1952). *Arch. Mikrobiol.* **17**, 34–53.
Allen, M. B. (1956). *Scient. Mon., N.Y.* **83**, 100–106.
Backer, C. A. (1929). "The Problem of Krakatao as Seen by a Botanist." The Hague.
Barkman, J. J. (1958). "Phytosociology and Ecology of Cryptogamic Epiphytes." Assen, Holland.
Becquerel, P. (1936). *C. r. hebd. Séanc. Acad. Sci., Paris,* **202**, 978.
Becquerel, P. (1942). *C. r. hebd. Séanc. Acad. Sci., Paris,* **214**, 986–988.
Bjälfve, G. (1962). *Physiologia Pl.* **15**, 122–129.
Bock, W. (1963). *Nova Hedwigia,* **5**, 199–254.
Bolȳshev, N. N. (1952). *Pochvovedenie,* **21**, 403–417. (Russian).

Bolỹshev, N. N. and Evdokimova, T. I. (1944). *Pochvovedenie*, **13**, 345–452. (Russian.)

Bond, R. D. and Harris, J. R. (1964). *Aust. J. Soil Res.* **2**, 111–122.

Booth, W. E. (1941). *Ecology*, **22**, 38–46.

Booth, W. E. (1946). *Proc. Mont. Acad. Sci.* **5/6**, 21–23.

Brendemühl, E. (1949). *Arch. Mikrobiol.* **14**, 407–449.

Bristol, B. M. (1919). *New Phytol.* **18**, 92–107.

Bristol Roach, B. M. (1926). *Ann. Bot.* **40**, 149–201.

Bristol Roach, B. M. (1927a). *J. agric. Sci.*, *Camb.* **17**, 563–588.

Bristol Roach, B. M. (1927b). *Ann. Bot.* **41**, 509–517.

Bristol Roach, B. M. (1927c). *Proc. Pap. 1st int. Congr. Soil Sci.* **3**, 30–38.

Bristol Roach, B. M. (1928). *Ann. Bot.* **42**, 317–345.

Brown, R. M. Jr., Larson, D. and Bold, H. (1964). *Science, N.Y.* **143**, 583–585.

Bunt, J. S. (1954). *Proc. Linn. Soc. N.S.W.* **79**, (1954), 34–56.

Bunt, J. S. (1961). *Nature, Lond.* **192**, 479–480.

Cameron, R. E. (1960). *J. Ariz. Acad. Sci.* **1**, 85–88.

Cameron, R. E. (1964). *Trans. Am. microsc. Soc.* **83**, 212–218.

Cameron, R. E. and Fuller, W. A. (1960). *Proc. Soil Sci. Soc. Am.* **24**, 353–356.

Clark, D. G. (1936). *Mem. Cornell Univ. agric. Exp. Stn.* No. 196.

Cribb, A. B. (1955). *Qd. Nat.* **15**, 46–48.

Cullimore, R. D. and Woodbine, M. (1963). *Nature, Lond.* **198**, 304–305.

De, P. K. (1939). *Proc. R. Soc. B.* **127**, 121–139.

De, P. K. and Mandal, L. N. (1956). *Soil Sci.* **81**, 453–458.

De, P. K. and Sulaiman, M. (1950). *Soil Sci.* **70**, 137–152.

Denffer, D. von (1949). *Arch. Mikrobiol.* **14**, 159–202.

Dorogostaĭskaya, E. V. (1959). *Bot. Zh. SSSR.* **44**, 312–321. (Russian.)

Drewes, K. (1928). *Zentbl. Bakt. ParasitKde.* Abt. II. **76**, 88–101.

Durrell, L. W. (1962). *Trans. Am. microsc. Soc.* **81**, 267–273.

Durrell, L. W. (1964). *Trans. Am. microsc. Soc.* **83**, 79–85.

Durrell, L. W. and Shields, L. M. (1961). *Trans. Am. microsc. Soc.* **80**, 73–79.

Duvigneaud, P. and Symoens, J. J. (1949). *Lejeunia.* **13**, 67–98.

Engle, H. B. and McMurtrey, J. E. (1940). *J. agric. Res.* **60**, 487–502.

Esmarch, F. (1911). *Jb. hamb. wiss. Anst.* 1910, **28**, 3 Beih., 62–82.

Evans, J. H. (1958). *J. Ecol.* **46**, 149–167.

Evans, J. H. (1959). *J. Ecol.* **47**, 55–81.

Eyster, C. (1958). *Ohio J. Sci.* **58**, 25–33.

Eyster, C. (1959). *Proc. IX Int. bot. Congr.* 1959, II, IIA, p. 109.

Eyster, C. (1964). *In* "Algae and Man." (D. F. Jackson), 86–119. New York.

Fay, P. and Fogg, G. E. (1962). *Arch. Mikrobiol.* **42**, 310–321.

Fedorov, M. V. (1952). "Biological fixation of atmospheric nitrogen." 2nd ed. Gosudarstv. Izdatel. Sel'skokhoz. Lit. Moscow. (Russian.)

Féher, D. (1933). "Untersuchungen über die Mikrobiologie des Waldbodens." Berlin. (Cited from Petersen, 1935.)

Féher, D. (1948). *Erdész. Kisérl.* **48**, 57–93.

Fletcher, J. E. and Martin, W. P. (1948). *Ecology*, **29**, 95–100.

Flint, E. A. (1958). *N.Z. Jl. agric. Res.* **1**, 991–997.

Flint, L. H. (1947). *Proc. La. Acad. Sci.* **10**, 30–31.

Florenzano, G., Balloni, W. and Materassi, R. (1963). *Annls Inst. Pasteur, Paris*, **105**, 195–201.

Fogg, G. E. (1953). "The Metabolism of Algae." London.

Fogg, G. E. (1960). *In* Proc. Symp. Algology, 138–143, *Indian Coun. agric. Res. New Delhi.*

Forest, H. S., Willson, D. L. and England, R. B. (1959). *Ecology*, **40**, 475–477.

Fott, B. (1956). *Preslia*, **28**, 145–150. (Czech.)

Füchtbauer, W. (1957a). *Arch. Mikrobiol.* **26**, 209–230.

Füchtbauer, W. (1957b). *Arch. Mikrobiol.* **26**, 231–253.

Fuller, W. H., Cameron, R. E. and Raica, N. (1960). *7th int. Congr. Soil Sci.* (Madison) **2**, 617–624.

Gäumann, E. and Jaag, O. (1950). *Phytopath. Z.* **17**, 218–228.

Geiger, R. (1950). "The Climate near the Ground" (transl. Stewart, M. N. *et al.*). Cambridge, Mass.

Gistl, R. (1932). *Arch. Mikrobiol.* **3**, 634–649.

Glade, E. (1914). *Beitr. Biol. Pfl.* **12**, 295–343.

Gollerbakh, M. M. (1936). *Trudy bot. Inst. Akad. Nauk SSSR.* Ser. 2, 99–301. (Russian.)

Gollerbakh, M. M., Novichkova, L. N. and Sdobnikova, N. V. (1956). *In* "Takȳrs of Western Turkmenistan and Ways of their Utilisation for Agriculture," 38–54, *Akad. Nauk U.S.S.R., Moscow.* (Russian.)

Gonsalves, E. A. and Yalavigi, V. S. (1960). *Proc. Symp. Algology, Indian Coun. agric. Res., New Delhi,* 335–342.

Hadfield, W. (1960). *Nature, Lond.* **185**, 179.

Harder, R. and Oppermann, A. (1953). *Arch. Mikrobiol.* **19**, 398–401.

Höfler, K. (1951). *Verh. zool.-bot. Ges. Wien.* **92**, 234–241.

Hustedt, F. (1942). *Ber. dt. bot. Ges.* **60**, 55–72.

Hutchinson, G. E. (1957). "A Treatise on Limnology." Vol. I. New York.

Jacob, H. (1954a). *C. r. hebd. Séanc. Acad. Sci., Paris,* **238**, 928–930.

Jacob, H. (1954b). *C. r. hebd. Séanc. Acad. Sci., Paris,* **238**, 2018–2020.

Jacob, H. (1961). *Revue gén. Bot.* **68**, 5–72.

John, R. P. (1942). *Ann. Bot.* N.S. **6**, 323–349.

Kärcher, H. (1931). *Planta*, 515–517.

Katznelson, H. (1946). *Soil Sci.* **62**, 343–354.

Katznelson, H. (1961). *In* "Recent Advances in Botany," 610–614. Univ. Toronto Press.

Kingsbury, J. M. (1956). *News Bull. phycol. Soc. Am.* **28**, p. 37.

Knapp, R. and Lieth, H. (1952). *Arch. Mikrobiol.* **17**, 292–299.

Knebel, G. (1935). *Hedwigia*, **75**, 1–120.

Kosheleva, I. T. and Novichkova, L. H. (1958). *Bot. Zh. SSSR*, **43**, 1478–1485. (Russian.)

Kovda, V. A., Bazilevich, N. I. and Rodin, L. E. (1956). *In* "Takȳrs of Western Turkmenistan and Ways of their Utilisation for Agriculture," 22–29. *Akad. Nauk U.S.S.R. Moscow.* (Russian).

Kovda, V. A., Letunov, P. A., Zemskiĭ, P. M., Budakova, A. A., Shabryzin, P. A. and Kuznetsova, T. V. (1956). *In* "Takȳrs of Western Turkmenistan and Ways of their Utilisation for Agriculture," 513–521. *Akad. Nauk U.S.S.R. Moscow.* (Russian).

Kühnelt, W. (transl. N. Walker, 1961). "Soil Biology." Faber and Faber, London.

Lackey, J. B. (1938). *Publ. Hlth. Rep., Wash.* **53**, 1499–1507.

Lange, O. L. (1953). *Flora, Jena*, **140**, 39–97.

Lewin, J. C. (1954). *J. gen. Microbiol.* **37**, 589–599.

Lewin, J. C. (1955a). *Pl. Physiol., Lancaster*, **30**, 129–134.

Lewin, J. C. (1955b). *J. gen. Physiol.* **39**, 1–10.
Lewin, J. C. (1957). *Can. J. Microbiol.* **3**, 427–433.
Lipman, C. B. (1941). *Bull. Torrey bot. Club*, **68**, 664–666.
Litvinov, M. A. (1956). *In* "The Takӯrs of Western Turkmenistan and Ways of their Utilisation for Agriculture," 55–74. *Akad. Nauk U.S.S.R. Moscow.* (Russian).
Lund, J. W. G. (1945–46). *New Phytol.* **44**, 196–219, **45**, 56–110.
Lund, J. W. G. (1947). *New Phytol.* **46**, 35–60.
Lund, J. W. G. (1962). *In* "Physiology and Biochemistry of Algae." (R. A. Lewin, ed.), 759–770. New York and London.
Martin, T. L. (1940). *Rep. Proc. 3rd int. Congr. Microbiol.* 1939, 697–698.
Miller, J. D. A. and Fogg, G. E. (1957). *Arch. Mikrobiol.* **28**, 1–17.
Mitra, A. K. (1951). *Indian J. agric. Sci.* **21**, 357–373.
Nielsen, C. O. (1949). *Natura jutl.*, **2**, 1–311.
Novichkova, L. N. (1955). "Communities of lower plants of the takӯrs of the foothill plain, Konet-Daga." (Russian.) Dissertation, Leningrad. (Cited from Troĭtskaya, 1961.)
Parker, B. C. (1961) *Ecology*, **42**, 381–386.
Parker, B. C. and Bold, H. C. (1961). *Am. J. Bot.* **48**, 185–197.
Parker, B. C., Bold, H. C. and Deason, T. R. (1960). *Science, N.Y.* **133**, 761–763.
Parker, B. C. and Turner, B. L. (1961). *Evolution, Lancaster, Pa.* **15**, 228–238.
Petersen, J. B. (1928). *In* "The Botany of Iceland." Vol. 2, 327–447.
Petersen, J. B. (1935). *Dansk bot. Ark.* **8**, 1–183.
Petit, M. P. (1877). *Bull. Soc. bot. Fr.* **24**, 367–369.
Piercy, A. (1917). *Ann. Bot.* **3**, 513–537.
Ponomareva, V. V. (1956). *In* "The Takӯrs of Western Turkmenistan and Ways of their Utilisation for Agriculture," 411–438. Moscow. (Russian.)
Potul'nitskiĭ, P. M. (1962). *Mikrobiologiya*, **31**, 116–120. (Russian.) *Microbiol.* **31**, 92–95. (English translation.)
Prát, S. (1955). *Preslia*, **27**, 225–233.
Pringsheim, E. G. and Pringsheim, O. (1956). *Arch. Mikrobiol.* **24**, 169–173.
Rieth, A. (1961). *Biol. Zbl.* **80**, 429–438.
Rieth, A. (1962a). *Kulturpflanze*, **10**, 167–194.
Rieth, A. (1962b). *Mber. dt. Akad. Wiss. Berl.* **4**, 488–492.
Rieth, A. and Sagromsky, H. (1964). *Biol. Zbl.* **83**, 489–500.
Roĭzin, M. B. (1960). *Bot. Zh. SSSR.* **45**, 997–1008. (Russian.)
Russell, E. J. (1950). "Soil Conditions and Plant Growth." 8th Ed., revised by E. W. Russell. Longmans, Green & Co. London, New York and Toronto.
Sauberer, F. and Härtl, O. (1959). *In* "Probleme der Bioklimatologie." V. Leipzig.
Saubert, S. and Grobbelaar, N. (1962). *S. Afr. J. agric. Sci.* **5**, 283–292.
Schlichting, H. E., Jr. (1964). *Lloydia*, **27**, 64–78.
Schwabe, G. H. (1960a). *Forschn Fortschr.* **34**, 194–197.
Schwabe, G. H. (1960b). *Öst. bot. Z.* **107**, 281–309.
Schwabe, G. H. (1963). *Pedobiologiya*, **2**, 132–152.
Sdobnikova, N. V. (1958). *Bot. Zh. SSSR.* **43**, 1675–1681. (Russian.)
Shelhorn, M. (1936). *Naturw. Landwirtsch.* **18**, 1–54.
Shields, L. M. and Durrell, L. W. (1964). *Bot. Rev.* 92–128.
Shields, L. M., Mitchell, C. and Drouet, F. (1957). *Am. J. Bot.* **44**, 489–498.
Shtina, É. A. (1954). *Trud. kirovsk. sel'skokhoz. Inst.* **10**, 59–69. (Russian.)
Shtina, É. A. (1956a). *Vest. mosk. gos. Univ.* 6 Ser. *Fiz. Mat. Estestven. Nauk*, **1956**, 93–98. (Russian.)

Shtina, É. A. (1956b). *Bot. Zh. SSSR.* **41**, 1314–1317. (Russian.)
Shtina, É. A. (1957). *Pochvovedenie,* **26**, 12–17. (Russian.)
Shtina, É. A. (1959a). *Bot. Zh. SSSR.* **44**, 1062–1074. (Russian.)
Shtina, É. A. (1959b). *Trudy bot. Inst. Akad. Nauk SSSR.* Ser. 2. Sporovye Rasteniya. **12**, 36–141. (Russian.)
Shtina, É. A. (1960). *Trans. 7th int. Congr. Soil Sci.* 1960, **2**, 630–634.
Shtina, É. A. (1961). *Trudy Inst. Mikrobiol., Mosk.* **11**, 130–138.
Shtina, É. A. (1963). *Agrobiologiya,* 1963, 585–588. (Russian.)
Shtina, É. A. (1964a). *Izv. Akad. Nauk SSSR Ser. biolog.* 1964, 72–80. (Russian.)
Shtina, É. A. (1964b). The role of blue-green algae in soil-forming processes. *In* "The Biology of Blue-green Algae." pp. 66–79. (Russian.)
Shtina, É. A. (1965). *In* "The Ecology and Physiology of the Blue-green Algae." (V. D. Fedorov and M. M. Telitchenko, eds.), pp. 160–177. (Russian.)
Shtina, É. A. and Yung, L. A. (1963). *Agrobiologiya,* **3**, 424–427. (Russian.)
Singh, R. N. (1961). "Role of Blue-green Algae in Nitrogen Economy of Indian Agriculture." *Indian Coun. agric. Res. New Delhi.*
Stokes, J. L. (1940a). *Soil Sci.* **49**, 171–184.
Stokes, J. L. (1940b). *Soil Sci.* **49**, 265–275.
Subrahmanyan, R., Relwani, L. L. and Manna, G. B. (1964a). *Proc. Indian Acad. Sci. B,* **60**, 293–297.
Subrahmanyan, R., Relwani, L. L. and Manna, G. B. (1964b). *Curr. Sci.* **33**, 485–486.
Sulaiman, M. (1944). *Indian J. agric. Sci.* **14**, 277–282.
Syrett, P. J. (1954). *In* "Autrotrophic Micro-organisms." (B. A. Fry and J. L. Peel, eds.), pp. 126–151. Cambridge Univ. Press, London.
Szolnoki, J. (1951). *Annls Inst. biol. Tihany. Hung. Acad. Sci.* **20**, 245–247. (Hungarian.)
Tchan, Y. T. (1952). *Nature, Lond.* **170**, 328–329.
Tchan, Y. T. (1953). *Proc. Linn. Soc. N.S.W.* **77**, 265–269.
Tchan, Y. T. (1959). *Pl. Soil,* **10**, 220–231.
Tchan, Y. T., Balaam, L. N., Hawkes, R. and Draette, F. (1961). *Pl. Soil,* **14**, 147–158.
Tchan, Y. T. and Beadle, N. C. W. (1955). *Proc. Linn. Soc. N.S.W.* **80**, 97–104.
Tchan, Y. T. and Bunt, J. S. (1954). *Nature, Lond.* **174**, 656.
Tchan, Y. T. and Whitehouse, J. A. (1953). *Proc. Linn. Soc. N.S.W.* **78**, 160–170.
Trainor, F. R. (1962). *News Bull. phycol. Soc. Am.* **15**, 3–4.
Trainor, F. R. and McLean, R. J. (1964). *Am. J. Bot.* **51**, 57–60.
Tret'yakova, A. N. (1965). *Mikrobiologiya,* **34**, 491–496. (Russian.)
Treub, M. (1888). *Annls Jard. bot. Buitenz.* **7**, 213–223.
Troïtskaya, E. H. (1961). *In* "Pastures of Uzbekistan." 204–213. *Akad. Nauk Uzbek SSSR,* Tashkent.
Vaidya, S. M. W. (1964). "Ecology of algae in Indian soils with special reference to the light factor." Ph.D. Thesis, University of London.
Vogel, S. (1955). *Beitr. Biol. Pfl.* **31**, 45–135.
Watanabe, A. (1960). *In* Symposium on Algology, 162–166. *Indian Coun. agric. Res. New Delhi.*
Watanabe, A., Hattori, A., Fujita, Y. and Kiyohara, T. (1959). *J. gen. appl. Microbiol., Tokyo,* **5**, 51–57.
Watanabe, A. and Kiyohara, T. (1960). *J. gen. appl. Microbiol., Tokyo,* **5**, 175–179.
Watanabe, A., Nishigaki, S. and Konishi, C. (1951). *Nature, Lond.* **168**, 748–749.

Wiessner, W. (1962). *In* "Physiology and Biochemistry of Algae." (R. A. Lewin, ed.), pp. 267–286, Academic Press, New York and London.
Williams, B. H. (1943). *Science, N.Y.* **97**, 441–442.
Wolters, B. (1960). *Arch. Mikrobiol.* **37**, 293–326.
Zauer, L. M. (1956). *Trudy Inst. Akad. Nauk SSSR.* Ser. 2, **10**, 33–174. (Russian.)

Chapter 6

Protozoa

J. D. STOUT

Soil Bureau, Department of Scientific and Industrial Research
Wellington, New Zealand

and

O. W. HEAL

Natural Environment Research Council, The Nature Conservancy
Merlewood Research Station, Grange-over-Sands, Lancashire, England

I. INTRODUCTION

The study of soil protozoa has been concerned with determining the nature of the fauna and its relation to different soil conditions, in estimating the size of the populations, and with the relationship between protozoa, the microflora and other microfauna.

Apart from the classical monographs on the group by Sandon (1927) and Grandori and Grandori (1934) recent reviews, dealing incidentally with the soil protozoa, are those of Thornton (1956), Thornton and Meiklejohn (1957) and Russell (1961). The present review concentrates on papers published since 1927.

II. METHODS

Basically three techniques are available: direct observation, extraction and culture.

A. DIRECT OBSERVATION

The soil may be examined undisturbed (Kubiena, 1938; Koffmann, 1934) or in prepared sections (Haarløv and Weiss-Fogh, 1953; Burges and Nicholas, 1961; Heal, 1964b); in water, with a stain added (Volz, 1951), or in a soil agar suspension, dried and stained (Bunt and Tchan, 1955; Jones and Mollison method by Heal, 1964b), by inserting into the profile slides or capillaries which are subsequently withdrawn for study (Linford, 1942; Starkey, 1938; Aristovskaya, 1962; Aristovskaya and Parinkina, 1962), or by inserting a substrate, such as cellulose, into the soil and subsequently mounting it for study (Tribe, 1961).

Direct study of undisturbed mineral soil rarely provides any indication of protozoan activity. This is partly because of the intimate association of the protozoa with the soil colloids and because the population is often encysted or resting. In preparations of soil, testacea are more readily recognized than other groups because their hard test can withstand the rough treatment of preparation. Consequently they are most commonly reported by these methods, but some success has been achieved with flagellates, amoebae and even ciliates, the most delicate soil protozoa, both in recording their numbers (Bunt and Tchan, 1955) and their activity (Kubiena, 1938; Aristovskaya and Parinkina, 1962; Aristovskaya, 1962; Biczók, 1955; Nikoljuk, 1956).

B. EXTRACTION

Extracting protozoa from soil has been almost entirely confined to testacea. Carbon dioxide or air is bubbled through the soil and the tests containing gas float to the surface (Bonnet and Thomas, 1958; Chardez, 1959; Décloitre, 1960). This is useful for qualitative studies. Extraction of ciliates using an electric current has been tried by Horváth (1949) and Hairston (1965).

C. CULTURE

Culture techniques are the most versatile and extensively used methods. Not only are they the most satisfactory methods for qualitative studies, but they provide the first step in establishing pure cultures of soil protozoa which are necessary for the detailed study of the morphology and physiology of individual species. The physiology of flagellates, amoebae and ciliates is better known than that of testacea chiefly because more extensive work has been done on pure cultures of these three groups.

The choice of culture medium depends on the purposes of study. Generally, agar plates, which permit direct microscopic observation, have replaced tubes as the initial means of soil culture. Non-enriched media are less selective than media enriched with peptone or yeast extract (Dixon, 1937; Stout, 1956c), and of the species of testacea recorded by direct examination of soil, Heal (1964b) recorded 85–100% in liquid soil extract and 61–76% on soil extract agar. The dilution-culture technique has been extensively used for estimating populations and was considerably refined by Singh (1946), whose methods have been adapted by later workers (Brzezińska-Dudziak, 1954; Stout, 1962). Most common soil protozoa are bacteria-feeders and growth is promoted in the cultures by the addition of a widely accepted bacterium such as *Aerobacter aerogenes*. Numbers of encysted protozoa are estimated by pre-heating the soil to 60°C, or by treating it with 2% HCl to kill unencysted individuals. Singh found the latter method the most reliable.

No single method provides a complete picture of the protozoa of soil and it is certainly desirable to employ more than one technique wherever possible.

III. THE PROTOZOAN FAUNA OF SOIL

A. COMPOSITION AND DISTRIBUTION

Bonnet and Thomas (1960) list 100 species of testacea considered to form the endogenous soil fauna and Thomas (1960) catalogued 182 species and varieties. These are chiefly species found in mineral soil: if forest soils and peats are included the number is much greater. Many soil ciliates were first described by Kahl (1930–35), and most are included in Wenzel's (1953) study of moss ciliates, which lists over 100 species, but there are many more. Gellért (1950a, b, 1955, 1956, 1957) recently described a number of new species from soil and related habitats. It is evident that the soil fauna comprises several hundred species, many of which are confined to soil habitats. Gray (1948), however, considered that there was a free interchange of ciliate species between the soil and inland waters. Identification of the small amoebae presents special problems and although Singh (1952) described some new species, their ecological status is uncertain.

Protozoan species are generally defined on morphological grounds, but this does not imply genetic interchange which is very rare if not altogether absent in rhizopods, and in ciliates and flagellates is confined within the mating types of distinct interbreeding varieties. Evidence suggests some geographical limitations in the distribution of these varieties (Elliott *et al.*, 1962; Elliott, 1965) and they are known to differ in physiological (Holz *et al.*, 1959) and ecological properties (Hairston, 1958). There is also evidence of geographical zonation for some testacea, particularly the genus *Nebela*. In New Zealand beechwood soils *Nebela* is more common than Centropyxidae but the position is reversed in European beechwoods. This suggests that similar ecological niches carry different faunas as a result of accidents of zoogeography. The generally cosmopolitan character of the protozoan fauna may be attributed to two factors; first to physical distribution of viable cells, and second, genetic stability of the species. Evidence of the distribution of soil protozoa is very limited (Maguire, 1963b) but suggests that some flagellates, amoebae, and ciliates are transported by birds, insects, or as airborne particles. This contrasts with the distribution of typical freshwater taxa, which appear to be transported by larger terrestrial animals, and may result from the greater tendency of soil protozoa to form resistant cysts. The most commonly recorded airborne taxon is the ciliate *Colpoda*, perhaps the most widespread of all soil protozoa. Nevertheless it seems that genetic stability is of even greater importance in maintaining the homogeneity of the soil protozoan fauna and it is significant that species of one of the most variable testaceans —*Nebela*—provide the best evidence of discontinuous geographical distribution. It may also be significant that encystment is less frequently recorded in the testacea and that there are no available records of viable airborne species.

Although many species are quite widespread they occur with different frequency under different soil conditions. Figures 1 and 2 show the frequency distribution of individual species in three grassland soils. For rhizopods, the pattern is the same for the three soil types and few species occur in more than half the samples. For ciliates, the pattern differs for the different soils and more species occur in more than half of the cultures. Figures 3 and 4 show a similar difference in the distribution of rhizopods and ciliates in a forest litter, the topsoil under litter and the same topsoil under grass. With the rhizopods there is a much greater distinction between habitats than with the ciliates. Relatively few rhizopod species occur frequently in the samples compared with ciliates suggesting a broad distinction between the ecology of the two groups. Factors influencing ciliate distribution are clearly different from those determining the distribution of rhizopod and particularly testacean species.

Since Sandon's classic monograph of 1927 there have been more than 70 papers listing, with varying degrees of completeness, the protozoan fauna of different soils. Most have little pedological significance because few samples were studied or the soil was inadequately described. Exceptions are the papers of Brodsky (1929), Brodsky and Yankovskaya (1929) and Varga (1936) on desert soils; those of Gellért (1957), Varga (1935a, b), Volz (1951), Rosa (1957, 1962) and Stout (1963) on forest soils; those of Stout (1958, 1960) on grassland soils and the recent papers of Chardez (1959, 1960a, b, 1962), Thomas (1959) and Bonnet (1958, 1961a, b, c, 1964) which, however, deal only with testacea.

The fauna of soils may be compared by considering the total number of species present, the dominant or most numerous species, or the distribution of species of strictly limited occurrence. The first method is the most usual and convenient, the second the most instructive for comparing soil with non-soil faunas and the third the most significant within a range of soil groups.

Three soil forming factors, climate, vegetation and parent material are of decisive importance in determining soil habitats: the first two distinguish

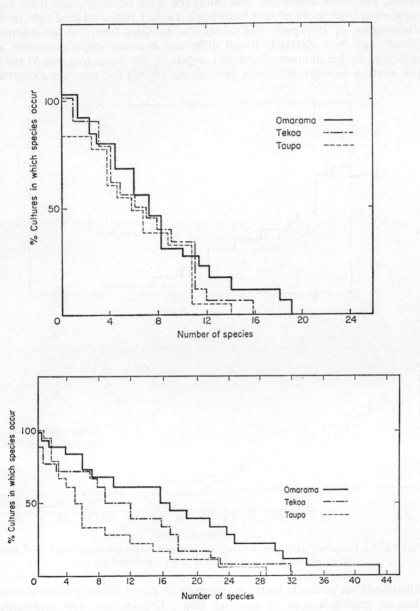

FIGS 1 and 2. Frequency of distribution of rhizopod and ciliate species in three New Zealand grassland soils.

desert, grassland, forest and peat land; the third separates acid from basic soils, mull from mor and fens from bogs. Table I shows selected data on the distribution of rhizopods and ciliates in samples from the sub-Antarctic islands and New Zealand. Broad difference between major categories are indicated by the number of species comprising the fauna (column *S*) and by the average number of species per culture (N/M) for each sample group.

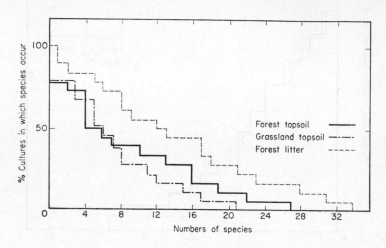

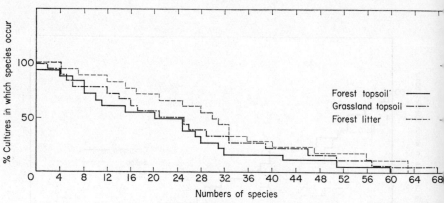

FIGS 3 and 4. Frequency of distribution of rhizopod and ciliate species in forest litter, forest topsoil and grassland topsoil of a New Zealand hill soil.

Rhizopods are generally better represented in forest litters and zonal peats than in grassland soils or lowland peats. Ciliates are well represented in all habitats but appear to prefer the type of litter found in beech forest and base rich grassland soil. The greatest differences lie between the broad zonal categories induced by climate and vegetation but the distinctions within these categories are also important. The figures used in these comparisons, namely

TABLE I

Faunal character of some New Zealand grassland soils, forest litters and peats

Soil habitat	No. samples M	Rhizopods No. species S	Total incidence N	Av. no. species N/M	Index of diversity k	Ciliates No. species S	Total incidence N	Av. no. species N/M	Index of diversity k
Grassland Soils									
Waiouru soil (medium base status) Alt. 900 m.	18	14	118	6·5	2·5	29	150	8·3	8·3
Tekoa soil (medium base status) Alt. 700 m.	18	16	127	7·0	3·4	32	208	11·6	7·5
Omarama soil (high base status) Alt. 900 m.	18	19	141	7·8	3·9	43	313	17·4	9·0
Forest Litters									
Podocarp litters (mor forming) Alt. 400 m.	9	33	89	9·9	14·2	21	40	4·4	14·6
Beech litters (mor forming) Alt. 600–900 m.	9	40	126	14·0	15·2	42	126	14·0	15·9
Beech litter (mor forming) Alt. 200 m.	50	45	812	16·2	9·4	59	932	18·6	12·2
Peats									
Zonal Sub-Antarctic	14	47	151	10·8	19·1	33	127	9·1	11·3
Alpine–sub-alpine	17	49	182	10·7	18·2	27	92	5·4	10·8
Lowland Paraparaumu	10	25	63	6·3	12·1	31	63	6·3	19·8
Maungaroa	10	19	50	4·0	11·6	36	71	7·1	24·3

the number of species and their total occurrence, are a function of the size of the sample or the number of cultures examined. This is a limitation common to all ecological work. Fisher, Corbet and Williams (1943) derived from similar data an index (α) of the faunal diversity of the area, that was independent of the sample size. An analogous value (k), derived by Darwin (1960) is included with the present data but while still indicating broad faunal differences, it is clearly less sensitive than the more direct comparison of the number of species or their total incidence.

Stout (1958, 1960) compared in more detail the fauna of some New Zealand grassland soils. The rhizopod fauna of these soils is very similar and consists of a limited number of species. The species found in soil under improved pasture are the same as under native grassland but they occur more frequently. There are more ciliate species, but they differ with different soils. Three main ecological groups are distinguished: (1) (Group (a), Fig. 5),

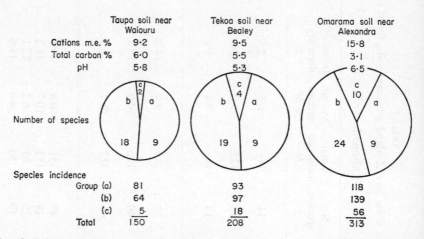

FIG. 5. Relative distribution of three ecological groups of ciliates in three New Zealand grassland soils (after Stout, 1958).

almost ubiquitous species, such as *Colpoda steinii*, small, morphologically simple and tolerant of a wide range of environmental conditions; (2) (Group (b), Fig. 5), less common species, such as *Chilodonella gouraudi*, generally similar to the first group but less well adapted to soil conditions; (3) (Group (c), Fig. 5), ciliates such as *Blepharisma* and *Frontonia*, morphologically more specialized and commonly with a less efficient encystment mechanism (Stout, 1956b), and consequently they have more exacting ecological requirements. The first two groups are well represented in all three grassland soils, but the third group is found chiefly in the base rich soil. In addition to these distinctions between the fauna of the different soils, there are also distinctions between the same soil under tussock grassland, established pasture and agricultural cropping, but these distinctions relate to the numbers of individuals rather than the species composition (Stout, 1960).

In three types of forest soil, a calcareous mull, an acid mull and a mor under beech (*Fagus sylvaticus*), Stout (1963; Fig. 6) found that the ciliate fauna differed less than the rhizopod fauna. The main difference lay between the testacea of the two acid soils, which contained the genus *Nebela*, and the

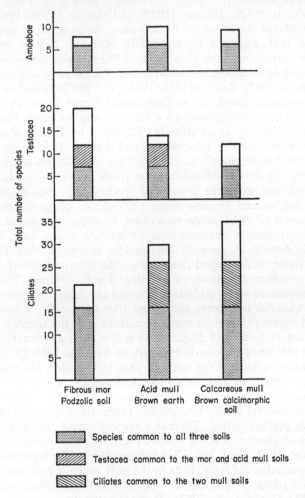

FIG. 6. Distribution of amoeba, testacean, and ciliate species in three beechwood soils on the Chiltern Hills, England

more restricted testacean fauna of the calcareous mull which resembled a grassland fauna. There appeared to be no difference in the amoeba fauna of the three soils. The ciliate faunas differed less than the testacean faunas and, unlike them, the main difference was between the mor and the two mull soils. Ciliate species particularly favoured the calcareous mull. In general amoebae, flagellates and ciliates favour conditions of high base status and a mellow humus with a high rate of mineralization, whereas the testaceans appear to favour a slow organic turnover particularly characteristic of raw humus (Stout, 1965).

Comparable studies, confined to testacea, have been made by Chardez (1959, 1960a, b, 1962), Thomas (1959) and Bonnet (1958, 1961c). Chardez (1960c) compared the fauna of fresh water, *Sphagnum* and moss, and soil, concluding that *Difflugia* is essentially aquatic, *Nebela* sphagnicolous, *Plagiopyxis* terricolous and *Trinema* and *Phryganella* ubiquitous. In other papers he distinguished the testacean fauna of a range of soil types (Chardez, 1959, 1960a, b, 1962). Bonnet (1958, 1961a, b, 1964*) studied in considerable detail the testacean fauna of the Bouillouses region in the Pyrénées, of the French Pyrénées generally and, to a lesser extent, of other French soils. In the Bouillouses region, at an altitude of 2,000 m he distinguished, like Chardez, between the fauna of mineral soil and that of "Hochmoor". In *Sphagnum* from the "Hochmoor" he identified the peat faunas described by Harnisch (1929), but this fauna was absent from mineral soils. In the mineral soils he distinguished three groups of species: (1) ubiquitous species like *Corythion dubium* and *Trinema lineare*, (2) species characteristic of skeletal soils (or azonal soils), *Assulina muscorum*, *Centropyxis vandeli* and *C. aerophila*, and (3) species characteristic of mature zonal soils, *C. sylvatica*, *Plagiopyxis declivis*, *P. penardi*, *Phryganella acropodia* and *Trinema complanatum*. Later he developed these ideas into a formal classification (Table II) of the testacean communities of mineral soils (Bonnet, 1961a, b, c). In young or immature soils (skeletal or azonal) the fauna is related to the kind of parent material or parent rock, and like the fauna of mosses consists largely of Centropyxideae. In zonal or mature soils the fauna is independent of the parent material and *Plagiopyxis* is the most characteristic genus. In comparing this work with earlier studies or with the New Zealand survey it is important to realize that the methods used by Chardez, Thomas and Bonnet are extraction methods and not culture techniques.

The extensive literature on the testacea of *Sphagnum* bogs (Schönborn, 1962a), is of interest chiefly because the fauna resembles that of forest litter with *Nebela* predominating. There is a marked stratification of the fauna on the *Sphagnum* plant with some species preferring the summit and others the base (Bonnet, 1958; Heal, 1962; Schönborn, 1963). The large testacean fauna and the preservation of their shells in the peat suggested the value of testacea for stratifying bogs and Harnisch's classification has often been used (Gilyarov, 1955; Grospietsch, 1952). However, the faunal pattern of mosses generally is very complex (Fantham and Porter, 1945) and though Harnisch's types are of some value, a wide range of intermediate communities exists. The chief distinction is between the hygrophils, the xerophils and the eurytopes (Bartoš, 1940) and between the fauna of bogs or acid peats and fens or alkaline peats (Heal, 1961, 1964a). Heal found that fen *Sphagnum* contained

---

* Results from this major work are not dealt with fully because it appeared after the chapter was written.

more species than bog *Sphagnum*. Sandon (1928), however, found that fen soils, as distinct from acid peat soils, contained no more testacea than ordinary mineral soils.

Although their pattern of distribution differs in many respects, the ciliate and testacean faunas of soil have much in common. Both are closely related to the fauna of mosses and *Sphagnum* and both reflect the moisture regime and base status of the habitat.

TABLE II

Classification of testacean communities (from Bonnet 1961c)

lass	Order	Alliance	Association	
		Acid soils *Corythion dubii*	Soils with Saxicole vegetation and roots Skeletal soils	*Centropyxidetum deflandrianae* *Centropyxidetum vandeli*
	Azonal soils low in organic matter *Centropyxidetalia*	Calcareous soils *Bullinularion gracilis*	Soils very low in organic matter	*Paraquadruleto-hyalosphenietum insectae*
			Soils with accumulated organic matter	*Centropyxidetum plagiostomae*
			Decalcified clays	*Pseudawerintzewietum calcicolae*
			White rendzinas Skeletal soils	*Geopyxelletum sylvicolae* *Arcelletum arenariae*
	Evolved soils rich in organic matter *Plagiopyxidetalia callidae*	Brown forest soils *Plagiopyxidion callidae*	Mor Mull	*Plagiopyxidetum callidae* *Plagiopyxidetum penardi*
		Grassland soils *Tracheleuglyphion acollae*	Humic alpine soils Calcareous grasslands	*Tracheleuglyphetum acollae* *T.a. Centropyxidetosum elongatae*
	Saline soils	Saline soils	Saline gleys	*Centropyxidetum halophilae*

B. MICROHABITAT

Microhabitats have seldom been examined although protozoa are often restricted in distribution within the soil profile. A marked stratification in forest soils is well documented for testacea (Volz, 1951; Bonnet, 1961c, Fig. 7; Schönborn, 1962b; Chardez, 1964) and is also shown by ciliates. Of the 40 ciliate species recorded from 3 beechwood soils on the Chiltern Hills, 39 were recorded from the organic horizons (L, F, H) but only 25 from the mineral topsoil (Ah). Similarly of the 21 testacean species recorded, all were present in the organic horizons, but only 9 in the mineral topsoil (Stout, 1963; Fig. 8). This distribution appears to be related to pore space, thickness of water film, resistance to desiccation and, for testacea, availability of test building materials. Those testacea with large pyriform tests (*Nebela, Heleopora*) are restricted to the organic layers, but those with flattened or small tests (*Centropyxis, Plagiopyxis, Corythion, Trinema*, and *Euglypha*) are common in mineral topsoil. This type of distribution has been demonstrated

6*

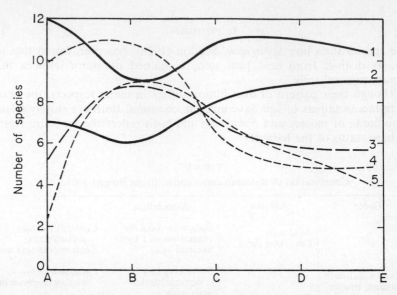

FIG. 7. Distribution of testacean species in forest soil horizons in France. 1, 2: *Ilex aquifolium*; 3, 4: *Pinus uncinata*; 5: *Fagus sylvatica*. A, B: A_0 horizon; C: top of A_1 horizon; D, E: upper half of A_1 horizon (after Bonnet, 1961b).

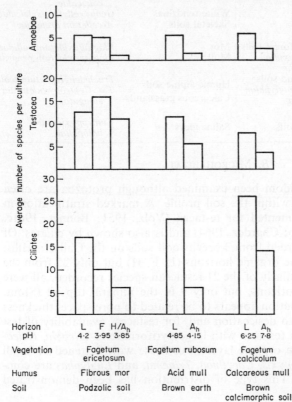

Horizon	L	F	H/A_h		L	A_h		L	A_h
pH	4·2	3·95	3·85		4·85	4·15		6·25	7·8
Vegetation		Fagetum ericetosum				Fagetum rubosum			Fagetum calcicolum
Humus		Fibrous mor				Acid mull			Calcareous mull
Soil		Podzolic soil				Brown earth			Brown calcimorphic soil

FIG. 8. Distribution of amoeba, testacean, and ciliate species in the organic and topsoil horizons of three beechwood soils in the Chiltern Hills, England.

statistically by Bonnet (1964) and Fig. 9 shows a detailed example from an acid brown forest soil under oak in northern England. Similar zonations occur on *Sphagnum* plants (Bonnet, 1958; Heal, 1962; Schönborn, 1963).

In saline soils (Solonetz-Solonchak) the populations is concentrated in the B_1 horizon (Szabó *et al.*, 1959) where the salt concentration is relatively low and an analagous zonation may be found in gleyed or waterlogged soils

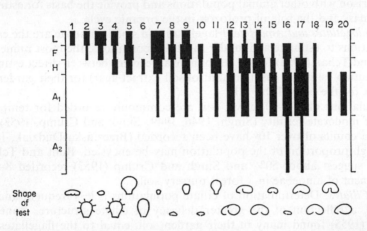

FIG. 9. The vertical distribution of 20 species of testacea in a woodland soil in relation to their test shape. The species are: (1) *Arcella arenaria*, (2) *Euglypha strigosa*, (3) *Corythion dubium*, (4) *E. ciliata*, (5) *Nebela tincta*, (6) *Hyalosphenia subflava*, (7) *Cryptodifflugia oviformis*, (8) *Trinema enchelys*, (9) *E. laevis*, (10) *T. complanatum*, (11) *N. militaris*, (12) *Centropyxis sylvatica*, (13) *C. aerophila*, (14) *Trigonopyxis arcula*, (15) *Phryganella acropodia*, (16) *T. lineare*, (17) *Plagiopyxis penardi*, (18) *Cyclopyxis kahli*, (19) *C. puteus*, (20) *Centropyxis orbicularis*. The percentage occurrence in ten cultures from each horizon is shown (O. W. Heal unpublished).

(Wilcke, 1963). Conversely, similar conditions may occur in the water film of superficially different habitats, such as soil, moss and forest litter, and this accounts for the widespread distribution of some protozoa.

C. ABUNDANCE AND BIOMASS

The most commonly used technique for estimating numbers of protozoa is the dilution culture, begun by Cutler (1920) and developed by Singh (1946). Early estimates by this method are probably unreliable because few replicates were used and culture conditions were unsuitable (Singh, 1946). Few results have been treated statistically. Direct methods of counting developed recently have been used chiefly to estimate testacean populations. Bunt and Tchan (1955) compared dilution methods with direct counting on a garden soil in Sydney, Australia, and a peat soil from Macquarie Island, in the sub-Antarctic region.

1. Numbers per unit mass

Numbers are commonly estimated on the basis of the wet or dry weights of soil. This is satisfactory for comparing mineral soils, and microflora numbers, but for comparing forest or organic soils with mineral soils the figures must be in numbers per unit area because densities of organic and mineral soils differ greatly. Numbers per unit area are also necessary for comparison with other animal populations and provide the basis for estimates of biomass and the role of protozoa in the organic cycle.

(a) *Flagellates and Amoebae.* Flagellates and small amoebae are the easiest populations to estimate and, under most soil conditions, the most numerous. Bunt and Tchan (1955) found reasonable agreement between direct estimates and dilution estimates (using mannitol soil extract agar) for their garden soil but not for the peat (Table III).

Populations of 10^3–10^5/g wet soil are commonly recorded for temperate soils of moderate fertility (Singh, 1946, 1949; Singh and Crump, 1953), but amoeba counts of over 10^6 have been recorded (Brzezińska-Dudziak, 1954).

A high proportion of the population may be encysted. Bunt and Tchan's figures suggest about 50% and Singh and Crump (1953) recorded 8–49% encystment of amoebae in a forest nursery soil.

(b) *Ciliates.* Determination of ciliate populations is less frequent and less certain, a reflection of the greater delicacy of ciliate structure. Bunt and Tchan (1955) found many in their garden soil, equal to the flagellates and more than the amoebae, though only 28% were active. Generally, however, estimates for temperate soils are less than 10^3/g wet soil for arable or grassland soils (Singh, 1946; Stout, 1962) though greater numbers are recorded for forest soils (Stout, 1963; Varga, 1958; Gellért, 1955, 1957).

(c) *Testacea.* Testacea are rarely recorded by dilution techniques because they need a long culture period for growth (cf. Bunt and Tchan, 1955, Table III). As many as 250/g wet soil have been found by this method for New Zealand grassland soils. The testacea are, however, particularly well suited for direct counts and up to 3,000/g and 7,000/g wet soil have been recorded for forest soils by Varga (1958) and Rosa (1962) respectively. Similar figures have been recorded by dilution counts (Stout, 1962). Using a modification of the Jones and Mollison technique Heal (1964b, 1965), found between 20,000 and 70,000 live cells/g dry soil for English deciduous woodland, grassland and moorland and for sub-Antarctic grassland (*Deschampsia*).

2. Numbers per unit area and biomass

Estimates of numbers per unit area involve assumptions such as the population being uniformly distributed and concentrated largely in the organic horizons and in the topsoil (say the top 10 cm). These may be invalid, so estimates of field populations and biomass based on them must be treated with caution. Nevertheless, it is probable that populations have been underestimated rather than overestimated.

In estimating biomass it is important to remember that the commonest

TABLE III

Abundance and biomass of soil protozoa.
Comparison of population estimates with dilution technique
and direct counting (after Bunt and Tchan, 1955)

| | Garden loam Sydney, Australia | | Peat Macquarie Island | |
	Dilution count	Direct count	Dilution count	Direct count
Flagellates	6250	4000	0	250
Amoebae	2380	1750	0	250
Testaceans	0	350	0	120
Ciliates	6250	1750	63	850
Cysts	0	5500	0	4000

Numbers and estimated biomass of protozoa in a Rothamsted soil
(after Singh, 1946)

	Flagellates	Amoebae	Ciliates
Nos g/wet soil	70,500	41,400	377
Est. biomass g/m^2	0·35	1·6	0·12

Distribution of testaceans in the horizons of two forest soils (after Volz,
1951) expressed as numbers/m^2 × 1,000

| | Beech forest | | Oak forest | |
	Live	Dead	Live	Dead
L	47·7	20·4	427	86
F	134·3	176·4	281	873
H	2968	35,714	—	—
A (0–5 cm)	3710	170,457	6394	11,180
(6–10 cm)	1400	82,144	702	6050
(20 cm)	—	—	0	6490
(c. 40 cm)	—	—	0	158
Total	8260	287,512	7804	24,679

species are generally the smallest (Cutler *et al.*, 1922) and that protozoa in soil are often smaller than in culture (Kubiena, 1938).

Estimates of flagellate and amoeba populations on an area basis are uncommon. Table III shows an estimate based on Singh's data (Singh, 1946) for three of the main populations of a Rothamsted soil estimated by the same technique. The dimensions given by Cutler *et al.* (1922) for the dominant flagellates and amoebae are used to estimate the mass. The mean diameter is assumed to be 5 μ for flagellates, 10 μ for amoebae and 20 μ for ciliates, giving volumes of about 50 μ^3, 400 μ^3, and 3,000 μ^3 respectively. These figures suggest that amoebae are the most important element in the population but that the total mass is only about 2 g/m². It is assumed that there were few testaceans in this soil, perhaps comparable to New Zealand grassland soils, and their mass would be comparable to that of the ciliates. In Bunt and Tchan's garden soil, however, the ciliates would be of major importance roughly equal to the amoebae which apparently were of comparable size. The flagellates appear to have been of less importance.

Estimates of live testaceans by direct methods, for oak and beech forest range from 5–8 × 10⁶/m² and for pine forest 25 × 10⁶/m² (Volz, 1951; Schön-born, 1962b). However, later figures by Volz (1964) and Heal (1964b, 1965) are in the region of 10⁶–10⁹/m² for various soils. Volz (1964) distinguishes between mull soils containing 1–2 × 10⁷ and moder types with about 5 × 10⁸/m². A biomass of 1 g/m² was given by Volz in his earlier work (Volz, 1951). Heal (1965) quotes 2 g/m² for Antarctic grassland and other population estimates indicate a biomass up to 10 g (wet weight)/m².

It seems likely, therefore, that in most temperate arable and grassland soils there is a comparatively small biomass, less than 5 g/m², but that in woodland soils or in cold grassland soils where there is accumulation of organic matter and conditions favouring the relatively large species of rhizopods, both amoebae and testacea, the biomass of protozoa may be appreciably greater, possibly up to 20 g/m². Similar figures may be obtained in exceptional conditions in other soils, since populations some thirty times greater than those given by Singh have been reported.

Competition is probably a very important factor influencing protozoa populations as indicated by the preliminary results of Hairston (1965). Since the classic studies of G. F. Gause many laboratory competition studies have involved protozoa (e.g. Burbanck and Williams, 1963) but these are not related to particular field studies. Analyses of field studies have seldom considered competitive relationships or the effects of intra- and inter-specific competition on numbers of protozoa and their distribution in soil. Maguire (1963a) discussed the exclusion of *Colpoda* from superficially favourable habitats in the presence of *Paramecium* and other protozoa.

3. Seasonal variation and relation to depth

Singh (1949) and Singh and Crump (1953) failed to observe any seasonal trends in the protozoan populations of two Rothamsted soils (Barnfield and Broadbalk) and a pine nursery soil. In an earlier study of the Barnfield soil, however, Cutler *et al.* (1922) made daily counts throughout the year and found a population increase in autumn, with lower populations in summer. This pattern has also been recorded for other soils in Europe; by Nikoljuk (1956) for irrigated cotton fields of south Russia and by Aristovskaya (1962) for a number of Russian soils, including a northern podzol. These latter studies, based on direct observations, also showed that in winter the protozoa only remained active below the frozen topsoil, although normally protozoan activity was greatest in the topsoil.

Activity, as measured by population size, may also vary in soils affected by compaction or by differences in the level of the water table and this may be reflected in the distribution of species in the profile (Wilcke, 1963). In saline soils, such as solonetzik or solonchak soils, where salt tends to accumulate at the surface, the population may be concentrated in the B_1 horizon (Szabó et al., 1959).

In forest soils the stratification of the population is more readily observed (Bonnet, 1961c, Fig. 10; Chardez, 1964; Schönborn, 1962b; Stout, 1962;

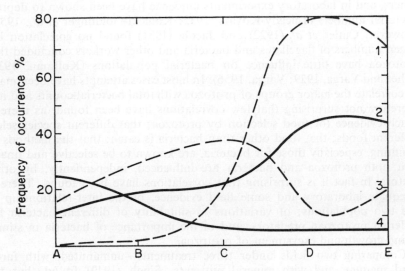

FIG. 10. Frequency of occurrence of *Centropyxis* (1, 2) and *Plagiopyxis* (3, 4) under *Pinus uncinata* (1, 3) and *Ilex aquifolium* (2, 4). A, B: A_0 horizon; C: top of A_1 horizon; D, E: upper half of A_1 horizon (after Bonnet, 1961b).

Volz, 1951; Table III). Testacea, for example, are relatively few in the upper litter horizons (L and F) and increase in the humus and topsoil layers (H and A_1). Numbers of species and individuals usually decrease markedly in the A_2 horizon or below about 10 cm depth. There is however, a difference between mull and mor soils, the population tending to be concentrated in the organic horizons of the latter. Testacea and ciliates also differ, the latter colonize fresh litter more rapidly and consequently maintain a relatively high population in the upper horizons.

These seasonal and horizon differences in the population reflect differences in the character of the soil environment and the response of the protozoan populations to them. They also stress the importance of the microhabitat in their growth.

4. Relationship to numbers of bacteria and plant growth

The close inter-relationship between populations of amoebae and bacteria in nature was first conclusively established by Cutler et al. (1922), who found that daily fluctuations in the two populations were not a function of temperature, moisture or aeration, but that the numbers of active amoebae were inversely related to those of bacteria on 86% of the days. Evidence indicated that this resulted from protozoan predation on the bacteria. Taylor (1936) found that, in general, short-term variations in numbers of protozoa were inversely related to total numbers of bacteria, but he also stated that "the accuracy of the protozoal counts does not justify statistical treatment". Similar results were obtained by Telegdy-Kovats (1928), Jacobs (1931) and others, and in laboratory experiments amoebae have been shown to depress bacterial numbers (Telegdy-Kovats, 1932; Kunicki-Goldfinger et al., 1957). However, Cutler et al. (1922) and Jacobs (1931) found no correlation between numbers of flagellates and bacteria and other workers concluded that protozoa have little influence on bacterial populations (Koffman, 1935; Fehér and Varga, 1929; Varga, 1956). In most cases attempts have been made to correlate the major groups of protozoa with total bacterial counts and it is therefore not surprising that few correlations have been found, as there is much evidence for food selection by protozoa; that different species select different foods; that food other than bacteria is eaten; that the methods of counting, especially those for bacteria, are known to be selective and finally that both protozoa and bacteria are influenced, independently, by other factors. In fact it is surprising that correlations have been found. There is adequate laboratory and some field evidence, of the inter-relationship of the two populations; of variations in suitability of different bacteria for different protozoan predators, and of the importance of bacteria in stimulating growth and excystment of protozoa.

Comparing two fields under three treatments—unmanured, with farmyard manure, and with mineral nutrients—Singh (1949) found that the numbers of amoebae were greater in the two manured plots than in the unmanured plots (Table IV). There were, however, comparatively small differences in the bacterial and fungal populations, and Russell (1961) remarked that only the protozoa tended to reflect differences in soil fertility. It seems plausible to argue, however, hat the increased bacterial activity was masked by the predation of the increased protozoa population. What is of interest is that the main difference lay between the unmanured soil and the much higher yielding manured soils, and was not therefore related to an increase in organic content but to an increase in plant activity, which would also be reflected in root growth and root exudates. The stimulating effect of root growth—the rhizosphere effect—has been well established for protozoa (see p. 178) and Biczók (1954, 1955, 1956) argued that seasonal changes in protozoan populations reflect differences in plant growth and root activity. Although the population may be stimulated by root growth, cultivation can have an adverse effect, particularly on the testacean population (Biczók, 1956).

TABLE IV

Amoeba counts of two cropped fields under different agricultural treatment—
(after Singh, 1949)

	Barnfield			Broadbalk		
	C*	M	O	C	M	O
pH	7·2	7·1	7·0	8·1	7·9	7·7
% Organic matter	0·8	0·8	2·5	1·1	1·2	2·6
Mean amoeba counts × 1,000/g dry wt						
Total	8	26	34	17	48	72
Active	5·3	23	28	10	40	52

* C, untreated; M, complete minerals; O, farmyard manure.

IV. THE BIOLOGY OF SOIL PROTOZOA

A. LIFE HISTORY

Few soil protozoa (apart from the Myxomycetes) are polymorphic and those that are show relatively little differentiation between the different life stages. Most of the flagellates are monomorphic, but certain of the related amoebae occur in either flagellated or limax form (Singh, 1952), a change induced by altered environmental conditions (Brent, 1957; Willmer, 1956). Other amoeboid organisms, such as the proteomyxids, have both a limax and a reticulate stage in their life history. Of the ciliates, some, such as *Tetrahymena rostrata*, have theront, trophont and tomite stages (Stout, 1954) and free swimming and tentaculiferous forms occur in the few soil suctorians.

The formation of cysts or other forms that resist desiccation is one of the most distinctive and common features of soil protozoa. There is great variation in the degree of de-differentiation in the cell, the thickness of the cyst membrane and the readiness with which the cysts are formed and activated.

Cysts of small amoebae are simple, typically spherical, with cyst walls varying in thickness and structure (Singh, 1952). They remain viable when dried and when treated with dilute HCl, a method used to differentiate encysted from trophic forms (Singh, 1946). Cysts of *Naegleria gruberi* and *Acanthamoeba* sp. endure exposure to picric acid up to 20% concentration (Hajra, 1959). Factors influencing encystment of amoebae have not been widely studied but Band (1963) using *Hartmannella rhysodes* in axenic culture concluded that although starvation, and a decrease in aeration and divalent salts could cause encystation, the main factor is desiccation i.e. an increase in the osmotic pressure. Oxygen supply also limits cyst formation in *H. rhysodes*, no cysts being formed at low oxygen tensions (Band, 1959). Excystment in some species may be obtained with water, others require the presence of bacteria or their metabolic products such as amino acids (Crump,

1950; Singh *et al.*, 1958). The available evidence suggests that cysts of flagellates and amoebae remain viable for long periods in soils (Goodey, 1915).

Testacea show several types of cyst formation (Volz, 1929). In the simplest case, first described by Penard (1902) for the common soil species *Trigono-pyxis arcula* (= *Difflugia arcula*), a wrinkled membrane or pellicle covers the cytoplasm, producing a pre-cyst whose formation may take only a few minutes (Bonnet, 1959, 1960, 1961c, 1964). In the second case a true cyst is formed inside the test, the cyst membrane, as with amoebae, varying in thickness and shape. Finally, associated with a true cyst, the mouth of the test may be plugged. The physiology of encystment and excystment in testacea is poorly understood. Physical and physiological drought appear to be important, but even under relatively constant culture conditions periodic encystment and excystment occurs (Bonnet, 1964).

Some authors describe cyst and spore-like stages in testacea that may be associated with sexual processes. Life cycles involving small naked amoeboid stages and individuals with small tests are also recorded (Bonnet, 1964; Chardez, 1965). All the information suggests that such complex life cycles are a feature of testacea, but pure cultures have not yet been used to verify them.

The literature on encystment of ciliates, particularly the common soil species of *Colpoda*, is very extensive (Stout, 1955). *Colpoda steinii* is perhaps the most widespread of soil ciliates and indeed of soil protozoa and may properly be considered one of the species best adapted to its environment. It is small, up to 50 μ in length, feeding on bacteria and perhaps yeasts in nature but capable of axenic culture. It forms at least three types of cysts; resting or resistant cysts, reproductive cysts, and unstable cysts. Resting or resistant cysts normally form after a period of growth under the twin influences of exhaustion of food and crowding. Such cysts may be activated by a hypotonic solution, such as distilled water, or by the presence of bacteria, other nutrients or even alcohol. The cells feed and grow and on reaching a certain size or after a certain period of time, they form reproductive cysts within which cell division takes place. Excystment follows cell division provided food and other conditions are favourable. Unstable cysts form in response to adverse conditions which tend to inhibit growth and division. These include high salinities (2–3% NaCl), low and high temperatures (4° and 35°c), and the absence of oxygen. If the inhibitory factor is removed the ciliates will excyst and continue to feed and divide. The cysts, particularly the resistant ones, can withstand very low (near absolute zero) and very high temperatures (near 100°c) and high carbon dioxide tensions. They remain viable for decades (Goodey, 1915; Bridgeman, 1957), *Colpoda* cysts representing the most efficient example. In *Sathrophilus muscorum* (Stout, 1956b) and *Frontonia depressa* (Stout, 1956a) the mechanism is less well developed with incomplete dedifferentiation, a thinner cyst membrane and lower viability. Moreover, in these genera only resting cysts appear to be formed, the cells divide outside a cyst membrane.

The aquatic soil environment is transitory in most soil habitats.

Consequently protozoa capable of rapid growth have a distinct advantage in filling these niches. In general, the flagellates, small amoebae and ciliates divide fairly rapidly, perhaps once or twice a day at temperatures of about 12°C. Some species divide more rapidly than others and all depend upon an adequate supply of food. Most testacea reproduce more slowly so population growth is slower than other groups. This is shown by the succession in laboratory cultures, flagellates preceding amoebae and ciliates which in turn are followed by testacea. Recovery of field populations after partial sterilization follows a similar sequence (Stout, 1961).

B. MORPHOLOGY

Compared with the fresh water and marine faunas, the most striking feature of the soil fauna is the absence of large, structurely elaborate protozoa. The common soil flagellates, such as *Cercomonas* and *Oikomonas* are minute, only several microns in length and even *Peranema trichophorum* one of the largest soil flagellates is only 70 μ long. The common soil amoebae are generally less than 50 μ long (Singh, 1952) and the commonest testacea, such as *Trinema lineare*, *Corythion dubium* and *Euglypha rotunda* are little bigger. Similarly, the common soil ciliates, *Colpoda* and *Enchelys* are less than 100 μ long. Where congeneric species differ in size, the smallest is almost invariably the commonest soil form. This is true of *Trinema* and *Euglypha* among testacea and of *Frontonia* and *Dileptus* among ciliates. The larger species of the same genus are either uncommon in soil or occur only in fresh water or marine habitats. When they occur in soil, larger amoebae, testacea and ciliates are either confined to habitats, such as forest litter, with extensive and better aerated water conditions or else tend to show some compensating morphological adaptations. Morphological variation within a species in relation to habitat variation has been shown by Chardez and Leclercq (1963) and Heal (1963b). Testacea confined to forest soils or peats include large species of *Nebela* and *Heleopora* and the large spined *Centropyxis aculeata*. Ciliates found only in moss or litter include *Stentor multiformis*, the only edaphic species of the genus and the smallest; *Bresslaua*, the largest and most complex genus of the Colpodidae; and *Phacodinium metschnicoffi*, morphologically perhaps the most elaborate if not the largest of all soil ciliates. At the other extreme, Varga (1960) states that ciliates are absent from compacted clay solonetz because of the very fine pore size.

Except for species such as *Trinema lineare*, *Euglypha rotunda* and *E. laevis*, the common soil testacea, as distinct from those found in forest litter, tend to be sub-spherical with a slightly flattened ventral surface containing the mouth or pseudostome. Spines or horns are absent (Chardez and Leclercq, 1963; Fig. 9). These features are thought to be adaptive and to allow the testacean to adhere to the substrate like a chiton and to extend its pseudopodia in the thin film of water surrounding the soil particles. The very small species lacking this form are thought to be sufficiently small to be able to exist within the water film (Volz, 1951; Schönborn, 1962b; Heal, 1964b; Bonnet,

1961c). Two other morphological features, plagiostomy and cryptostomy, are considered to be adaptations to life in soil; both involve a reduction in the size of the pseudostome in proportion to the test and the formation of a vestibule (Fig. 11) and both tend, therefore, to protect the cell against desiccation (Bonnet, 1961a, 1964). Many of the morphological features of testacea present in primary biotopes such as lakes, pre-adapt them for life in secondary terrestrial habitats, while other characteristics of soil species are post-adaptive changes (Schönborn, 1964).

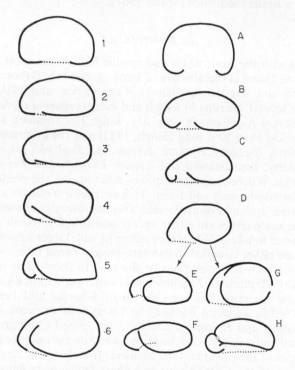

FIG. 11. Comparison of the form of the test of testacea showing increasing cryptostomy in the genus *Plagiopyxis* (2–6) and increasing plagiostomy in the genera *Centropyxis* (B–G) and *Paracentropyxis* (H) (after Bonnet, 1961b).

With ciliates, the chief morphological features are the relatively simple form and the tendency towards plasticity that is also shared by flagellates and amoebae. This plasticity enables even the larger species to use the very thin water film surrounding the soil particles and to occupy the minute pores in which moisture is usually retained. Many of the ciliates are flattened and, apart from a single species of *Vorticella*, none of the common species is attached to the substrate. Even the *Vorticella* can detach itself and form a free-swimming telotroch very rapidly (Stout, 1956c; Horváth, 1949).

C. PHYSIOLOGY

1. Movement

Losina-Losinsky and Martinov (1930) studied the movement of an amoeba (*Vahlkampfia* sp.), a ciliate (*Colpoda steinii*) and a bacterium (*Bacterium radicicola*) in different mechanical fractions of a sterilized garden soil at different moisture levels. They found that activity depended both upon the moisture and the physical structure of the soil. In the α–0·1 mm fraction, movement of the bacterium and the protozoa was limited, though greater at 25% moisture than at either 15% or 20%. In the 0·1–0·25 mm fraction movement appeared to be directly proportional to the moisture status, amoebae moving more freely than ciliates. In the 0·25–0·5 mm fraction the organisms moved more freely and showed a similar dependence on soil moisture. Ciliates, however, moved only at 25% moisture and then moved 3 cm in a day compared with 1 cm a day for amoebae at that moisture level. It was concluded that movement was a function of the proportion of moisture in relation to the water holding capacity (w.h.c.) of the soil. At moisture contents up to 40% w.h.c. the protozoa move slowly or not at all. Above this level they move more freely; ciliates, for example, diffusing over 190 cm^2 in two days at 59% w.h.c. Similar results were obtained for other soils and for sand (Losina-Losinsky, 1932, Figs. 12, 13). Singh (1947) found that the amoebae of *Dictyostelium* moved at a similar rate. Biczók (1959) recorded movement of 0·4–0·5 cm/day for *Colpoda fastigata* in sterile garden soil. Bonnet (1961a) measured the rate of movement of testacea in culture in terms of body length and found that small species moved relatively faster than larger species (Fig. 14).

2. Nutrition and respiration

In axenic culture protozoa reveal exacting nutritional requirements. The flagellate *Peranema trichophorum*, for example, required thiamine, riboflavin, B_{12} (cobalamin), tryptophan, methianine, nucleic acid components (satisfied by a combination of uracil, cytidylic, guanylic and adenylic acids) and traces of fat-soluble and water soluble materials not yet identified (Storm and Hutner, 1953). Similarly complex requirements were found for the amoeba-flagellate *Tetramitus rostratus* (Brent, 1955), and some small soil amoebae, the latter needing thiamine, B_{12} and various organic acids (Adam, 1959; Band, 1959; Neff *et al.*, 1958). Adam (1964a) has shown that hartmanellid amoebae may differ in their amino-acid requirements, one strain requiring only 6 essential amino-acids plus glycine and synthesizing histidine, lysine, threonine and tryptophan. The ciliate *Colpoda steinii* required thiamine, riboflavin, nicotinamide, pyridozine, pantothenic acid, several heat-stable and heat labile factors of plasmoptyzate including, perhaps, thioctic acid (van Wagtendonk, 1955a). The absence of specific growth factors will induce encystment even when an adequate energy supply is available (Garnjobst, 1947). However, the ecological significance of these nutritional requirements is not clear and the diversity of the soil microflora is such as to supply the known requirements of the protozoa. It has been suggested that the soil flagellates may be osmotrophic, especially in nutrient rich soils (Varga, 1959; Nikoljuk, 1956) but the evidence is slight.

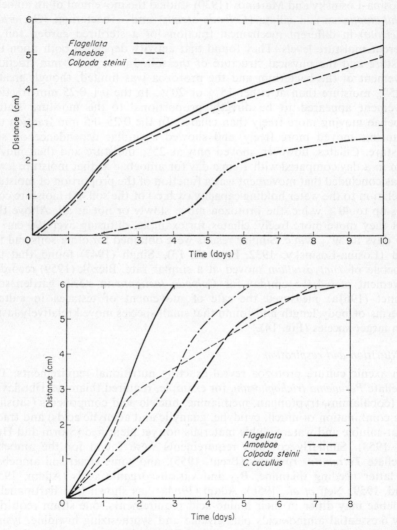

FIGS 12 and 13. Rate of movement of protozoa in soil at 20% (Fig. 12) and 35% (Fig. 13) moisture. *Colpoda cucullus* is a larger species than *C. steinii* (after Losina-Losinsky, 1932).

Respiratory activity of protozoa depends closely upon the available nutrients. Reich (1948, Table V) found the respiratory rate of fed *Mayorella palestinensis* (101 mm^3/O_2/mg wet wt/hr) greater than that of starved cells and much greater than that of the cysts. The respiratory rate was also slightly greater in a nutrient solution than in a balanced salt solution. *M. palestinensis* could metabolize added peptone but not added glucose, whereas Neff *et al.* (1958) found that *Acanthamoeba* metabolized glucose but not peptone. The R.Q. was 0·86 for both species. Adam (1964b) from a comparative study of hartmanellid amoebae, including *Mayorella palestinensis* and Neff's strain of *Acanthamoeba*, concluded that they belonged to a single species whose correct name is *Hartmanella castellanii* Douglas. Reich found little difference in the respiration at pH 6·0 and 8·0 although originally he recorded marked differences in growth (Reich, 1933). There was no change in respiratory rate with oxygen tensions between 5–50% of normal but at 1–2% of normal tension respiration fell to 42–43% of normal. Ormsbee (1942) found a difference between the respiration of the ciliate *Tetrahymena pyriformis* in the stationary

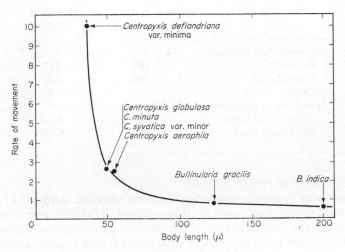

FIG. 14. Rate of movement per unit body length per second of testacea in relation to the size of the body (after Bonnet, 1961a).

and exponential phase and in nutrient and non-nutrient solutions (Table V). Pace (1946) found the R.Q. of this ciliate generally greater than unity and this agrees with its known ability for anaerobic fermentation. The respiratory rate of the typical soil ciliate *Colpoda*, fed on *Chlamydomonas*, is similar to that of *Tetrahymena* (Adolph, 1929). Like *M. palestinensis* little variation with oxygen tension occurs unless it is reduced to about 5 mm Hg when the oxygen consumption of the ciliate falls to 31% of its normal rate (at 156 mm Hg). Adolph also observed that at lower oxygen tension (40 mm Hg) the ciliates divided earlier before attaining normal size. This indicates that small or "dwarf" *Colpoda* in soil (Kubiena, 1938) may result from reduced oxygen tensions as well as from reduced food supply. The advantage of small size is that it allows oxygen to diffuse more rapidly to the centre of the cell. The cysts of *Colpoda* have a low respiratory rate, 35 mm³/hr/mg dry wt. at 22°c

(Thimann and Commoner, 1940). There is little work on the respiration of soil flagellates but work on *Chilomonas paramoecium* suggest a rate comparable to that of *Mayorella* (Hutchens, 1941).

This evidence shows that respiratory activity is a function of oxygen tension, food supply and the physiological state of the population, which all vary greatly in soil.

TABLE V

Respiratory rate of the amoeba *Mayorella palestinensis* at 27°c (after Reich, 1948) and the ciliate *Tetrahymena pyriformis* at 26·8°c (after Ormsbee, 1942) expressed as $mm^3O_2/hr/10^7$ cells

Species	Non-nutrient buffer	Nutrient solution
Mayorella palestinensis		
Fed cells	102	117
Starved cells	84	102
Cysts	—	22
Tetrahymena pyriformis		
Exponential stage	1402	4330
Stationary stage	1337	6330

3. Moisture, salinity and temperature

The moisture regime is probably the most selective attribute of the soil environment to which protozoa must be adapted. It involves alternate wetting and drying of the soil, restriction of the water to narrow pores, capillaries and thin surface films often associated with mineral and organic colloids, and variations in osmotic tension. The activity of ciliates has been related to wetting and drying of soil (Horváth, 1949) but there is little direct evidence of the effect on protozoa of changes in moisture content within a soil.

Cutler *et al.* (1922) found no significant effect of soil moisture on protozoan numbers or encystment in their daily counts of the Barnfield plots where the moisture varied only from 12–22%. But in the same soil Cutler and Dixon (1927), showed that reproduction of protozoa fell when moisture content fell below half the water holding capacity of the soil. Of the four species studied, only *Cercomonas crassicauda*, could excyst and reproduce at a moisture content below ⅙ w.h.c. and although excystment took place there was little or no multiplication of any of the species at ⅓ w.h.c. (Table VI). These results correspond quite well with those of Losina-Losinsky and Martinov (1930) for movement of protozoa in soil (p. 171). Encystment appears to be an adequate defence against drought which Sandon (1927) concluded was not an important factor limiting the distribution of the protozoa in soil.

Most common soil protozoa can adapt to a wide range of salinities, up to

25–45‰ (Reich, 1933), though increasing salinities may inhibit reproduction and lead to encystment (Stout, 1955; Band, 1963). Conversely, reduction of osmotic tension may lead to excystment and growth. High cation concentrations cause the amoeba-flagellate, *Naegleria gruberi*, to transform to the amoeba stage whereas low concentrations or anions such as phosphate and bicarbonate favour the flagellate stage. This indicates conservation of cations by the flagellates and conservation of water by the amoebae (Willmer, 1963).

TABLE VI

Populations of three flagellate species and an amoeba (× 1000/g) in samples of Barnfield soil at different moisture content (Cutler and Dixon 1927)

| Time | $\frac{1}{3}$ W.H.C.* | | | | $\frac{1}{2}$ W.H.C. | | | |
| | 0 | | 24 hr | | 0 | | 24 hr | |
	No.	% Active	No.	% Active	No.	% Active	No.	% Active
Cercomonas crassicauda	230	0	230	86	44	0	420	86
Heteromita globosa	21	0	44	96	41	0	140	84
Oikomonas termo	10	0	10	87	1·8	0	44	92
Naegleria gruberi	1·8	0	65	21	7·3	0	21	88

* The water holding capacity of the soil is 37·9%.

Experiments have shown that in most cases increasing temperature up to about 30° C favours metabolism and reproduction of protozoa (Reich, 1933). Higher temperatures are adverse with death point about 35–40° C. (Maguire, 1960), but cysts can survive much higher temperatures (Stout, 1955). Simple relationships between temperature and protozoan activity in soil have not been shown and there appear to be no data on temperature adaptation in forms found in extreme temperature ranges.

4. pH

Although there is a wide range of pH in different soils, variation within a particular soil is slight (not more than 1 pH unit) compared with poorly buffered fresh water ponds. Little experimental work has been done on the pH tolerance of individual species. Both the distributional evidence and the limited experimental data (Stout, 1956c) suggest that most flagellates, amoebae, and ciliates will grow over a relatively wide range but Cutler and Crump (1935) found that *Cinetochilum margaritaceum* did not occur in glucose filters below pH 5·7 and Wang (1928) found this eurytopic species in the range 6·2 to 7·05. Watson (1944) found that *Balantiophorus minutus* had a range from 4·65 to 9·25 and Nasir, quoted by Cutler and Crump, found that *Colpoda cucullus* had a range from 3·5 to 9·75, which is similar to that of *C. steinii* (Stout, 1955) and is probably typical of the range of the more widespread soil protozoa.

With the testacea, distributional evidence strongly suggests more limited tolerance of pH variation. Again there is little experimental data. Cutler and Crump (1935) found that *Arcella vulgaris* preferred a strongly acid reaction, below pH 6·0, and this range appears to be preferred by many of the species

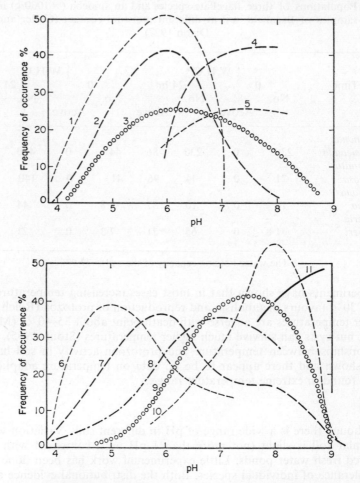

Figs 15 and 16. Distribution of testacean species in relation to pH (after Bonnet, 1961b): (1) *Centropyxis deflandriana*; (2) *Corythion dubium*, (3) *Plagiopyxis declivis*, (4) *Heleopora petricola* var. *humicola*, (5) *Bullinularia gracilis*, (6) *Centropyxis vandeli*, (7) *Tracheleuglypha acolla*, (8) *Arcella arenaria*, (9) *Centropyxis plagiostoma*, (10) *Geopyxella sylvicola*, (11) *Centropyxis halophila*.

found in acid mors and *Sphagnum*. Conversely Bonnet (1961c) listed species which appear to be restricted to neutral or alkaline soils whereas eurytopic species such as *Trinema lineare* appear to have the same pH tolerance as the common ciliates and flagellates (Figs. 15, 16). Studies on the distribution of testacea in fens and bogs also indicate the importance of pH (de Graaf, 1957; Heal, 1961, 1964a). Experiments with *Difflugia tuberculata* show that it will not reproduce below pH 4·5, corresponding closely with the observed distribution (Heal, 1964a). Kuhnelt (1963), found the distribution of testacea on leaf litter was related to pH and tannin content, which are influenced by the growth of fungi, particularly *Clitocybe infundibuliformis*.

5. Oxygen and carbon dioxide tensions

In most environments, including soil, variation in pH is associated with fluctuating concentrations of carbon dioxide. Thus Sekera, quoted by Kubiena (1938) found that in a soil of pH 6·0, the pH near root hairs ranged from 4·9 to 5·8 due to the evolution of carbon dioxide and also no doubt to secretion of organic acids. Most of the experimental work on tolerance of high carbon dioxide tensions has been done with ciliates (Stout, 1956c). Polysaprobic species which include the most common soil species, such as *Leptopharynx sphagnetorum*, and *Colpoda* spp. are remarkably tolerant of high concentrations of carbon dioxide. They will also tolerate but will not excyst or divide in the absence of oxygen. This appears to be equally true of the small amoebae (Neff *et al.*, 1958). The readiness with which many of the common soil protozoa encyst is also an advantage in surviving conditions of low oxygen or high carbon dioxide tensions since the cysts are often much more resistant than the trophic cells. Slight increases in carbon dioxide tension may stimulate protozoan activity.

D. COMPARISON OF THE MAJOR GROUPS

The morphological and physiological characters that appear to favour the existence of protozoa in soil are: small size and simple structure; a capacity for rapid multiplication under favourable conditions; encystment and excystment mechanisms adapted to fluctuations of soil moisture, salinity, aeration and food supply; tolerance of a wide range of pH and temperature; the ability to absorb nutrients in dissolved or particulate form. These properties are well illustrated by *Colpoda steinii* (Stout, 1955) and are generally shared by the small amoebae such as *Naegleria*, and the flagellates such as *Oikomonas* or *Cercomonas*. Testacea, however, with some notable exceptions such as *Trinema lineare*, reproduce more slowly, have less perfect encystment mechanisms, poorer tolerance of high carbon dioxide tensions and salinities and low oxygen tensions. Such differences account for the differences in their ecology (Stout, 1965). Thus, Sandon (1927) found a strong correlation between the distribution of the flagellates, amoebae and ciliates but not between these three groups and the testacea. These differences, described earlier in the chapter, were also emphasized by Grandori and Grandori (1934).

V. RELATION TO VEGETATION AND TO OTHER SOIL ORGANISMS

A. RELATION TO VEGETATION

Apart from its pedogenetic role, vegetation has an immediate effect on the soil fauna through the accumulation of plant residues and changes brought about in the rhizosphere. The "rhizosphere" effect has been studied by several authors (Biczók, 1953, 1954; Agnihothrudu, 1956; Katznelson, 1946; Rouatt, Katznelson and Payne, 1960; Nikoljuk, 1949, 1964; Shilova and Kondrat'eva, 1955; Formisano, 1957; Stout, 1960; Varga, 1958). In all cases differences were recorded between the rhizosphere and the non-rhizosphere population but the composition of the fauna was generally the same, the rhizosphere simply stimulating greater protozoan activity. For example, Varga found that total numbers were similar but there were more cysts in the soil than on the hairs of sugar beet. Shilova and Kondrat'eva, Biczók, Nikoljuk, and Katznelson found greater numbers in the rhizosphere of grasses, cotton, wheat and mangels. Geltzer (1963) observed that as well as being more numerous, there was a greater diversity of species in the rhizosphere than in the soil. He also found that amoebae only developed and accumulated where there was an active development of bacteria. The importance of the increased bacterial food supply is also stressed by Nikoljuk (1964).

Gellért (1958) found only slight differences in the growth of maize and oats with and without soil protozoa. However, Nikoljuk (1956, 1965) has shown that when cotton seeds are treated with amoebae and ciliates the resulting plants are bigger and stronger than plants from untreated seed. Phytopathogenic fungi (*Rhizoctonia solani* and *Verticillium dahliae*) affecting cotton plants are reduced by direct and indirect action of the protozoa. Irradiated ciliates (*Colpoda maupasi*) tended to be more effective than non-irradiated ciliates (Nikoljuk and Marlyanova, 1963a).

Grandori and Grandori (1934) studied the effect of different kinds of plant debris on the protozoan population. They collected dry leaves of various trees, added them to soil and then examined the protozoa fauna. They found appreciable differences in the number of species associated with the decomposition of the different species of leaves, the largest number being associated with *Robinia* and *Gelso* and the smallest with red oak and Canadian poplar. They attributed these differences partly to the nitrogen content of the different leaves and associated differences in the decomposition rate. They also found that the fauna of a soil under *Robinia* was richer than the same soil under *Calluna* or under *Pinus*.

B. RELATION TO MICROFLORA

Sandon (1932) reviewed the food preferences of protozoa, particularly of soil and sewage species. It is generally accepted that the majority of soil protozoa feed on bacteria and to a lesser extent on yeasts, algae, fungal spores and mycelium. However, many of the records in the literature of feeding on fungi and algae are based on the observation of these materials in the protoplasm of protozoa. Such evidence must be treated carefully until evidence of digestion is produced, because particles may be rejected from the body uneaten (Heal, 1963a).

Information on the food of amoebae has been obtained mainly from experiments in culture, but for ciliates many observations have been made on animals obtained directly from soil or in mixed cultures developed from soil (Gellért, 1955, 1957; Horváth, 1949). In various papers, ciliate species have been classified as algal, bacterial, fungal or detrital feeders or as carnivores, but the available information suggests that many species are not specific in their feeding requirements and feed on a range of microflora, probably depending upon availability. Thus *Colpoda steinii* is recorded as feeding on algae and fungi (Gellért, 1955) and on bacteria and detritus (Gellért, 1957). Similarly *C. fastigata* is classed as an algal feeder by Gellért (1957) and bacterial and fungal feeder by Horváth (1949). *Spathidium amphoriforme* is carnivorous on other ciliates according to Gellért (1955) but feeds also on bacteria and algae according to Horváth (1949). Feeding experiments on the range of food eaten by individual species are required with details of the availability of food.

The small flagellates are probably mainly bacterial feeders because of their size, but they are also regarded as osmotrophic (Varga, 1959; Nikoljuk, 1956). Soil testacea are believed to feed mainly on bacteria but also on algae, fungi, and on other testacea (Biczók, 1954; Varga, 1958; Rosa, 1957; Volz, 1951). However, Schönborn (1965) has suggested that they are able to feed on humus in soil.

1. Bacteria as food

There is little doubt that predation on the bacterial flora is selective, although the evidence is somewhat conflicting. Two factors may be important: first, the correct identification of the organisms and, second, establishing comparable experimental conditions. For example, the age and concentration of the bacterial culture can be important (Leslie, 1940a, b). Further, the division rate of protozoa grown on a particular bacterial strain is determined partly by its previous culture history (Burbanck, 1942; Burbanck and Gilpin, 1946).

There is considerable literature dealing with bacteria as food for ciliates. Some maintain a high rate of ciliate growth, others a low rate, while some cause the premature death of the ciliate (Kidder and Stuart, 1939a, b). Different strains may vary as much as different species in suitability (Leslie, 1940a, b; Hetherington, 1933) but generally the Gram-negative Enterobacteriaceae support the highest division rates and the Bacillaceae the lowest (Burbanck, 1942). The soil ciliate most intensively studied is *Colpoda steinii*, perhaps the most typical of soil protozoa. Kidder and Stuart (1939a) found that *Aerobacter cloacae* supported the best growth of *C. steinii* and in mixed bacterial cultures edible strains were selected, leaving inedible strains which consequently increased in number. In the presence of an inedible strain *C. steinii* encysts, as it would in a non-nutrient medium (Singh, 1941b). Kidder and Stuart found that pigmented strains of *Pseudomonas* and *Serratia* were toxic to active and encysted *Colpoda*, and this was confirmed by Singh (1942b, 1945), who found that nearly all red, green, violet, blue and fluorescent pigmented bacteria were inedible to soil amoebae and *C. steinii*. The unsuitability of chromagenic bacteria for ciliates was earlier studied by Chatton and Chatton (1927a, b).

The most extensive studies of the relationship between soil protozoa and the bacterial flora have been by Singh (1941a, b; 1942 a, b; 1945; 1948; Anscombe and Singh, 1948; Singh *et al.*, 1958) and this work was reviewed recently (Singh, 1960; Thornton and Crump, 1952). Using many bacterial strains and a wide range of soil flagellates, amoebae, and the ciliate *C. steinii* Singh concluded that bacteria could be classified into four groups: (1) strains readily and completely eaten, (2) strains slowly but completely eaten, (3) strains partly eaten, and (4) inedible strains. No correlation between Gram-staining, motility, presence of proteolytic ferment, or slime production and edibility was found. Altogether 87 strains of bacteria were tested using 8 micropredators (2 amoebae, 1 proteomyxid, 2 species of Acraseiae, and 3 species of Myxobacteria). Only 8% of the bacterial strains were not attacked by any predator, about half were attacked by one and 14% were attacked by all the predators. Strains of *Rhizobium* were generally resistant to attack (Singh, 1942a).

As with the ciliate, edibility of bacteria by the two amoebae was related to pigment production. Of the 56 colourless strains 71% were eaten; of the 32 yellow, orange and brown strains 75% were eaten but only 1 (7%) of the 14 red, violet, blue, green and fluorescent organisms was edible. The pigments of some of these inedible strains were shown to be toxic (Singh, 1945). Similar results are recorded for flagellates (Hardin, 1944) and for amoebae (Groscop and Brent, 1964; Knorr, 1960; Graf, 1958; Chang, 1960; and Imszeniecki quoted by Kunicki-Goldfinger *et al.*, 1957). In particular *Pseudomonas aeruginosa*, and *P. fluorescens* are recorded as toxic. Studies on the filtration of bacteria through soil profiles by Knorr (1960) showed that *P. fluorescens* pass through the soil while other bacteria are retained. He related this to the toxicity of *Pseudomonas*, the others being edible. A toxic extra-cellular substance consisting of 6 amino-acids plus a fatty acid was isolated from *P. fluorescens* (Graf, 1958) and Knorr (1960) also found that *P. aeruginosa* was poisonous when ingested by amoebae, causing death or the production of deformed cysts. However, Kunicki-Goldfinger *et al.* (1957) found that *P. aeruginosa* was readily eaten by amoebae and concluded that food selection by amoebae was only slightly influenced by pigment production. Chang (1960) also showed that amoebae can develop tolerance towards the yellow pigment of *Flavobacterium*.

The feeding experiments of Kunicki-Goldfinger *et al.* (1957, Fig. 17) and Heal and Felton (1965 and unpublished) showed amoebae grew best with sarcinae, cocci and Gram-negative rods, poorer growth occurred with bacilli and diphtheroids. They and Groscop and Brent (1964) suggest that size of bacteria, and the physical characteristics of their surfaces are more important than chemical differences, such as pigment production, in the selection of food by amoebae. The age of the bacterial culture was again shown to be an important factor influencing the growth of amoebae.

The soil flagellates *Oikomonas termo* and *Cercomonas crassicauda* eat a wide range of bacteria, *C. crassicauda* having similar food preferences to two species of soil amoebae and also eating some bacteria toxic to amoebae (Hardin, 1944; Singh, 1942a).

These studies indicate that most species of soil protozoa can feed on a wide range of bacteria and can also select one bacterial species from mixed

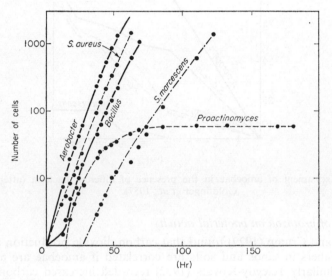

FIG. 17. Growth of amoebae with different bacteria as food (after Kunicki-Goldfinger *et al.*, 1957).

populations. Bacteria differ considerably in their edibility and nutritive value, and a limited number of species produce toxic substances in culture. Whether or not these toxins are effective in the soil is not known, although there is some correlation between the presence of *Serratia* and a limited ciliate fauna (Stout, 1958). Drożański (1956, 1963a, b) recently recorded a lethal bacterial parasite of soil amoebae.

2. Effect of bacteria on encystment and excystment

Much work has also been done on the effect of bacteria on encystment and excystment of amoebae (Kunicki-Goldfinger *et al.*, 1957; Drożański, 1961; Dudziak, 1955; Oura, 1959; Band, 1963; Singh *et al.*, 1958). The earlier work was reviewed by van Wagtendonk (1955b). In general encystment and excystment of protozoa is closely related to edibility of the bacteria. Thus Kunicki-Goldfinger *et al.* (1957) and Dudziak (1955) found that presence of edible forms caused much more rapid excystment than inedible species (Fig. 18). Crump (1950) found differences between soil amoebae, one species requiring the presence of living bacteria for excystment, another excysting readily in water. Singh *et al.* (1958) and Drożański (1961) showed that extracts of *Aerobacter aerogenes* and *Escherichia coli* and amino-acids stimulate excystment of soil amoebae.

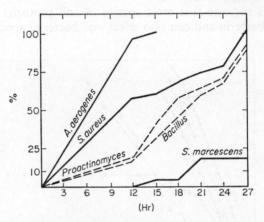

FIG. 18. Excystment of amoebae in the presence of different bacteria (after Kunicki-Goldfinger *et al.*, 1957).

3. Effect of protozoa on bacterial activity

Cutler and Crump (1929) found that carbon dioxide production and bacterial numbers in sands and soils are correlated if amoebae are absent or scarce. Similarly Telegdy-Kovats (1932) recorded increased carbon dioxide production in sand cultures in the presence of small numbers of protozoa. Bacteria were fewer when protozoa were present but they produced more carbon dioxide. Increasing the carbon-nitrogen ratio of the medium had little effect on carbon dioxide production when protozoa were absent but it increased when they were present. Meiklejohn (1930) found that in sand culture amoebae decreased the numbers of bacteria but increased the rate of ammonia production and the same was true for a ciliate (Meiklejohn, 1932). Early work by Telegdy-Kovats (1928), Federowa-Winogradowa and Gurfein (1928) and Hirai and Hino (1928) showed that the protozoa favoured nitrogen fixation by *Azotobacter* (Waksman, 1930) and this view was confirmed by Hervey and Greaves (1941) who worked with sterilized soils of varying moisture and organic matter content. They showed that nitrogen fixation increased in the presence of protozoa if the bacteria had a sufficient supply of energy material. Nitrogen fixation was encouraged not only by the presence of living protozoa but also by suspensions of heat-killed protozoa, "suggesting the provision by the protozoa of vitamins or other growth-stimulating substances". Once again we have no information of the importance of this phenomenon in soil, and stimulation of nitrogen-fixation by *Azotobacter* has also been recorded in the presence of other bacteria (Panosyan *et al.*, 1962). Nikoljuk (1956) reviewed recent literature, and has continued to work on this subject (Nikoljuk and Mavlyanova, 1963b). Greatest stimulation of nitrogen fixation was obtained with irradiated ciliates (*Colpoda maupasi*).

4. Actinomycetales

Despite the considerable interest shown in the antibiotic activity of this group, studies on the relationship between free-living protozoa and actinomycetes are few and concern small soil amoebae. Kunicki-Goldfinger *et al.* (1957), Dudziak (1962) and Heal and Felton (1965) found *Streptomyces* spores and mycelium were inedible, but some strains of *Nocardia* (= *Proactinomyces*) and *Mycobacterium* could support reproduction of amoebae. In particular, the *Nocardia* strains that produced bacteria-like colonies were more edible than those producing *Streptomyces*-like colonies.

Protozoa are usually considered more resistant to antibiotics than are bacteria though they are sensitive to some, *viz.* chloromycetin, bacitracin, neomycin and actidione (Loefer, 1951, 1952; Loefer and Matney, 1952; Blumberg and Loefer, 1952). Zaher *et al.* (1953) showed that exudates of 32% of 82 actinomycetes isolated from soil retarded growth of *Tetrahymena geleii* (*T. pyriformis*), *Euglena gracilis* and *Herpetomonas culicidarum*. Of 20 anti-protozoal actinomycetes, 9 (45%) were not active against bacteria. Exudates from soil *Streptomyces* are also toxic to soil amoebae and exudates from at least one *Nocardia* sp., although not toxic, caused increased encystment (Heal and Felton, unpublished work). The effectiveness of antibiotic exudates in natural soil is still uncertain, but more directly applicable to soil conditions is the release of an intra-cellular toxin by mycobacteria after ingestion by amoebae (Dudziak, 1962).

It seems that Actinomycetales are, in general, unsuitable as food for amoebae and can have strong antagonistic effects. Pfennig (1958) recorded growth of *Streptomyces* spores on dead amoebae in soil which suggests possible advantages to the actinomycetes of this antagonism. Detailed field and microhabitat studies are needed for more information on the effect of antibiotics on protozoa in soil, and by direct observation Geltzer (1963) found that reproduction of amoebae in a rhizosphere was suppressed by large growths of actinomycetes and fungi.

5. Fungi

Experimental evidence shows that protozoa only rarely feed on spores and hyphae of mycelial fungi (Sandon, 1932; Hardin, 1944; Heal, 1963a) but observations on ciliates from the field and in mixed cultures suggest that some species may feed on hyphae (Gellért, 1955; 1957; Horváth, 1949).

7+s.b.

Brodsky (1941) gives evidence that *Colpoda steinii* suppresses growth of *Verticillium dahliae* in soil.

Scattered observations suggest that yeasts are eaten by protozoa (Sandon, 1932; Hardin, 1944; Soneda, 1962; Nero, Hedrick and Traver, 1964) and Heal (1963a) showed that 19 species of yeasts were eaten by at least one of four species of amoebae. Exudates from yeasts also retard encystment of starved amoebae (Heal and Felton, unpublished data). Yeasts present in temperate soil vary from 10^3–10^6/g and may form a significant food source for soil protozoa.

Observations on the antagonistic effect of fungi on protozoa are lacking, but the more direct effect of zoophagaceous fungi feeding on amoebae and testacea has been recorded frequently in cultures (see Duddington, 1957).

6. Algae

In most soils the organic cycle is dominated by the higher plants and the contribution of algae is insignificant. But in soils bare of higher vegetation, such as deserts, algae are of prime importance. Few protozoa are obligate algal feeders but the ciliate genus *Nassula* and possibly some larger rhizopods characteristically feeds on algae. Small hartmannellid amoebae showed little or no growth on fourteen strains of soil algae (Heal and Felton, 1965).

C. RELATION TO MICROFAUNA AND MACROFAUNA

The other members of the microfauna are generally much larger than the protozoa and are, therefore, more commonly predators than prey. It seems likely that the nematodes and rotifers that feed on small particles ingest some protozoa as well as bacteria and yeasts in their somewhat indiscriminate diet. Similarly, animals such as aquatic oligochaetes, turbellarians, copepods and ostracods in forest litter, which all consume much plant debris, must ingest many protozoa commonly associated with such food. Conversely, when they die, these animals provide a ready substrate for bacterial proliferation and hence a direct or indirect food source for the protozoa. The macrofauna are similar in consuming protozoa in their normal diet and providing a transient centre of microbial activity when they die.

Miles (1963) suggested a more essential relationship. He found that the earthworm *Eisenia foetida* grew poorly in sterile soil recolonized only by fungi and bacteria, but grew normally if protozoa were also added, and concluded that soil protozoa are an essential part of this worm's diet. Van Gansen (1962) also concluded that *E. foetida* lives on soil micro-organisms. She found that it could be fed on yeasts or dead bacteria, but with yeasts alone there was a high mortality and with dead bacteria only limited growth.

More intimate association of the protozoa and the soil fauna may occur. First, there are obligate endocommensals and parasites such as the enteric ciliates of oligochaetes, the flagellates of termites or the gregarines of earthworms. This group includes ciliates and suctorians associated with copepods (Precht, 1936), tardigrades (Matthes, 1951, 1955), oligochaetes (Baer, 1952) and isopods (Remy, 1928). Second, there are obligate and casual epibionts of soil animals (Stammer, 1963). These include the testacea, which are thought to be distributed by mites (Chardez, 1960b). Third, there are facultative parasites, of which the best authenticated are the ciliates *Colpoda steinii*, known to infect the lung of pulmonate gastropods (Reynolds, 1936), and *Tetrahymena rostrata*, a histophage normally scavenging dead protozoa, rotifiers, tardigrades or nematodes but also capable of invading living enchytraeids through damaged setal follicles (Stout, 1954). Other records of ciliate parasitism implicating *Tetrahymena* species are those of Warren (1932), Lom (1959), Kazubski (1958), and Kozloff (1957). This literature is reviewed by Corliss (1960). The ecology of the soil amoebae is seldom as well established. Recently Weber *et al.* (1952) described a proteomyxid which destroyed nematode larvae and similar organisms have been found associated with diseased crops (McLennan, 1930). Hawes (1963) isolated a small amoeba which is a parasite of a snake and which he believed to be a soil inhabitant.

VI. THE ROLE OF SOIL PROTOZOA

Russell and Hutchinson (1909) initiated the serious study of soil protozoa and proposed that the infertility of "sick" soils resulted from protozoa preying on the beneficial flora. Partial sterilization, which appeared to benefit such "sick" soils was supposed to suppress the protozoa and so permit beneficial bacteria to grow. It is now considered that protozoa are unlikely permanently to suppress the bacterial population of soil and that the effects of partial sterilization are far more complex than was originally supposed. Further, although partial steam sterilization is generally followed by increasing numbers of bacteria, it is also followed by a marked increase in the size of the protozoan population (Singh and Crump, 1953; Stout, 1955). This was observed by Oxley and Gray (1952), the numbers of bacteria and protozoa showing a series of "pulses" with a succession of protozoan species associated with changes in the composition of the microflora. A similar pattern is found in soils following over-burning (Miller *et al.*, 1955; Stout, 1961). The present view is that a balance or equilibrium between the two populations is temporarily altered or upset by partial sterilization, but a new equilibrium is rapidly attained. Similarly, although protozoa can feed selectively on bacteria there is no conclusive evidence that they modify the composition of the normal soil bacterial flora. Thus, Nikoljuk (1961) found that although they preferred the oligonitrophilic bacteria their predation appeared to favour the activity of these bacteria. It is possible, however, that the rapid disappearance of coliform bacteria in soil may result from the activity of micropredators such as protozoa rather than from antibiotic activity because they belong to a group of bacteria particularly favoured by protozoan predators whereas they resist antibiotics more than most soil bacteria. On the whole, the population both of the bacteria and of the associated protozoan fauna is determined by other soil conditions—the nature of the organic cycle, the moisture status and the base status. Acid peats or arid soils which have few micropredators generally also have few bacteria, particularly of the readily accepted *Aerobacter*, whereas soils with high numbers of *Aerobacter* likewise have many micropredators (Stout, 1962). Further, the unrestricted diet of many edaphic protozoa ensures their distribution in soils, such as those of Antarctica, with an entirely different flora to that of soils in temperate zones (Décloitre, 1956; Flint and Stout, 1960). In general, protozoa, like other micropredators, may cause local and diurnal fluctuations in bacterial populations, as first recorded by Cutler *et al.* (1922), but they are unlikely to change the normal soil flora permanently. Occasional invaders, such as the bacteria from the phyllosphere, enteric contaminants, such as the coliform bacteria or enterococci, and even plant pathogens, such as *Erwinia* (Hino, 1934), whose rapid disappearance in soil is well known, may be destroyed by protozoa. Similarly, protozoan parasitism probably has little effect on the fauna and flora, although it may decrease slug populations slightly (Reynolds, 1936).

Protozoa mainly affect the organic cycle indirectly. Their constant predation on bacteria contributes to the general turnover of readily available nutrients and appears to favour biochemical activity. An interesting illustration is given by Tribe (1961), who followed the decomposition of cellulose in a light sandy soil, the associated immobilization and release of soil nitrogen, and the succession of microflora and microfauna. He found that fungal growth was associated with nitrogen immobilization and that nitrogen release was associated with subsequent autolysis or bacteriolysis of the mycelium, and with the growth of protozoa particularly testacea, which were considered to accelerate the release of ammonium nitrogen. Doyle and Harding (1937) concluded that the ciliate *Tetrahymena pyriformis* (*Glaucoma pyriformis*) eliminated most of the ingested bacterial nitrogen as ammonia approximately 6 hours after ingestion. Ammonia, as with most aquatic animals, appears to be the chief nitrogenous end-product of protozoa. The release of phosphates may be accelerated, as shown by Hooper and Elliott (1953) with *Tetrahymena pyriformis*.

In very acid environments, such as *Sphagnum* peat or forest mors, bacterial activity and fungal growth may be small and the chief actively growing organisms are the rhizopods, particularly testacea. It is possible that they can digest cellulose (Tracey, 1955) and play a direct role in the organic cycle (Schönborn, 1965). Similarly, testacea may assist chemical weathering through mobilizing silicates to synthesize the scales of their tests.

In assessing the importance of protozoa in the organic cycle the turnover of the population must be considered. Population studies on protozoa have considered the standing crop without attempting to estimate reproductive rate, production or mortality. Such estimates raise considerable technical difficulties, but very approximate estimates can be made from the 365 days results of Cutler, Crump and Sandon (1922). For each of six species, the standing crop is taken as the mean number/g for the 365 days. Wherever there is a significant rise in numbers, the number of individuals at the beginning (*a*) and at the end (*b*) of the rise are used to calculate the annual production

$[\sum(b-a)]$ and the number of generations per year $[\sum(\log b - \log a)/\log 2]$. The accuracy of these calculations is considerably limited by statistical and sampling errors, but the results are given in Table VII. They indicate that for small amoebae and flagellates the amount of protoplasm produced and re-cycled during the year varies from 50 to 300 times the standing crop. The average generation time over the year, under field conditions, varies from 1–3 days. This rapid production and turnover suggests that although the standing crop of protozoa, measured as biomass, is smaller than that of many other soil animals their role in the cycle of organic matter is greater.

It is difficult to assess the relative importance of the different protozoan groups. Morphological and physiological features favouring the existence of protozoa in soil, estimates of populations, and the evidence of laboratory cultures suggest that flagellates and small amoebae best fulfil the exacting demands of the soil environment. Large ciliates and testacea have very extensive distributions and consistant, if not very great, populations. This suggests that they are also well adapted to life in soil and that they may be more important than either the flagellates or the small amoebae, particularly in the more favourable habitats such as forest soils.

Estimates of protozoan activity in soil are necessarily speculative. Using the population figures of Singh (Table IV) for the Rothamsted soil (Broadbalk) and the respiratory rates for *Mayorella palestinensis* (Table V) as a guide and correcting for temperature, the rate of oxygen uptake for this field could be of the order of 20 $l/m^2/yr$ without top-dressing, 80 for the mineral-dressed field and 100 for the field with added farmyard manure. This corresponds to about 80, 320 and 400 $Kcal/m^2/yr$ respectively. This is a conservative figure, treating the amoebae activity in this soil as of principal importance (cf. Table IV). It represents, however, only a small fraction of the total activity, about 8% without top dressing and 3% for the top-dressed (Russell, 1961). Viewed another way, the release of carbon dioxide, roughly 17, 69 and 86 l/m^2 per yr respectively, may be considered equal to the weight of substrate metabolized, or roughly 150, 700 and 900 $g/m^2/yr$. If this is principally bacterial cells, then it represents about 1·5, 7, and 9×10^{14}, assuming 10^{12} bacterial cells/g wet wt. Overgaard Nielsen (1961) suggested that protozoa consume approximately the standing crop of bacteria. This, however, is misleading. As has been shown, the protozoa are selective feeders for two reasons. First, protozoa are generally confined to pore spaces or colloidal films and an appreciable part of the bacterial population is not directly accessible to them. Second, not all bacteria are equally acceptable as food, some are unacceptable and some are toxic. Generally, then, they will feed on the flora in the pore spaces and particularly on such readily acceptable bacteria as *Aerobacter* and *Azotobacter*, part of the zymogenous flora of Winegradsky, a population generally at a low level (less than 10^6/g wet wt., generally 10^3–10^4), probably largely because of protozoan predation. The zymogenous population is roughly comparable to the plate count (as contrasted with the direct count) or about 5×10^7/g equal to about 10 g/m^2. Consequently, in Broadbalk, the yearly predation by protozoa is equal to about 15, 65 and 85 times

TABLE VII

Estimates of the standing crop, production and number of generations per year from the results of Cutler, Crump and Sandon (1922)

	Dimastigamoeba gruberi*	Sp. α	Heteromita sp.	Sp. γ	Cercomonas sp.	Oicomonas termo
Standing crop (×10³/g)	130	19	242	42	127	93
Annual production (×10³/g)	13,213	5015	11,889	8166	15,535	16,438
Ratio S.C.:A.P.	1:101	1:257	1:49	1:194	1:333	1:176
No of generations/year	190	366	110	340	244	288

* = *Naegleria gruberi*

the standing crop of readily available bacteria. In these plots, the actual plant crop is not returned to the soil which derives its energy from root material, root excretions and stubble. The differences between the three plots are reflected less in the level of bacterial or fungal populations than in the protozoan population, but there is clearly an absolute dependence upon the input of photosynthesis, which limits the activity of the population irrespective of its size or character.

ACKNOWLEDGEMENTS

We are indebted to Mr G. V. Jacks of the Commonwealth Bureau of Soils, Rothamsted Experimental Station, for the preparation of a Bibliography on Soil Protozoa and to the librarians of the British Museum (Natural History), the Science Library, Rothamsted Experimental Station, and the Balfour and Newton Libraries, Cambridge, for their hospitality and assistance in tracing the literature.

REFERENCES

Adam, K. M. G. (1959). *J. gen. Microbiol.* **21**, 519–529.
Adam, K. M. G. (1964a). *J. Protozool.* **11**, 98–100.
Adam, K. M. G. (1964b). *J. Protozool*, **11**, 423–430.
Adolph, E. F. (1929). *J. exp. Zool.* **53**, 269–311.
Agnihothrudu, V. (1956). *Experientia* **12**, 149–150.
Anscombe, F. J. and Singh, B. N. (1948). *Nature, Lond.* **161**, 140–141.
Aristovskaya, T. V. (1962). *Pochvovedeniye* No. 1, 7–16.
Aristovskaya, T. V. and Parinkina, O. M. (1962). *Microbiologiya* **31**, 385–390.
Baer, J. G. (1952). *Acta trop.* **9**, 366–370.
Band, R. N. (1959). *J. gen. Microbiol.* **21**, 80–95.
Band, R. N. (1963). *J. Protozool.* **10**, 101–106.
Bartoš, E. (1940). *Arch. Protistenk.* **94**, 93–160.
Biczók, F. (1953). *Agrokém. Talajt.* **2**, 45–64.
Biczók, F. (1954). *Annls. Biol. Univ. Hung. 1952*, **2**, 385–394.
Biczók, F. (1955). *Allatt. Közl.* **45**, 21–32.
Biczók, F. (1956). *Acta zool. hung.* **2**, 115–147.
Biczók, F. (1959). *Acta biol., Szeged* **5**, 97–108.
Blumberg, A. J. and Loefer, J. B. (1952). *Physiol. Zoöl.* **25**, 276–282.
Bonnet, L. (1958). *Bull. Soc. Hist. nat. Toulouse* **93**, 529–543.
Bonnet, L. (1959). *C. r. Acad. Sci.* **249**, 2617–2619.
Bonnet, L. (1960). *Bull. Soc. zool. Fr.* **85**, 43–52.
Bonnet, L. (1961a). *Bull. Soc. Hist. nat. Toulouse* **96**, 80–86.
Bonnet, L. (1961b). *Bull. soc. zool. Fr.* **86**, 17–28.
Bonnet, L. (1961c). *Pedobiologia* **1**, 6–24.
Bonnet, L. (1964). *Revue Écol. Biol. Sol.* **1**, 123–408.
Bonnet, L. and Thomas, R. (1958). *C. r. Acad. Sci.* **247**, 1901–1903.
Bonnet, L. and Thomas, R. (1960). Faune terrestre et d'eau douce des Pyrénées-Orientales. Fasc. 5, "Thécamoebiens du Sol," 103 pp. Hermann, Paris.
Brent, M. M. (1955). *Biol. Bull. mar. biol. Lab. Woods Hole* **106**, 269–278.
Brent, M. M. (1957). *Nature, Lond.* **179**, 1029.
Bridgeman, A. J. (1957). *J. Protozool.* **4**, 17–19.

Brodsky, A. L. (1929). *Acta Univ. Asiae mediae 12a Geog.* **5**, 1–42.
Brodsky, A. L. (1941). *Dokl. Akad. Nauk SSSR.* **33**, 81–83.
Brodsky, A. L. and Yankovskaya, A. (1929). *Acta Univ. Asiae media. 12a Geog.* **6**, 1–36.
Brzezińska-Dudziak, B. (1954). *Acta microbiol. Pol.* **3**, 121–124.
Bunt, J. S. and Tchan, Y. T. (1955). *Proc. Linn. Soc. N.S.W.* **80**, 148–153.
Burbanck, W. D. (1942). *Physiol. Zoöl.* **15**, 342–362.
Burbanck, W. D. and Gilpin, D. W. (1946). *Physiol. Zoöl.* **19**, 236–242.
Burbanck, W. D. and Williams, D. B. (1963). *In* "Progress in Protozoology." (J. Ludvík, J. Lom and J. Vavra, eds.) pp. 304–307. Czech. Acad. Sci., Prague.
Burges, N. A. and Nicholas, D. P. (1961). *Soil Sci.* **92**, 25–29.
Chang, S. L. (1960). *Can. J. Microbiol.* **6**, 397–405.
Chardez, D. (1959). *Hydrobiologia* **14**, 72–78.
Chardez, D. (1960a). *Hydrobiologia* **16**, 197–202.
Chardez, D. (1960b). *Bull. Inst. agron. Stns. Rech. Gembloux* **28**, 118–131.
Chardez, D. (1960c). *Bull. Inst. agron. Stns. Rech. Gembloux* **28**, 132–138.
Chardez, D. (1962). *Bull. Inst. agron. Stns. Rech. Gembloux* **30**, 263–272.
Chardez, D. (1964). *Bull. Inst. agron. Stns. Rech. Gembloux* **32**, 26–32.
Chardez, D. (1965). *Bull. Inst. agron. Stns. Rech. Gembloux* **33**, 26–34.
Chardez, D. and Leclercq, J. (1963). *Bull. Inst. agron. Stns. Rech. Gembloux* **31**, 21–27.
Chatton, É. and Chatton, M. (1927a). *C. r. Séanc. Soc. Biol.* **97**, 289–292.
Chatton, É. and Chatton, M. (1927b). *C. r. Séanc. Soc. Biol.* **97**, 292–295.
Corliss, J. O. (1960). *Parasitology*, **50**, 111–153.
Crump, L. M. (1950). *J. gen. Microbiol.* **4**, 16–21.
Cutler, D. W. (1920). *J. agric. Sci. Camb.* **10**, 136–143.
Cutler, D. W., Crump, L. M. and Sandon, H. (1922). *Phil. Trans. R. Soc. B.* **211**, 317–350.
Cutler, D. W. and Crump, L. M. (1929). *Ann. appl. Biol.* **16**, 472–482.
Cutler, D. W. and Crump, L. M. (1935). *In* "Problems in Soil Microbiology," 104 pp. Longmans, Green and Co., London.
Cutler, D. W. and Dixon, A. (1927). *Ann. appl. Biol.* **17**, 247–254.
Darwin, J. H. (1960). *Biometrics* **16**, 51–60.
Décloitre, L. (1956). *Acta Sci. Indust. 1242 Expéd. Pol. Fr. Missions Paul-Emile Victor* **8**, 1–105.
Décloitre, L. (1960). *Bull. Mus. Hist. nat. Paris* **32**, 242–251.
Dixon, A. (1937). *Ann. appl. Biol.* **24**, 442–456.
Doyle, W. L. and Harding, J. T. (1937). *J. exp. Biol.* **14**, 462–469.
Drożański, W. (1956). *Acta microbiol. Pol.* **5**, 315–317.
Drożański, W. (1961). *Acta microbiol. Pol.* **10**, 147–153.
Drożański, W. (1963a). *Acta microbiol. Pol.* **12**, 3–8.
Drożański, W. (1963b). *Acta microbiol. Pol.* **12**, 9–24.
Duddington, C. L. (1957). *In* "Microbial Ecology" (R. E. O. Williams and C. C. Spicer, eds.), pp. 218–237. University Press, Cambridge.
Dudziak, B. (1955). *Acta microbiol. Pol.* **4**, 115–126.
Dudziak, B. (1962). *Acta microbiol. Pol.* **11**, 223–244.
Elliott, A. M. (1965). *In* "Progress in Protozoology," London (1965), p. 249. Excerpta Medica Foundation, Amsterdam.
Elliott, A. M., Addison, M. A. and Carey, W. E. (1962). *J. Protozool.* **9**, 135–141.
Fantham, H. B. and Porter, A. (1945). *Proc. zool. Soc. Lond.* **115**, 97–174.

Federowa-Winogradowa, T. and Gurfein, L. N. (1928). *Zentbl. Bakt. ParasitKde. II* **74**, 14–22.

Fehér, D. and Varga, L. (1929). *Zentbl. Bakt. ParasitKde II* **77**, 524–542.

Fisher, R. A., Corbet, A. S. and Williams, C. B. (1943). *J. Anim. Ecol.* **12**, 42–58.

Flint, E. A. and Stout, J. D. (1960). *Nature, Lond.* **188**, 767–768.

Formisano, M. (1957). *Annali Fac. Agr. Portici* **22**, 1–34.

van Gansen, P. (1962). "Structures et fonctions du tube digestif du lombricien *Eisenia foetida* Savigny," 120 pp. Imp. Medicale et Scientifique (S.A.), Bruxelles.

Garnjobst, L. (1947). *Physiol. Zoöl.* **20**, 5–14.

Gellért, J. (1950a). *Annls. biol. Univ. szeged.* **1**, 295–312.

Gellért, J. (1950b). *Annls. biol. Univ. szeged.* **1**, 313–319.

Gellért, J. (1955). *Acta. biol. hung.* **6**, 77–111.

Gellért, J. (1956). *Acta. biol. hung.* **6**, 337–359.

Gellért, J. (1957). *Annal. Biol. Tihany* **24**, 11–34.

Gellért, J. (1958). *Annal. Biol. Tihany* **25**, 29–35.

Geltzer, J. G. (1963). *Pedobiologia* **2**, 249–251.

Gilyarov, M. S. (1955). *Pochvovedenie* **10**, 61–65.

Goodey, T. (1915). *Ann. appl. Biol.* **1**, 395–399.

de Graaf, F. (1957). *Hydrobiologia* **9**, 210–317.

Graf, W. (1958). *Arch. Hyg. Bakt.* **142**, 267–275.

Grandori, R. and Grandori, L. (1934). *Boll. Lab. Zool. agr. Bachic, R. Ist. sup. agr. Milano* **5**, 1–339.

Gray, E. (1948). *Nature, Lond.* **161**, 854–855.

Groscop, J. A. and Brent, M. M. (1964). *Can. J. Microbiol.* **10**, 579–584.

Grospietsch, T. (1952). *Naturwissenschaften* **39**, 318–323.

Haarløv, N. and Weis-Fogh, T. (1953). *Oikos* **4**, 44–57.

Hairston, N. G. (1958). *Evolution* **12**, 440–450.

Hairston, N. G. (1965). *In* "Progress in Protozoology," London (1965), p. 114. Excerpta Medica Foundation, Amsterdam.

Hajra, B. (1959). *Naturwissenschaften* **46**, 582.

Hardin, G. (1944). *Ecology* **44**, 274–297.

Harnisch, O. (1929). Die Biologie der Moore. 146 pp. Erwin Nagele, Stuttgart.

Hawes, R. S. J. (1963). *In* "Progress in Protozoology." (J. Lud′ik, J. Lom and J. Vavra, eds.), p. 262. Czech. Acad. Sci., Prague.

Heal, O. W. (1961). *J. Linn. Soc. Zool.* **44**, 369–382.

Heal, O. W. (1962). *Oikos* **13**, 35–47.

Heal, O. W. (1963a). *In* "Soil Organisms." (J. Doeksen and J. van der Drift, eds.), pp. 289–296. North Holland Publishing Co., Amsterdam.

Heal, O. W. (1963b). *Arch. Protistenk.* **106**, 351–368.

Heal, O. W. (1964a). *J. Anim. Ecol.* **33**, 395–412.

Heal, O. W. (1964b). *Pedobiologia* **4**, 1–7.

Heal, O. W., (1965). *British Antarctic Survey Bulletin* **6**, 43–47.

Heal, O. W. and Felton, M. J. (1965). *In* "Progress in Protozoology," London (1965), p. 121. Excerpta Medica Foundation, Amsterdam.

Hervey, R. J. and Greaves, J. E. (1941). *Soil Sci.* **51**, 85–100.

Hetherington, A. (1933). *Arch. Protistenk.* **80**, 255–280.

Hino, I. (1934). *Bull. Miyazaki Coll. Agric. For.* **6**, 19–84.

Hirai, K. and Hino, I. (1928). *Proc. 1st Int. Congr. Soil Sci. Washington 1927*, **3**, 160–165.

Holz, G. G. Jr., Erwin, J. A. and Davis, R. J. (1959). *J. Protozool.* **6**, 149–156.

7*

Hooper, F. F. and Elliott, A. M. (1953). *Trans. Am. microsc. Soc.* **72**, 276–281.
Horváth, J. (1949). *Ann. Inst. Biol. Fer. Hung.* **1**, 151–162.
Hutchens, J. O. (1941). *J. cell. comp. Physiol.* **17**, 321–332.
Jacobs, S. E. (1931). *Ann. appl. Biol.* **18**, 98–136.
Kahl, A. (1930–1935). *In* "Die Tierwelt Deutschlands." (F. Dahl, ed.), Parts 18, 21, 25, 30. Gustav Fischer, Jena.
Katznelson, H. (1946). *Soil Sci.* **62**, 343–354.
Kazubski, S. L. (1958). *Bull. Acad. pol. Sci. Cl. II Sér. Sci. biol.* **6**, 247–252.
Kidder, G. W. and Stuart, C. A. (1939a). *Physiol. Zoöl.* **12**, 329–340.
Kidder, G. W. and Stuart, C. A. (1939b). *Physiol. Zoöl.* **12**, 341–347.
Knorr, M. (1960). *Schweiz. Z. Hydrol.* **22**, 493–502.
Koffman, M. (1934). *Arch. Mikrobiol.* **5**, 246–302.
Koffman, M. (1935). *Proc. 2nd Intern. Congr. Soil Sci. Leningrad-Moscow 1930*, **3**, 268–271.
Kozloff, E. N. (1957). *J. Protozool.* **4**, 75–79.
Kubiena, W. (1938). "Micropedology," 243 pp. Collegiate Press, Iowa State College, Ames, Iowa.
Kühnelt, W. (1963). *In* "Soil Organisms." (J. Doeksen and J. van der Drift, eds.), pp. 281–288. North Holland Publ. Co., Amsterdam.
Kunicki-Goldfinger, W., Drożański, W., Blaszczak, D., Mazur, J. and Skibińska, J. (1957). *Acta microbiol. Pol.* **6**, 331–344.
Leslie, L. D. (1940a). *Physiol. Zoöl.* **13**, 243–250.
Leslie, L. D. (1940b). *Physiol. Zoöl.* **13**, 430–438.
Linford, M. B. (1942). *Soil Sci.* **53**, 93–103.
Loefer, J. B. (1951). *Physiol. Zoöl.* **24**, 155–163.
Loefer, J. B. (1952). *Tex. J. Sci.* **4**, 73–76.
Loefer, J. B. and Matney, T. S. (1952). *Physiol. Zoöl.* **25**, 272–276.
Lom, J. (1959). *J. Parasitol.* **45**, 320.
Losina-Losinsky, L. (1932). *Proc. 2nd Intern. Congr. Sci. Leningrad-Moscow 1930*, **3**, 272–275.
Losina-Losinsky, L. and Martinov, P. F. (1930). *Soil Sci.* **29**, 349–362.
Maguire, B. Jr. (1960). *Physiol. Zoöl.* **33**, 29–38.
Maguire, B. Jr. (1963a). *Ecology* **44**, 781–784.
Maguire, B. Jr. (1963b). *Ecol. Monogr.* **33**, 161–185.
Matthes, D. (1951). *Zoöl. Anz.* **146**, 135–136.
Matthes, D. (1955). *Arch. Protistenk.* **100**, 435–446.
McLennan, E. T. (1930). *Aust. J. exp. Biol. med. Sci.* **8**, 9–44.
Meiklejohn, J. (1930). *Ann. appl. Biol.* **17**, 614–637.
Meiklejohn, J. (1932). *Ann. appl. Biol.* **19**, 584–608.
Miles, H. B. (1963). *Soil Science* **95**, 407–409.
Miller, R. B., Stout, J. D. and Lee, K. E. (1955). *N. Z. Jl. Sci. Technol.* **37**, 290–313.
Neff, R. J., Neff, R. H. and Taylor, R. E. (1958). *Physiol. Zoöl.* **31**, 73–91.
Nero, L. C., Traver, Mae G. and Hedrick, L. R. (1964). *J. Bact.* **87**, 220–225.
Nielsen, C. O. (1961). *Oikos* **12**, 17–35.
Nikoljuk, V. F. (1949). *Dokl. Akad. Nauk. uzbek. S.S.R.* **4**, 22–24.
Nikoljuk, V. F. (1956). "Soil Protozoa and their Role in Cultivated Soils of Uzbekistan," 144 pp. Tashkent.
Nikoljuk, V. F. (1961). *Uzbk. biol. Zh.* **6**, 3–5.
Nikoljuk, V. F. (1964). *Pedobologia* **3**, 259–273.

Nikoljuk, V. F. (1965). *In* "Progress in Protozoology", London (1965), pp. 118–119. Excerpta Medica Foundation, Amsterdam.

Nikoljuk, V. F. and Mavlyanova, M. I. (1963a). *Uzbk. biol. Zh.* **4**, 59–61.

Nikoljuk, V. F. and Mavlyanova, M. I. (1963b). *Dokl. Akad. Nauk. uzbek. S.S.R.* **7**, 48–50.

Ormsbee, R. A. (1942). *Biol. Bull. mar. biol. Lab. Woods Hole* **82**, 423–437.

Oura, H. (1959). *Nisshin. Igaku.* **46**, 735–745.

Oxley, C. D. and Gray, E. A. (1952). *J. agric. Sci.* **42**, 353–361.

Pace, D. M. (1946). *Yb. Am. phil. Soc.* **1946**, 160–162.

Panosyan, A. K., Arutyuryan, R. Sh., Avetisyan, N. A. *et al.* (1962). *Isv. Akad. Nauk. armyan. S.S.R. Biol. Nauki*, **15**, 12–24.

Penard, E. (1902). "Faune rhizopodique du Bassin du Léman," 714 pp. Kündig, Geneva.

Pfennig, N. (1958). Arch. *Mikrobiol.* **31**, 206–216.

Precht, H. (1936). *Zoöl. Anz.* **115**, 217–218.

Reich, K. (1933). *Arch. Protistenk.* **79**, 76–98.

Reich, K. (1948). *Physiol. Zoöl.* **21**, 390–412.

Remy, P. (1928). *Ann. Parasitol. Paris* **6**, 419–430.

Reynolds, B. D. (1936). *J. Parasitol.* **22**, 48–53.

Rosa, K. (1957). *Přirodov. Sb. ostrav. Kraje* **18**, 17–75.

Rosa, K. (1962). *Acta Univ. Carol. Bidogica Suppl. 1962*, 7–30.

Rouatt, J. W., Katznelson, H. and Payne, T. M. B. (1960). *Proc. Soil Sci. Soc. Am.* **24**, 271–273.

Russell, E. J. and Hutchinson, H. B. (1909). *J. agric. Sci. Camb*, **3**, 111–144.

Russell, E. W. (1961). "Soil Conditions and Plant Growth." 688 pp., 9th Ed. Longmans, Green and Co., London.

Sandon, H. (1927). "Composition and Distribution of the Protozoan Fauna of the Soil," 237 pp. Oliver and Boyd, Edinburgh.

Sandon, H. (1928). *Nat. Hist. Wicken Fen* **4**, 366–370.

Sandon, H. (1932). *Publs Fac. Sci. Egypt. Univ.*, No. 1, 187 pp. Misr-Sokkar Press, Cairo.

Schönborn, W. (1962a). *Limnologica* **1**, 111–182.

Schönborn, W. (1962b). *Limnologica* **1**, 231–254.

Schönborn, W. (1963). *Limnologica* **1**, 315–321.

Schönborn, W. (1964). *Limnologica* **2**, 321–335.

Schönborn, W. (1965). *In* "Progress in Protozoology," London (1965), pp. 120–121. Excerpta Medica Foundation, Amsterdam.

Shilova, E. I. and Kondrat'eva, K. B. (1955). *Vest. Leningrad Univ.* **4**, 17–24.

Singh, B. N. (1941a). *Ann. appl. Biol.* **28**, 52–64.

Singh, B. N. (1941b). *Ann. appl. Biol.* **28**, 65–73.

Singh, B. N. (1942a). *Ann. appl. Biol.* **29**, 18–22.

Singh, B. N. (1942b). *Nature, Lond.* **149**, 169.

Singh, B. N. (1945). *Br. J. exp. Path.* **26**, 316–325.

Singh, B. N. (1946). *Ann. appl. Biol.* **33**, 112–119.

Singh, B. N. (1947). *J. gen. Microbiol.* **1**, 361–367.

Singh, B. N. (1948). *J. gen. Microbiol.* **2**, 8–14.

Singh, B. N. (1949). *J. gen. Microbiol.* **3**, 204–210.

Singh, B. N. (1952). *Phil. Trans. R. Soc. B.* **236**, 405–461.

Singh, B. N. (1960). *Proc. 47th Indian Sci. Congr., Agricultural Section, Bombay, 1960*, pp. 1–14.

Singh, B. N. and Crump, L. M. (1953). *J. gen. Microbiol.* **8**, 421–426.

Singh, B. N., Mathew, S. and Anand, N. (1958). *J. gen. Microbiol.* **19**, 104–111.

Soneda, M. (1962). *Trans. Mycol. Soc. Japan* **3**, 36–42.

Stammer, H. J. (1963). *In* "Progress in Protozoology." (J. Ludvík, J. Lom, and J. Vavra, eds.), pp. 347–363. Czech. Acad. Sci., Prague.

Starkey, R. L. (1938). *Soil Sci.* **45**, 207–249.

Storm, J. and Hutner, S. H. (1953). *Ann. N.Y. Acad. Sci.* **56**, 901–909.

Stout, J. D. (1954). *J. Protozool.* **1**, 211–215.

Stout, J. D. (1955). *Trans. R. Soc. N.Z.* **82**, 1165–1188.

Stout, J. D. (1956a). *J. Protozool.* **3**, 28–30.

Stout, J. D. (1956b). *J. Protozool.* **3**, 31–32.

Stout, J. D. (1956c). *Ecology* **37**, 178–191.

Stout, J. D. (1958). *N.Z. Jl. agric. Res.* **1**, 974–984.

Stout, J. D. (1960). *N.Z. Jl. agric. Res.* **3**, 237–244.

Stout, J. D. (1961). *N.Z. Jl. Sci.* **4**, 740–752.

Stout, J. D. (1962). *J. Soil Sci.* **13**, 314–320.

Stout, J. D. (1963). *J. Anim. Ecol.* **32**, 281–287.

Stout, J. D. (1965). *In* "Progress in Protozoology," London (1965), p. 119. Excerpta Medica Foundation, Amsterdam.

Szabó, I., Marton, M., Szabólcs, I. and Varga, L. (1959). *Acta. agron. hung.* **9**, 9–39.

Taylor, C. B. (1936). *Proc. R. Soc. B.* **119**, 269–295.

Telegdy-Kovats, L. de (1928). *Kiserl. Közl.* **31**, 223–231.

Telegdy-Kovats, L. de (1932). *Ann. appl. Biol.* **19**, 65–86.

Thimann, K. V. and Commoner, B. (1940). *J. Gen. Physiol.* **23**, 333–341.

Thomas, R. (1959). *P-V. Soc. Linn. Bordeaux* **97**, 1–27.

Thomas, R. (1960). *Bull. Soc. Pharm. Bordeaux* **99**, 13–22.

Thornton, H. G. (1956). *Proc. R. Soc. B.* **145**, 364–374.

Thornton, H. G. and Crump, L. M. (1952). *Rep. Rothamsted exp. Stn. 1952*, 164–172.

Thornton, H. G. and Meiklejohn, J. (1957). *A. Rev. Microbiol.* **11**, 123–148.

Tracey, M. V. (1955). *Nature, Lond.* **175**, 815.

Tribe, H. T. (1961). *Soil Sci.* **92**, 61–77.

Varga, L. (1935a). *Zentbl. Bakt. ParasitKde II*, **93**, 32–38.

Varga, L. (1935b). *Zentbl. Bakt. ParasitKde II*, **93**, 128–137.

Varga, L. (1936). *Annls. Inst. Pasteur, Paris* **56**, 101–123.

Varga, L. (1956). *Magy. tudom. Akad. Agrártud. Osztal. Közl.* **9**, 57–69.

Varga, L. (1958). *Agrokém. Talajt.* **7**, 393–400.

Varga, L. (1959). *Acta zool. hung.* **4**, 443–478.

Varga, L. (1960). *Agrokém. Talajt.* **9**, 237–244.

Volz, P. (1929). *Arch. Protistenk.* **68**, 349–408.

Volz, P. (1951). *Zool. Ja. Abt. Syst. Oekol.* **79**, 514–566.

Volz, P. (1964). *Verh. Deutsch. Zool. Ges. Kiel 1964*, 522–532.

Wagtendonk, W. J. van (1955a). *In* "Biochemistry and Physiology of Protozoa." (S. H. Hutner and A. Lwoff, eds.), Vol. II. pp. 57–84. Academic Press, New York.

Wagtendonk, W. J. van (1955b). *In* "Biochemistry and Physiology of Protozoa." (S. H. Hutner and A. Lwoff, eds.), Vol. II, pp. 85–90. Academic Press, New York.

Waksman, S. A. (1930). *Fortschr. naturw. Forsch.* **10**, 1–116.

Wang, C. C. (1928). *J. Morph.* **46**, 431–478.

Warren, E. (1932). *Ann. Natal Mus.* **7**, 1–53.

Watson, J. M. (1944). *Jl. R. microsc. Soc.* **64**, 31–67.

Weber, A. P., Zwillenberg, L. O. and Van der Laan, P. A. (1952). *Nature, Lond.* **169**, 834–835.

Wenzel, F. (1953). *Arch. Protistenk.* **99**, 70–141.

Wilcke, D. E. (1963). *Z. Acker-u. PflBau.* **118**, 1–44.

Willmer, E. N. (1956). *J. exp. Biol.* **33**, 583–603.

Willmer, E. N. (1963). *Advmt. Sci., Lond.* **20**, 119–127.

Zaher, F., Isenberg, H. D., Rosenfeld, M. H. and Schatz, A. (1953). *J. Parasitol.* **39**, 33–37.

Chapter 7

Nematoda

C. OVERGAARD NIELSEN

Department of Zoology
Copenhagen University, Copenhagen, Denmark

I. INTRODUCTION

The study of soil and plant nematodes has developed greatly in the last 20 years and has been accompanied by a sizeable increase in the number of nematologists studying plant parasitic forms. In this period a great many new species have been described from all parts of the world, many old descriptions have been revised and numerous life-histories and morphological and biological details made known. However, the study of all aspects of soil, marine and animal and plant parasitic nematodes has not been integrated into a coherent subject. One reason for this is that most nematologists have been too preoccupied with applied problems relating to nematode parasites of man, livestock, agricultural, forestry or garden products to give much time to studying basic problems of nematode physiology, biochemistry, cytology, genetics and ecology. Moreover, University Departments of Zoology have neglected nematodes in their teaching and research.

Recent progress in nematology has been accompanied by several textbooks and reviews and by a helpful practice of concentrating papers on soil and plant nematology in few journals. Christie (1959) and Thorne (1961) published textbooks on nematology emphasizing practical work with plant parasites including the recognition of economically important species, symptoms of damage, and control measures. Sasser and Jenkins (1960) edited a series of papers, by several specialists, dealing with most aspects of nematology.

This review deals mainly with aspects of recent developments in nematode ecology not covered in recent textbooks and reviews.

II. FUNDAMENTAL PROBLEMS OF NEMATODE TAXONOMY

Details or principles of nematode taxonomy are not presented here, but taxonomy cannot be left out altogether because it often enters problems that seem to be detached from the taxon. Goodey (1963) gives a thorough introduction to the subject and much detailed information for the advanced student. Even so, monographs of genera and many papers describing new species are still indispensable because nematode taxonomy is developing so rapidly.

For plant parasitic nematodes, Mai and Lyon (1960) is a great help to the beginner.

The class Nematoda has successfully colonized almost all major habitats. There are about 10,000 known species and the number increases daily. Of these only about 2,000 soil inhabiting species concern us, the rest are parasitic in vertebrates or invertebrates or occur in the sea. Many non-marine, free-living nematodes occur chiefly or only in freshwater, and these cannot be distinguished sharply from soil nematodes (see below).

Although little more than 1,000 species of true soil nematodes are known their taxonomy presents many difficulties. Some of the more important reasons are as follows:

(1) Few useful taxonomic characters are known at the species level, and of these absolute and relative measurements are important. But measurements vary and the range of intraspecific variation is unknown and can rarely be assessed in natural populations. The conscientious nematologist is often unable to name specimens when he has few or only one.

(2) Soil nematodes are small, transparent thread-like animals. Good optical equipment is essential because the taxonomic characters of nematodes are often subtle structures or minute organs.

(3) Published descriptions of species vary in quality because (a) some omit descriptions of characters that have since been recognized as taxonomically important, (b) often the range of variation of measurements and indices is not stated and, when it is, the total variation within the species is unknown, and (c) type specimens often do not exist or have deteriorated so countless synonyms have arisen and are only gradually being discarded.

However, in recent years much has been done to improve taxonomic standards using new techniques. Further progress will depend on the following factors:

(1) Improvement in the detailed description of new species (Goodey, 1959).

(2) Revision of a number of the more important and difficult genera. The plant parasites have attracted most attention, but several genera of freeliving nematodes have also been thoroughly revised, e.g. the genus *Plectus* by Maggenti (1961).

(3) Enlargement of nematode collections now being built up in various parts of the world. This and increasing international contact has made it easier to compare material and identify specimens of different origin.

(4) Development of culture techniques for freeliving and plant-parasitic nematodes in the laboratory. This is an important advance because it makes a rational study of intraspecific variation possible.

(5) Cytological study of nematodes which will give information on chromosome numbers, polyploidy, the occurrence of parthenogenesis, etc., and may put nematode taxa on a more reliable basis.

Until valid taxonomic categories have been established (by quantitative study of intraspecific variation of the few distinctive characters that can be used) to separate species, several genera, such as *Tylenchus, Ditylenchus, Helicotylenchus, Pratylenchus Aphelenchoides* and *Rhabditis*, will remain difficult, and the suggested species little more than a provisional list used for sorting out samples of nematodes. A study of the variation of many individuals descended from a single female and exposed to widely different environmental conditions is needed. Some genera can, with difficulty, be cultured in quantity, but so far little has been done on these lines. Allen (1952), Dropkin (1953) and Triantaphyllou and Sasser (1960) have worked with the genus *Meloidogyne*, and von Weerdt (1958) with the species *Radopholus similis*. In several genera, e.g. *Meloidogyne* and *Ditylenchus*, visible characters and quantitative measures and indices may be inadequate to distinguish genuine species, and biochemical and serological techniques will have to be applied before progress can be made.

III. GEOGRAPHICAL DISTRIBUTION

Although nematode taxonomy is inadequate, it seems reasonably certain that many nematodes are widely distributed. Allen (1955) gives examples of species of *Tylenchorhynchus* occurring in Europe, and the U.S.A.: Maggenti (1961) has examined specimens of *Plectus parientinus* Bastian from Hawaii, several states of continental United States, the Antarctic, Australia, Canada, England, Ireland and the Netherlands. This species, like several others, is truly cosmopolitan, but for most of them all the specimens have not been identified by one person.

IV. NEMATODE ECOLOGY

The growing interest in nematodes shown by applied biologists has been accompanied by a declining interest amongst ecologists. Consequently, there is still little known about nematode ecology, although knowledge of the biology of plant-parasitic nematodes has increased greatly in recent years. Nielson (1949) summarized information up to 1949 and Winslow (1960) discussed later contributions. The present review reappraises nematode ecology, emphasizing their physiology. Aspects that have received little attention since 1949 are not considered in detail. Attention is drawn to papers on nematode biology that relate to the ecology of nematodes and emphasis is given to work not discussed in detail by Winslow (1960) or that has been done since. An attempt has been made to indicate where knowledge of important aspects of nematode ecology is lacking. Aspects of the biology of plant parasites that are relevant to soil nematodes generally are considered as well as freeliving nematodes.

A. GENERAL BIOLOGY OF NEMATODES

Although the general biology of freeliving and plant-parasitic nematodes has received much attention (Winslow, 1960), many aspects of their biology remain obscure, and no general synthesis has been possible. Within recent years nematodes have become laboratory animals. This is an important milestone because it makes large-scale experimental work possible by providing large numbers or amounts of homogeneous material. Dougherty (1960), who with his associates has contributed much to this development, gives a detailed survey of the techniques and their uses. Freeliving species, particularly microbial feeders, were used in the first large-scale attempts to get mass cultures. Monoxenic culture of several species is now possible and *Caenorhabditis briggsae*, including a mutant *C. elegans* (two strains) and *Rhabditis anomala* have been maintained in axenic culture for several years.

Axenic culture of plant parasitic species is not yet possible but several species can be maintained in xenic or monoxenic culture. Since Dougherty's survey, plant tissue cultures have been used successfully as a medium for culturing plant-parasitic nematodes. Mountain (1955) cultured *Pratylenchus minyus*, Darling; Faulkner and Wallendal (1957) cultured *Ditylenchus destructor*; Peacock (1959) cultured *Meloidogyne incognita*; and Krusberg (1960, 1961) cultured *Ditylenchus dipsaci*. Monoxenic culture of representatives of three such different genera makes it possible to study their intraspecific variation as a first step towards solving problems of their taxonomy. Culture techniques have also opened up the study of several fundamental ecological problems such as host–parasite relationships (Mountain, 1960a, b, c), the nature of host specificity, and other physiological and biochemical problems (Krusberg, 1960a, b).

The wide variation in sex ratio among different species and among different populations of the same species, ranging from a large excess of males to an even larger excess of females, is a well-known feature of nematode populations and affects them greatly.

Nigon (1949) studied the cytology and sex determination in five species of *Rhabditis*, one *Panagrolaimus* sp. and one *Diplogaster* sp. and demonstrated great cytological differences between such closely related species. Mulvey (1960a, b, c) and Hirschmann (1960) have reviewed work on the cytology of reproduction and sex determination. The latest addition to the various types of nematode reproduction known to occur is the environmental determination of the sex ratio. Ellenby (1954) found the sex ratio in *Heterodera rostochiensis* varied with the population density and the location of the population in the host root system. Lindhardt (1961) found a similar increase in the proportion of males in *Heterodera major* as population density increased. Triantaphyllou (1960) and Triantaphyllou and Hirschmann (1960) described and analysed an example of sex reversal caused by environmental factors. This important work helps in studying intersexes, best known from *Ditylenchus triformis* studied by Hirschmann and Sasser (1955).

With improved optical equipment and techniques, several different types of nematode sense organs have recently been detected. However, their function is unknown and nematologists are forced to conclude, with Wallace (1960), "To sum up the work on orientation in nematodes it can be said that there is strong evidence for the occurrence of chemotaxis, galvanotaxis, and thermotaxis, but quantitative evidence from controlled experiments is lacking. There is little evidence that the other types of orientation occur at all."

B. WATER RELATIONS OF NEMATODES

The oxygen consumption of nematodes is about 1,000 ml./kg/hr (Nielsen 1949), which is fairly high. Special respiratory organs are absent but, because nematodes are small and threadlike, sufficient oxygen for respiration can diffuse through the cuticle even in relatively large species, such as *Mononchus*, with a relatively high respiratory metabolism. Because their cuticle is permeable to water (the rate of water loss is similar to that from a free water surface), nematodes are restricted to habitats with a saturated atmosphere. Their osmotic relations, which have been little studied, are summarized by Brand (1960).

The microhabitat of soil nematodes is primarily the labyrinth system of the soil and the water films extending over the soil particles and nematodes. For some species it includes plant roots, either by a superficial association or by actual penetration. The closely applied leaves in buds and the air spaces in plants are habitats physically resembling soil. Nematodes are therefore typical members of the interstitial fauna of soil, along with protozoa, rotifers, gastrotrichs, turbellarians and tardigrades.

Direct observation of nematodes in soil is almost impossible. Wallace (1959a) studied the movement of *Heterodera schachtii* and *Aphelenchoides ritzemabosi* in water films. They differ greatly in habit and habitat. Both move by undulatory propulsion. *Aphelenchoides* usually moves by crawling in thin films and by swimming in films thicker than the diameter of its body. The two types of locomotion merge in films of intermediate thickness. Wallace defines the condition for maximum speed in a shallow uniform film (absence of lateral slip). However, the natural environment of nematodes is more complicated. First, ultra-thin films alternating with water pouches where soil particles meet cause spatial variation of the forces exerted by surface tension on moving nematodes. Second, particle size varies; and third, other geometric features of the soil are not standard. Consequently, Wallace's model cannot be applied directly to individual nematodes moving in their natural environment, but it contributes much to fundamental knowledge of nematode movement. The ability of nematodes to swim in a deep water film depends greatly on their activity and probably on their length and shape also.

Wallace (1958a, b, c) also analysed the importance of the moisture content and geometry of the environment for migration of *Heterodera schachtii* larvae in soil. Speed was greatest in pores of 30–60 μ diameter, which corresponds to a particle size of 150–250 μ. In channels appreciably wider than 100 μ, the diameter of the nematodes, there is less restriction to lateral movement and a corresponding reduction of forward movement. Nematodes seem unable to pass through pore necks appreciably narrower than their own diameter (pores less than 20 μ prevent movement). Nematodes scarcely disturb the surrounding soil particles, so they are restricted to the existing soil pores. The water content also influences movement in soil and nematodes move faster when relatively large amounts of water are retained where soil particles meet, while the bulk of the pore space is empty except for the thin water films covering the soil particles. This condition corresponds to the steep section of the log suction/moisture content curve. In most natural soils this part of the curve is less steep and the pores empty less dramatically than in artificial soils made from graded particles.

Wallace (1958b, c, 1959b, c, 1960) discussed the movement of nematodes in relation to water content, particle size, temperature, body length, etc., and (1955a, b) the influence of the moisture regime on the emergence of larvae from cysts of *Heterodera schachtii*.

Undoubtedly soil moisture also influences the survival and distribution of nematodes, although this has been little studied. The amount of water needed to support nematode activity should be studied.

The water content of a soil fluctuates, and is determined by soil type, rainfall, percolation and evaporation. Its availability to soil organisms is determined by the capillary potential, which is expressed by the pF scale of soil moisture (chapter 1).

The percentage of water held at a given pF differs for different soils. Three soils studied by the author had the following water contents (in % of dry weight) at pF 2·7: a coarse sandy soil 3%, a similar soil with increased organic matter content 9%, and an organic soil about 52%. Because these percentages represent water of the same *availability* to the organisms it is clear that water content, expressed merely as a percentage, has no biological meaning when different soils are compared.

Activity of nematodes is confined to the lower part of the pF scale, from pF 0 to some point between pF 2·7 and 4·0. Unpublished data of C. A. Nielsen, suggests that the upper limit is within the range pF 3 to 4. The exact point of desiccation would be of considerable interest. It is likely to be almost identical for all soil nematodes and, therefore, generally applicable when considering nematode activity in relation to soil moisture.

Dehydration of nematodes is likely to occur when the pF is between 3 and 4. In the central part of Denmark (NW Sjalland, N Fyn, Samsø and the eastern-most part of Jylland) the rainfall is rather low, approximately 500 to 525 mm annually, the soils are sandy, and the upper few centimetres of the soil dry out to pF 3 to 4 several times during most summers. This need not affect the vegetation seriously because the plants can get water from deeper horizons, but the soil fauna is very much affected because it is most abundant in the upper 1 to 5 cm. of the soil (Nielsen, 1955, 1961). Similar situations may occur frequently and in shallow soils or thin moss cushions covering stones, rocks, tree trunks, and thatched roofs the nematode fauna is exposed to violent fluctuations in the moisture regime.

A study of the species composition of the fauna shows that anabiosis is ecologically important when there is risk of desiccation. Unfortunately, the ability to survive complete dehydration has not been studied systematically in nematodes, although several species can survive repeated desiccations without harm. Wallace (1962) dehydrated *Ditylenchus dipsaci* in an atmosphere of 50% relative humidity (corresponding to pF 6) for 34 days. About 90% of the animals regained activity when immersed in water. The power of moss-dwelling nematodes (and rotifers, tardigrades and protozoa) to survive desiccation is well known (May, 1942; Rahm, 1923), and there is evidence that desiccation also affects the species composition of soil faunas.

The following list of species, based on my own samples, shows in group (1), abundant species which have been found in habitats which are *known* to be subjected to desiccation beyond (approximately) pF 4 several times in most summers, and in group (2), abundant species which have only been found in soils which never dry up.

It is suggested that all members of group (1) can survive desiccation, but not necessarily to the same extent, because the list has been compiled from several sample sites, and not necessarily in all developmental stages. The less abundant species may be less abundant because desiccation affects them more, but if their eggs were fully drought resistant, sparse populations might survive. This is well known to occur with enchytraeid worms (Nielsen, 1955).

A study of the biology of freeliving nematodes in thin moss cushions exposed to sun and wind on a thatched roof also illustrates the effects of desiccation.

In summer (June–August), the cushions dry up completely every day if there is no rain and they are usually wetted by dew at night. The side of the roof facing south has cushions of *Tortula ruralis* 2–3 cm thick (density approx. 30 shoots cm²), a spongy litter layer at the bottom approx. 1 cm and, sticking out of this, shoots 1–1·5 cm tall which do not touch appreciably. The side facing north has cushions of *Ceratodon purpureus* 3–4 cm thick (approx. 135 shoots/cm²), a spongy litter layer approx. 2 cm thick and shoots 1–1·5 cm tall, so densely set that they touch. There are also scattered cushions of *Ceratodon* on the side facing south.

Table I summarizes the climate affecting the cushions and gives the amplitudes of temperature and relative humidity, and the number of hours when the saturation deficit was less than 5 mm Hg for a typical 24-hour period in July. The measurements were made with micro-climate recorders (Krogh, 1940) at the surface of the moss cushions at 1 cm depth and at 5 cm depth, i.e. in the thatched roof well below the base of the cushions.

The climate on the side facing south is much more extreme than on the north side for, in the 24-hour period studied, the relative humidity in the cushions never reached 100% during the night (due to absence of dewfall). The readings at 1 cm depth, where most of the fauna occurs, compare the

Group (1)	Group (2)
Cephalobus persegnis Bastian	*Teratocephalus palustris* de Man
Cephalobus nanus de Man	*Aphanolaimus attentus* de Man
Cervidellus vexilliger (de Man) Thorne	*Bastiania gracilis* de Man
Acrobeles ciliatus v. Linstow	*Prismatolaimus intermedius* (Bütschli) Filipjev
Teratocephalus terrestris (Bütschli) de Man	*Punctodora ratzeburgensis* (Linstow) Filipjev
Teratocephalus crassidens de Man	
Tylenchus davainei Bastian	*Achromadora dubia* (Bütschli) Micol.
Tylenchus filiformis Bütschli*	*Ethmolaimus pratensis* de Man
Tylenchorhynchus dubius (Bütschli) Filipjev	*Ironus ignavus* Bastian
	Trilobus allophysis (Steiner) Micol.
Ditylenchus dipsaci (Kühn) Filipjev	*Dorylaimus limnophilus* de Man
Ecphyadophora tenuissima de Man	*Dorylaimus stagnalis* Dujardin
Aphelenchoides parietinus (Bastian) Steiner	*Dorylaimus centrocercus* de Man
	Dorylaimus brigdamensis de Man
Plectus parietinus Bastian	*Dorylaimus longicaudatus* Bütschli
Plectus rhizophilus de Man	*Dorylaimus rhopalocercus* de Man
Plectus longicaudatus Bütschli	
Plectus cirratus Bastian	
Anaplectus granulosus (Bastian) de Coninck & Schn. Stekh.	
Wilsonema auriculatum (Bütschli) Cobb	
Wilsonema otophorum (de Man) Cobb	
Rhabdolaimus terrestris de Man	
Monhystera vulgaris de Man†	
Monhystera villosa (Bütschli)	
Prismatolaimus dolichurus de Man	
Mononchus papillatus (Bastian) Cobb	
Dorylaimus carteri Bastian	
Dorylaimus obtusicaudatus Bastian	
Tylencholaimus mirabilis? (Bütschli) de Man	
Alaimus primitivus de Man	

* The species is ill-defined and may represent more than one genuine species.

climates best; the south side had only 6 hours whereas the north side had 20 hours with a saturation deficit of less than 5 mm Hg.

Table II shows that this difference is associated with a great number of species in cushions on the north side. The reason for the greater number of individuals in the cushions on the south side is not known.

It seems that *Plectus rhizophilus* is the most drought resistant freeliving nematode on the roof. It is also the most drought resistant freeliving nematode known to the author. When habitats characterized by violent temperature fluctuations and frequent desiccation are examined (e.g. shallow moss cushions on stones and tree stems in the open, shallow layers of soil on stones

TABLE I

Climatic extremes in moss cushions on thatched roof during one 24 hour period in July (no dew fall during night)

Orientation of roof and depth (cm)	Temperature (°c)			Relative humidity (%)		Saturation deficit < 5 mm (hr)
	max.	min.	amplitude	max.	min.	
South 0	46	7	39	100	18	12
North 0	43	9	34	100	32	17
South 1	39	12	27	84	22	6
North 1	31	11	20	100	64	20
South 5	29	15	14	78	36	2
North 5	25	13	12	100	100	24

TABLE II

Density of fauna (no./cm²) in Tortula and Ceratodon cushions on south- and north-facing sides of thatched roof

	South-facing		North-facing
	Tortula	Ceratodon	Ceratodon
Plectus rhizophilus	200	330	51
Plectus cirratus	—	—	47
Aphelenchoides parietinus	—	—	8
Paraphelenchus pseudoparietinus	—	—	1
Prionchulus muscorum	—	—	1
Rotifers	150	230	62
Tardigrades*	40	95	2

* Three species occur, *Hypsibius oberhauseri*, *Macrobiotus hufelandii*, and *Milnesium tardigradum*, in order of decreasing abundance.

and rocks), the nematode population is often a monoculture of this species. Continuous studies of the populations on the thatched roof have shown that all developmental stages of this species can survive frequent, severe, and prolonged dehydration.

It exploits this particular habitat by undertaking extensive migrations up and down the moss stems. Sampling at night or during showers showed that most of the population was concentrated in the "canopy" of the moss cushion, whilst sampling during dry periods of the day showed a concentration in the "litter" layer. The revival after hydration lasts only a few minutes. The same applies to the tardigrades, rotifers and protozoa inhabiting the south side of the roof. All are species which are exceptionally well adapted to exploit this extreme habitat.

The other species listed in Table II, *Plectus cirratus, Aphelenchoides parietinus, Paraphelenchus pseudoparietinus, Prionchulus muscorum*, and a few others from similar situations: *Monhystera vulgaris, Wilsonema auriculatum, Monhystera villosa*, and the ill-defined *Tylenchus filiformis* must also be among the species of freeliving nematodes best adapted to survive desiccation.

Stalfelt (1937) points out that summer showers can *wet* moss cushions and make them turn a fresh green colour, but they are not wet long enough for assimilation to start, so the mosses spend the summer almost quiescent. This suggests that the nematodes can exploit short wet periods better than the mosses which are their habitat.

A systematic study of drought resistance in freeliving and plant parasitic nematodes would throw much light on the ability of different species to colonize habitats with contrasting climates. No nematodes are active when water is absent, but species which tolerate frequent dehydration probably have a better chance of building up dense populations in droughty areas than less resistant species. This factor may have had a selective effect on the nematode faunas of particular habitats.

Artificial irrigation is increasingly used in agriculture to maintain water supplies for plant growth during periods of drought. This is likely to affect nematode populations by creating conditions where species which are not drought resistant can increase in numbers. Freeliving nematodes may respond first, but because plant parasite numbers are also affected by the growth of their host plants artificial irrigation could affect them also, and a study of drought resistance in nematodes may be economically desirable. Already there is evidence that high water tables or irrigation increases soil populations of some plant nematodes such as *H. schactii* in the Fenlands of Britain and elsewhere, and *H. rostochiensis* under irrigation.

C. NUTRITION OF NEMATODES

Nielsen (1949) suggested that nematodes might be divided into 3 ecological categories:

(1) species depending on liquid food (largely cell contents and plant juices got by piercing roots and cell walls): Tylenchida and Dorylaimoidea;

(2) species depending on particulate food (largely bacteria and small algae): the majority of freeliving nematodes except those belonging to groups (1) and (3).

(3) species feeding on other relatively large organisms (e.g. protozoa, nematodes, rotifers, etc.): *Mononchus* (s.l.), *Choanolaimus, Tripyla*.

To this grouping was added a fourth category (comprising *Monhystera* and *Prismatolaimus*) with unknown food preferences.

Although no comprehensive studies have been published the food of nematodes has received much attention during recent years. Banage (1963) proposes a classification into (1) plant feeders (Tylenchida, among which are some fungal feeders), (2) microbial feeders, (3) miscellaneous feeders (Dorylaimoidea), and (4) predators.

The main difference between this classification and mine is that the *Dorylaimoidea*, which I thought fed largely on algae, are now supposed to have a more varied diet. Although Hollis (1957) succeeded in culturing *Dorylaimus ettersbergensis* on algae and algae certainly play an important part in the food of *Dorylaimus*, there is also much evidence that they have a rather varied diet (including bacteria, protozoa, nematodes, plant roots, fungi, etc.), so Banage's classification is preferable. However, the Dorylaimoidea also include apparently obligate plant-parasitic species (*Longidorus, Xiphinema, Trichodorus*).

Although the precise feeding habits of *Monhystera* and *Prismatolaimus* seem to be unknown it is very probable that these two important genera are microbial feeders, although I have watched a marine species of *Monhystera* ingest large quantities of a microscopic alga.

It has recently been realized that the Tylenchida comprise a fairly large number of species which are obligate or facultative fungus feeders that get their food by piercing fungal hyphae with their stylet.

Two important features emerge from all known details of nematode nutrition:

(1) the food of nematodes seems, invariably, to be "protoplasm," be it obtained as cell contents, plant sap, the contents of fungal hyphae, algae, bacteria, actinomycetes, protozoa, or other animals;

(2) the dead organic matter and plant remains of the soil play a considerable role as a substratum for the organisms on which nematodes feed, but do not form part of the nematode diet. Hirschmann (1952) found *Rhabditis strongyloides* could not reach sexual maturity if the bacteria offered as food had been killed by exposure to low temperatures.

Although "protoplasm" may vary considerably in composition it seems that few animals have a better defined feeding biology than nematodes. The basic chemical variation between different nematode foods is largely restricted to differences in the relative abundance of proteins, carbohydrates and lipids and to differences in the total concentration of organic matter. Because the substances typically associated with cell walls and skeletal structures (cellulose, lignin, chitin, etc.) are usually not ingested or are only present in negligible amounts, most of the food is presumably easily assimilated and the proportion utilized correspondingly high.

Consequently, if the respiratory metabolism and gross composition of the food of nematodes is known, it is possible to estimate approximately the amount of, say, bacteria, necessary to support a given population of bacterial feeders. Although the accuracy of such estimates is unknown, fairly realistic figures might be obtained. In this respect nematodes are a particularly favourable group to study because they are aquatic and little energy is used for locomotion; when completely narcotized by urethane their oxygen consumption usually falls by less than 10% (Nielsen, 1949). Consequently differences in respiratory rate resulting from different levels of activity will be proportionately smaller and insignificant compared with the total metabolism of the population. This is not so in most other soil animals (Nielsen, 1961).

D. Size and Metabolic Activity of Nematode Populations

Winslow (1960) discusses recent estimates of nematode populations. Figures that are generally valid are not available. The number of nematodes in two adjacent samples from an apparently homogeneous field may differ by a factor of 100, so hundreds of samples are needed to estimate accurately the population of even small areas. Only orders of magnitude can be discussed, and most authors now seem to agree that a few million nematodes per square metre are usual. However, little is known about the factors that affect nematode abundance. Although nematodes are aquatic, wet soils do not always contain so many nematodes as might be expected. For example Nielsen (1949) studied two meadows, two moors and a bog (fen) soil and found 0·33 to 1·5 million nematodes/m², whereas ten times as many have been found in several soils with lower and more variable water content. Banage (1963) records slightly higher numbers, although of the same order, from Pennine moorlands. He concludes "it seems that their importance (see Macfadyen, 1957) has been overestimated in the past." Because there are usually few nematodes in acid and permanently wet soil their importance may be relatively small there, and much greater *numbers* have been found in several less extreme situations. Five to ten million individuals/m² may turn out to be an average figure. The most recorded so far are 19 and 20 million/m² in grass fields (Nielsen, 1949), and almost 30 million in an oak forest on mull soil (Volz, 1951) compared with about 12 million in the raw humus of a beech forest. The *biomasses* quoted by Nielsen (l.c.) may be slight over-estimates compared with those of Andrassy (1956), but this does not affect the estimates for *respiration* because the respiratory rates were calculated on the same basis. Consequently if the biomass was over-estimated the respiratory rates would be correspondingly under-estimated.

E. Ecological Significance of Nematodes

Although nematodes seem to feed on "protoplasm" their activity affects the other soil organisms because their food comes from the entire microflora, the microfauna and higher plants. Because of their biomass and metabolism, microbial feeders and plant feeders seem to be the most important groups and may often be 50% of the entire nematode fauna, with plant feeders usually dominant in grass fields or other habitats with dense vegetation and bacterial feeders dominant in forest litter, compost heaps, etc.

Nematodes cannot participate in the *direct* decomposition of dead plant matter nor can they significantly affect the mechanical or physical properties of the soil.

Their ecological importance is related to: (i) primary production (plant and algal feeders), (ii) primary decomposition (microbial feeders), and (iii) higher consumer levels (predators).

1. Nematodes and primary production

This has important applied aspects and many examples of complete or partial crop failure resulting from attacks of plant-parasitic nematodes could be given. Obligate plant parasites are the important agents in this connection and the cost of their damage and its effect on yield can often be calculated. Except for plant pests, however, the chief damage caused by nematodes may be secondary effects such as bacterial infection through the lesions caused by feeding, or when nematodes act as virus vectors.

Although crop losses caused by nematodes are important economically and so receive much attention, they may be small compared with the combined effect of all nematode species on the growth and yield of plants (primary production).

2. Nematodes and primary decomposition

Primary decomposition starts with the living plant or with dead plant remains. The first has been discussed; the second will be discussed in relation to the decomposition of various kinds of leaf litter produced annually.

Various chemical compounds are extensively withdrawn from leaves before they fall, so shed leaves differ chemically from those still living attached. This applies to several inorganic compounds, amino acids and other nitrogenous compounds (see, e.g., Olsen, 1948). However, some trees shed their leaves before any extensive re-absorption takes place. The newly shed leaf consists mainly of structural polysaccharides (cellulose, xylan, pectin, etc.), lignin, and inorganic substances.

There is little evidence that soil and litter invertebrates possess the enzymes needed to split these products (Nielsen, 1962), although a few, such as snails, may do so. On the other hand there is evidence that animals play some part in this aspect of primary decomposition.

There is abundant evidence that the soil microflora as a whole possess all the necessary enzymes for primary decomposition of litter and actually does most of it. Although some of the litter fauna may help, there is evidence that primary decomposition attributed to soil and litter invertebrates is brought about by enzymes secreted by their intestinal flora.

Consequently it seems that the ecological importance of nematodes that are microbial feeders must lie in their effect on the total microbial activity of the substratum through predation on the microflora. Whether this predation would promote or delay microbial activity or change the species composition of the bacterial flora is not known. The relationship between bacterial feeders among the nematodes and the activity of the bacterial flora is of fundamental importance ecologically and needs to be studied.

3. Nematodes and higher consumer levels

Predators occur in most animal groups, and the problems they pose are of the same type. The size of nematodes is such that their prey belongs to the microfauna (protozoa, nematodes, rotifers, small enchytraeids, etc.). It has been proposed to employ nematodes, especially *Mononchus*, in the biological control of plant-parasitic nematodes, but the prospects do not seem very promising.

REFERENCES

Allen, M. W. (1952). *Proc. helm. Soc. Wash.* **19**, 44–51.
Allen, M. W. (1955). *Univ. Calif. Publs. Zool.* **61**, 129–166.
Andrassy, I. (1956). *Acta zool. Budapest*, **2**, 1–15.
Banage, W. B. (1963). *J. Anim. Ecol.* **32**, 133–140.
von Brand, Th. (1960). *In* "Nematology." (Sasser and Jenkins, eds.), pp. 249–256. Univ. N. Carolina Press, Chapel Hill.
Christie, J. R. (1959). "Plant Nematodes, their economics and control." Florida agric. Exp. Stn. Gainsville.
Darling, H. M., Faulkner, L. R. and Wallendal, P. (1957). *Phytopathology*, **47**, 7.
Dougherty, E. D. (1960). *In* "Nematology". (Sasser and Jenkins, eds.), pp. 297–318. Univ. N. Carolina Press, Chapel Hill.
Dropkin, V. H. (1953). *Proc. helminth. Soc. Wash.* **20**, 32–39.
Edney, E. B. (1957). "The Water Relations of Terestrial Arthropods." Cambridge University Press.
Ellenby, C. (1954). *Nature, Lond.* **174**, 1016–1019.
Goodey, J. B. (1959). *Nematologica*, **4**, 211–216.
Goodey, T. (1963). "Soil and Freshwater Nematodes." 2nd Ed. Methuen, London.
Hirschmann, H. (1952). *Zool. Jb.* (*Systematik*), **81**, 313–436.
Hirschmann, H. (1960). *In* "Nematology." (Sasser and Jenkins, eds.), pp. 140–146. Univ. N. Carolina Press, Chapel Hill.
Hirschmann, H. and Sasser, J. N. (1955). *Proc. helminth. Soc. Wash.* **22**, 115–123.
Hollis, J. P. (1957). *Phytopathology*, **47**, 468–473.
Krogh, A. (1940). *Ecology*, **21**, 275–278.
Krusberg, L. R. (1960a). *Phytopathology*, **50**, 9–22.
Krusberg, L. R. (1960b). *Phytopathology*, **50**, 643.
Krusberg, L. R. (1961). *Nematologica*, **6**, 181–200.
Lindhardt, K. *Tidskr. PlAvl*, **64**, 889–896.
Macfadyen, A. (1957). "Animal Ecology, Aims and Methods." Pitman, London.
Macfadyen, A. (1962). *In* "Advances in Ecological Research." (J. B. Cragg, ed.), **1**. pp. 1–34. Academic Press, London and New York.
Maggenti, A. R. (1961a). *Proc. helminth. Soc. Wash.* **28**, 118–130.
Maggenti, A. R. (1961b). *Proc. helminth. Soc. Wash.* **28**, 139–166.
Mai, W. F. and Lyon, H. H. (1960). "Pictorial Key to Genera of Plant Parasitic Nematodes." Dept. Pl. Path. N.Y. St. Coll. Agric. Ithaca.
May, R.-M. (1942). *Bull. Soc. zool. Fr.* **67**, 24–33.
Mountain, W. B. (1955). *Proc. helminth. Soc. Wash.* **22**, 49–52.
Mountain, W. B. (1960a). *In* "Nematology". (Sasser and Jenkins, eds.), pp. 419–421. Univ. N. Carolina Press, Chapel Hill.

Mountain, W. B. (1960b). *In* "Nematology". (Sasser and Jenkins, eds.), pp. 422–425. Univ. N. Carolina Press, Chapel Hill.

Mountain, W. B. (1960c). *In* "Nematology". (Sasser and Jenkins, eds.), pp. 426–431. Univ. N. Carolina Press, Chapel Hill.

Mulvey, R. H. (1960a). *In* "Nematology". (Sasser and Jenkins, eds.), pp. 321–322. Univ. N. Carolina Press, Chapel Hill.

Mulvey, R. H. (1960b). *In* "Nematology". (Sasser and Jenkins, eds.), pp. 323–330. Univ. N. Carolina Press, Chapel Hill.

Mulvey, R. H. (1960c). *In* "Nematology". (Sasser and Jenkins, eds.), pp. 331–335. Univ. N. Carolina Press, Chapel Hill.

Nielsen, C. O. (1948). *Naturv. Skr. Laerde Selsk. Skr.* **1**, 1–98, Arhus.

Nielsen, C. O. (1948). *Natura jutl.* **1**, 273–277.

Nielsen, C. O. (1949). *Natura jutl.* **2**, 1–131.

Nielsen, C. O. (1955). *Oikos*, **6**, 153–169.

Nielsen, C. O. (1961). *Oikos*, **12**, 17–35.

Nielsen, C. O. (1962). *Oikos*, **13**, 200–215.

Nigon, V. (1949). *Annls. Sci. nat. Zool.* **11**, 1–132.

Olsen, C. (1948). *C.r. Trav. Lab. Carlsberg*, **26**, 5.

Oostenbrink, M. (1954). *Meded. LandbHoogesch. OpzoekStns*, Gent **19**, 377–408.

Oostenbrink, M. (1960). *In* "Nematology". (Sasser and Jenkins, eds.), pp. 85–102. Univ. N. Carolina Press, Chapel Hill.

Overgaard, C. (1948). See Nielsen, C. O. (1948).

Peacock, F. C. (1959). *Nematologica*, **4**, 43–55.

Rahm. (1923). *Z. f. allg. Physiol*, **20**, 1–32.

Sasser, J. N. and Jenkins, W. R. (1960) "Nematology" pp. 1–480. Univ. N. Carolina Press, Chapel Hill.

Seinhorst, J. W. (1956). *Nematologica*, **1**, 249–267.

Seinhorst, J. W. (1962). *Nematologica*, **8**, 117–128.

Stalfelt, M. G. (1937). *Svenska SkogsvFör. Tidskr.* 161–195.

Thorne, G. (1961). "Principles of Nematology." McGraw-Hill, New York.

Triantaphyllou, A. C. (1960). *Annls Inst. phytopath. Benaki*, **3**, 12–31.

Triantaphyllou, A. C. and Hirschmann, H. *Annls Inst. phytopath. Benaki*, **3**, 1–11.

Triantaphyllou, A. C. and Sasser. (1960). *Phytopathology*, **50**, 724–735.

Volz, P. (1951). *Zool. Jb. (Systematik)*, **79**, 449–638.

Wallace, H. R. (1955a). *J. Helminth.* **29**, 3–16.

Wallace, H. R. (1955b). *Ann. appl. Biol.* **43**, 477–484.

Wallace, H. R. (1956). *Nature, Lond.* **177**, 287–288.

Wallace, H. R. (1958a). *Ann. appl. Biol.* **46**, 74–85.

Wallace, H. R. (1958b). *Ann. appl. Biol.* **46**, 68–94.

Wallace, H. R. (1958c). *Ann. appl. Biol.* **46**, 662–668.

Wallace, H. R. (1959a). *Ann. appl. Biol.* **47**, 366–370.

Wallace, H. R. (1959b). *Ann. appl. Biol.* **47**, 131–139.

Wallace, H. R. (1959c). *Ann. appl. Biol.* **47**, 350–360.

Wallace, H. R. (1959d). *Nematologica*, **4**, 245–252.

Wallace, H. R. (1960). *Ann. appl. Biol.* **48**, 107–120.

Wallace, H. R. (1961). *Nematologica*, **6**, 222–236.

Wallace, H. R. (1961a). *Helminth. Abstr.* **30**, 1–22.

Wallace, H. R. (1962). *Nematologica*, **7**, 91–101.

van Weerdt, L. G. (1958). *Nematologica*, **3**, 184–196.

Winslow, R. D. (1960). *In* "Nematology". (Sasser and Jenkins, eds.), pp. 341–415. Univ. N. Carolina Press, Chapel Hill.

Chapter 8

The Enchytraeidae

F. B. O'CONNOR

Department of Zoology
University College, London, England

I. INTRODUCTION

A. TAXONOMY AND IDENTIFICATION

The Enchytraeidae are a family of microdrilid oligochaetes most closely related to the Naididae and Tubificidae (Černosvitov, 1937). Anatomically they form a relatively simple and uniform group. Figure 1 shows the typical body form. The smallest species are less than 1 mm long as adults whilst the largest species reach up to 5 cm in length. Because of the relative uniformity of bodily organization throughout the group, generic and specific distinctions must be based on combinations and permutations of a limited number of taxonomic criteria (Černosvitov, 1937). Until recently (Nielsen and Christensen, 1959, 1961, 1963) the taxonomy of the Enchytraeidae was confused. This was due largely to inadequate definitions of many genera and species, combined with the failure of many workers in the past to recognize the wide intraspecific variation for which the group is remarkable. In addition, the attentions of amateurs have added considerably to the confusion; thus of 70 "species" described by the Rev. Hildric Friend only two have survived critical revision (Černosvitov, 1937, 1941; Nielsen and Christensen, 1959).

The most fundamental contribution of Nielsen and Christensen's review of the taxonomy of European species was to establish a standard set of criteria for the description and identification of genera and species. The most clearly

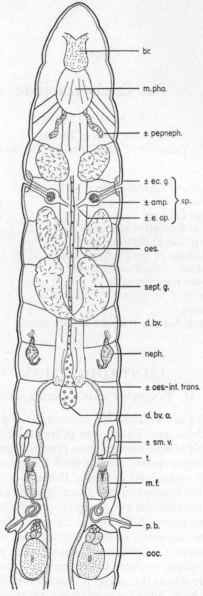

FIG. 1. The typical body form of an enchytraeid worm; ± indicates features which may be present or absent.

amp., ampulla; br., brain; d.bv.o., origin of dorsal blood vessel; d.bv., dorsal blood vessel; ec.g., ectal glands; e.op., ental opening; m.f., male funnel; m.pha., muscular pharynx; neph., nephridia (1 pr/seg.); oes., oesophagus; oes.-int. trans., oesophageal-intestinal transition; ooc., oocytes; p.b., penial bulb; pepneph., peptonephridia; sept.g., septal glands (1–2 pr./seg., 3 prs ± 2); sm.v., seminal vesicles; sp., spermatheca; t., testes.

recognized and widely used criteria are shown in Fig. 1; all these features are visible in live specimens under a light microscope. Nielsen and Christensen (1959, 1961, 1963) now recognize 21 genera containing 141 European and 191 non-European species. In addition they list 75 inadequately described doubtful species. Their key to the European genera is reproduced below. Sufficient illustration for the operation of the key is given in Figs 2 to 8, most of which are taken from Nielsen and Christensen (1959).

Key to the European genera of the Enchytraeidae
(After Nielsen and Christensen, 1959)

I. Setae absent. *Achaeta*, Vejdovsky, 1877.

II. Setae sigmoid, forked at distal end (Fig. 2(a)).
Propappus, Michaelsen 1905.

III. Setae sigmoid, simple with nodules (Fig. 2(b)).

1. Medium or large sized worms. Egg sac present. Post-septal part of nephridium bi-lobed; efferent duct arising between the lobes (Fig. 3(a)). *Mesenchytraeus*, Eisen 1878.

2. Small or very small worms. Egg sac absent. Post-septal part of nephridium entire; efferent duct terminal (Fig. 3(b)).
Černosvitoviella, Nielsen and Christensen 1959.

IV. Setae sigmoid, simple, without nodules (Fig. 2(c)).

1. Dorsal blood vessels originating in the ante-clitellar region.

A. Oesophagus merging gradually into the intestine; oesophageal and intestinal diverticula absent. Spermathecae without opening to oesophagus. Dorsal vessel originating in segment ix. Only nucleate lymphocytes present.
Stercutus, Michaelsen 1888.

B. Sudden transition between oesophagus and intestine at septum vii/viii; oesophageal appendages in segment iv; one or two large intestinal diverticula at septum vii/viii (Fig. 5(a)). Spermathecae attached to the oesophagus (Fig. 6(a)). Dorsal vessel originating from anterior end of intestinal diverticula. Small, hyaline, a-nucleate corpuscles present in addition to nucleate lymphocytes (Fig. 4). *Buchholzia*, Michaelsen 1887.

2. Dorsal vessel originating in intra- or post-clitellar region.

A. Four oseophageal diverticula in segment vi (Fig. 5(b) and 6(b)). Spermathecae merging into a common, narrow canal which communicates with the oseophagus dorsally (Fig. 6(b)). Lymphocytes discoid or slightly oval.
Bryodrilus, Ude 1892.

B. No oesophageal diverticula. Spermathecae free or communicating separately with the oeseophagus. Lymphocytes not discoid.

(a) Spermathecae free (Fig. 6(c)). Seminal vesicle compact. Efferent duct of nephridia long, narrow, arising antero-ventrally (Fig. 3(c)). Genital organs often displaced forwards. Usually white, slender worms inhabiting limnic or wet terrestrial habitats.

Cognettia, Nielsen and Christensen 1959.

(b) Spermathecae attached to oesophagus. Seminal vesicles regularly lobed (Fig. 7). Efferent duct of nephridia short, stout, arising mid- or postero-ventrally (Fig. 3(d)). Genital organs in normal position. Usually reddish or greenish worms inhabiting marine (littoral) habitats.

Lumbricillus, Ørsted 1844 (partim).

(c) Spermathecae attached (in *M. riparia* occasionally free). Seminal vesicle compact—or almost absent. Efferent duct of nephridia terminal (Fig. 3(e)). Genital organs in normal position. Small worms inhabiting marine and limnic littoral or wet terrestrial habitats.

Marionina, Michaelsen 1889 (partim).

V. Setae straight or bent, simple, without nodules (Fig. 2(d), (e)).

1. Salivary glands present.

A. Salivary glands (peptonephridia) unpaired, dorsal (Fig. 8(a)). Spermathecae free. Dorsal vessel arising in segments xii–xiii. Small bisetose species. Dorsal pores absent. Only nucleate lymphocytes present. *Hemienchytraeus*, Černosvitov 1935.

B. Salivary gland paired (Fig. 8(b)). Spermathecae attached to and communicating with the oesophagus (Fig. 6(d)). Dorsal vessel arising behind the clitellum (segments xiv–xxv). Setae 2–16 arranged fanwise within the bundles with the shortest pair at the centre (Fig. 2(d)). Dorsal pores present from segment vii. Nucleate lymphocytes and a-nucleate corpuscles present (Fig. 4). *Fridericia*, Michaelsen 1889.

C. Salivary glands paired (Fig. 8(c)). Spermathecae attached to and communicating with the oesophagus. Dorsal vessel arising in segments xii–xviii. Setae of equal length within the bundles (Fig. 2(e)). Dorsal pores absent. Only nucleate lymphocytes present. *Enchytraeus*, Henle 1837.

2. Salivary glands absent.

A. Sudden transition between oesophagus and intestine. Intestinal diverticula often present at transition.

(a) Dorsal vessel arising well in front of the clitellum (in segment viii or ix) with heart-like pulsating expansions in 2 to 3 segments near origin. 0, 2 or 4 intestinal diverticula in segment vii (Fig. 5(c)). Always more than 2 setae per bundle, with shortest near centre but not arranged pairwise. *Henlea*, Michaelsen 1889.

(b) Dorsal vessel arising in segment xiii; no pulsating heart-like expansions. Two lateral intestinal diverticula in segment vi. Two setae per bundle; dorsal bundles absent in segments viii–xi.

Enchytronia, Nielsen and Christensen 1959.

B. Gradual transition between oesophagus and intestine. Intestinal diverticula absent.

(a) In addition to nucleate lymphocytes, numerous small hyaline a-nucleate corpuscles present.

Hemifridericia, Nielsen and Christensen 1959.

(b) No a-nucleate corpuscles present.

i. Seminal vesicles well developed, regularly or somewhat irregularly lobed (Fig. 7). Ante-septal of nephridia consisting of funnel only (Fig. 3(d)). Blood usually red. *Lumbricillus*, Ørsted 1844 (partim).

ii. Seminal vesicles absent or well developed, compact when present. Ante-septal of nephridium with coils of nephridial canal (Fig. 3(e)) (exceptions: *M. tubifera*, *M. cambrensis*—with spermathecae merging before entering oesophagus). Blood colourless (exception: *M. filiformis*—with intensely white lymphocytes).

Marionina, Michaelsen 1889 (partim).

Thirteen of the 21 genera recognized contain less than 5 species; Table I shows the numbers of species in the remaining 8 genera.

TABLE I

Numbers of species in the most common genera of the Enchytraeidae

Genus	European	Non-European	Species dubiae
Fridericia	33	31	30
Lumbricillus	19	30	11
Marionina	17	25	12
Enchytraeus	13	14	6
Mesenchytraeus	10	45	4
Achaeta	9	1	—
Henlea	8	26	7
Cognettia	5	—	—

B. Distribution

The Enchytraeidae have been recorded from every continent, but because of their sensitivity to drought they reach their greatest abundance in moist temperate climates. In the Tropics they tend to occur at high altitudes. The family has been commonly supposed to be of Arctic origin (Stephenson, 1930); certainly the Enchytraeidae are well represented in the Arctic and

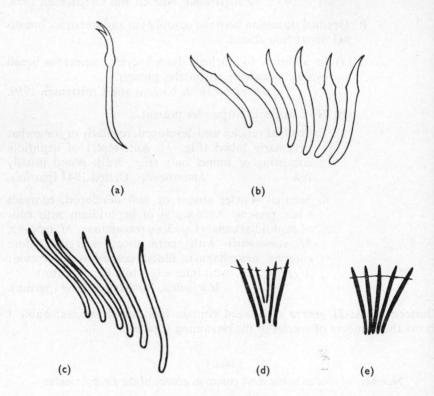

Fig. 2. Setae of (a) *Propappus*, (b) *Mesenchytraeus*, (c) *Lumbricillus*, (d) *Fridericia*, (e) *Enchytraeus*.

North Temperate zones, but the smaller number of records from the southern hemisphere is probably due to a lack of study rather than of Enchytraeidae. They are now known to occur commonly in soils within the Antarctic zone (J. B. Cragg, personal communication). As Nielsen and Christensen (1959) remark, the unsatisfactory state of the taxonomy of the Enchytraeidae, even now only partly resolved, makes a detailed discussion of the geographical distribution of genera and species impracticable at present. Such a study can be expected to throw light upon the origin and evolution of the family.

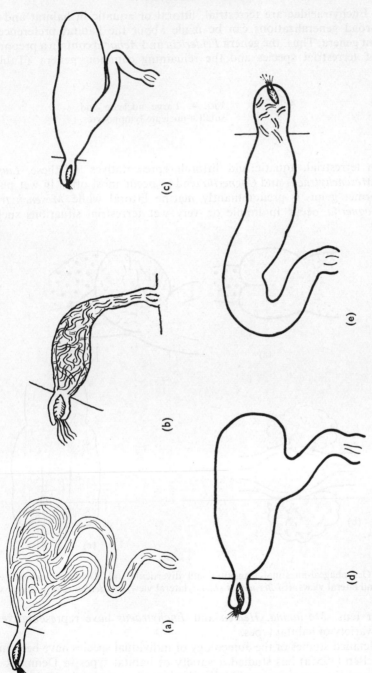

FIG. 3. Nephridia of (a) *Mesenchytraeus*, (b) *Cernosvitoviella*, (c) *Cognettia*, (d) *Lumbricillus*, (e) *Marionina*.

The Enchytraeidae are terrestrial, littoral or aquatic in habitat and only very broad generalizations can be made about the habitat preferences of different genera. Thus, the genera *Fridericia* and *Achaeta* contain a preponderance of terrestrial species and the remaining common genera (Table I)

Fig. 4. Large nucleate and small a-nucleate lymphocytes.

contain terrestrial, aquatic and littoral representatives. Of these, *Lumbricillus, Mesenchytraeus* and *Cognettia* tend to occur most often in wet places. The former genus is predominantly marine littoral while *Mesenchytraeus* and *Cognettia* occur in limnic or very wet terrestrial situations such as

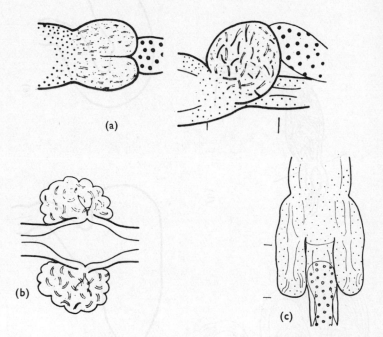

Fig. 5. Oesophageal-intestinal transition and diverticula. (a) *Buccholzia appendiculata*, dorsal and lateral views, (b) *Bryodrilus ehlersi*, lateral view, (c) *Henlea similis*, dorsal view.

bogs or fens. *Marionina, Henlea* and *Enchytraeus* have representatives in a wide variety of habitat types.

No detailed studies of the autecology of individual species have been made but Nielsen (1955a) has studied a variety of habitat types in Denmark and remarks on the surprisingly wide distribution of many species. Of 10 species

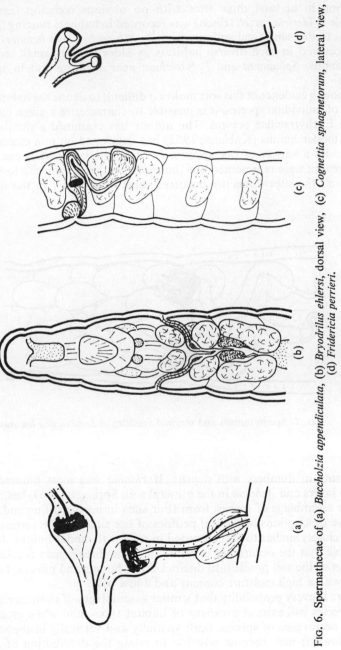

Fig. 6. Spermathecae of (a) *Buccholzia appendiculata*, (b) *Bryodrilus ehlersi*, dorsal view, (c) *Cognettia sphagnetorum*, lateral view, (d) *Fridericia perrieri*.

recorded in his sampling sites only one was restricted to a single site, the rest occurring in at least three sites with no obvious common features. For example *Fridericia ratzeli* (Eisen) was recorded in habitats ranging from water courses to dry sandy soil and raw humus. *Mesenchytraeus beumeri* (Michaelsen) occurred in such diverse habitats as alder swamp, small streams, old tree stumps, *Sphagnum* and *Polytrichum* near a spring and in spruce raw humus.

Although evidence of this sort makes it difficult to define the habitat requirements of individual species, it is possible to characterize a given habitat type by the Enchytraeidae present. The author has examined a number of sites where moder humus (Kubiena, 1953) has developed on non-calcareous silty soils under a variety of tree species. In three similar habitats examined the same genera were represented but the species differed from site to site (Table II). In all the sites *Cognettia* occurred most abundantly in the litter layer,

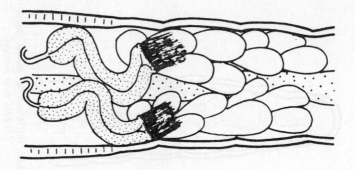

Fig. 7. Sperm funnels and seminal vessicles of *Lumbricillus lineatus*.

decreasing in numbers with depth; *Marionina* was most numerous in the humus layers and *Achaeta* in the mineral soil. Springett (1963) has recorded a similar assemblage of species from four sites in northern England. She does not give descriptions of the soil profiles of her sites but the vertical distribution is closely similar to that recorded in soils with moder humus. It is highly probable that the occurrence together of these three genera is related to the division of the soil profile into distinct litter, humus and mineral layers combined with a high moisture content and a low pH.

There is every probability that similar assemblages of characteristic genera and species will exist in a variety of habitat types, and when precise details of the occurrence of species, both spatially and vertically in the soil profile, are known it may become possible to relate the distribution of species to measurable factors in the soil.

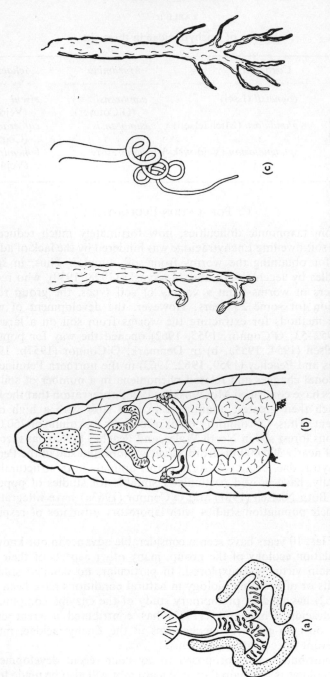

FIG. 8. Salivary glands of (a) *Hemienchytraeus bifurcatus*, (b) *Fridericia*, (c) *Enchytraeus albidus*.

TABLE II

Species of Enchytraeidae in three sites

Site	Cognettia	Marionina	Achaeta
Douglas fir	cognettii (Issel)	cambrensis (O'Connor)	eiseni (Vejdovsky).
Oak	glandulosa (Michaelsen)	cambrensis	camerani (Cognetti)
Beech	sphagnetorum (Vejdovsky)	cambrensis	bohemica (Vejdovsky)

C. POPULATION ECOLOGY

Apart from taxonomic difficulties, now fortunately much reduced, the study of the soil-dwelling Enchytraeidae was hindered by the lack of adequate techniques for obtaining the worms from soil samples. Thus, in spite of pioneer studies by Jegen (1920) and Moszyński (1928, 1930), who recorded large numbers of worms from a variety of soil types, the group received little attention for some 25 years. However, the development of reliable quantitative methods for extracting the worms from soil on a large scale (Nielsen, 1952–53; O'Connor, 1955, 1962) opened the way for population studies. Nielsen (1954, 1955a, b) in Denmark, O'Connor (1957b, 1958) in North Wales and Peachey (1959, 1962, 1963) in the northern Pennines have studied seasonal changes and related phenomena in a number of soil types. These studies have confirmed Moszyński's (1928) observation that the Enchytraeidae reach their greatest abundance in acid soils with a high organic matter content. Thus, O'Connor (1957b) recorded a maximum of $250,000/m^2$ in a coniferous forest soil in North Wales, and Peachey (1963) has recorded a maximum of nearly $300,000/m^2$ from a *Juncus* moorland soil in the Pennines.

The Enchytraeidae, being relatively simple animals both structurally and physiologically, have proved particularly suitable for studies of population respiration. Both Nielsen (1961) and O'Connor (1963a) have integrated the results of their population studies with laboratory estimates of respiratory rates.

While the last 10 years have seen a considerable advance in our knowledge of the population ecology of the group, many other aspects of their life in the soil remain virtually unexplored. In particular, no detailed studies of feeding habits or of breeding biology in natural conditions have been made. Nielsen (1962) has made a preliminary study of the enzyme compliment of some enchytraeids. Christensen (1961) has contributed a great deal of information on cyto-genetical mechanisms in the Enchytraeidae, much of which is relevant to ecological problems.

In this contribution it is proposed to consider recent developments in population ecology as the main theme. An attempt will also be made to draw

together a number of autecological observations, particularly on the reproductive and feeding biology, more in order to point out the need for further
work than with any claim of completeness.

II. THE EXTRACTION OF ENCHYTRAEIDAE FROM SOIL

The extraction of enchytraeids from soil on a large scale can be carried
out by two methods. Both rely on the movement of the worms in response to
physical stimuli but differ considerably in their mode of operation. The details
of construction and the dimensions of the two types of apparatus are shown
in Figs 9 and 10.

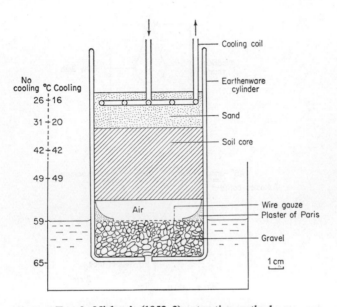

FIG. 9. Nielsen's (1952–3) extraction method.

In Nielsen's (1952–53) method, soil cores are removed from the field using a
stainless steel cylinder designed to take soil cores of 7·3 cm diameter and
6 cm depth. The cores slide directly from the corer into the extraction cylinders. Deep cores are stratified into 6 cm layers before being placed in the
cylinders. The cylinders are then placed in a water bath which is heated so
that a temperature gradient, high at the bottom and low at the top of the
column, is established. At the same time, water evaporating from the lower
gravel layer recondenses in the lower part of the soil core and a moisture
gradient is established, again high at the base and low at the top of the
column. Under the influence of these two gradients, worms present in the core
move into the upper sand layer. When extraction is complete this layer is
removed, and the worms separated by repeated washing and decanting.

Extraction takes 3 hours, and any number of cylinders can be used together. In practice three cooling coils are connected in series, several series being supplied with water at 10°c from a single, rake-shaped manifold.

The alternative method (O'Connor, 1955, 1962) uses soil cores of 6·3 cm diameter taken with a cylindrical corer split longitudinally so that it can be opened and the core subdivided into as many 2 cm deep layers as desired without forcing the core from the corer. This method has the advantage that the profile can be separated into its natural divisions before extraction. In highly compacted silt or clay soils great force is required to remove a soil core from the corer; this results in damage to the worms and a loss of extraction efficiency. The split corer obviates this difficulty.

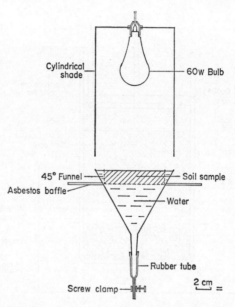

FIG. 10. Wet-funnel extraction method (O'Connor, 1955, 1962).

The sub-cores are placed upside down in the wire gauze sieves and the funnels filled with water. During extraction, the heat intensity is increased by means of a variable resistance at such a rate that the surface of the soil reaches a temperature of 45°c after 3 hours. By this time the worms will have moved through the sieve into the water below and can be run off with a little water from the bottom of the funnel.

Both methods have been used widely for studies of population density change (Nielsen, 1955a; O'Connor, 1957b; Peachey, 1959, 1963). The efficiency of the methods has been compared on a variety of soil types (O'Connor, 1955, 1962; Peachey, 1962). In general it seems that there is little difference in the efficiency of the methods when used for extraction from sandy or alluvial soils, but the wet funnel method is better for soils with a high organic matter content. The final choice of extraction method for any particular study will be decided not only on the basis of efficiency but also on the availability of materials and the ease of construction of the apparatus. From this point of view the wet funnel method has the advantage of simplicity and ease of operation; heat control is easy and extraction is a single process. Nielsen's method is more readily modified for larger diameter soil cores, since the form of the temperature gradient is not affected by core diameter. The extractor units of the wet funnel apparatus cannot be increased in diameter without modification of the heating system because horizontal temperature gradients tend to be established in large funnels.

III. FEEDING HABITS OF THE ENCHYTRAEIDAE

No detailed studies of the feeding biology of the Enchytraeidae have been made and the information presented here is gathered from a variety of sources of varying reliability. Jegen (1920) states that they ingest plant remains and particles of silica and, while burrowing in the soil, assist in the subdivision of plant detritus and mix it with the mineral soil. Clark (1949) recorded Enchytraeidae in Australian forests ingesting finely divided plant remains together with considerable quantities of fungal mycelium. Zachariae (1963) has observed that, in the leaf litter of coniferous and deciduous forests, Enchytraeidae consume the droppings of litter-feeding Collembola, along with all other loose particles of leaf material. He also states that the Enchytraeidae produce crumb-like droppings of finely divided plant remains in which there are no cellulose residues. These can form a considerable proportion of the moder humus of coniferous forest soils. Kubiena (1955) states that, in some mineral soils, the Enchytraeidae can form a micro-sponge structure, analogous to that produced by earthworms but on a smaller scale, in which clay-humus complexes form water-stable aggregates. The Enchytraeidae of sewage beds feed extensively on algae, fungi and bacteria (Reynoldson, 1939a). His observations suggest that *Lumbricillus lineatus* (Muller) feeds on the alga *Phormidium* in the live state. The Enchytraeidae of wrack beds, *L. lineatus*, *L. rivalis* (Levinson) and *Enchytraeus albidus* (Henle), ingest large quantities of decaying seaweed and must play a major part in its decomposition. In laboratory culture they are capable of reducing fresh seaweed to a dark-brown amorphous mass of faeces in a short space of time.

Enchytraeus albidus is often aggregated in large numbers in and around the bodies of dead fish and marine birds thrown ashore with seaweed. Kühnelt (1961) states that a liquid given off by the worms liquefies the flesh of the dead animal and that the resulting mess is sucked up by the worms. His evidence for this statement is obscure, and it seems equally possible that the worms rely upon saprophytic bacteria to perform the preliminary softening of the body. Jegen (1920) observed large numbers of Enchytraeidae, of unspecified species, in and around the roots of nematode-infested strawberry plants. He contended that enchytraeids are able to kill root-feeding nematodes: they enter the roots of the infected plant and collect where nematodes are present, converting them into a liquid mass and consuming the resulting fluid. In pot experiments, Jegen found that nematode infections of strawberry plants could be checked by introducing enchytraeids to the soil in the early stages of damage. If, however, the attack had proceeded too far the Enchytraeidae accelerated the process of decomposition.

The actual feeding mechanism of the Enchytraeidae appears to involve, in some species at least, a preliminary softening of the food material before ingestion. Stephenson (1930) and other authors have observed the pharyngeal plate extruded onto the food prior to ingestion. The septal glands in many enchytraeids are connected by strands of tissue to the dorsal surface of the pharyngeal plate and, according to Stephenson (1930), the strands convey disintegration products of the septal glands to the exposed surface of the pharyngeal plate. This material, presumably liquid in life, may have a digestive function. Kühnelt (1961), without stating his authority, claims that the attack on plant residues is achieved by the release of a strongly alkaline secretion from the salivary glands (septal glands?) and that the material is already softened before being ingested. Reynoldson (personal communication) has also observed extrusion of the pharyngeal plate onto algal food prior to ingestion by the Enchytraeidae of sewage beds. Christensen's (1956) observations on the use of the pharyngeal plate in cocoon laying indicates that its secretions are mucilaginous in nature—so its use in feeding may only be for lubrication.

In an attempt to investigate the possibility of selective feeding in the soil-dwelling Enchytraeidae, O'Connor (1957a) made a preliminary study of 3 species from a moder soil under Douglas fir in North Wales. The proportions of plant, fungus and silica ingested by the worms were estimated from squash preparations of the gut contents from the 3 species. The quantities of each component were expressed in arbitrary units, each measurement corresponding to the number of squares of a lattice over the high-power field of a microscope occupied by the various components. These estimates were compared with the proportions of plant, fungus and silica present at different levels in the profile. Figure 11 shows the results of this comparison, based upon an examination of 10 specimens of each species from each layer of the profile. No estimates were possible for Achaeta eiseni from the litter layer nor Cognettia cognetti from the mineral soil layer because of their scarcity in these layers. It was impossible to estimate the proportions of plant, fungus and silica in the litter layer because of the presence of a great many whole fir needles. From Fig. 11 it is apparent that Achaeta and Cognettia from the humus layer tend to consume about twice as much fungus as would be expected if they ingested their substrate at random: Achaeta apparently avoids plant material and Cognettia avoids siliceous material. In the mineral soil, Achaeta again tends to avoid plant material. Marionina cambrensis shows no great selectivity in either the humus or mineral layers. No direct comparison between gut contents and substrate is possible for the litter layer but the high proportion of fungus taken by *Cognettia* in comparison with *Marionina* suggests that it is feeding selectively on fungus in this layer also.

While these results support the view that the Enchytraeidae, in general, are important agents in mixing plant debris and mineral soil, it is apparent that two out of the three species examined eat more fungus than would be expected if they fed entirely at random.

Recent work by Nielsen (1962) upon the carbohydrases of soil- and litter-dwelling invertebrates indicates that the four species of Enchytraeidae which he has examined do not possess enzymes which would enable them to

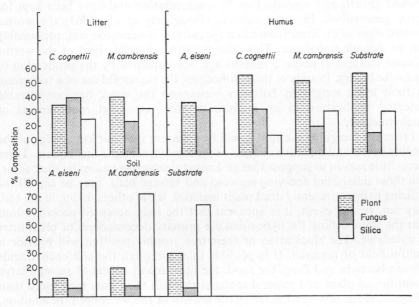

Fig. 11. Feeding preferences of *Cognettia cognetti, Marionina cambrensis,* and *Achaeta eiseni* in coniferous forest soil.

utilize the complex structural polysaccharides of higher plants. Indeed, this seems to apply equally to the large group of soil invertebrates currently regarded as primary decomposers. Nielsen suggests that the primary decomposition of plant remains is largely attributable to the soil micro-flora (bacteria, actinomycetes and fungi) and that, with the exception of snails, some tipulid larvae and possibly Protozoa, the so-called decomposing soil fauna is in reality a group of primary consumers utilizing the micro-flora as food.

The selective fungal feeding reported above is in line with Nielsen's observations, and the apparent lack of any structural change in plant remains while passing through the guts of enchytraeids becomes explicable. Unfortunately, no account was taken of the bacterial content of the food ingested and, in any case, it is difficult to see how selective bacterial feeding

could be accomplished by an enchytraeid worm. However, it is probable that
bacteria, ingested along with other materials, will form an important component of the food. In this connection Dougherty and Solberg (1960) have succeeded in rearing *Enchytraeus fragmentosus* (Bell), a species which reproduces
asexually by fragmentation, in monoxenic culture with the bacterium *Escherichia coli* growing on agar slants. However, it was necessary to add a few
grains of autoclaved rolled oats to the surface of the agar slant for continued
vigorous growth and reproduction. More recently, Dougherty and Solberg
(1961) succeeded in keeping *E. fragmentosus* in axenic culture on nutrient
agar supplemented with heated lamb liver extract. On this medium the worms
showed growth and reproduction by fragmentation and have been kept for
many generations. In some cultures (Dougherty *et al.*, 1963) the worms
showed signs of disintegration when the cultures became too wet, presumably
due to osmotic unbalance. They also reported complete lysis of the worms
in some cultures of about 3 months age, accompanied by the production of
virus-like bodies. In spite of these difficulties, the successful use of a bacterium
as food lends weight to Nielsen's views and the work has considerable
potential application in an analysis of the nutritional requirements of
Enchytraeidae.

From the foregoing account it will be apparent that our knowledge of the
feeding habits and digestive abilities of the Enchytraeidae is inadequate. There
seems little reason to suppose that all Enchytraeidae have a similar diet; some,
like those inhabiting decaying seaweed and sewage beds, may be capable of
utilizing living or recently dead plant material, while others, living in the soil,
may not. In any event, it is apparent that the long accepted generalization
that the soil-dwelling Enchytraeidae are primary decomposers of plant litter
is untenable. The elucidation of their true trophic position will provide a
fruitful field of research. It is possible that, although the soil enchytraeids
rely on bacteria and fungi for food, the mechanical effects of passing large
quantities of plant and mineral material through their guts may more than
compensate for this by stimulating the growth of the microflora. In addition,
the mechanical processes of feeding are likely to have an important effect upon
the development of soil humus forms; the role of Enchytraeidae in this respect
is but little understood.

IV. REPRODUCTIVE BIOLOGY OF THE
ENCHYTRAEIDAE

Christensen (1961) states that the normal method of reproduction in the
Enchytraeidae is by mutual transference of spermatozoa between herma-
phrodites, though some species are parthenogenetic and a few cases of
asexual reproduction have been recorded. In the majority of Enchytraeidae
copulation and mutual transference of sperm takes place, the penes of one
worm being inserted into the spermathecae of the other. Ova are passed into a
mucilaginous cocoon secreted by the clitellum and, as the cocoon passes
forward over the spemathecae, spermatozoa are passed into it and the eggs

develop into worms of 1 to 2 mm length; hatching takes place by rupture of the cocoon wall.

The only detailed studies of breeding biology of the Enchytraeidae are those of Reynoldson (1939b, 1943) on *Lumbricillus lineatus* and *Enchytraeus albidus* from sewage bacteria beds and Ivleva (1953) on *E. albidus* from laboratory cultures. Table III summarizes data from these sources. Reynoldson

TABLE III

Summary of data on reproductive biology of *Lumbricillus lineatus* and *Enchytraeus albidus*

	Data of Reynoldson		Data of Ivleva
	L. lineatus	*E. albidus*	*E. albidus*
Cocoon size (mm)	1·8 × 0·84	0·59 × 0·55	0·5–1·8 (length)
Eggs/cocoon	6–7	4–5	1–35 (av. 10)
Cocoons/worm/day	0·13	0·22	0·40 (young worms) 0·13 (old worms)
Fertile eggs (%)	76	83	—
Hatching success (%)	74	97	—
Viable eggs/worm/day	0·073	0·177	—
Incubation period (days)	15·7 ± 0·9	23·8 ± 1·7	12
Maturation period (days)	101 ± 6·4	44·5 ± 0·9	21
Size at hatching (mm)	1·0 (13 segs)	—	1·5–3·0
Total life cycle (days)	117·0	68·3	261 (mean max. longevity)
Temp. range for reproduction (°c)	7–20	5–25	

(1943) gives 10°c as an average annual sewage bed temperature and the table shows the results of his breeding experiments at this temperature. Ivleva's results are for worms kept at 18°c, the optimum temperature for laboratory culture. The cocoons of the two species vary from 0·5 to 1·8 mm in length, depending on the size of the parent worm; large cocoons tend to contain more eggs. Cocoon production continues throughout the life of the worm, but is more rapid in young than in old worms. Temperature has an important influence on the reproduction of Enchytraeidae. Multiplication is possible over the range 7 to 20°c for *L. lineatus* and 5 to 25°c for *E. albidus*. The fertility of the eggs of *E. albidus* was fairly constant at approx. 83% over the range 4 to 20°c, dropping sharply outside these limits. In *L. lineatus* egg fertility showed a maximum of 76% at 10°c, declining above and below this. It is interesting to note that sterile eggs were consumed by the surviving embryos in the cocoon. The hatching success of cocoons showed little variation with temperature within the tolerable range, but was always higher for *E. albidus*. The incubation and maturation periods both declined with increasing temperature up to a lethal limit between 20 and 25°c.

From a consideration of the entire life cycle, the optimum breeding temperature for both species will be around 18°C. At sewage bed temperatures *E. albidus* produces viable eggs at more than twice the rate of *L. lineatus*, and the eggs develop to maturity in half the time. Thus, *E. albidus* has a decisive reproductive advantage over *L. lineatus*.

Christensen (1961) states that, in addition to this normal sexual reproduction, parthenogenesis is not uncommon in the Enchytraeidae. Parthenogenetic reproduction has been established with certainty in 5 species and probably occurs in at least 6 others. In 2 species the eggs have to be activated by spermatozoa before development proceeds (Christensen and O'Connor, 1958). In a number of other parthenogenetic species spermatozoa are produced and enter the cocoons as they are laid, but it is not known whether pseudo-fertilization is necessary for the development of the eggs. In one species only very few worms produce spermatozoa and no spermathecae are present in polyploid individuals so that activation of the eggs is presumably unnecessary.

Recently, a number of cases of asexual reproduction have been reported. Bell (1959) has described a new species, *Enchytraeus fragmentosus*, in which sexual maturity has not been observed. Fully grown worms break into 3 to 11 fragments, of about 5 segments each, and the fragments regenerate into complete worms in about 10 days. Christensen (1959) has observed asexual reproduction by a similar fragmentation process in the species *Cognettia sphagnetorum*, *C. glandulosa* and *Buchholzia appendiculata* (Buchholz). *Cognettia sphagnetorum* has occasionally been observed to lay eggs but they never complete their development. *C. glandulosa* and *B. appendiculata* are able to produce eggs which develop normally as well as to reproduce by fragmentation. The eggs of *C. glandulosa* develop parthenogenetically, but the mode of development is unknown in *B. appendiculata*. In natural populations of these last 3 species sexual maturity occurs only for a short period during the winter.

Out of a total of 88 cytotypes examined, Christensen (1961) recorded 41 polyploids. He regards this high proportion of polyploids, and the fact that a number of genera contain polyploid parthenogenetic and non-parthenogenetic types as well as normal amphimictic diploids as evidence that the family Enchytraeidae is evolving rapidly by polyploidy.

No studies comparable to those of Reynoldson (1939b, 1943) and Ivleva (1953) have been made for the fully terrestrial enchytraeids, but Christensen (1956) used glass observation chambers (Fig. 12) in order to describe the process of cocoon production in a number of littoral and terrestrial species. In all the Enchytraeidae the cocoon is laid as a clear-walled mucilaginous bag containing 1 to 35 eggs depending on the species and the individual. In the genera *Enchytraeus*, *Fridericia* and *Henlea*, but not in *Lumbricillus* the worms actively cover their cocoons with a layer of sand grains and organic debris. The particles are picked up by the protrusible pharyngeal plate and plastered onto the wall of the cocoon with mucus secreted from the pharyngeal region. The covering process results in a complete disguise of the cocoon and accounts for the difficulty experienced by several authors in finding cocoons of Enchytraeidae in soil samples. Personal observation of cocoon production in *Achaeta eiseni, Cognettia cognetti* and *Marionina cambrensis* has shown no indication of cocoon covering. Reynoldson (1939a, b, 1943) does not report cocoon covering in *E. albidus* or *L. lineatus* from sewage bacteria beds. Figure 13 shows the two cocoon types.

The habit of cocoon covering may be of ecological significance in relation to drought resistance. Nielsen (1955a, b) has noted that, in a sandy permanent pasture in Denmark, a population consisting predominantly of *Fridericia bisetosa* (Levinson) was severely decimated by drought. However, at the onset of rain in the autumn, the population recovered by the sudden appearance of large numbers of young worms which could only have hatched from cocoons already in the soil prior to the drought. By contrast, a population of 3 species

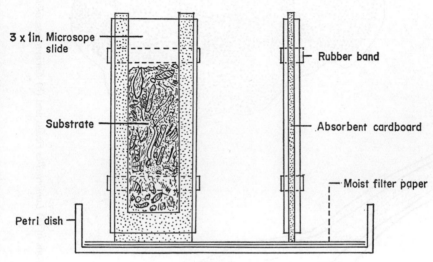

FIG. 12. Observation slide (after Christensen, 1956).

from North Wales, which do not cover their cocoons, were unable to survive even moderate drought. The fact that Reynoldson did not observe cocoon covering in *E. albidus* may be related to the permanently moist conditions of the sewage bed habitat. Evidence of this sort is strongly suggestive of some advantage for covered cocoons during drought. An experimental investigation into this problem would be justified and would present no great technical difficulties.

Several authors have noted that a greater proportion of the individuals in enchytraeid populations are sexually mature in winter. It has been argued from this that the Enchytraeidae are of Arctic origin. However, there is no evidence from Reynoldson's (1943) study of the life cycles of *L. lineatus* and *E. albidus* in relation to temperature to suggest obligatory winter breeding.

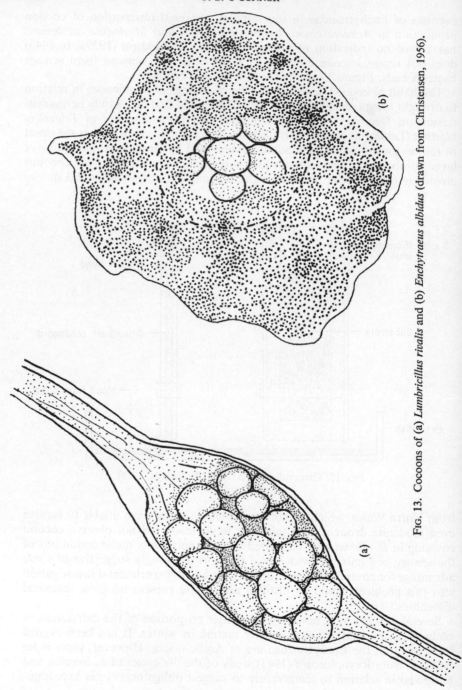

FIG. 13. Cocoons of (a) *Lumbricillus rivalis* and (b) *Enchytraeus albidus* (drawn from Christensen, 1956).

V. POPULATION ECOLOGY OF THE ENCHYTRAEIDAE

Studies of population ecology have recently been made on a variety of habitats in Denmark (Nielsen, 1955a, b), in a coniferous woodland in North Wales (O'Connor, 1957b, 1958) and on peaty moorland in the northern Pennines (Peachey, 1959, 1962, 1963). These habitats cover a wide range of environmental conditions. The North Wales habitat is remarkable for the relative stability of temperature and soil moisture conditions. The moorland habitats have, in a normal year, a relatively stable moisture regime but a much longer and colder winter than North Wales. The Danish habitats undergo wide changes in both temperature and soil moisture status. It is thus instructive to compare the course of seasonal change in population density in these habitats and, in examining the causes of differences between the regions, to arrive at some general conclusions regarding the factors controlling the numbers of Enchytraeidae in natural populations.

Figure 14 summarizes population changes in selected sites from the three regions and Table IV shows the annual mean density levels in three of Nielsen's sites, in North Wales and in the Pennines. The data, in general, support

TABLE IV

Annual mean density in different habitats

Author and Region	Site	Nos, $10^3/m^2$	Biomass g/m^2
Nielsen, Denmark	sandy permanent pasture, Stn 1	44	2·97
	4	30	3·03
	18	74	10·50
O'Connor, North Wales	Coniferous wood	134·3	10·79
Peachey, pennine moorland	alluvial grassland	10– 25	15
	Juncus moor	130–290	53
	Nardus grass	37–200	35
	eroded peat	12– 50	10

the long-accepted view that organic soils contain the greatest number of Enchytraeidae. Thus, the highest densities and biomass are recorded from Juncus squarrosus moor and the lowest from alluvial and sandy grassland soils. A comparison of seasonal changes in population density in relation to environmental factors is more revealing than a consideration of general density levels.

In the permanently moist habitats, with the exception of Peachey's Nardus grassland site, maximum densities occur in summer followed by a decline

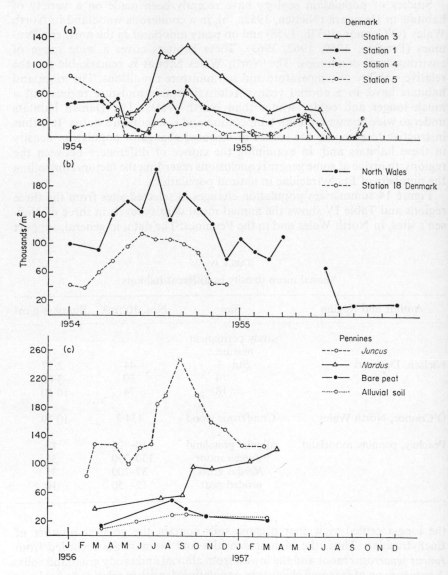

Fig. 14. Population density of Enchytraeidae in (a) dry, (b) warm and wet, and (c) cold moorland situations. (Data from Nielsen, 1955a, b; O'Connor, 1957b; Peachey, 1963.)

throughout the winter to a minimum in late winter. A comparison of population changes with the seasonal variation in temperature (Fig. 15) reveals closely parallel trends. The peak density occurs in July in North Wales, in August in Denmark and September–November in the Pennines. The position of the peak density is probably related to the duration of the cold season; the spring increase in temperature occurs earliest in North Wales and latest in the Pennines. While coincidence of temperature and population density changes does not necessarily imply cause and effect, such a relationship could be deduced from Reynoldson's (1943) data on the life cycles of *L. lineatus* and *E. albidus* in relation to temperature. He has shown that the minimum temperature for breeding is 5 to 7°c and the optimum about 18°c. In addition,

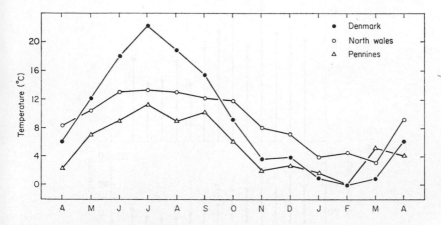

FIG. 15. Seasonal temperature change in Denmark, North Wales and the Pennines.

the age class composition of the population and the incidence of sexual maturity have been used as evidence of breeding activity, underlying the seasonal trend in population density in North Wales (O'Connor, 1958). The population studied consisted of 3 species, but the trends in age, class composition and the incidence of sexual maturity were similar in all 3, so that they can be considered together. Figure 16 shows the seasonal trend in numbers and percentage of juvenile worms (less than 2 mm in length) in relation to the trend in total population density. It is at once apparent that the number and percentage of juvenile worms is greatest in the early summer when population density is increasing. There is a slow decline in the prevalence of juveniles throughout the late summer and winter, with an increase apparent in the following spring. Both Nielsen (1961) and Peachey (1963) have shown a similar decline in the average weight of individuals during population increase and conversely, an increase in average weight as population density declines. When the numbers and percentage of mature worms are considered (Fig. 16) it appears, somewhat surprisingly, that there is an inverse relationship between sexual maturity and the prevalence of juveniles, and that the number of sexually mature worms is always small. It is apparent from the graphs that marked changes in the population were occurring in April. Accordingly, a more detailed examination of the inverse relationship was made for the month of April. Figure 17 shows changes in the population at weekly intervals for April 1954 and April 1955 and the inverse relationship is apparent for both. As indicated in Fig. 17, the changes in the population were preceded by, and doubtless related to, a rise in temperature. The rapid decline in the number of mature worms, coinciding with the increase in the

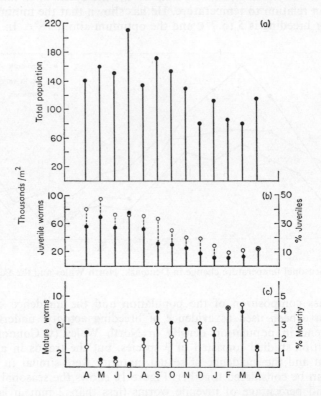

FIG. 16. Seasonal trend in population density in relation to numbers (●) and percentage (○) of juvenile and mature worms (from O'Connor, 1958).

number of juveniles, suggests that mature worms either die or undergo regression of their sexual organs at this time. In spite of this, the population continued to increase, and can only have done so by the hatching of cocoons accumulated in the soil over winter. It is hardly conceivable that the small number of mature worms remaining in the population during May–July could have been capable of producing the observed increase in the juvenile population. The final proof of this hypothesis must await more detailed knowledge of the rate of cocoon production, development and hatching in relation to temperature.

There is no evidence of temperature-induced mortality in the Enchytraeidae; population density tends to decline slowly throughout the cold season. The

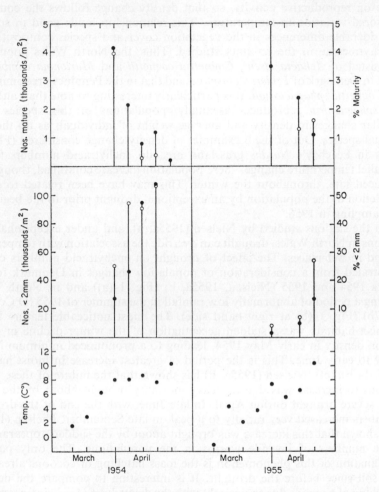

FIG. 17. Changes in numbers (●) and percentage (○) of mature and juvenile worms in April 1954 and 1955. (After O'Connor, 1958.)

decline is always associated with a reduction in the proportion of juveniles present in the population or an increase in the average weight of individuals; this suggests that the decline results more from a cessation of cocoon hatching or of asexual reproduction than from mortality. Nielsen (1955a) reports that a spell of severe frost (-10 to $-18°$c) lasting for 28 days produced no sudden decrease in enchytraeid numbers and concludes that they are able to survive the Danish winter without appreciable loss.

The available evidence strongly supports the hypothesis that enchytraeid numbers in permanently moist habitats are regulated by the effect of temperature on reproductive activity, so that density change follows the course of seasonal variation in temperature. This relationship holds good in spite of considerable differences in the vegetation cover and species composition of Enchytraeidae in the habitats studied. Thus, the North Wales population consisted of *Achaeta eiseni, Cognettia cognettii* and *Marionina cambrensis*, that in Denmark of *Fridericia bisetosa* and that in the Pennines predominantly of *Cognettia sphagnetorum*. It is particularly interesting to note that, although *C. sphagnetorm* reproduces asexually, populations of this species show similar changes in density and average weight of individuals as do those of sexual species. Out of the 6 examples of density change considered (Fig. 14) only in Peachey's *Nardus* grassland area do enchytraeid numbers fail to parallel temperature change—here population increase continued, though at a reduced rate, throughout the winter. This may have been related to severe depletion of the population by an exceptional drought prior to the beginning of sampling in 1956.

In the stations studied by Nielsen (1955a, b), and under exceptional conditions in North Wales, drought can override the association with temperature found in wet places. The effect of drought on enchytraeid numbers can be illustrated from a consideration of population changes in Denmark for the years 1954 and 1955 (Nielsen, 1955a, b) (Fig. 14(a)) and in North Wales during a period of abnormally low rainfall in the summer of 1955 (O'Connor, 1957b) (Fig. 14(b) at right-hand side). The most noticeable feature in the Danish habitats was a sudden accentuation of the winter decline in population density in early May 1954, leading to a pronounced minimum in late May to early June. This is the period of greatest increase in moist habitats (Fig. 14(b), (c)). Nielsen (1955a, b) has shown that the failure of these populations to increase was due to heavy mortality brought about by the onset of a severe drought during April. In late June, with the end of the drought, numbers increased very rapidly to a peak in late September. Nielsen (1955b) has shown that this increase was brought about by the sudden appearance of large numbers of juvenile worms in the populations. The only possible explanation of this phenomenon is the mass hatching of cocoons already in the soil since before the drought. It is interesting to compare the delayed hatching of cocoons due to drought with the delay due to low winter temperatures postulated for the North Wales habitat. It certainly seems possible that the eggs or embryos of some enchytraeids are capable of suspended development in the face of adverse physical conditions.

In 1955 drought occurred in both Denmark and North Wales, beginning in late May in Denmark and in early June in North Wales, and persisting in both regions until late September. The slight delay in onset of drought as compared with 1954 permitted the expected temperature-dependent spring increase to occur, but drought soon resulted in a premature curtailment of this increase, earlier and more severe in Denmark than in North Wales. In both cases low densities persisted until the following autumn.

There are indications that the Danish populations recovered from drought more readily than did the North Wales population. Nielsen (1955b) has observed that the severity and duration of drought affects the subsequent recovery of the population. In the less severely desiccated habitats the populations were capable of rapid recovery by the hatching of cocoons in the soil. In North Wales, although more than 6,000 worms/m² survived the drought, artificially increased water content of experimental plots during August caused no increase in population density even when soil moisture contents were restored to a normal level for the time of year. Thus, although the minimal density recorded during the drought in North Wales was high compared with the same period in Denmark, it is apparent that no viable cocoons were present in the soil at the time of the watering experiment. This differential survival of cocoons may well be related to the fact that the Danish populations studied by Nielsen consisted predominantly of *Fridericia bisetosa*, a species with covered cocoons, while none of the species from the North Wales habitat have covered cocoons.

From the available evidence, it seems that the seasonal trend in density in permanently moist habitats is controlled largely by the effect of temperature on the rate of population increase. No evidence for temperature-induced mortality was found, but exceptionally dry soil conditions result in severe mortality and can override the normal association with temperature. In continental conditions, where low rainfall combined with high summer temperatures generally leads to summer drought, the increase in numbers in response to rising temperatures in the spring is prevented, sooner or later, by the onset of low soil moisture conditions. This will result in a summer minimum with peaks of density in spring and autumn, the relative size of which will depend on the timing and severity of summer drought.

It is interesting to find that fluctuations in the numbers of Enchytraeidae in widely different habitats can, in general, be explained in relation to only two physical factors in the environment. In no terrestrial population has it been necessary to invoke competition for food or space, nor predatory mortality in order to explain the observed population phenomena. The available evidence suggests that the numbers of Enchytraeidae in terrestrial populations are regulated by the balance of favourable and unfavourable conditions in the environment, as suggested by Andrewartha and Birch (1954).

An important element in the hypothesis of population regulation presented above is the over-wintering of cocoons in permanently moist situations and the survival of cocoons during drought in continental climates. While there is considerable circumstantial evidence for these phenomena, an experimental study of survival and development of cocoons under controlled conditions would be of great value in confirming the hypothesis, and would present no great technical difficulties.

VI. AGGREGATION IN THE ENCHYTRAEIDAE

The detailed distribution of individuals of enchytraeid populations in small areas is probably better documented than that of other organisms in the soil. Certain peculiarities of the distribution of observations about sample means, calculated from routine population census data, led Nielsen (1954)

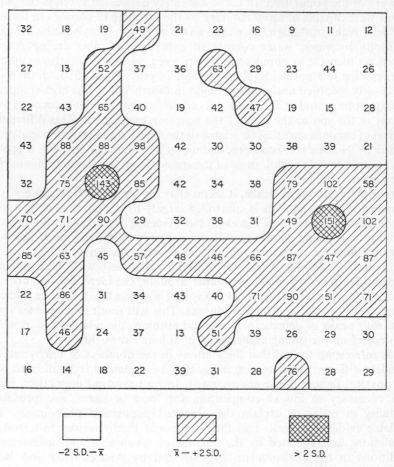

FIG. 18. Distribution pattern of worms in a coniferous forest soil. (After O'Connor, 1957a.)

to study the micro-distribution of Enchytraeidae by means of complete enumerations of the population in several small plots of a sandy permanent pasture. Similar studies have been made in a coniferous woodland in North Wales (O'Connor, 1957a, b) in a variety of moorland soils (Peachey, 1959, 1962, 1963) and in oak woodland soils (O'Connor, unpublished work). These studies have an intrinsic value in that they throw some light on the biology of the soil-dwelling Enchytraeidae and an applied value in relation to the interpretation of routine estimates of population density.

Figures 18 and 19 show maps of the spatial distribution of Enchytraeidae in areas of 0·75 × 0·75 and 1 × 1·2 m respectively. Figure 18 refers to a plot

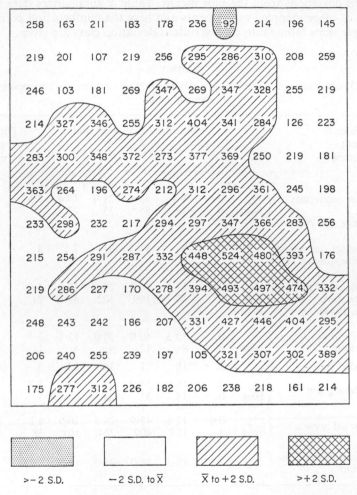

Fig. 19. Distribution pattern of worms in a sandy permanent pasture. (After Nielsen, 1954.)

from a coniferous woodland in North Wales where *Marionina cambrensis* was the most abundant species and *Achaeta eiseni* occurred in small numbers. The population was estimated by removing soil cores of 6·3 cm diameter as close together as possible, and extracting the worms separately from each core. Figure 19 is based upon data obtained by Nielsen (1954) from a sandy permanent pasture where *Fridericia bisetosa* was the only important species. Nielsen used cores of 7·3 cm diameter. In both cases about 80% of the total area was removed. These maps were selected in order to show distribution patterns at extremes of high and low population density. The contours and shading indicate areas of different density expressed in terms of unit standard deviations from the plot means. Table V summarizes data from a variety of other mapping experiments and here the numbers and percentage of sample units falling into each standard deviation class are given.

TABLE V

Distribution of observations about sample means for mapping experiments

Site and Author		-3	-2	-1	x̄	+1	+2	+3	Total no. of sample units
N. Wales coniferous forest (O'Connor, 1957b)	%	0	8·1	53·1	21·9	14·4	2·5		
	Nos	0	13	85	35	23	4		160
Lake district oak wood (O'Connor, unpub.)	%/Nos	0	7	51	31	7	4		100
Denmark sandy permanent pasture (Nielsen, 1954)	%	0·4	12·7	44·2	27·1	10·9	4·6		
	Nos	2	57	199	122	49	21		450
N. Pennines *Juncus* moor	%	0	13·3	40·0	30·0	13·3	3·3		
	Nos	0	4	12	9	4	1		30
eroded peat	%/Nos	2	18	27	38	12	3		100
Nardus grass	%	0	16·0	37·9	33·3	6·9	5·7		
	Nos	0	14	33	29	6	5		87
Total for all areas	%	0·4	12·1	43·9	28·5	10·9	4·1		
	Nos	4	113	407	264	101	38		927
Theoretical normal distribution	%	2·35	13·5	34·0	34·0	13·5	2·35		100

(The rows for N. Pennines *Juncus* moor, eroded peat, and *Nardus* grass are bracketed under (Peachey, 1959).)

The most striking feature of this considerable body of data is the similarity of distribution patterns obtained from a variety of habitats in spite of considerable differences in species composition. In all cases the distribution of observation about sample means is skewed, with a small number of large positive deviates balanced by an excess of negative deviates falling just below the plot mean. The large positive deviates result from the presence of small areas of very high density while the high proportion of small negative deviates results from the fact that about half the area of the plots is occupied by a general background density a little below the plot mean. Between the two, the density gradient is non-linear; Fig. 20 shows the size and form of an idealized aggregation based on data from Fig. 18. This illustrates the dimensions of an aggregation and the form of the density gradient expressed in standard deviation units.

It has not been possible to relate the position of aggregation centres to

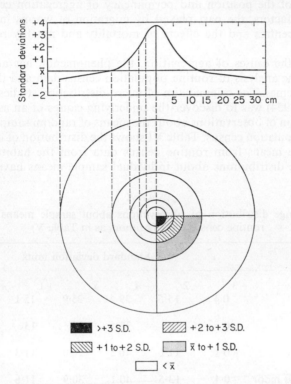

FIG. 20. An idealized diagram of an aggregation based on data from Fig. 18. (After O'Connor, 1957a.)

physical factors in the environment existing at the time of the studies (Nielsen, 1954). This, however, does not preclude the possibility that aggregations are related to some factor operative before the study was made. Both Nielsen (1954) and O'Connor (1957a) have observed that aggregation centres contain a high proportion of young worms and hence may form centres of breeding activity. Unfortunately, no quantitative data is available on this point. It is possible that aggregation centres result from differential survival of cocoons during drought or low temperature (see p. 233). This, however, is unlikely, since Peachey (1959) has shown that *Cognettia sphagnetorum*, a species which reproduces asexually, is just as markedly aggregated as are sexual cocoon-producing species. In the North Wales study, an analysis of species composition at aggregation centres showed that the two species present at the time of the study aggregated independently. However, the consistency of pattern in the distribution of different species, in spite of very different environmental conditions, suggests that aggregation is a result of some behaviour pattern characteristic of the Enchytraeidae in general. The underlying causes of the distribution pattern remain obscure and, as Nielsen (1954) points out, the relationship of the position and permanency of aggregation centres to environmental factors, the part played by migration of worms in and out of aggregation centres and the effects of mortality and natality remain to be analysed.

Whatever the causes of aggregation, the phenomenon has an important bearing on the analysis of routine population census data and the design of sampling schemes. The original aim of micro-distribution studies carried out by Nielsen (1954) was to discover the underlying causes of an asymmetry in the distribution of observations about the means of random samples obtained during his population census. Table VI shows the distribution of observations about sample means from routine census data from the habitats listed in Table V. The distributions about individual sample means have been sum-

TABLE VI

Percentage distribution of observations about sample means from
routine census data (Authors as in Table V)

	Standard deviation units						
	-3	-2	-1	$\bar{x}$	$+1$	$+2$	$+3$
N. Wales	0·4	15·5	39·4	25·9	15·1	3·7	
Lake District	0	18	38	27	13	4	
Denmark	0·1	11·6	46·5	26·0	11·3	4·5	
Pennines *Juncus* moor	0·4	13·5	40·1	30·9	11·6	3·5	
All areas	0·4	13·1	39·6	30·2	14·4	2·2	
Overall routine	0·26	14·3	40·7	28·0	13·1	3·6	
Micro-distribution	0·4	12·1	43·9	28·5	10·9	4·1	

mated to arrive at the values shown. There is a striking similarity between the distributions for different habitats and between these and the values obtained from the micro-distribution plots (Table V). Histograms based on the entire body of data for random sampling and micro-distribution sampling are shown in Fig. 21; their similarity is obvious. A consequence of the aggregative distribution pattern is that the standard deviation about sample means is related to the size of the mean. Figure 22 shows this relationship for the North Wales sample data. Nielsen (1955a) and Peachey (1959) have produced remarkably similar graphs for their sample data. The similarity between distribution of observations about sample means for randomly sited and intensive sampling indicates that the distribution for randomly sited sample

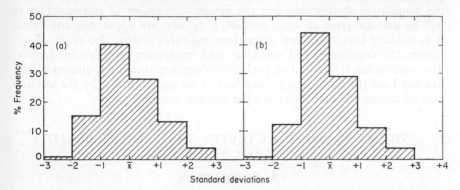

FIG. 21. Frequency distribution of observations about sample means for random sampling and micro-distribution sampling.

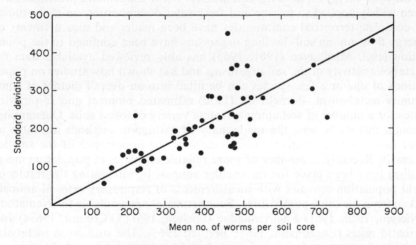

FIG. 22. Relationship between standard deviation and mean size for random sampling from a coniferous forest soil. (After O'Connor, 1957b.)

units is a reflection of the aggregative distribution of the worms. It is apparent that the variance associated with sample means from aggregated populations of this sort will be due in part to random sampling errors and in part to non-random distribution in the population. For the purpose of statistical analysis of routine sample data the effects of the aggregative distribution can be

9+s.b.

removed by a logarithmic transformation. This has the effect of normalizing the distribution of observations about sample means and of rendering the standard deviation independent of the size of the mean (O'Connor, 1957b).

Reynoldson (1957) has pointed out that the aggregative distribution provides a safety mechanism against the possibility of extinction of the population when unfavourable physical conditions occur. Since neither the population distribution nor the severity of action of physical factors will be uniform over an area, and since the two are apparently unrelated, it is unlikely that maximum percentage mortality during the onset of unfavourable conditions will coincide with maximum population density. This mechanism is likely to be particularly important in a population which, like the Enchytraeidae, is regulated largely—if not entirely—by the alternation of favourable and unfavourable weather conditions.

VII. METABOLIC ACTIVITY OF ENCHYTRAEID POPULATIONS

A. INTRODUCTION

Lindeman (1942) indicated the possibility of relating quantitative measurements of energy flow through different trophic levels or species populations to the total energy input to the community. While Lindeman's principles have been widely applied to marine and freshwater communities, no such studies of complete terrestrial communities have been made, and measurements of energy flow among soil-dwelling organisms have been confined to the population level. Macfadyen (1961, 1963) has ably reviewed available data on metabolic activity of the soil organisms and has shown how studies on populations of one or a few species can be fitted into an overall picture of community metabolism. Bornebusch (1930) estimated biomass and respiratory rates for a number of soil animals from a variety of forest soils. Outstanding though this study was, the inadequacy of extraction methods available at that time led to a relative underestimate of the importance of the smaller animals. Recently, a number of more reliable estimates of population metabolism have been made for the smaller animals by integrating the results of field population censuses with measurements of respiratory rates of animals taken from the same populations. Such estimates are available for Nematoda (Nielsen, 1949, 1961) Enchytraeidae (Nielsen, 1961; O'Connor, 1963a) and oribatid mites (Engelmann, 1961; Berthet, 1963). The studies on metabolic activity of enchytraeid populations reported here were made with the ultimate aim of a synopsis of soil community metabolism in mind.

B. RESPIRATORY ACTIVITY (OXYGEN CONSUMPTION)

The data on respiratory activity of the Enchytraeidae fall into two categories: (1) general information on levels of oxygen uptake in different genera and species, and (2) data on individual species obtained specifically for the calculation of population metabolism in well documented habitats. For laboratory estimates of oxygen consumption Nielsen (1961) and O'Connor (1963a) used the Cartesian diver respirometer (Holter, 1943) for detailed studies of particular populations and the author used both the diver and the Warburg respirometer for a more general study.

Before embarking on a discussion of the results of these studies, it is relevant to consider the applicability of respiration measurements made on worms living in water in a glass vessel to the actual activity in natural substrates. As Nielsen (1961) points out, there is no factual basis for discussing this problem at present. He regards the work done by a worm writhing in a water film inside a respirometer flask as small, and observes that in nematodes the oxygen uptake of active worms is only 5% greater than in immobilized worms. It is probable that the movements of enchytraeids in water result in a similar increase above the basal metabolism. All except the very smallest Enchytraeidae make burrows through the soil in which they live and so the work performed in the soil will tend to be larger than in a respirometer. Thus, laboratory measurements of oxygen uptake will tend to underestimate actual respiratory rates in the soil. The magnitude of the underestimate will presumably increase with the size of the individual. In large enchytraeids such as *Fridericia galba* and *F. ratzeli* the expenditure of energy in burrowing may well be larger than 5%.

Nielsen has also considered the possible effects of oxygen tension in the soil on the respiratory rate. He has shown that a 10% reduction in oxygen tension does not produce a significant change in respiratory rate. Since the majority of Enchytraeidae live in the upper few centimetres of soil, they are not likely to encounter appreciable oxygen deficiencies.

1. General level of oxygen uptake

The respiratory rate of many of the common species of Enchytraeidae have been measured, and the available data is combined in Fig. 23. The curves for *Lumbricillus* and *Enchytraeus* are plotted from data obtained with the Warburg respirometer and the others are based partly on Nielsen's (1961) studies with the Cartesian diver and partly on the author's own diver and Warburg data. Most of the measurements were made at a standard temperature of 20° C, but a few made at lower temperatures were corrected to 20° C from the curve relating oxygen uptake to temperature (Fig. 24). Nielsen's results were converted from μl. $O_2/\mu g$ N per hr to μl. O_2/g live weight per hr. As shown in Fig. 23, the rate of oxygen uptake for the genera studied declines with increasing size up to a weight of about 1 mg. Above this weight the rate is fairly constant, irrespective of size, but clear-cut differences between the levels of oxygen uptake at which size ceases to influence respiratory rate can be detected for the genera studied. They can be placed in order of descending respiratory rate as follows: *Lumbricillus, Enchytraeus, Henlea, Fridericia*. Further curves are likely to emerge as more genera are studied in detail; already some estimates for *Mesenchytraeus* suggest a position intermediate between *Henlea* and *Fridericia*.

The underlying physiological basis of these inter-generic differences remains obscure. It is, however, worth noting that the genera studied so far form a series of increasing adaptation to the terrestrial environment. *Lumbricillus* and *Enchytraeus* are normally found in the wettest habitats and *Fridericia* in the driest with *Henlea* falling in between. It may well be that the low respiratory rate of *Fridericia* species is associated with reduction of water loss through the relatively thick body wall characteristic of the genus.

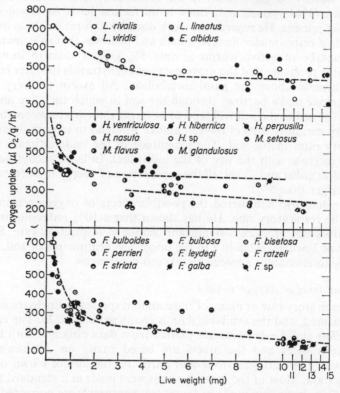

FIG. 23. The relationship between size and oxygen uptake at 20°C.

Direct observation of worms from the three respiratory groups leaves the firm impression that high respiratory rate is associated with greater mobility, both in water and when the worms are kept in semi-natural conditions in observation slides (Christensen, 1956). It would be of interest to know the extent to which differences in activity are associated with utilization of different substrates. Measurements of respiratory quotients would go some way towards answering this question, but the work remains to be done.

The results described so far were all obtained at a temperature of 20°C and, although of value for a discussion of some general problems, they are somewhat unrealistic in relation to field conditions. In order to relate the curves shown in Fig. 23 to field temperatures, supplementary measurements were made over a range of temperatures for a number of species. Worms stored at 5°c for about 24 hours were placed in a Warburg respirometer and their oxygen uptake measured for about 30 minutes at 5, 10, 15, 20, 25 and sometimes 30°c. The worms used were all of more than 1 mg body weight so as to rule out variations in oxygen uptake with size. Figure 24 shows a temperature–respiration curve based on at least 2 species from each of the 3

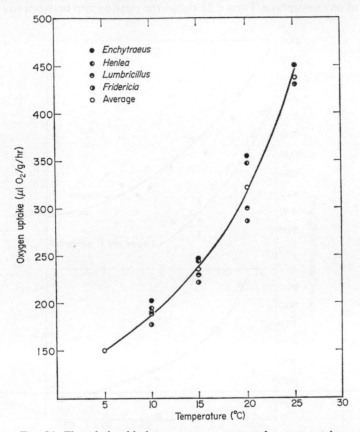

FIG. 24. The relationship between temperature and oxygen uptake.

respiratory groups indicated in Fig. 23. The rate of increase in oxygen uptake with temperature was comparable for all species, so that a single temperature–respiration curve can be drawn. Inter-generic differences in respiration were removed by placing the curves for all species at the same height above the base line. Another series of experiments in which worms were stored for long periods at different temperatures prior to being used for respiration measurements indicated that temperature adaptation does not occur to any great extent in the Enchytraeidae.

The information presented in Figs 23 and 24 will permit an interpretation of population census data for many common species in terms of population metabolism.

2. Metabolism of natural populations

The population studies made by Nielsen in Denmark and the author in North Wales (see above) have been integrated with laboratory measurements of oxygen uptake. Figure 25 shows the relationship between live weight

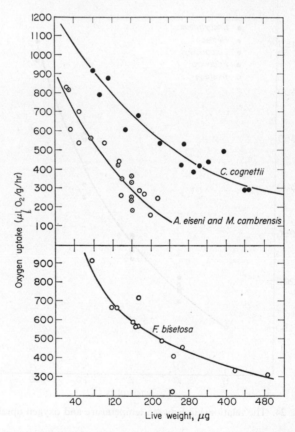

FIG. 25. The relationship between size and oxygen uptake for *Cognettia cognetti*, *Marionina cambrensis*, *Achaeta eiseni* (after O'Connor, 1963a) and *Fridericia bisetosa* (recalculated from Nielsen, 1961).

and oxygen uptake at 20° C for the species present. The curve for *Fridericia* is recalculated from Nielsen's (1961) data and those for *Marionina*, *Cognettia* and *Achaeta* are taken from O'Connor (1963a). In both studies the population metabolism was calculated for each month as the product of population biomass and oxygen uptake corrected to field temperature; the size structure and species composition of the populations was also taken into account.

Table VII shows the mean annual levels of density, biomass and metabolic activity for Nielsen's Station 1, 4 and 18 and the North Wales population.

TABLE VII

Mean annual levels of density, biomass and metabolic activity (after O'Connor, 1963a)

	Density $(10^3/m^2)$	Biomass (g/m^2)	Metabolic activity (ml. O_2/m^2 per hr)	(l. O_2/m^2 per annum)
North Wales	134·3	10·79	3·61	31·6
Denmark				
Stn 1	44	2·97	0·84	7
Stn 4	30	3·03	1·10	10
Stn 18	74	10·5	3·70	32

Nielsen's stations form a series showing decreasing effects of summer decimation of the population by drought. The North Wales habitat is wetter than any of Nielsen's stations. There is an increase in the general level of metabolic activity with decreasing drought effect in the Danish stations. The similarity of population metabolism in Station 18 and North Wales cannot be more than coincidence because of differences in species composition, though both are permanently moist situations.

The comparison between seasonal trends in population density already made can be extended to a consideration of population metabolism. It is generally accepted that the Enchytraeidae are a relatively homogeneous group with respect to their reaction to environmental conditions, and so such a comparison will not be invalidated by differences in species composition between the sites. Figure 26 shows the population metabolism in Nielsen's Stations 1, 4 and 18 and in North Wales, plotted on the same graph for ease of comparison.

In both the permanently moist situations, North Wales and Station 18, the seasonal variation in the average size of individuals in the population is small, and this factor has only a small influence upon changes in respiratory activity. Summer maxima and winter minima of population density and biomass are related to temperature. This fact, combined with the increase in respiratory rate at higher temperatures, produces a summer maximum in population metabolism. The greater amplitude of temperature variation in Denmark results in a more pronounced seasonal change in population metabolism than in the more temperate conditions of North Wales.

The situation where temperature has a controlling influence on population metabolism can be contrasted with Nielsen's Station 1. Here the depletion of the population by summer drought and its almost complete replacement by the mass hatching of cocoons lead to pronounced changes in the average size of individuals in the population. The effect of these events on population metabolism is to override the association with temperature found in wet situations. During the onset of drought in April, population metabolism

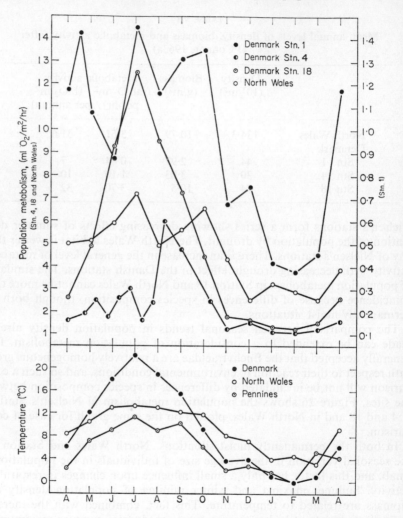

FIG. 26. Comparison of population metabolism in Denmark (from Nielsen, 1961) and North Wales (from O'Connor, 1963a). (Note different scale for Station 1.)

follows the fall in biomass in spite of rising temperatures. During recovery from drought, the small size of the newly hatched worms results in an increase in respiration sufficient to counteract the expected decrease associated with falling temperature in the autumn. During the winter months temperature becomes the most important factor determining the rate of population metabolism.

Station 4 is intermediate between the wet conditions of Station 18 and North Wales and the extreme summer drought of Station 1. In this locality drought did not result in a marked drop in population metabolism, but merely delayed the occurrence of the summer peak by some two months as compared with the wetter sites.

3. Calorific requirement of enchytraeid populations

It is possible to calculate an approximate figure for the calorific equivalent of oxygen consumption of enchytraeid populations. The respiratory quotient has not been determined for any enchytraeids; however, their diet consists of organic debris, fungi, bacteria and probably other soil organisms. Thus, it seems reasonable to use the calorific equivalent of 4·775 kcal/l. O_2 (Heilbrunn, 1947). Table VIII shows the average calorific equivalent of oxygen consumption for the four populations studied in detail. For the sake of completeness,

TABLE VIII

Habitat	l. O_2/g per annum	kcal/g per annum	g/m^2	kcal/m^2 per annum
North Wales	2·90	13·84	10·79	149·5
Denmark				
Stn 1	2·40	11·46	2·97	34·0
Stn 2	3·30	15·76	3·03	47·7
Stn 18	3·10	14·80	10·50	155·4
Northern Pennines				
Limestone grassland			15	210
Juncus moor	—	14	53	742
Nardus grassland			35	490
Bare peat			10	140

* Biomass figures for N. Pennine habitats from Cragg (1961).

Peachey's biomass figures (quoted from Cragg, 1961) for a number of moorland habitats are expressed in the same terms in the lower part of the table, using an approximate value of 14 kcal/g per annum as the calorific equivalent of oxygen consumption.

A complete assessment of the energy utilization of these populations is impossible from respiratory data alone. To estimate the amount of energy used in growth and replacement of individuals in the population, data on the rate of cocoon production, growth rate of individuals, and the distribution of mortality between age classes in the population will be required. In addition, the calorific value of cocoons and worms will be required. The data

9*

available for terrestrial enchytraeid populations is inadequate for a meaningful calculation of this component of energy flow to be made.

Macfadyen (1957) suggests that the utilization of energy for growth and replacement will be low compared with that for respiration. However, Engelmann (1961) has shown that 18% of the total energy output from an oribatid mite population is in the form of egg and adult mortality. Since the fecundity of enchytraeid populations is high (Reynoldson, 1939a, b) it is quite probable that the use of energy for replacement will be considerably more than for Engelmann's mite population. The assessment of this component of energy flow for the Enchytraeidae must await further work.

The relative importance of a population in a community can be calculated as the percentage of the total annual rate of energy input into the system released by the population. In the Douglas fir plantation studied in North Wales the total energy input was contained in approximately 300 g dry weight of litter/m^2 per annum. Using Ovington and Heitkamp's (1960) figure of approximately 4,500 cal/g dry weight of Douglas fir litter, this amounts to an annual calorific input of 1,350 kcal/m^2. The respiratory activity of the Enchytraeidae releases 150 kcal/m^2 per annum or 11% of the total annual energy input. This will represent a minimum figure to which must be added the use of energy for body building. Nonetheless, the figure is high in relation to Macfadyen's (1963) estimate that, in general, *all* the animals in a community release between 10 and 20% of the total energy input. The figures serve to illustrate the importance of the Enchytraeidae in the energy balance of a moder type coniferous forest soil. Their contribution to energy flow will doubtless be considerably less in mull soils.

REFERENCES

Andrewartha, H. G. and Birch, L. C. (1954). "The Distribution and Abundance of Animals." University of Chicago Press, Chicago.
Bell, A. W. (1959). *Science, N.Y.* **129**, 1278.
Berthet, P. (1963). *In* "Soil Organisms." (J. Doeksen and J. van der Drift, eds.), pp. 18–31. North-Holland Publ. Co., Amsterdam.
Birch, L. C. and Clark, D. P. (1953). *Q. Rev. Biol.* **28**, 13–36.
Bornebusch, C. H. (1930). *Forst. ForsVæs. Danm.* **11**, 1–224.
Černosvitov, L. (1937). *Bull. Ass. Russe. Rech. Sci. Praha*, **5**, 263–295.
Černosvitov, L. (1941). *Proc. zool. Soc. Lond.* **111**, 197–236.
Christensen, B. (1956). *Oikos*, **7**, 302–307.
Christensen, B. (1959). *Nature, Lond.* **184**, 1159–1160.
Christensen, B. (1961). *Hereditas*, **47**, 396–450.
Christensen, B. and O'Connor, F. B. (1958). *Nature, Lond.* **181**, 1085–1086.
Clark, D. P. (1949). Thesis (unpub.) University of Sydney. (Quoted by Birch and Clark, 1953.)
Cragg, J. B. (1961). *J. Ecol.*, **49**, 477–506.
Dougherty, E. C. and Solberg, B. (1960). *Nature, Lond.* **186**, 1067–1068.
Dougherty, E. C. and Solberg, B. (1961). *Nature, Lond.* **192**, 184–185.
Dougherty, E. C., Ferral, J., Brody, B. and Gotthold, M. L. (1963). *Nature, Lond.* **198**, 973–975.

Englemann, M. D. (1961). *Ecol. Monog.* **31**, 221–238.
Heilbrunn, L. V. (1947). "An Outline of General Physiology" (2nd ed.). Saunders, Philadelphia and London.
Holter, H. (1943). *C.r. Trav. Lab. Carlsberg, Ser. chim.* **24**, 399–478.
Ivleva, I. V. (1953). *Zool. Zh. ukr.* **32**, 394–404.
Jegen, G. (1920). *Landw. Jb. Schweiz,* **34**, 55–71.
Kubiena, W. L. (1953). "The Soils of Europe." Murby, London.
Kubiena, W. L. (1955). *In* "Soil Zoology." (D. K. McE. Kevan, ed.), pp. 73–82. Butterworths, London.
Kühnelt, W. (1961). "Soil Biology." Faber and Faber, London.
Lindeman, R. L. (1942). *Ecology,* **23**, 399–418.
Macfadyen, A. (1957). "Animal Ecology." Pitman, London.
Macfadyen, A. (1961). *Ann. appl. Biol.* **49**, 215–218.
Macfadyen, A. (1963). *In* "Soil Organisms." (J. Doeksen and J. van der Drift, eds.), pp. 3–17. North-Holland Publ. Co., Amsterdam.
Moszyński, A. (1928). *Kosmos. J. Soc. Polon. Nat. Kopernik.* **53**, 731–766.
Moszyński, A. (1930). *Annls. Mus. zool. pol.* **9**, 65–127.
Nielsen, C. O. (1949). *Natura. jutl.* **2**, 1–131.
Nielsen, C. O. (1952–3). *Oikos,* **4**, 187–196.
Nielsen, C. O. (1954). *Oikos,* **5**, 167–178.
Nielsen, C. O. (1955a). *Natura. jutl.* **4**, 1–58.
Nielsen, C. O. (1955b). *Oikos,* **6**, 153–159.
Nielsen, C. O. (1961). *Oikos,* **12**, 17–35.
Nielsen, C. O. (1962). *Oikos,* **13**, 200–215.
Nielsen, C. O. and Christensen, B. (1959). *Natura. jutl.* **8/9**, 1–160.
Nielsen, C. O. and Christensen, B. (1961). *Natura. jutl.* **10**, Suppl. 1, 1–23.
Nielsen, C. O. and Christensen, B. (1963). *Natura. jutl.* **10**, Suppl. 2, 1–19.
O'Connor, F. B. (1955). *Nature, Lond.* **175**, 815–816.
O'Connor, F. B. (1957a). Thesis (unpub.) University of Wales.
O'Connor, F. B. (1957b). *Oikos,* **8**, 161–199.
O'Connor, F. B. (1958). *Oikos,* **9**, 271–281.
O'Connor, F. B. (1962). *In* "Progress in Soil Zoology." (P. W. Murphy, ed.), pp. 279–285. Butterworths, London.
O'Connor, F. B. (1963a). *In* "Soil Organisms." (J. Doeksen and J. van der Drift, eds.), pp. 32–48. North-Holland Publ. Co., Amsterdam.
O'Connor, F. B. (1963b). *Ann. Mag. Nat. Hist.* **5**, 761–766.
Ovington, J. D. and Heitkamp, D. (1960). *J. Ecology,* **48**, 639–646.
Peachey, J. E. (1959). Thesis (unpub.) University of Durham.
Peachey, J. E. (1962). *In* "Progress in Soil Zoology." (P. W. Murphy, ed.), pp. 286–293. Butterworths, London.
Peachey, J. E. (1963). *Pedobiologia,* **2**, 81–95.
Reynoldson, T. B. (1939a). *Ann. appl. Biol.* **26**, 138–164.
Reynoldson, T. B. (1939b). *Ann. appl. Biol.* **26**, 782–798.
Reynoldson, T. B. (1943). *Ann. appl. Biol.* **30**, 60–66.
Reynoldson, T. B. (1957). *Cold. Spring. Harb. Symp. quant. Biol.* **22**, 313–327.
Springett, J. A. (1963). *In* "Soil Organisms." (J. Doeksen and J. van der Drift, eds.), pp. 414–419. North-Holland Publ. Co., Amsterdam.
Stephenson, J. (1930). "The Oligochaeta." Oxford University Press.
Zachariae, G. (1963). *In* "Soil Organisms." (J. Doeksen and J. van der Drift, eds.), pp. 109–124. North-Holland Publ. Co., Amsterdam.

Chapter 9

Lumbricidae

J. E. SATCHELL

Merlewood Research Station, Grange-over-Sands
Lancashire, England

I. INTRODUCTION

The Lumbricidae is the characteristic Oligochaete family of the Palaearctic region. It comprises about 220 species and is a recent and dominant group possessing great powers of adaptation to new surroundings. About 19 species are common over the greater part of Europe and have been carried by man to many parts of the world, where they have locally replaced the indigenous earthworm fauna. In soils where they flourish they dominate the inverte- brate biomass and, because of their large size, their effect on the gross physical structure of their habitat is unique amongst the mesofauna.

As a classroom type of the Annelida, "the earthworm" is familiar to every biology student. Its basic biology is described in standard textbooks and is not repeated here. As classical subjects for laboratory experiment the lumbricids have an extensive literature which was surveyed by J. L. Stephenson in his monograph *The Oligochaeta*, published in 1930. M. S. Laverack's *The Physiology of Earthworms* (1963) provides a critical survey of more recent work in the light of modern physiological concepts and a recent key to the British Lumbricidae is available in Gerard (1964).

II. GENERAL BIOLOGY

Although water is the main constituent of earthworms—about 80–90% of their fresh weight (Grant, 1955a)—the ability to withstand desiccation is one of the most remarkable features of their biology. *Lumbricus terrestris* can survive losing 70% of the water content of its body, and *Allolobophora chlorotica*, 75% (Roots, 1956), and many species can withstand several months of drought in a quiescent state. Nevertheless, although the Lumbricidae are remarkably successful as a terrestrial group, they have a basically aquatic organization.

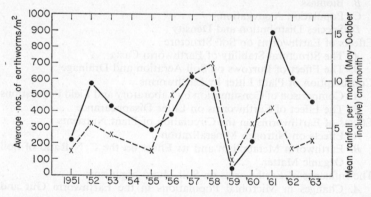

FIG. 1. Earthworm population density and summer rainfall in a Welsh pasture (Reynoldson, unpublished work).

Allolobophora caliginosa, A. chlorotica and *A. rosea* comprised 90% of the population. –x—x–, rainfall (cm/month); —●—●—, numbers of earthworms/m².

They lack special respiratory organs and so must maintain a constantly moist body surface for gaseous exchange. Their main nitrogenous excretion is ammonia, which needs a copious hypotonic urine for its elimination. Locomotion and burrowing depend on the hydrostatic pressure of the coelomic fluid and cannot proceed normally if the water content of the body falls by more than 18% (Wolf, 1940). Consequently, the avoidance of desiccation is a keystone in earthworm ecology (Fig. 1).

Evidence will be given later to suggest that competition for food amongst earthworms is often intense and that most of what is known of lumbricid behaviour and distribution may be interpreted in terms of these two basic requirements, water and food.

Except for species with specialized sub-aquatic habitats, the Lumbricidae fall into two main groups, those like *Dendrobaena octaedra* and *Bimastos eiseni* that live in surface organic horizons and ingest little mineral material, and those like *Octolasium cyaneum* and *Allolobophora caliginosa* that live predominantly in the mineral soil. The division is not absolute, for example *L. terrestris* feeds on plant remains drawn from the surface into its burrow and it also ingests soil; *L. rubellus* lives like *L. terrestris* in mull soils but in soils with raw humus is found only in the organic layers. Nevertheless, there are distinctive differences between the two groups of species. In surface feeding species the body wall is deeply coloured with reddish pigments, identified from *L. terrestris* as protoporphyrin and protoporphyrin methyl ester (Laverack, 1960). Subterranean species lack this pigmentation and are predominantly pale in colour. Except for *L. terrestris*, which remains partly in its burrow while feeding, the surface feeders wander over the ground surface*, whereas subterranean species (Table I) rarely do so, and only when sexually mature.

TABLE

The proportions of pigmented and unpigmented Lumbricidae found in soil samples from limestone grassland and collected on the surface at night (from Svendsen, 1957a)

	Pigmented species	Unpigmented species
Soil samples	168	221
Free on the surface at night	103	25

The pigmentation has been supposed to protect the surface active species from damage by ultra-violet irradiation (Merker and Braunig, 1927) but Kalmus, Satchell and Bowen (1955) found that the unpigmented form of *Allolobophora chlorotica* was unaffected by ultra-violet irradiation several times greater than occurs in daylight. Moreover, *L. terrestris*, which is pigmented, is crepuscular and nocturnal and so is unlikely to need protection

* This occurs during and after rainfall under appropriate temperature conditions and has been reported (Svendsen, 1957a) to take place in Pennine moorland equally in daylight and darkness. This seems inconsistent with what is known of the response to light of *L. terrestris*, which is photonegative to strong light and photopositive to light intensities below about 0·0018 metre candles (Hess, 1924) resulting in the restriction of surface feeding to the hours of dusk and darkness. However, unpigmented species, particularly *O. cyaneum*, which are strongly photonegative to all but the weakest light, are frequently seen in daylight on the surface after heavy rain. Some authors (Merker and Braunig, 1927; Merker, 1928; Nagano, 1934) have regarded this as a response to oxygen deficiency in the soil water, but Roots (1955) considered that water-avoiding reaction alone would explain the worms' behaviour after heavy rain.

from ultra-violet irradiation. The close tonal match between the dorsal surface of pigmented earthworms and soil and dead leaves suggests that pigmentation may be a cryptic adaptation to predation by birds (cf. Southern,
1954). There is experimental evidence that the green pigmented form of *A.
chlorotica* survives better than the unpigmented form when subjected to bird
predation (Satchell, unpublished work).

A. REPRODUCTION AND LIFE HISTORY

Reproduction: Reproduction in the Lumbricidae varies from strict cross
breeding in most British *Allolobophora* and *Lumbricus* species to facultative
parthenogenesis in *Dendrobaena* and obligate parthenogenesis in *Octolasium,
Eiseniella, Allolobophora rosea* and *Dendrobaena rubida* f. *tenuis* (Muldal,

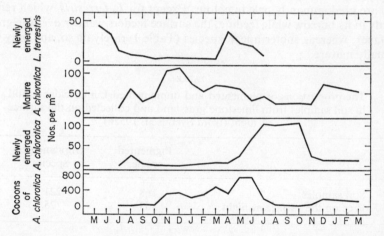

FIG. 2. Seasonal abundance of *A. chlorotica* in "Pastures," Rothamsted 1958–60 (from
Gerard, 1960) and of newly-emerged *L. terrestris* in Heaning Wood, Lancs., 1962–63.

1950). *L. terrestris* mates on the surface; other species mate below ground. So
far as is known, mating occurs throughout the year except when soil conditions are unsuitable (see pp. 269–271) or the worms are in diapause.

Similarly, cocoon production occurs throughout the year when conditions
are suitable. For example, Fig. 2 shows that the number of *A. chlorotica*
cocoons in the soil increases from late summer until May–June, when they
hatch faster than they are produced.

In many situations, particularly at the limits of their range, earthworm
populations may be prevented by adverse moisture and temperature conditions from exploiting the available food resources fully. In less rigorous
habitats competition for food appears to be normal. The fecundity of earthworms depends greatly on the food supply (see p. 280), and this homeostatic
mechanism regulates the abundance of competing populations. A population

that is greatly decreased, e.g. by prolonged drought (see 1959 data in Fig. 1), may take up to 2 years to recover when conditions are favourable, but usually the reproductive potential is sufficient for populations to adjust rapidly to improved conditions. Table II shows the differing fecundity of

TABLE II

Number of cocoons produced per worm per annum in laboratory cultures (Evans and Guild, 1948)

Species	Year	
	1945	1946
L. rubellus	106	79
L. castaneus	65	—
D. subrubicunda	—	42
D. mammalis	17	—
A. caliginosa	27	27
A. chlorotica	27	25
A. nocturna	3	—
A. longa	8	—
A. rosea	—	8
E. foetida	—	11
O. cyaneum	—	13

lumbricid species kept in laboratory cultures, and although the data may bear little relation to fecundity in the field, there is a striking relationship between the numbers of cocoons produced by the different species and the severity of the environmental hazards they are likely to encounter in nature. For example, the deepest burrowing species (Fig. 3), *A. nocturna, A. longa* and *O. cyaneum*, which are most protected from desiccation, produced 3 to 13 cocoons in a year (Evans and Guild, 1948); *L. terrestris*, which also burrows deeply, produces a similar number of cocoons per annum. *A. caliginosa* and *A. chlorotica*, which inhabit the top-soil, produced 25 to 27 cocoons per annum; and *L. rubellus, L. castaneus* and *D. subrubicunda*, which live at the soil surface and are most exposed to heat, drought and predation, produced 42 to 106 cocoons in a year.

Moreover, fecundity depends greatly on soil humidity and temperature (Figs. 20 and 23), as does the incubation period of the cocoons. Cocoons of *A. chlorotica* hatch under favourable moisture conditions in about 36 days at 20, 49 days at 15 and 112 days at 10° c (Gerard, 1960). For some species the range in incubation period is extremely large (Fig. 4). For example, Evans and Guild (1948) record that batches of *A. caliginosa* and *L. castaneus* cocoons, all laid within a fortnight, hatched in two distinct groups separated by 10 to 12 weeks of low winter temperatures. The physiology of incubation is not understood, but a flexible incubation period that enables a species to survive adverse seasons is clearly an advantage. Normally the factors that control cocoon production and incubation period in *L. terrestris*, *L. castaneus* and *A. chlorotica*, and probably other species, synchronize to produce pronounced peaks of emergence in the spring and early summer (Fig. 2), when the growth rate may be 3 to 4 times greater than at other times of the year (Satchell and Skellam, unpublished work).

Like incubation, the growth period from emergence to sexual maturity is flexible and depends on environmental conditions (Table III and Fig. 5). For example, the periods recorded for *A. chlorotica* are 13 weeks at 18°C (Michon, 1954), 17 to 19 weeks at 15°C (Graff, 1953) and 29 to 42 weeks in an

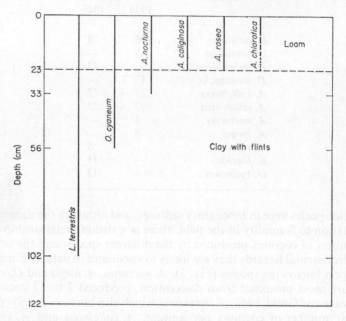

FIG. 3. Vertical distribution of earthworms in a Rothamsted pasture (from Satchell, 1953).

unheated cellar (Evans and Guild, 1948). In woodlands near Merlewood Research Station, Lancashire, there is a peak emergence of this species in early summer, and the population contains the greatest proportion of adults

TABLE III

Growth period (days) from emergence to sexual maturity of *Eisenia foetida* kept at constant temperature (Michon, 1954)

Food	28°C	18°C
Dung	46	59
Tilia leaves	62	91

in the winter following. Development to sexual maturity therefore appears to take about 6 months. *L. terrestris* matures in these sites in about 1 year.

The breeding life of most lumbricids is probably quite short, rarely more than a few months, and much interrupted by unfavourable conditions (see

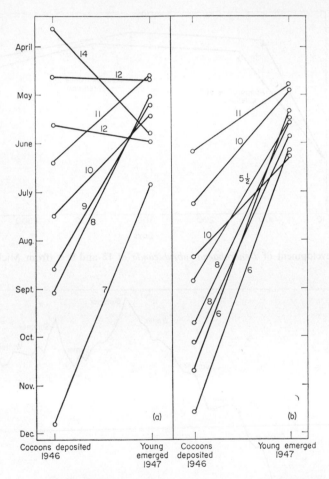

FIG. 4. Incubation periods of cocoons (adapted from Evans and Guild, 1948).
$-\text{o}\frac{6}{\quad}\text{o}-$, incubation time in months. (a) *L. castaneus*; (b) *A. caliginosa*.

p. 266). In the laboratory, individual specimens of *E. foetida, L. terrestris* and *A. longa* have been kept for $4\frac{1}{2}$, 6 and $10\frac{1}{4}$ years respectively (Korschelt, 1914), but these represent the ends of very skew longevity distributions. An average life of rather less than 2 years has been recorded for 10 common field species kept at 18°C, ranging from 15 months for *A. chlorotica* to 31 months for *A. longa* (Michon, 1954). The phenology of maturation, reproduction and senescence observed in these cultures (Fig. 5) differed from that of *L. terrestris* in cultures kept in the ground outdoors (Satchell, 1963) (Fig. 6). These worms became sexually mature at about 1 year, and about half survived at least 3

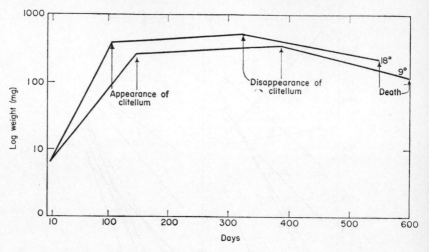

FIG. 5. Development of *Dendrobaena subrubicunda* at 18 and 9°c (from Michon, 1954).

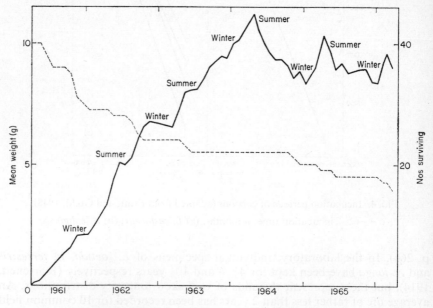

FIG. 6. Growth increment and mortality (---------) of *L. terrestris* reared outdoors.

years showing no sign of senescence. The mortality rate was approximately constant throughout, individuals losing weight before death. The causes of death are unknown, but some individuals which lost weight contained hyphae of a phycomycete in a dense web surrounding the intestine. Growth rate studies and size class frequencies in field populations suggest that the average life of this species is about 15 months, although a few individuals may survive for 8 or 9 years.

B. Seasonal Activity in Relation to Soil Moisture, Temperature and Food Resources

Earthworm activity in the field is markedly seasonal. The production of faeces in the form of wormcasts on the soil surface shows marked maxima in spring and autumn and may cease completely at other times of the year (Fig. 7). Similarly, the numbers of earthworms collected by vermifuge

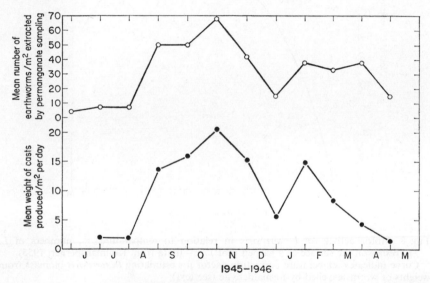

Fig. 7. Seasonal variation in worm cast production and numbers of earthworms extracted by permanganate sampling, Great Field, Rothamsted (redrawn from Evans and Guild, 1947).

sampling, which depends on the activity of the worms to bring them to the soil surface, tend to show spring and autumn maxima (Fig. 7). In both these examples activity has been shown to be correlated with soil temperature and soil moisture (Evans and Guild, 1947), but the response to these factors varies considerably between species.

1. Seasonal activity in L. terrestris

For *L. terrestris*, the relationship between activity and soil temperature can be represented approximately by the curve shown in Fig. 8. This is derived from the numbers of worms collected from woodland sites near Merlewood by a standardized sampling procedure using dilute formaldehyde as an expellant. It is based on a large number of samples taken over a period of 2

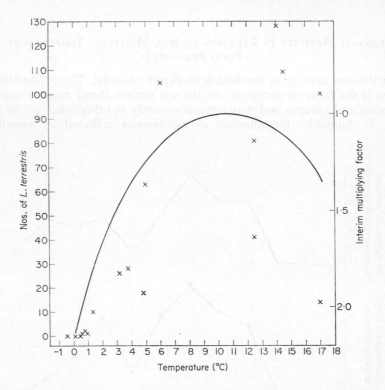

FIG. 8. Motor activity of *L. terrestris* in relation to temperature. ×, numbers of *L. terrestris* on the surface of a garden plot 17 m² (data from Kollmansperger, 1955).
Curve indicates temperature correction factor for estimating *L. terrestris* biomass from weights of worms expelled by formaldehyde (see text).

years, and is corrected for variations in population density. The optimum soil temperature (at a depth of 10 cm) for response to the expellant appears to be about 10·5° c.

The numbers of worms found on the soil surface at night can also be used as an index of activity, provided population density is constant. In Fig. 8 the numbers of worms active on the surface of a garden plot in Germany and the prevailing ground temperatures are shown (Kollmannsperger, 1955), with the formaldehyde sampling temperature curve superimposed. The data,

which are selected to include only nights after recent rain, are consistent with
the curve and suggest an optimum temperature of about 10·5°C for surface
activity. Figure 9 shows similar data for earthworms active on a close mown
lawn at Merlewood.* They represent the worms, mainly *L. terrestris*, seen
on a permanently marked-out area of 12 m² during counts begun at 1 a.m. on
40 nights in March–May 1962. The records suggest that the nights most

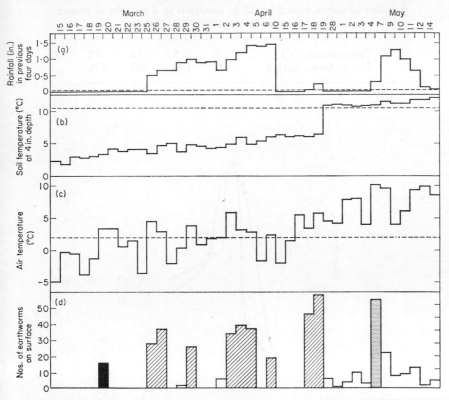

FIG. 9. Surface activity of *L. terrestris* in relation to rainfall and temperature.
(a) Rainfall (in) in previous four days; (b) soil temperature (°C) at 4 in depth; (c) air
temperature (°C); (d) numbers of earthworms on surface: ■, temperature rise after 7
nights below zero; ▨, air temperature above 2°C, soil temperature below 10·5°C, rainfall
during previous 4 days; ▦, rainfall following 12 rainless days.

suitable for earthworm activity were those when grass air-temperatures were
above 2°C, when soil temperatures did not exceed 10·5°C and when there had
been some rain within the previous 4 days. All the main peaks of activity
occurred in such conditions except two, and both of those followed long
periods of inactivity. If it is sufficiently hungry, *L. terrestris* will apparently
come out to feed when it would not otherwise be active on the surface. The

* Recorded by J. M. Nelson.

number of leaves buried by *L. terrestris* kept at constant temperature (Table IV) also suggests that the optimum temperature for motor activity is near 10°c. This is about 2·5°c less than the optimum found by Laverack (1961a) (Fig. 10) for segmental nerve preparations for *L. terrestris*, but the difference may be accounted for by cerebral or synaptic inhibition of motor response.

TABLE IV

Number of leaves buried by 20 *L. terrestris* in 4 months at constant temperatures (Raw, unpublished data)

Temperature (°c)	0	5	10	15
No. of leaves buried	0	178	204	174

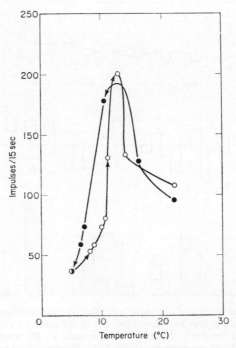

FIG. 10. Graph showing steady rate curve of nervous activity for a range of temperatures. The number of impulses rises towards an optimum at 13°c and then falls as the temperature increases further (from Laverack, 1961a).

The surprisingly low level of the optimum temperature for activity raises questions as to its ecological significance. It can be of no importance as a protection against heat death because the upper lethal temperature for *L. terrestris*, 28°c (Wolf, 1938a), is unlikely to be encountered by earthworms in nature. The negative phototaxis of *L. terrestris* restricts it to crepuscular and nocturnal surface activity, and its deep burrows protect it from the hazards of desiccation in the topsoil, encountered by many species. Moreover, earthworms move away from drying air irrespective of the temperature (Parker and Parshley, 1911; Wolf, 1938b).

Except in very cold weather and during nocturnal surface activity, *L. terrestris* generally occupies the topsoil where, in temperate forests, the temperature rarely exceeds 10·5°c except between mid-May and October (Fig. 32). At this season food supplies from one leaf fall have virtually ended and have not yet been replenished from the next (see Fig. 29). If the respiration rate of *L. terrestris* increased with increasing temperature during this period, death by starvation could follow. The basal metabolic rate of *L. terrestris* increases with rising temperature almost to the thermal death point (Pomerat and Zarrow, 1936), but the reduction of motor activity at temperatures above 10·5°c may counteract this (see pp. 268) and could actually decrease metabolism. The control of motor activity by ambient temperature can thus be regarded as an indirect mechanism that limits oxidative metabolism at a time when food is scarce.

2. *Seasonal activity in* Allolobophora *spp.*

The activity of sexually mature *Allolobophora longa* and *A. nocturna* is interrupted by summer diapause. In nature this begins in May, when soil temperatures are rising and soil moisture is falling. The worm stops feeding, lines a small cell with mucus, rolls into a ball and enters an inactive state during which it loses its secondary sexual characters. It cannot be aroused by changes in soil temperature or humidity, but diapause ends spontaneously in late September or October. Michon (1954) found that diapause did not occur in worms reared at about 9° c with adequate food and soil moisture but more recent work (Doeksen and van Wingerden, 1964) has not confirmed this.

Diapause contrasts with the quiescent state which occurs in immature specimens and also in *A. chlorotica*, *A. caliginosa* and *A. rosea* (Evans and Guild, 1947), when the worms roll up into a ball as the soil becomes too cold or too dry (Table V) and become active again immediately soil conditions become favourable. The ecological significance of this difference is not understood. There is considerable disagreement in the reports of various authors

TABLE V

Percentage of *Allolobophora* spp. in aestivation in an irrigated and a covered plot. Rothamsted 1959–60 (Adapted from Gerard, 1960)

	July	Aug.	Nov.	Feb.	May
% Aestivating					
Irrigated plot	3·8	0	0	0	6·3
Covered plot	100	100	28·5	0	48·1
% Soil Moisture (0–20 cms)					
Irrigated plot	18·2	21·2	23·7	23·6	23·2
Covered plot	11·5	10·2	10·0	18·3	9·4

(Avel, 1929; Evans and Guild, 1947; Michon, 1957; Doeksen and van Wingerden, 1964; Doeksen, 1964) on details of the behaviour of a number of species, and the subject requires further study, particularly of the neurosecretory mechanisms involved.

Fig. 7 shows seasonal changes in wormcast production by *A. longa* and *A. nocturna*.

III. EARTHWORM POPULATIONS— BIOMASS, DISTRIBUTION AND REGULATION

A. METHODS OF POPULATION SAMPLING

Of the numerous methods used to sample earthworm populations, none are equally suitable for all species and all habitats. Evans and Guild (1947), in their pioneering studies on the earthworm populations of agricultural soils in Britain, used potassium permanganate solution to expel worms from the soil, a method limited by the penetration of the solution and the variable response of the earthworms to it. Sorting soil samples by hand is a more efficient procedure for soils that can be easily crumbled (Svendsen, 1955b), but most specimens less than 2 cm long are missed (Nelson and Satchell, 1962). For sampling small species, such as *Eiseniella tetraedra*, in wet, matted hill grassland, Raw (1960) used a method of flotation in magnesium sulphate solution which extracted more than twice the number found by hand sorting. Hand sorting is also impracticable for sampling *L. terrestris*, which when disturbed retreats down its burrow a metre or more deep. The discovery of formaldehyde solution as an expellant for this species (Raw, 1959) and the development of a method of biomass estimation which allows for the effect of soil temperature on the proportion of the population expelled (Satchell, 1963), has opened up the study of this important species in soil biology.

B. BIOMASS

Estimates of earthworm biomass (Table VI) based on formaldehyde sampling, approximately 100 to 250 g/m², suggest that the weight of earthworms in mull sites where *L. terrestris* is present is considerably greater than earlier methods indicated. In particular, Bornebusch's (1930) estimate of 61 g/m², which is much quoted in comparative studies of energy turnover by soil fauna, is much too low to be typical of woodland mull. Present estimates suggest that the earthworm biomass of grassland and woodland are similar on similar soils. Lower weights are found in arable land, but they can exceed 100 g/m² in fields heavily dressed with dung (Raw, 1961a). Estimates of up to 5 g/m² for woodland raw humus and acid moorland sites (Table VI) indicate that the earthworm fauna there differs from that of other habitats and lacks the large, deep burrowing species.

All the above figures are subject to large standard errors arising from seasonal and spatial variation. In a mixed population of *A. caliginosa* and

TABLE VI

Numbers and weights of earthworms in various habitats

	No./m²	g/m²	Sampling method	Locality	Authority
Eriophorum moor	0·01		Dung baiting	Moor House, Westmorland	Svendsen (1957b)
Calluna moor	0·1–0·5		Dung baiting	Moor House, Westmorland	Svendsen (1957b)
Picea raw humus (2 sites)	18–31	0·9–1·5	Tullgren funnels	Denmark	Bornebusch (1930)
Fagus raw humus (2 sites)	23–81	1·2–5·4	Tullgren funnels	Denmark	Bornebusch (1930)
Pseudotsuga raw humus	14	4·7	Hand sorting	Bangor, N. Wales	Reynoldson (1955)
Picea mull	101	5·1	Tullgren funnels and hand sorting	Denmark	Bornebusch (1930)
Fagus mull (3 sites)	73–177	5·9–54	Tullgren funnels and hand sorting	Denmark	Bornebusch (1930)
Quercus mull	122	61	Tullgren funnels and hand sorting	Denmark	Bornebusch (1930)
Mixed wood mull	157	40	Hand sorting	Bangor, N. Wales	Reynoldson (1955)
Mixed wood mull (2 sites)	78–493	148–162*	Formaldehyde	Lake District	Satchell (unpublished)
Apple orchards under grass (23 plots)	25–500	11–122	Hand sorting	Holland	Van Rhee and Nathans (1959)
	848	287	Hand sorting and formaldehyde	Wisbech, Cambs.	Raw (1959) [(1961)
Apple orchards under arable cultivation (4 plots)	13–30	11–23	Hand sorting	Holland	Van Rhee and Nathans (1959)
	196	153	Hand sorting and formaldehyde	Wisbech, Cambs.	Raw (1959) [(1961)
Arable land	220	48	Wet sieving	Germany	Krüger (1952)
Arable land	287	76	Hand sorting	Bardsey Island	Reynoldson et al. (1955)
Arable land	146	50	Hand sorting	Bangor, N. Wales	Reynoldson (1955)
Arable land (4 sets of plots)	389–470	50–106	Formaldehyde	Rothamsted	Raw (1961a)
Base rich grassland (2 sites)		52–110†	Hand sorting	Moor House, Westmorland	Svendsen (1957b)
Base rich grassland (2 sites)	390	56	Hand sorting	Bardsey Island	Reynoldson et al. (1955)
Base rich grassland (2 sites)	481–524	112–120	Hand sorting	Bangor, N. Wales	Reynoldson (1955)

* Yearly averages corrected for temperature variation.
† *L. terrestris* is uncommon on these sites. Only 1 m² was sampled for each estimate.

L. rubellus in a New Zealand pasture the weight of earthworms found by Waters (1955) varied, during $2\frac{1}{2}$ years monthly sampling, between approximately 140 g/m² in the summer to about 269 to 324 g/m² in the winter (Fig. 11). A similar seasonal fluctuation in the biomass of *L. terrestris* occurred in woodland mulls near Merlewood (Fig. 11).

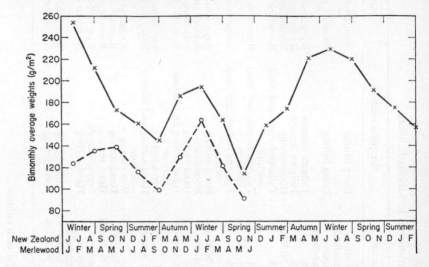

FIG. 11. Seasonal variation of earthworm biomass. –x–x–, *A. caliginosa* (1951–54, New Zealand; from Waters, 1955); – o — o –, *L. terrestris* (1960–61, Merlewood; Satchell, unpublished work).

C. POPULATION AGGREGATION

On one of these sites near Merlewood 10 quadrats, each 0·5 m², were sampled by the formaldehyde method on each of 31 occasions. On one occasion the biomass of *L. terrestris* in individual quadrats ranged from 24 to 113 g. The standard error for the 10 samples varied on the 31 occasions between 6 and 17% of the mean.

The very patchy distribution which these figures reflect is typical of earthworm distribution generally. It is common amongst such species as *L. castaneus* (Fig. 12) which roam over the ground surface and aggregate under dung or similar localized food sources. It also occurs, however, where there is no particular concentration of food as a result of localized concentrations of cocoons. *L. terrestris*, for example, deposits its cocoons in the topsoil near the mouth of its burrow so that a "family" group is formed when the cocoons hatch in the spring. In species such as *L. castaneus*, with a marked seasonal abundance, the spatial distribution passes from a highly aggregated phase in the early summer when the population consists mainly of immature worms, through an intermediate phase when the aggregation is weakened by dispersal and mortality to a winter phase when the population is low, predominantly adult and randomly distributed (Satchell, 1955).

D. SPECIES DISTRIBUTION AND DENSITY REGULATION

Unless saline or very deficient in organic matter, few soils in the temperate zone are incapable of supporting some species of earthworm. Barley (1961) expresses this in the working rule that where temperate grasses can grow, some species of earthworm can also grow. Many factors affect their distribution, the physical and chemical characteristics of the soil, the type of vegetation, and land management, but in most soils the primary factors that determine the population are the supplies of available water and food.

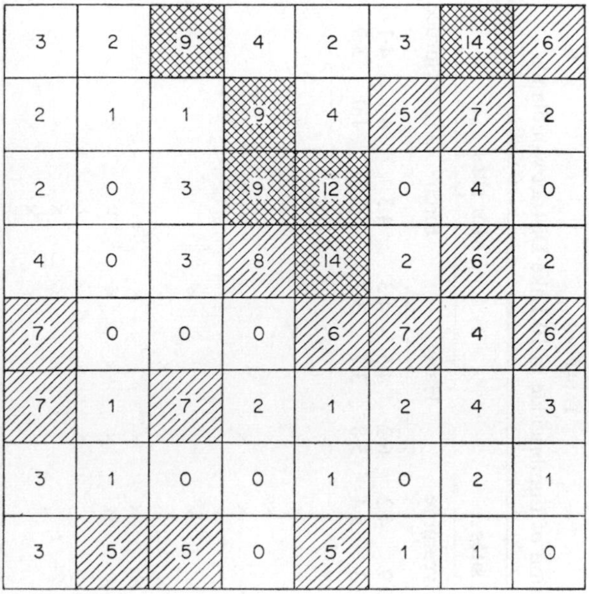

FIG. 12. Distribution of *L. castaneus* in a quadrat 8×8 yd (approx. $53 \cdot 5$ m^2). ▨, more than 8 *L. castaneus*/yd^2; ▨, 5–8 *L. castaneus*/yd^2; □, less than 5 *L. castaneus*/yd^2.

1. Distribution in mull and mor

Table VII shows the distribution of some common earthworm species collected from some Lake District woodlands by hand sorting. The five mull sites are on base rich soils overlying carboniferous limestone, the sites with mor humus, which is of a moder type, overlie base poor slates and shales of the Bannisdale series. Table VIII, taken from Guild (1948), shows the earthworm distribution in a similarly contrasting pair of sites under rich pasture and moorland herbage. In the mull sites, about 8 characteristic species are found, of which three, *L. terrestris*, *A. longa*, *O. cyaneum*, are large worms several grams in weight. In the moder or peaty sites, rarely more than 4 species occur, all are less than 1 gram weight and the largest, *L. rubellus*, is much less

TABLE VII

Distribution of Lumbricidae in 10 Lake District woodlands

	Mull sites							Mor sites			Average size of mature field specimens (g fresh wt.)
	Yew		Sycamore		Hazel			Birch	Oak	Spruce	
pH of litter	6·6	7·5	5·9	4·2	6·2	4·5	4·3	4·3	4·1	4·1	
pH at 15 cm	8·0	6·7	6·3	5·4	5·8	3·7	3·7	3·3	4·0	3·9	
A. rosea	x	x	x	x	x						0·41
A. longa	x	x	x	x	x						2·29
A. caliginosa		x	x	x	x						0·47
A. chlorotica	x	x	x	x	x						0·40
Octolasium cyaneum	x	x	x	x	x	x	x				1·98
L. castaneus	x	x	x	x	x	x	x				0·25
L. terrestris	x	x	x	x	x	x	x				5·58
L. rubellus		x	x	x	x	x	x	x	x		0·75
D. rubida agg.	x						x	x			0·20
D. octaedra						x	x	x	x	x	0·13
Bimastos eiseni						x	x	x	x	x	0·25

TABLE VIII

Species composition of two earthworm populations sampled by
the permanganate method (from Guild, 1948)

Species	Good quality pasture with much clover (No./m²)	Acid peaty soil with coarse herbage and heather (No./m²)
A. longa	1·2	—
A. chlorotica	0·2	—
A. caliginosa	19·5	—
A. rosea	4·4	—
O. cyaneum	1·4	—
L. terrestris	5·8	0·1
L. castaneus	8·2	0·1
L. rubellus	15·3	5·3
D. rubida	1·3	2·0
D. octaedra	0·1	1·8
B. eiseni	—	3·1

abundant than in mull sites. Under increasingly eutrophic conditions, *L. rubellus* and species of the *D. rubida* complex decrease until only *D. octaedra*, and *B. eiseni* remain (Fig. 13) as the characteristic species of such extreme habitats as *Calluna* heath and conifer mor. It is interesting that although these species are adapted to mor sites and are most abundant there, their total biomass is small despite the abundant energy supplies present in the organic matter. Although it is commonly stressed that a mor fauna contains few

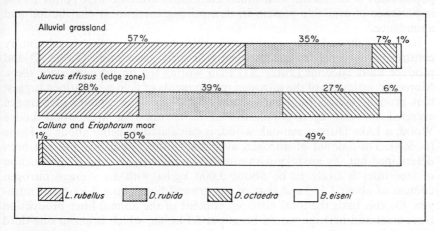

FIG. 13. The relative proportions of 4 species of lumbricids found aggregated in sheep dung on different vegetation types on Moor House National Nature Reserve (from Cragg, 1961).

species, there are many species of enchytraeids, microarthropods, larval Diptera and other groups adapted to mor conditions. The fact that organic horizons persist despite their presence shows that they, and the microflora on which many of them feed, are physiologically unable to fully exploit mor forming litter as food. Handley (1954) suggests that the organic nitrogenous material in mor is less easily digestible than that in mull.

2. Food as a population determinant

(a) *The effect of added food supplies on field populations.* It has already been stated that competition for food is a primary population determinant. One form of evidence for this is the population increase which occurs when food is supplied experimentally in the field. Examples from arable land, grassland and heath are given in Table IX. The first, Broadbalk, is under continuous wheat cropping, and the earthworm population of the plot that receives 14 tons (approx. 35 m. tons/ha) of farmyard manure per acre annually is 3 to 4 times as great as that on an unmanured plot. On Park Grass, a permanent mowing meadow, the earthworm population of a plot receiving 14 tons of farmyard manure and 6 cwt of guano (0·75 m. tons/ha) per acre every fourth year was, in 1952, three times greater than that of an unmanured plot. On Silpho Moor, an acid *Callunetum*, occupied almost solely by *Bimastos eiseni*, 8 years of applying birch litter to the heather at rates simulating natural leaf fall increased the population from less than 1 worm per 20 m^2 to between 1 and 5 worms/m^2.

(b) *Nitrogen as a limiting food constituent.* In the Silpho Moor experiment the nitrogen content of the birch litter was 2 to 3 times that of the *Calluna* litter, and the treated plots on Broadbalk and Park Grass at Rothamsted received heavy dressings of organic nitrogen. The response of the earthworm populations is consistent with much additional evidence that points to the importance of available protein in determining earthworm distribution and abundance.

Barley (1959) and Evans and Guild (1948) have shown that in laboratory cultures earthworms fed on nitrogen rich diets grow more (Table X) and produce more cocoons (Table XI) than worms fed on nitrogen poor diets. Moreover, estimates of the nitrogen requirements of field populations suggest that protein supplies limit earthworm abundance. The amount of nitrogen excreted annually by a population of *L. terrestris* in Merlewood Lodge Wood, a Lake District ash-oak wood, is calculated as being about 33 kg/ha (p. 304). The amount of nitrogen available to this population has not been determined but, by analogy with similar woodlands, the annual production of tree litter is likely to be about 3,000 kg/ha with an average nitrogen content of about 1·5% and that of the ground flora about 8 kg/ha of nitrogen. On this basis the total nitrogen content of the annual litter production from trees and herbage would be about 50 kg/ha, which is about one-third more than the estimate of the amount excreted annually by the *L. terrestris* population.

TABLE IX

Earthworm populations of plots treated with organic materials and control plots
(No./m²)

1. Arable
Broadbalk, Rothamsted
(from A. C. Evans, unpublished work)

	Control	Dung
No. (all species)	74.1	271.8
Weight (all species) (g/m²)	5.0	50.3

Barnfield, Rothamsted
(from Raw, 1961)

Inorganic nitrogen fertilizer	g/m² (all species)	
	Control	Dung
NH₃SO₄	2.5	106.1
NaNO₃ (+ rape cake)	24.1	78.8
NaNO₃	10.2	62.4
None	3.9	49.5

2. Grassland
Park Grass, Rothamsted
(from Satchell, 1955)

	Control	Dung
A. caliginosa	2.9	8.0
A. nocturna	1.3	18.9
A. chlorotica	1.6	0
A. rosea	10.0	21.3
L. castaneus	16.0	59.6
L. terrestris	13.1	22.5
O. cyaneum	6.9	24.5
Total	51.8	154.8

3. Heather Moor
Silpho Moor, N. Yorkshire
(from Satchell, unpublished work)

B. eiseni	Control	Birch Litter
Replicate 1	0	1.4
Replicate 2	0	3.0
Replicate 3	0	5.4
Replicate 4	0	0.6

However, *L. terrestris* ingests, besides litter, a considerable amount of soil. Specimens of various sizes taken from Merlewood Lodge Wood population in March 1961 contained 100 mg of soil (oven dry wt.) per gram body weight. In this species food passes through the gut in about 20 (Parle, 1963b) −24 hours (Satchell, unpublished) so the rate of ingestion appears to be about 100 to 120 mg/g per day. This will of course vary with soil temperature and internal factors affecting the metabolic rate, but if it were maintained for 200 days in a year, the total annual soil intake by the population which had a

TABLE X

Change in body weight of *A. caliginosa* when fed for 40 days on various diets (from Barley, 1959)

	% N content of diet	% Wt. change in worms
Sandy loam soil	0·04	− 53
Phalaris tuberosa roots	0·8	− 26
Phalaris tuberosa leaves	2·0	− 26
Clover roots	2·6	− 2
Clover leaves	4·5	+ 18
Dung on surface	3·3	+ 71
Dung incorporated		+ 111

TABLE XI

The cocoon production of two species of earthworms on various types of organic matter (from Evans and Guild, 1948)

	Mean no. of cocoons produced by 5 earthworms in 3 months	
Organic matter	*A. chlorotica*	*L. castaneus*
Fodder	0·8	9·4
Oat straw	1·4	12·0
Bullock droppings	12·4	73·2
Sheep droppings	14·0	76·0

mean biomass of 120 g/m^2 would be about 2,640 g/m^2. The nitrogen content of the soil at 10 cm depth in Merlewood Lodge Wood is 0·46% (oven dry wt.), so the amount of nitrogen ingested in soil would be about 121 kg/ha. The total nitrogen available to the population from ingested soil and the entire leaf fall would therefore be about 170 kg/ha. Barley (1959) has shown that of the insoluble nitrogen ingested by *A. caliginosa*, 6·4% is excreted in soluble metabolized forms. If a similar proportion of the ingested organic nitrogen is metabolized by *L. terrestris*, and if the food materials were ingested only once in one year, then the total nitrogen excreted annually would be about 11 kg/ha, which is only one-third of that estimated from the excretion data referred to on p. 304. It may be that *L. terrestris* digests protein more efficiently than *A. caliginosa*, but even if it were three times as efficient it would still need the whole of the woodland's litter output to balance its nitrogen excretion rate. As there are other competitors for the litter, the demand must be met by selective feeding on some additional richer source of nitrogen. The soil organic matter of a woodland mull (Heaning Wood) similar to that in Merlewood Lodge Wood has a nitrogen content of 4·9% (Howard, personal communication) and although it can only be inferred that this forms an important nutrient resource for *L. terrestris*, there is substantial evidence that earthworms feed selectively on materials with a high nitrogen content.

(c) *Food selection. Lumbricus terrestris, L. rubellus, A. longa, A. caliginosa, A. rosea, E. foetida* and *D. octaedra* all show ability to distinguish between different kinds of litter (Lindquist, 1941). Food selection has been studied mainly in *L. terrestris*, which preferentially selects the leaves it draws into its burrows when offered a choice of different kinds (Table XII). In general,

TABLE XII

Order of preference of *L. terrestris* for leaves of different plant species
(from Bornebusch, 1953)

(i) *Mercurialis perennis, Urtica dioica, Oxalis acetosella, Agrostis* sp., *Sambucus nigra*

(ii) *Crataegus* sp., *Alnus glutinosa, Ulmus* sp., *Fraxinus excelsior, Prunus padus, Coryllus avellana, Betula* sp., *Acer pseudoplatanus, Carpinus betulus, Ribes* sp.

(iii) *Prunus serotina, Fagus sylvatica, Quercus robur* s.l., *Q. borealis*

(iv) *Abies alba, Pseudotsuga taxifolia*

(v) *Pinus mugo, P. sylvestris, P. nigra* var. *austriaca*

(vi) *Picea abies, Larix decidua, L. leptolepis*

---

leaves of mull species such as ash or *Mercurialis* are preferred to those of oak or beech or conifer needles. Darwin (1881) ascribed the order of selection to the shape and texture of the leaves, but in choice experiments where the effect of leaf shape is removed by using uniform-sized leaf discs or short lengths of conifer needle the order of selection is little changed. Wittich (1953) observed that protein rich litters are more readily taken than litters containing less protein, and this is supported by other experiments showing a correlation between the palatability of various litters and their nitrogen content (Fig. 14). However, litters with a high nitrogen content generally also have a high sugar content (Fig. 15) and, as earthworms are capable of detecting sweet tasting substances (Mangold, 1953; Laverack, 1960), this may explain their selection of protein-rich litter.

The palatability of litter may be much increased by a short period of weathering (Table XIII), and this may result from the breakdown of certain distasteful polyphenolic substances (Fig. 16). Brown, Love and Handley (1963) have recently shown that leaves of spruce, larch, beech and oak, which all produce unpalatable litter, contain condensed tannins which are absent

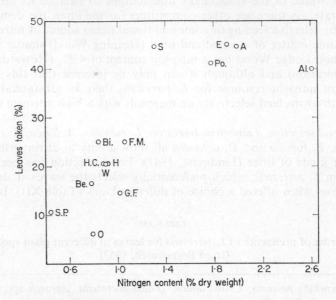

FIG. 14. Palatability of litter in relation to its nitrogen content.
A, Ash; Al, Alder; Be, Beech; Bi, Birch; E, Elder; F, Giant Fir; F.M, Field Maple; H, Hazel; H.C, Horse Chesnut; O, Oak; P, Scots Pine; Po, Poplar; S, Sycamore; W, Walnut.

from *Mercurialis*, nettle, elderberry, ash and Wych elm which are all highly palatable to earthworms. Moreover, it can be shown (Fig. 17) that (+)-catechin, a commonly occurring leaf polyphenol, is repellant to *L. terrestris*, which withdraws from solutions of (+)-catechin at speeds directly related to their concentration.

TABLE XIII

Number of leaf discs removed from the soil surface by *L. terrestris* in laboratory experiments (Satchell, unpublished work)
(6 discs of each kind given nightly for 11 nights)

Duration of weathering after leaf fall	Beech	Oak	Hazel	Birch
—	57	59	77	87
6 weeks	80	74	89	92
12 weeks	88	90	98	101

The increased palatability of oak litter after weathering appears to result from microbial activity. In selection experiments with *L. terrestris* (Table XIV), fresh oak litter discs kept in running tap water for 14 days were not taken in significantly greater numbers than untreated discs, but their palatability was increased considerably by incubation in water at room temperature

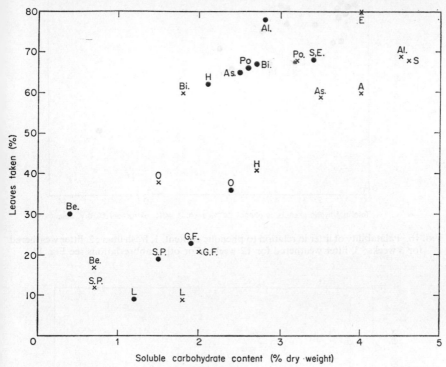

FIG. 15. Palatability of litter in relation to its soluble carbohydrate content. Percentage of leaf discs and conifer needles removed from the soil surface by *L. terrestris* in laboratory experiments.

Six discs or needle lengths of each kind given nightly for 33 nights.

x, Fresh litter. ●Weathered litter; As, Aspen; L. Larch. For other abbreviations see Fig. 14.

for 2 weeks following exposure outdoors for 48 hours. It is known that the so-called white rot fungi produce enzymes capable of oxidizing phenols and that *Penicillium solitum* and *Aspergillus niger* can decompose substances such as (+)-catechin (Bocks, Brown and Handley, 1963) and it may be that related microbial enzyme systems degrade the leaf constituents unpalatable to earthworms.

3. *The response of earthworms to soil acidity*

The distribution of earthworms in relation to mull and mor (Tables VI, VII and VIII) appears to be controlled by their response to the pH of their

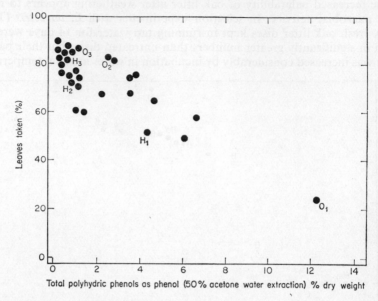

Fig. 16. Palatability of litter in relation to phenolic content. 1, fresh litter; 2, litter weathered for 6 weeks; 3, litter weathered for 12 weeks. For other abbreviations see Fig. 14.

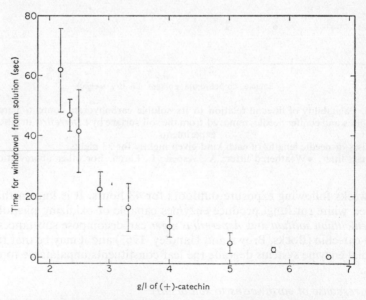

Fig. 17. Reaction of *L. terrestris* to aqueous solutions of (+)-catechin. Means of 5 replicates, and 95% confidence limits.

TABLE XIV

Selection by *L. terrestris* of leached and incubated oak litter discs
(Satchell and Lowe, in press)

Disc treatment	Replicate	No. of discs taken out of 50 supplied	
		Treated	Control
14 days in running water	1	15	16
	2	26	16
14 days' incubation in 5 cc water at 17°c after 2 days' exposure outdoors	1	34	12
	2	42	16
14 days' incubation in 5 cc water at 26°c after 2 days' exposure outdoors	1	35	5
	2	42	19

environment. In laboratory experiments the response of different species to solutions of different acidity has been found to correspond with their distribution in relation to pH in nature (Laverack, 1961b). For example, *A. longa* inhabits soils down to pH 4·5, *L. rubellus* soils down to about pH 3·7 to 3·8 and *L. terrestris* soils down to pH 4·1 and occasionally lower. By flooding the body wall of these species with buffer solutions and recording the action potentials in the segmental nerves, Laverack (1961b) showed that the threshold for stimulation in *A. longa* lay between pH 4·6 and 4·4; *L. terrestris* had a threshold at pH 4·3 to 4·1; and *L. rubellus* at pH 3·8 (Fig. 18).

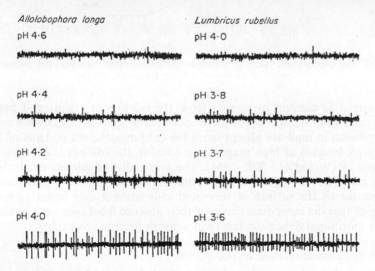

FIG. 18. Oscilloscope recordings of electrical activity in segmental nerves of earthworms stimulated by solutions of different pH (from Satchell, 1960).

Laverack supported this neurophysiological evidence with experiments on behaviour. Specimens of the same 3 species were held so that the anterior segments dipped into buffer solutions. *A. longa* withdrew the prostomium abruptly from solutions of pH 4·4 and below, *L. terrestris* responded similarly at a threshold of about pH 4·0 and *L. rubellus* at about pH 3·8 (Fig. 19). These thresholds correspond to the acidity tolerance of each species in the field. Another type of experiment confirmed this. When *A. longa* and *L. rubellus* were placed in pots of soil of acidities ranging from pH 4·0 to 4·9, *L. rubellus* burrowed into all the soils, but *A. longa* only burrowed into the soils of pH 4·6 and above. On soils of pH 4·4 to 4·0 the *A. longa* searched actively for a time and then became quiescent on the surface, where they eventually died.

It has been customary for many years to ascribe the absence of the larger earthworms from very acid soils to the soils' deficiency in calcium. Calcium

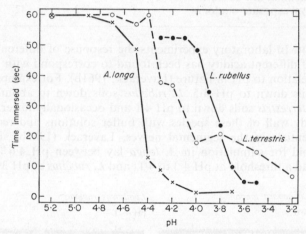

FIG. 19. The average time taken to withdraw the prostomium from acid pH solutions in 3 species of earthworm (from Laverack, 1961b).

is excreted as calcium carbonate from the calciferous glands and plays an important role in earthworm metabolism. The species of earthworms normally found in mull are absent from the calcium-deficient podzols of Rhum although, because of high magnesium content, the soil pH is between about 5·0 and 7·0 (Wragg and Ball, 1964). The availability of calcium or nitrogen or both may limit the earthworm population directly, but the fact that mull species die on the surface of very acid soils without ever ingesting any soil suggests that the immediate cause of their absence from mor soils generally is not a nutritional deficiency but their sensory response to acidity.

4. Distribution in relation to soil moisture

Various behaviour mechanisms by which Lumbricidae avoid desiccation have already been described. Although the inhibition of feeding by drought

(reflected in *Allolobophora* spp. by reduced casting and in *L. terrestris* by reduced surface activity) helps individuals to survive, it reduces population
densities by decreasing the rate of cocoon production. The effect of soil
moisture on cocoon production by *A. chlorotica* is illustrated (Fig. 20) by

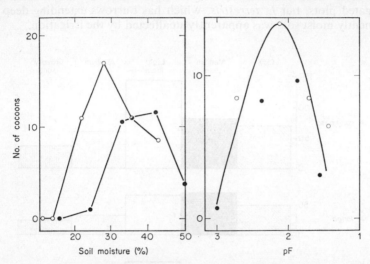

FIG. 20. Relationship between soil moisture and cocoon production by *A. chlorotica* in 2
Rothamsted fields (from Evans and Guild, 1948).
●—● Westfield; o—o, Bones Close

the work of Evans and Guild, who found an optimal soil moisture tension for
cocoon production somewhat above the sticky point in the region of pF 2.

The distribution of earthworms in relation to soil types recorded by Guild
(1948) (Fig. 21) probably reflects a combination of the effects of soil moisture
and available food, but the differences between species in their tolerance of
drought are greater than Fig. 21 may suggest. Table XV illustrates the

TABLE XV

Earthworm populations of irrigated and unirrigated plots on Lower
Greensand (Woburn, Beds., May, 1960) (adapted from Gerard, 1960)

| | No./8·9 m² | |
| | (Sampled by formaldehyde method) | |
Species	Irrigated	Un-irrigated
L. terrestris	231	224
A. longa	3	1
A. chlorotica	83	2
A. caliginosa	39	0
A. rosea	33	0

10*

striking effect of deficient soil moisture on the earthworm populations
of irrigated and un-irrigated plots on sandy soils on the lower Greensand at
Woburn (Gerard, 1960). The topsoil species *A. chlorotica*, *A. caliginosa*
and *A. rosea* were common on irrigated plots and virtually absent from
un-irrigated plots, but *L. terrestris*, which has burrows extending deep into
permanently moist soil, was apparently unaffected by the irrigation.

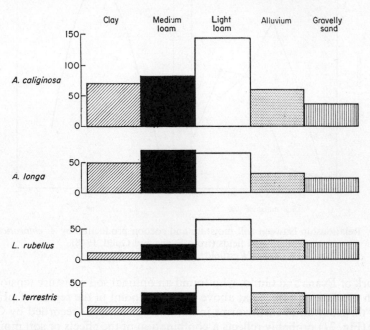

FIG. 21. Density of earthworm populations (thousands/acre) in various soil types in
Scotland (adapted from Guild, 1948). ▨, clay; ■, medium loam; □, light loam; ▩,
alluvium; ▥, gravelly sand.

The two colour forms of the polymorphic *A. chlorotica* provide an interesting example of the effect of soil moisture on distribution at sub-specific level.
A. chlorotica inhabits a wide range of habitats from the permanently sub-
merged root zone of *Phragmites* beds in Lake Windermere to forest, field and
garden soils. The two morphs are occasionally found together but generally
they form separate populations, the green form in wet sites and the pink form
in drier sites. Table XVI shows this for soils in northern England. The physiological basis for the different distributions of the two forms has not yet been
elucidated (Roots, 1955, 1956).

5. *Distribution in relation to soil temperature*

In arable soils in continental climates the earthworm population may be
largely destroyed by autumn frosts (Hopp, 1947), but it is exceptional under

TABLE XVI

Occurrence of the two colour forms of *A. chlorotica* in relation to soil moisture in summer

Habitat	Location	% Green form (Sample size: 100–300 worms)	% Soil moisture, September 1959
Marshy ground and beside tarns, streams and rivers	Long Sleddale (W)*	100	41
	Colt Park Spring (Y)	100	41
	Meathop Marsh (L)	99	41
	Sunbiggin Tarn (W)	99	52
	River Gilpin (W)	93	17
	Kendal Fell Tarn (W)	91	53
Lowland pastures	Foulshaw (W)	45	26
	Sampool (W)	4	30
Upland limestone grassland	Blawith Fell (L)	8	17
	Helsington Fell (W)	0	17
	Kendal Fell (W)	0	21
Gardens	Merlewood (L)	0	20
	Levens (W)	0	21
	Kendal (W)	0	13
Woodland	Witherslack (L)	0	20
	Eggerslack (L)	0	22
	Brigsteer (W)	0	24

* (L) = Lancs., (W) = Westmorland, (Y) = Yorks.

grass or forest cover for the soil to freeze deep enough to affect the population. Under natural conditions, the upper lethal temperature determined experimentally as 28°C for *L. terrestris* (Wolf, 1938a; Hogben and Kirk, 1944), 25°C for *E. foetida* and 26°C for *A. caliginosa* (Grant, 1955b), depends on soil moisture (Table XVII). Like terrestrial gastropods, the earthworm can maintain a lower body temperature than that of its surroundings by evaporating body water. At relative humidities above 37% the body temperature of *L. terrestris* does not exceed that of a wet bulb thermometer by more than 2°C (Hogben and Kirk, 1944).

Body temperature may also be controlled to some extent by thermotaxis. In temperature choice experiments with worms conditioned at 20° C, Grant (1955b) found that *E. foetida* moved into temperatures between 15·7° C and 23·2° C and *A. caliginosa* congregated between 10° C and 23·2° C.

In the field, response to temperature changes is probably the main cause of seasonal movement up and down the soil profile (Fig. 22), and in nature it is unlikely that earthworms are ever unable to avoid lethal temperatures or temperatures too high for optimum cocoon production (Fig. 23). Neverthe-

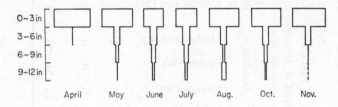

FIG. 22. Seasonal distribution of *Allolobophora* spp. in a pasture field, Rothamsted, 1959 (adapted from Gerard, 1960).

less, soil temperature is of fundamental importance in earthworm ecology because of its effects on motor activity and metabolic rate.

6. Distribution in relation to soil aeration

The ability to tolerate submergence differs greatly between lumbricid species. Populations of *A. chlorotica* occur entirely below water in Lake Windermere. Aquatic populations of *A. caliginosa* and *A. longa* are unknown but when offered a choice of water-saturated and air-filled soil a few are always found in the saturated soil. *L. rubellus* occurs in sewage beds but avoids immersion in water when offered a choice (Roots, 1956), while *L. terrestris* and *D. rubida subrubicunda* are never found in aquatic habitats. Whereas all these species can survive many months in aerated water, *Helodrilus oculatus* can live permanently in habitats of very low oxygen tension, such as the mud under the River Thames (Dobson and Satchell, 1956).

The effect of soil aeration on earthworm distribution is at present not well documented although it is undoubtedly important, particularly in moorland,

TABLE XVII

Number of *A. chlorotica* dead and aestivating after 30 days in experimental cultures (initially 10 worms per culture) (from Gerard, 1960)

Soil temperature (°C)	Soil Moisture							
	Very wet		Moist		Dry		Very dry	
	No. aestivating	No. dead	No. aestivating	No. dead	No. aestivating	No. dead	No. aestivating	No. dead
5	0	0	0	0	1	7	—	10
10	0	0	1	0	3	4	—	10
14	1	0	1	0	2	7	—	10
20	1	0	7	1	4	6	—	10
25	5	1	5	5	—	10	—	10

bog and similar highly organic sites. The distribution of *B. eiseni* and *D. octaedra* appears to be limited in some sites by the minimum oxygen tensions occurring at certain seasons, but this is difficult to demonstrate because factors such as soil water content, the presence of raw humus, the plant cover and soil microflora, which may have independent effects on earthworms, are linked as causes or effects to variations in the soil atmosphere. For example, on Silpho moor, an acid heather moor (see p. 278), dung bait trapping showed (Satchell, unpublished work) that *Bimastos eiseni* was relatively abundant in drier areas but scarce or absent in wetter areas characterized by the presence

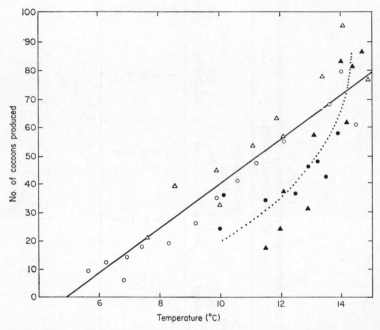

Fig. 23. Relationship between cocoon production by *L. rubellus* and increasing and decreasing temperature (Evans and Guild, 1948).
Increasing temperature, △ (1945), ○ (1946); decreasing temperature, ▲ (1945), ● (1946).

of *Eriophorum*. The calcium and nitrogen concentrations in the upper layers were correlated with the earthworm distribution but could not account for the marked difference between wet and dry areas. However, oxidation-reduction potentials measured after heavy rainfall in November (Fig. 24) showed that extremely low oxygen tensions sometimes occurred in the surface horizons of the wetter areas. As *B. eiseni* can survive in aerated water, it seems likely that low oxygen tensions rather than water were responsible for the scarcity of worms in these areas.

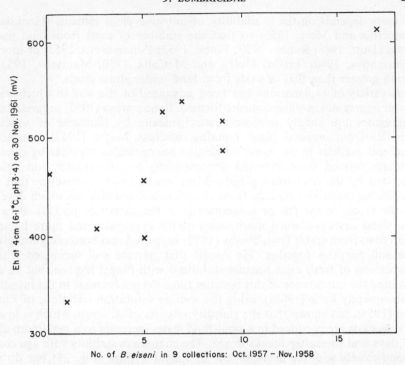

FIG. 24. Distribution of *Bimastos eiseni* in relation to oxidation-reduction potentials at 10 trapping points on Silpho moor, Yorkshire.

IV. EFFECTS OF EARTHWORMS ON SOIL STRUCTURE

A. THE STRUCTURAL STABILITY OF EARTHWORM CASTS

The aeration and water-holding capacity of soil are largely determined by its physical structure: with a good crumb structure water is retained in the capillary spaces within the aggregates, allowing continuous gaseous diffusion between them. Mull is characterized by an aggregated structure, and in defining mull, Kubiena (1953) states, "Practically all the aggregates are earthworm casts or residues of them." Consequently, one of the most important effects of earthworm activity appears to be its influence on the crumb structure of mull soil.

From the evidence of wet-sieving and water-drop stability tests it has been generally agreed by numerous workers (Bassalik, 1913; Joachim and Pandittesekera, 1948; Bakhtin and Polsky, 1950; Nijhawan and Kanwar, 1952) that worm casts contain more water-stable aggregates than non-cast soil and, in laboratory experiments, that worm-worked soils are more water stable than unworked soils (Gurianova, 1940; Hopp, 1946; Guild, 1955). The stability of casts depends on the availability of nutritive plant remains (Hoeksema, Jongerius and Meer, 1956) so that the stability of casts from land under grass (Dutt, 1948; Swaby, 1950; Finck, 1952; Ponomareva, 1953) or lucerne (Gurianova, 1940; Teotia, Duley and McCalla, 1950; Mamytov, 1953) is much greater than that of casts from land under straw crops.

A variety of explanations has been advanced of the way in which water stable aggregates in wormcasts are formed. Ponomareva (1953) suggested that aggregates are simply reinforced mechanically by filaments of vascular bundles from ingested plant remains, whereas Meyer (1943) considered that soil particles in the worm's intestine are cemented together by calcium humate formed from ingested decomposing organic matter and calcite excreted by the calciferous glands. Most workers agree, however, that the stabilizing materials originate from the microbial populations which develop in the faeces in the gut or subsequently in the casts (see p. 313). Because grassland casts contained more water stable aggregates and more bacteria than casts from arable land, Swaby (1950) suggested that bacterial gums glued the soil particles together. He found that pasture soil incubated with a suspension of fresh casts became stabilized with fungal hyphae, but he discounted the importance of this because fungi do not increase in the intestine. Subsequently Parle (1963a), using the sodium saturation technique of Emerson (1954), has shown that the stability of casts of *A. longa*, which is low at first as casts are produced in a semi-fluid state, increases to a maximum after 15 days and thereafter breaks down. The changes in stability with age correspond closely with the development of fungal hyphae (Fig. 25) but do not

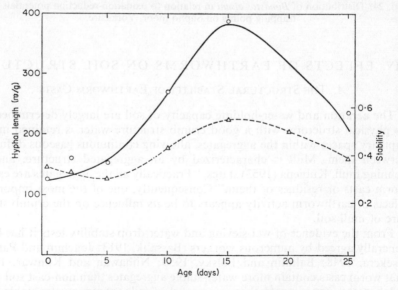

FIG. 25. Length of hyphae in m/g and aggregate stability in ageing casts (from Parle, 1963a).
–o——o–, hyphae; --△---△--, stability.

correspond with changes in the polysaccharide content of the casts. This could mean that the development of fungal hyphae after defaecation is the principal factor in the stability of wormcasts.

In order to assess the importance of wormcasting in the stability of the crumb structure of the soil it is necessary to know both how long the stability of earthworm faeces persists and the rate of faeces production. Evans (1948) calculated the latter on the basis of cast production on the soil surface by *A. nocturna* and *A. longa*. This varied considerably from 1 to 25 tons/acre per annum (approx. 2·5 to 63 m. tons/ha) dry weight. Assuming that, weight for weight, the other species consumed an equal amount of soil but voided it underground, the total soil consumption by earthworms in 8 fields at Rothamsted was estimated at 4 to 36 tons/acre per annum (approx. 10 to 90 m. tons/ha). In four fields this amounted to an annual consumption of 8·7, 5·0, 4·7 and 1·25% of the total weight of the topsoil to a depth of 10 cm which, Evans therefore concluded, would pass through the alimentary tracts of the earthworm population in $11\frac{1}{2}$–80 years. Barley (1959) estimated that an Australian population of *A. caliginosa*, active for 150 days/year, and with a biomass of 80 g/m², would take 60 years to eat a weight of soil equal to that in the top 15 cm of the profile. It is unlikely, however, as these calculations may be taken to assume, that an earthworm population would consume the whole of the topsoil before reingesting any part of it. The rates of ingestion for the four Rothamsted fields, re-calculated on the assumption that the soil was all equally likely to be ingested at any time, are represented in Fig. 26.

If cast stability lasts for less than a month and if, as Evans' figures suggest, less than 10% of the topsoil passes through earthworms annually, then the effect of earthworm activity on the structural stability of soil is likely to be small. However, a number of relevant factors have not yet been sufficiently investigated to warrant this conclusion. For example, the persistence of the stability of earthworm faeces deposited below ground has not been studied, nor has the effect on soil aggregation of burial of plant remains by earthworms been taken into account. Iimura and Egawa (1956) observed a great increase in water-stable aggregates when various soils were incubated in the presence of plant residues. As in the casts studied by Parle, the greatest increase, during the first 16 days, coincided with a vigorous development of fungal hyphae. With the subsequent disappearance of the hyphae the larger aggregates decreased and the smaller aggregates increased in quantity, and the authors suggested that the binding effect of the hyphae was taken over by the cementing effect of bacterial gums. The continual enrichment of burrow walls with mucus and urine could have more influence on aggregating microorganisms than earthworm faeces, but no estimate of the effect of this on soil structure has been made.

In assessing the role of earthworms and soil structure the following comment by Jacks (1963) should be remembered: "It may be justifiable to make the rather sweeping generalization that in the two great plant-ecologically distinguished worlds of the soil, the movement of plant roots is the major structure-forming factor in grassland soils, and the movement of animals in

forest soils. It may be noted that, although the role of earthworms in helping
to create the crumb structure of Russian chernozems has been accepted since
the time of Dokuchaev, these animals do not commonly occur in North
American prairie soils. Crumb-mull structure can be produced in grassland
soils without earthworms though they appear to be essential for its formation
in at least temperate forest soils."

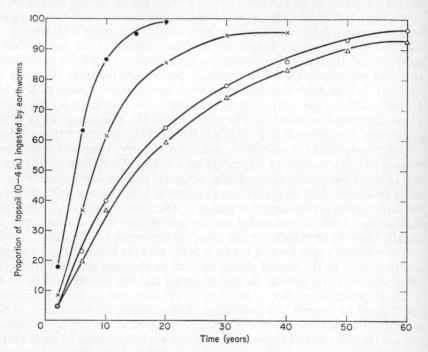

FIG. 26. Rate of turnover of topsoil in 3 grass fields at Rothamsted (recalculated from
Evans, 1948).

•, Hypothetical population of 200 g/m²; ×, Parklands; o, Pastures; △, Great Field III.

B. THE EFFECT OF BURROWS ON SOIL AERATION AND DRAINAGE

The space occupied by earthworm burrows may account for about two-
thirds of the air capacity of some soils, and Stöckli (1949) claimed that the
volume of earthworm tunnels under grass was as much as 0·05 cc/cc of soil.
However, species which defaecate below ground can only open the soil at
one point at the expense of consolidating it at another or filling in existing air
spaces and, apart from effects on crumb structure, the only activity which can
increase soil air space under field conditions is surface casting. Evans' data
for cast production at Rothamsted suggest that the volume of soil ejected
annually onto the surface by earthworms amounts to only about 0·5 to 6·0%

of the soil in the top 10 cm, the total pore space amounting to 40 to 59% of its volume. Since the rate of casting on the Rothamsted pastures appears to be about average for western Europe, it seems that the effect of earthworms on soil aeration is of only minor importance.

The effect of worm burrows on drainage may, however, be considerable. Slater and Hopp (1947) have shown that infiltration is generally much faster in field soils with high earthworm populations than where populations are low. Although it is difficult to believe that earthworm populations were the only differing factor in their sites, their results are supported by Guild's (1955) laboratory experiments, in which he found that water passed through containers of light sandy soil in 2 days when the soil was worm-worked and in 8 days in the absence of worms. In a number of laboratory experiments (Kahsnitz, 1922; Archangels'kii, 1929; Hopp and Slater, 1948), where yields from plants grown in containers have been higher in the presence of earthworms, the increase has been attributed to improved aeration and drainage. In an apple orchard in Cambridgeshire, Raw (1959) counted an average of 18·5 *L. terrestris* burrows opening at the surface per quadrat of 4 ft². If the average diameter of such burrows is reckoned as $\frac{1}{4}$ in, this would be equivalent in cross section to a drainage pipe 1·75 in (44 mm) in diameter in each metre square.

V. CONSUMPTION OF PLANT LITTER BY EARTHWORMS

A. COMPARISON OF CONSUMPTION BY LABORATORY AND FIELD POPULATIONS

The quantity of plant litter and other organic materials eaten or buried by earthworms is difficult to estimate, but several lines of evidence (see, for example, p. 278) suggest that where earthworms flourish the amount of organic matter they consume is limited by the availability of supplies rather than their capacity to ingest it. Laboratory data for a number of species illustrate this: Guild (1955) fed cultures of *A. longa, A. caliginosa* and *L. rubellus* for 2 years on cow dung and calculated the average dry weight of dung consumed per worm per annum. The weights obtained for the 3 species were respectively 35 to 40, 20 to 24 and 16 to 20 g. Consumption of dung by immature specimens of *A. caliginosa* at the rate of 80 mg oven dry matter/g fresh body weight, almost twice that found by Guild for this species, has been recorded by Barley (1959). Guild calculated that the annual consumption of dung by a moderate density field population of 100,000 adults acre (approx. 25/m²) each of *A. longa, A. caliginosa* and *L. rubellus* would be about 7 to 8 tons/acre (approx. 17 to 20 m. tons/ha) with a total consumption, allowing for immature individuals, of about 10 to 12 tons/acre (approx. 25 to 30 m. tons/ha). Cows produce about 52 lb (approx. 24 kg) dry weight of dung daily and if, say, two-thirds of this fell on the fields of a dairy farm stocked at a density of 1 cow/2 acres (0·8 ha), the amount falling annually to the pasture would be of the order of $2\frac{1}{2}$ to 3 tons/acre (approx. 6 to $7\frac{1}{2}$ m. tons/ha) or about one-quarter of the estimated potential consumption by the earthworm population.

A similar excess of laboratory consumption over field supplies is suggested by the quantity of leaf litter eaten by earthworms under experimental conditions. Franz and Leitenberger (1948) fed *L. rubellus* on hazel litter and recorded an average daily consumption of 20·39 mg dry weight per worm, about 27 mg/g fresh weight of worm. Van Rhee (1963) fed alder leaves and orchard and grassland vegetation to 6 species of earthworms and from 16 trials found an average food consumption of 27 mg/g fresh weight of worm. Needham (1957) fed *L. terrestris* on elm leaves and found a maximum consumption of 80 mg/g worm per day and an average of about one-third of this, similarly about 27 mg/g per day. In the first experiment the hazel litter was collected fresh, air dried and fed in this relatively unpalatable state, and in Needham's experiment a number of worms lost weight. The rate of litter consumption under optimal conditions would therefore seem likely to be higher than 27 mg/g per day.

The weight of leaves falling annually in temperate deciduous woodland is generally of the order of 3,000 kg/ha (Galoux, 1953). A population of *L. terrestris* such as that of Merlewood Lodge Wood, if it fed at the rate of 27 mg/g per day, would consume the entire annual leaf fall in about 3 months. Leaves may in fact, under favourable conditions, be removed from the ground surface by earthworm action, if not actually ingested, at rates similar to this, as illustrated by Raw's (1962) studies of litter disappearance in apple orchards. In one experiment apple leaves were placed under netting in amounts equivalent to 2,000 kg/ha in a cultivated orchard containing approximately 168 g/m² of *L. terrestris*. After 2 months (8 February to 8 April, 1960) only 0·5% by weight of the leaves remained on the surface, all but 14 out of 1,000 leaves having been buried by earthworms. The rate of disappearance, including loss by microbial decomposition while on the surface, calculated from the initial weight of the leaves and the number pulled into earthworm burrows, appears to have been approximately 20 mg/g per day. Data for another orchard under grass with a *L. terrestris* biomass of 53·03* g/m² yields the same rate over a period of 1 month (27 February to 31 March, 1961). The rate of leaf removal by *L. terrestris* is affected, however, by soil temperature, the quantity of leaves present, and the availability of alternative food resources; the average rate for a series of five orchards during three winters was approximately 5 mg/g per day (Figs 27, 28). The low average rate of activity reflects the low average soil temperature, which was 5·0°c at 30 cm depth.

No comparable data are available for forests, but the work of Bocock *et al.* (1960) demonstrates the different rates of litter disappearance in woodland sites with differing earthworm populations. Ash and oak litter was put out at leaf-fall in coarse meshed nets on two sites, on a moder with a low density earthworm population in which *Bimastos eiseni* was the only species found, and a mull containing numerous *L. terrestris* and *A. rosea*. On the latter site, ash litter disappeared so rapidly that, after about 6 months, only a few midribs remained. Both ash and oak leaves on the moder lost weight slowly and,

* Estimate based on 15% loss of weight on preservation in formalin.

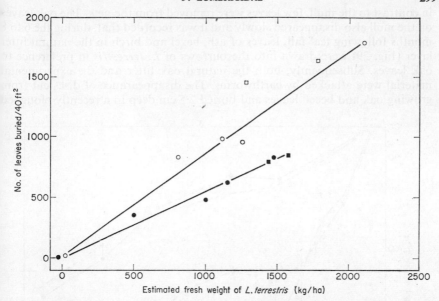

FIG. 27. Effect of initial amount of leaf litter on amount buried by *L. terrestris* in 5 grass and 2 arable orchards. ●, cages with 100 leaves; ×, cages with 200 leaves; ■, □, arable orchards, regression lines for grass orchards only (adapted from Raw, 1962).

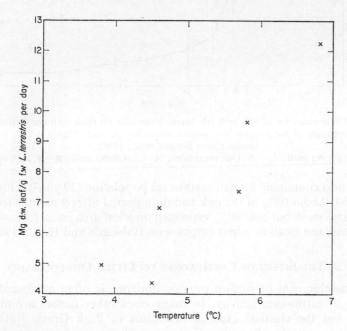

FIG. 28. Weight of leaves buried in apple orchards (and loss of weight prior to removal) during periods of 5-12 weeks (adapted from Raw, 1962).

in contrast to the mull, few leaves were removed from the nets. The oak leaves
on the mull also disappeared slowly and it was recorded that, during the 6 to 8
months following leaf fall, leaves of ash, hazel and birch in the natural litter
layer (Fig. 29) were drawn into the burrows of *L. terrestris* in preference to
oak leaves. Subsequently, both the natural oak litter and the experimental
material were attacked by earthworms. The disappearance of discs cut from
growing oak and beech leaves and buried 2·5 cm deep in a recently ploughed

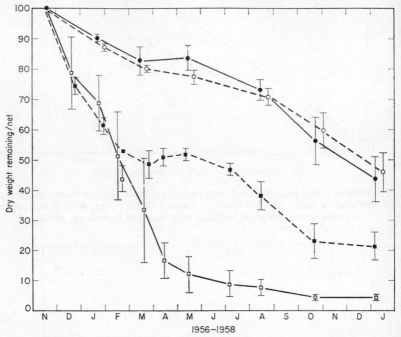

FIG. 29. Disappearance of oak and ask leaves from nets on sites with contrasting humus
types. Percentage of the original dry weight remaining per net. Means ±95% confidence
limits (from Bocock *et al.*, 1960).
●—●, Oak on mull; ○ --- ○, Oak on moder; □—□, Ash on mull; ■—■, Ash on moder.

pasture field containing a small earthworm population (39 g/m²) is illustrated
in Fig. 30. About 95% of the oak had disappeared after 9 months from nets
with a large mesh but only 40%, estimated on a leaf area basis, from nets with
a mesh size too small to admit earthworms (Edwards and Heath, 1963).

B. The Effect of Earthworms on Litter Disappearance

The development of surface organic horizons is often attributed to the
absence of earthworm activity. In many cases other factors are more important but the classical experimental plots of Park Grass, Rothamsted
provide an example where the effects of earthworm activity may be fairly

:learly defined. As a result of repeated applications of ammonium sulphate
the acidity on some plots has eliminated the earthworm population completely and a thick mat of dead vegetation has developed. It has been suggested that the mat of partly decomposed herbage which accumulated
was formed because the intense acidity of the soil retarded the decay of
organic matter. This is evidently only part of the explanation, for when the
organic matter is mixed with the soil it decomposes readily. Probably the
primary cause of the formation of a "mat" in these plots is the complete
absence of worms to pull the dead herbage into the soil (Richardson, 1938).
A comparable accumulation of organic matter in an orchard under grass

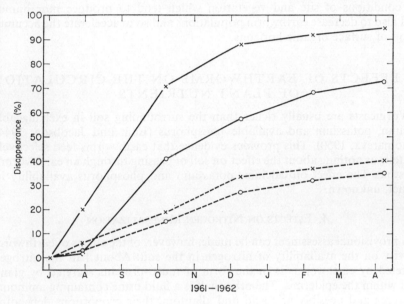

FIG. 30. Decomposition of leaf discs by soil animals (from Edwards and Heath, 1963).
×—×: oak leaf discs in 7 mm mesh bags; o—o: beech leaf discs in 7 mm mesh
bags; ×---×: oak leaf discs in 0·5 mm mesh bags; o---o: beech leaf discs in 0·5 mm
mesh bags.

occurred where the earthworm population had been poisoned by copper
sulphate spray (Raw, 1962). Both soil profiles showed the clear dis-
junction between the organic layer and the mineral soil and the absence of
crumb structure which are characteristic of mor soil. In New South Wales,
Australia, irrigated pastures from which earthworms are absent may accumulate surface mats up to 4 cm thick and containing as much as 147 kg/ha of
organic nitrogen. In some of these sites where earthworms have been introduced experimentally, the mixing of voided earth with the litter has led to the
disappearance of the mat as a discrete layer (Barley and Kleinig, 1964).

The decomposition curves presented in Fig. 29 for leaf litter on a moder site suggest that where there are few earthworms or other large litter-feeding invertebrates, even such a readily decomposed material as ash litter would tend to accumulate in a North European climate. Whether the resulting humus form would be like that of mor formed from oak, beech or conifer litter is unknown but seems unlikely in view of the difference in the poly-phenolic constituents of the materials. Handley (1954) states, "There are indications that some undetermined properties of the vegetable debris control the soil fauna, so that the soil fauna cannot be regarded as a primary deter-mining factor in the formation of mull and mor." Studies on the palatability of litter to earthworms reported on p. 281–3 and the responses of earthworms to environmental acidity (described on p. 283–6) support this view. It appears that the conditions of site and vegetation which tend to produce mor humus tend also to decrease earthworm populations and so to accelerate the accumu-lation of surface organic horizons.

VI. EFFECTS OF EARTHWORMS ON THE CIRCULATION OF PLANT NUTRIENTS

Wormcasts are usually richer than the surrounding soil in exchangeable calcium, potassium and available phosphorus (Lunt and Jacobson, 1944; Ponomareva, 1950). This provides evidence that earthworms feed selectively but tells us nothing about the effect on soil of passing through an earthworm's intestine. The effect on calcium, potassium and phosphorus availability is, in fact, unknown.

A. EFFECTS ON NITROGEN MINERALIZATION

A provisional assessment can be made, however, of the effects of earthworm activity on the availability of nitrogen in the soil. About half the nitrogen excreted by earthworms is in the form of muco-proteins secreted by gland cells within the epidermis. The other half is a fluid urine containing ammonia and urea and possibly uric acid and allantoin, their proportions depending upon the species of worm and whether it is fasting or feeding (Needham, 1957). All these substances are either soluble in soil solution or rapidly become so as a result of microbial action. In an experiment with young *A. caliginosa* kept in a mixture of soil and ground clover leaves, Barley and Jennings (1959) showed that 6·4% of the non-available nitrogen ingested was excreted in forms available to plant roots.

The body tissue of earthworms, of which up to 72% of the dry weight is protein (Lawrence and Millar, 1945), decomposes rapidly at death and pro-vides a further source of readily mineralized nitrogen. Fig. 31 illustrates the course of nitrogen mineralization of dead *L. terrestris* decomposing in jars of garden soil at 12°C under laboratory conditions. The amount of nitrogen added to each jar was calculated from the weight of the dead earthworms and analysis of a sample of them, and the proportion of worm nitrogen subse-quently accounted for in mineralized forms was determined by comparing the soils to which dead worms had been added with controls without worms. After 2 to 3 weeks the worms had disappeared completely and nitrogen fractions in the soil were roughly in equilibrium. Of the nitrogen added as worm tissue about 25% was present as nitrate, about 45% as ammonia and about 3% as soluble organic compounds. Of the approximately 27% unaccounted for, a little was probably held as undecomposed elements of the chaetae and cuticle and the remainder mainly as microbial protein.

Figure 31 also shows some results from a similar experiment (Russell, 1910) in which the decomposition of dead earthworms in jars of soil was recorded. The two experiments suggest that a large part of the nitrogen of

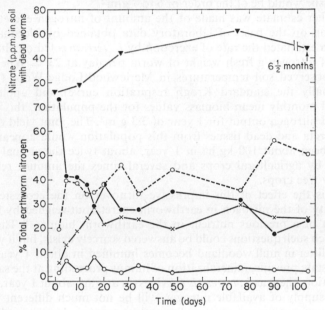

FIG. 31. Mineralization of nitrogen from dead *L. terrestris* (data from Satchell (unpublished) and from Russell, 1910).

o — o, Soluble organic N; ×—×, Insoluble organic N; o ‥ o, Extractable NH_4–N; •—•, Residual N.

decomposing earthworms may become adsorbed onto soil colloids as ammonia with nitrification either becoming completely inhibited or proceeding very slowly. This may have arisen in the experiments from the aeration conditions of the soil and Harmsen and van Schreven (1955) point out that in most soils only a minor part of the total amount of NH_4-ions is available for nitrification, varying between none and about 30%. Whatever may be the rate of nitrification of earthworm nitrogen, it seems likely that under normal conditions a minimum of about 70% of the nitrogen in dead earthworm tissue, and probably considerably more, becomes mineralized in 10–20 days.

If it is assumed that earthworm tissue decomposes without significant loss of nitrogen to the atmosphere, an approximate estimate of the amount of earthworm nitrogen mineralized in a year can be made for a particular population. A first attempt at such an estimate has been made by Skellam and Satchell (Satchell, 1963) for the Merlewood Lodge Wood population of *L. terrestris* (referred to on p. 278). From arguments based on the size structure of the field population and the growth rates of specimens from it reared in culture, the weight of tissue produced in 1 year was estimated to be about 3 times the average weight of the population, about 364 g/m². The nitrogen content of *L. terrestris* is about 1·75% of the fresh weight so that, on the steady state assumption that the amount of dead tissue returning to the soil is equivalent to the amount of live tissue produced, the nitrogen returned to the soil as tissue would be of the order of 6 to 7 g/m².

A further estimate was made of the amount of nitrogen excreted by this population on the basis of laboratory data obtained by Needham (1957). Needham estimated the rate of excretion by *L. terrestris* fed on elm leaves as 269 μg of nitrogen/g fresh weight of worm per day at 23°C. When adjusted for the observed soil temperatures in Merlewood Lodge Wood (employing provisionally the standard Krogh respiration curve) and applied to the estimated monthly mean biomass values for the population, this yielded an estimated nitrogen output for 1 year of 3·3 g/m². The joint yield of nitrogen from excreta and dead tissues from this population would appear therefore to have been about 100 kg/ha in 1 year, about twice the annual uptake of nitrogen by agricultural crops and several times the amount retained annually by tree crops.

What is the effect of this impressive turnover on the ecosystem? Is the availability of the nitrogen in earthworm excreta outweighed by the immobilization of a precious nutrient in the earthworm biomass? The evidence from which such questions could be answered scarcely exists, but if we suppose that leaf litter in mull woodland becomes humified in about 1 year and that a steady state prevails, mineralization of humus proceeding at the same rate as humification, then, as *L. terrestris* survives on average about 1 year, it appears that the supply of available nitrogen will be not much different whether it derives from earthworm tissue or from plant remains decomposed by microbial action. The acceleration of mineralization of plant litter on conversion to earthworm excreta appears, however, to be a bonus on this system. It will be seen, moreover, from Fig. 32 that in three woodland populations sampled in different years the maximum output of excreted nitrogen apparently occurs in early summer at the time of maximum nitrogen demand for plant growth. However, it should be remembered that some assumptions on which these estimates are based, notably that excretion rates are related to soil temperatures in the manner of the Krogh respiration curve, though reasonable, are not yet verified.

There appears to be a vacant niche in temperate forest soils for a holothurian-like earthworm, feeding in the subsoil on low grade organic matter, of large size, occupied mainly by intestine, conserving its energy by a sluggish subsurface existence and its protein supplies by a low reproductive rate and great longevity—in fact, a holarctic equivalent of the 4 ft long Australasian megascolecid *Spenceriella gigantica* (Lee, 1959). However, the ideal litter feeding animal, from the point of view of obtaining the fastest return of available nitrogen to the ecosystem and narrowing the C:N ratio of plant residues, would combine a high metabolic rate with a short life span. *Eisenia foetida*, the brandling of compost and dung heaps, with a nitrogen excretion rate of 402 µg/day per gram of worm (Needham, Table XVIII) is probably the earthworm most nearly approaching this ideal.

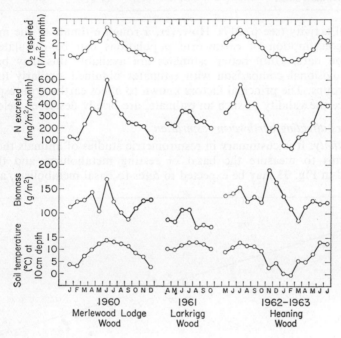

FIG. 32. Estimates of oxygen consumption and nitrogen excretion by 3 woodland populations of *L. terrestris*.

B. EARTHWORM METABOLISM AND ITS EFFECT ON THE C:N RATIO OF SOIL ORGANIC MATTER

The C:N ratio of organic matter added to the soil is of primary importance to the course of mineralization; generally only material with a C:N ratio of 20:1 or lower can directly provide mineral nitrogen (Harmsen and van Schreven, 1955). The following C:N ratios of freshly fallen leaves of common forest trees are given by Wittich (1953): Elm 24·9, Ash 27·6, Lime 38·2, Oak 42·0, Birch 43·5, Rowan 54·0, Scots Pine 90·6. The effect of earthworms in narrowing the C:N ratio of plant remains is not easy to assess directly because, in experimental cultures, earthworms not only metabolize carbon themselves but also increase organic matter decomposition by stimulating

TABLE XVIII

Nitrogen excretion rates of Lumbricidae feeding on elm leaves
Output at 23°C μg/g per day (Needham, 1957)

Species	Ammonia + amino N	Urea	Total N
E. foetida	156·5	48·3	401·8
L. terrestris	54·0	40·8	268·8
A. caliginosa	37·4	19·9	87·5

microbial activity (see p. 317). However, a rough estimate of the minimum carbon consumption of earthworm populations can be calculated from respiration data. Until better estimates are available this may be useful for a provisional comparison with estimates obtained similarly for other faunal groups. The principal factors known to affect earthworm respiration, and hence the validity of such an estimate, are briefly described below:

1. Factors affecting earthworm respiration

(a) *Activity.* It is customary in respirometric studies of animals the size of earthworms to measure the basal or resting metabolism, and the data presented in Fig. 33 may be expected to refer to basal metabolism, although

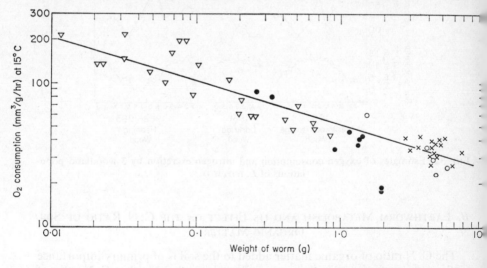

FIG. 33. Oxygen consumption by *L. terrestris* and *E. foetida* at 15°C. ▽, *E. foetida* (Kruger, 1952); ×, *L. terrestris* (Konopacki, 1907); ●, *L. terrestris* (Davis and Slater, 1928); ○, *L. terrestris* (Raffy, 1930).

this is not explicitly stated by all the authors on whose work the figure is based. The respiration rates obtained take no account of motor activity such as burrowing or feeding, nor of any special metabolic conditions which may prevail during diapause.

(b) *Diurnal rhythm.* Fig. 34 illustrates, from the work of Ralph (1957), the existence of diurnal rhythms of oxygen consumption and activity in *L. terrestris*. The two apparently do not entirely coincide and Ralph suggested that earthworms may incur oxygen debts during periods of high activity.

(c) *Oxygen tension.* Certain species undoubtedly occupy habitats with very low oxygen tensions, e.g. *Helodrilus oculatus* in lake muds and at the bottom of wells. Although it has never been directly demonstrated, *L. terrestris* may also encounter oxygen concentrations sufficiently low to have a marked effect

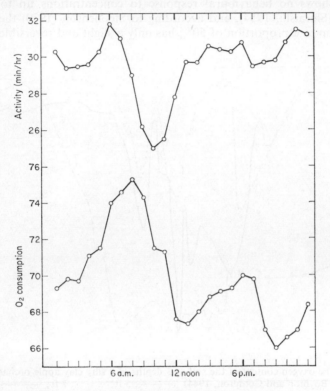

FIG. 34. Diurnal activity in *L. terrestris* (from Ralph, 1957). Units of oxygen consumption not given in original.

on oxygen consumption. In experiments continued for 2 hours at 10°c, Johnson (1942) found that when *L. terrestris* was kept in various concentrations of oxygen in nitrogen its oxygen consumption fell when the concentration of O_2 was decreased to 10% (partial pressure 76 mm Hg) and below. In 10% O_2 and in 5% O_2, oxygen consumption was about 93% and 47% of what it was at atmospheric concentration (20%). There appear to have been few studies in temperate regions of the composition of the soil atmosphere at the depths to which *L. terrestris* burrows, but the data of Boynton and Compton (1944) for a silty clay soil from an apple orchard at Cornell show oxygen concentrations below 10% for about 11 weeks in the year at a depth of 3 ft and for 6 months of the year at a depth of 5 ft. Concentrations below 5% occurred for about 11 days and 4 months respectively at 3 and 5 ft (Fig. 35). It has been suggested that low oxygen tensions are responsible for earthworms leaving their burrows after heavy rain (Merker, 1928), but the evidence is inconclusive.

(*d*) *Carbon dioxide concentration.* It is generally believed that carbon dioxide concentrations in the soil do not affect respiration greatly. *Eisenia foetida* shows no behavioural response to concentrations up to 25% by volume (Shiraishi, 1954), and according to Stephenson (1930) the presence of CO_2 up to a proportion of 50% has only a slight and reversible effect on

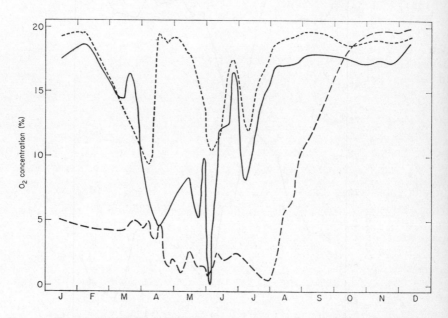

FIG. 35. The oxygen content of the soil at 3 depths of a silty clay apple orchard (adapted from Boynton and Compton, 1944). — — —, 5 ft; ······, 7 ft; ———, 3 ft.

worms. Extreme limits of CO_2 concentration in soils quoted by Russell (1950) range between 0·01 and 11·5%.

(e) *Exposure to light.* The respiratory rate of *L. terrestris* is affected by exposure to light. Davis and Slater (1928) found that the rate was doubled in bright light and Johnson (1942) recorded a 30% increase in the rate of oxygen consumption when worms were first exposed to darkness and then to diffuse daylight. This may be significant in surface feeding species.

(f) *Ambient temperature.* The rate of earthworm respiration is greatly affected by the ambient temperature, and this is likely to be one of the most important factors affecting earthworm metabolism under field conditions.

The rate of pulsation of the dorsal blood vessel and the pseudohearts varies according to temperature (Rogers and Lewis, 1914) as do the dissociation curves of earthworm haemoglobins (Haughton, Kerkut and Munday, 1958).

The respiration rate rises with increasing temperature. In poikilotherms generally the magnitude of the temperature effect, described by the Arrhenius constant, μ, has a value of 11,500 calories for a wide variety of respiratory processes (Prosser et al., 1950). From experiments done at temperatures ranging from 9 to 27° c, a μ value of $11,040 \pm$ calories has been found for L. terrestris (Pomerat and Zarrow, 1936), so the relationship between temperature and respiratory rate in earthworms appears to be similar to that reported for other poikilothermous animals.

However, the effect of temperature on respiration may be expected to vary seasonally as a result of acclimatization. In the tropical earthworm, Megascolex mauritii, the rate of oxygen consumption for winter animals at 20° c, determined in January 1960, was greater than that for summer animals, determined in June 1960, by about one-third in large specimens to four times in small specimens (Saroja, 1961). Attempts to induce respiratory acclimatization experimentally in E. foetida (Kirberger, 1953) have been inconclusive, but there seems no reason to suppose that acclimatization is less significant in the ecology of temperate than in tropical earthworms.

(g) Body size. In the Lumbricidae, as in other groups, the respiratory rate per unit weight is higher for small specimens of a given species than for large specimens. This is well illustrated by Gromadska's (1962) data for L. castaneus and Krüger's (1952) data for E. foetida and is consistent with Konopacki's (1907), Davis and Slater's (1928) and Raffy's (1930) observations on L. terrestris (Fig. 33). Müller (1943) found no such relationship for L. terrestris but as the individual weights of the specimens used in her experiments are not stated, the data are difficult to interpret. It will be seen from Fig. 33 that the respiration rates of L. terrestris and E. foetida are similar for animals of the same size. A. caliginosa has a lower metabolic rate, half grown worms of mean weight 0·5 g consuming 75 µl./hr per gram fresh weight at 15° c (Barley and Jennings, 1959) in contrast with about 125 µl./hr per g by E. foetida at this weight and temperature.

Although these respiratory studies were carried out at different temperatures by a variety of workers using different techniques, the results are reasonably consistent. They also agree with Needham's (1957) excretion data in showing that A. caliginosa has a relatively low metabolic rate, and they suggest that the difference in total nitrogen output of L. terrestris and E. foetida may largely result from their different body sizes.

2. Computation of carbon combustion by field populations

The direct contribution made by earthworms to decay can be estimated from respirometer data. Such an estimate has been made for an Australian population of A. caliginosa by K. P. Barley (1964) from whose work the following paragraph is quoted.

"At 15° c the oxygen consumption of worms of bodyweight 0·2 g—a mean commonly found for field populations—is in the region of 100 µl. per g bodyweight per hr. The metabolic rate in the field is likely to be less than that measured in a respirometer, and a generous estimate is 50 µl per g per hr. For a population of 80 g/m² active for 150 days this rate corresponds to an oxygen consumption of 14 l./m²/yr. This figure may be compared with the total amount of oxygen consumed in decay each year on pasture land at Adelaide. A pasture producing 7,000 lb dry matter per acre (8,000 kg/hectare) returns the following amounts (8,000 lb/acre) of material to the soil: herbage litter 3·5 (Carter 1962); dung, 1·4 (Hutchinson and Porter 1958); dead roots, 1·4 (root: shoot ratio 1:5); total 6,300 lb/acre. The increase in residual organic matter per year, corresponding to an addition of 0·004% nitrogen in the top 6 in. of soil, is 1,600 lb/acre. The amount of material oxidised is 6,300–1,600 = 4,700 lb/acre ≃ 500 g/m². This is nearly equivalent to the weight of oxygen consumed or to a volume of $500/32 \times 22\cdot4 = 350$ l./m²/yr. Thus, neglecting other members of the food chain, earthworms bring about only a small fraction, of the order of 4% of the total decay."

A similar conclusion is reached when Fig. 33 is used to estimate the oxygen consumption of woodland populations of *L. terrestris*. In the study of *L. terrestris* in Merlewood Lodge Wood and Heaning Wood every worm collected was weighed individually. The monthly biomass estimates (Fig. 32) were then apportioned to weight groups differing by half gram units and a mean oxygen consumption rate for each group was obtained from Fig. 33. After summing the products of this rate and the biomass for each size group the total was adjusted to the prevailing soil temperature using the Krogh curve. Estimates of the annual oxygen consumption by the two populations obtained by summing the monthly estimates are given in Table XIX, together with closely similar results calculated by a simpler method.

At the mean soil temperature for the year's sampling in Merlewood Lodge Wood, 22·87 l./m² of oxygen is equivalent to a carbon consumption of 118·6 kg/ha. A reasonable estimate of the litter fall and composition on this site would be about 3,000 kg/ha dry weight and, on an ash free basis, a carbon content of about 50% and a C:N ratio of about 38. The carbon combustion by the *L. terrestris* population might therefore amount to about 8% of the total, which would reduce the C:N ratio to a little below 35. Only material with a C:N ratio of 20 or lower can directly provide mineral nitrogen, so that the effects of the earthworm's respiratory metabolism may be less in this respect than those of other groups such as nematodes with a lower biomass but a higher metabolic rate.

The foregoing calculation is based on the respiratory rate of inactive animals, so the true consumption of carbon by the field population is likely to be higher than the 8% indicated. There is little direct evidence of how the metabolic rates of active and inactive worms compare nor of the duration of activity in the field. Ralph's (1957) oxygen consumption data for periodically active *L. terrestris* (Fig. 34) show a maximum consumption about 13% higher than the minimum consumption, and Raffy (1930) found the consumption of

L. terrestris exposed to light at 16° c between 31% and 64% higher than at the same temperature in the dark. As exposure to light produces strong negative phototaxic activity, it seems unlikely that the difference between resting metabolism and active metabolism in the field would be greater than observed in this experiment. The amount of carbon respired by the population may therefore be as much as 12% of that present in the litter fall, but is unlikely to be more.

TABLE XIX

Annual Oxygen Consumption of *L. terrestris* populations

	Merlewood Lodge Wood Jan.–Dec. 1960	Heaning Wood May 1962– April 1963
Total number of *L. terrestris* taken by formaldehyde sampling	2,837	13,974
Total weight of *L. terrestris* taken by formaldehyde sampling	7,735 g	30,026 g
Mean weight/worm	2·7 g	2·2 g
O_2 consumption at 15°c at mean weight/worm from Fig. 33	36 μl./g per hr	39 μl./g per hr
Mean soil temperature for year	9.0°c	8·2°c
Krogh correction factor	0·545	0·491
O_2 consumption at mean soil temperature at mean weight/worm	19·6 μl./g per hr	19·1 μl./g per hr
Mean of monthly biomass estimates	121·4 g/m²	133·0 g/m²
Estimated annual O_2 consumption by population	22·52 l./m²	22·25 l./m²
Estimate obtained as described in text	22·87 l./m²	22·77 l./m²

3. Comparison of population metabolism of earthworms and other groups

Mellanby (1960) pointed out that Hansen's famous statement that, "the weight of earthworms in pasture land may exceed the weight of stock grazing on it" may be misleading if taken as more than a picturesque analogy. Because the metabolic rate of earthworms is less than that of mammals and may be decreased by aestivation and cold torpor, Mellanby concluded that an earthworm biomass of 1,000 lb/acre would be "biologically equivalent" not to a 1,000 lb bullock but to a 10 lb hare. A possible corollary might be that if the energy demand on the ecosystem by earthworms is only about 1% of that of bullocks for the maintenance of the same biomass, the attention of agronomists might be directed to the possibilities of cropping earthworms as a source of animal protein. However, the concept of "biological equivalence" is generally used by soil zoologists to mean that the contribution of different animals to the transformation of plant residues in the soil may be

11 + s.b.

estimated by comparing their oxygen consumption. Macfadyen (1963), for example, states that, "the population which exploits the greatest quantity of stored energy is contributing most to the rapid liberation of nutrient substances."

The estimates of the oxygen consumption of the *L. terrestris* populations of Merlewood Lodge Wood and Heaning Wood (p. 311) enable provisional comparisons with livestock and other soil groups to be made.

On the assumptions that:

(1) an "average" pasture carries about 500 kg of stock per hectare;
(2) the basal oxygen consumption of a bullock is 132 cc/kg per hr (Brody, 1945);
(3) the energy required for normal activity by stock is about twice that of its basal metabolism (Brody, 1945);

the annual oxygen consumption of dairy stock may be estimated as of the order of 115 l./m². The estimates of the annual oxygen uptake by the *L. terrestris* populations of Merlewood Lodge Wood and Heaning Wood, both about 23 l./m², suggest that the energy loss in agricultural grassland may indeed be greater through the stock than through the earthworms, though by a factor nearer 5 than 100.

Recent estimates of the oxygen consumption of field populations of oribatid mites (Berthet, 1963) and Enchytraeidae (O'Connor, 1963) are available. Despite obvious differences from the Lumbricidae in behaviour, all three groups appear to feed on a mixed diet of plant litter, humic material and micro-organisms, so that there is some justification for using the oxygen consumption of these groups for comparing their contribution to soil metabolism. Berthet calculated that the adult oribatids of a broad-leaved forest consumed about $4 \cdot 5$ l.O_2/m² per annum, and considered this would be trebled if nymphs had been included in the estimate. Even so, the annual respiration of oribatid populations appears to be less than that of the earthworm populations of woodland mull, their higher metabolic rate failing to compensate for their small biomass. O'Connor (1963) has estimated that the enchytraeid population of a conifer plantation in Wales with a mean biomass of $10 \cdot 8$ g/m² consumed approximately 31 l. O_2/m² per annum, about a third more than the Lake District *L. terrestris* populations weighing about 12 times as much. O'Connor calculated that the energy of respiration for the enchytraeids was about 150 kcal./m² per annum. For the *L. terrestris* populations it would be about 110 kcal./m² per annum (R.Q. $=0 \cdot 78$, av. of 18 determinations by Konopacki, 1907) or about 10 and 8% respectively of the energy content of an annual litter fall of 3,000 kg/ha. The importance of other groups of soil animals may therefore exceed that of the Lumbricidae in their direct contribution to soil metabolism. However, earthworms are unique amongst soil animals in the extent to which they bury organic debris, mix organic and inorganic matter in their excreta and modify the structure of the soil with their burrow systems, and their direct effect in mobilizing nutrient substances may be insignificant compared with the catalytic effects of their activity on microbial metabolism. It must be stressed again that the estimates given of rates of nitrogen, carbon and energy flow through earthworm populations involve many assumptions and are to be regarded as imaginative speculations aimed at exploring the implications of the little knowledge we have.

VII. THE INFLUENCE OF EARTHWORMS ON SOIL MICRO-ORGANISMS

A. CHANGES IN MICROBIAL POPULATIONS IN THE EARTHWORM GUT AND FAECES

Publications on the influence of earthworms on the microflora of the soil contain many conflicting observations, but it is now generally agreed that the earthworm gut contains essentially the same kinds of organisms as are present in the soil in which the worms are living. Bassalik (1913) isolated more than 50 species of bacteria from the alimentary canal of *Lumbricus terrestris* and found none which was not present in the soil from which the worms came. More recently, Parle (1963b) examined the gut of 3 species of earthworm and found no micro-organisms which are not common in soil or plant remains. In particular, he investigated the possibility that the cellulase and chitinase present in the alimentary canal of earthworms might be secreted by special symbiotic micro-organisms such as occur in molluscs. He concluded that although some cellulolitic and chitinolitic activity was attributable to soil organisms present in the gut contents, the enzymes were secreted mainly by the earthworms themselves. It seems likely therefore that earthworms possess no indigenous gut microflora.

The extent to which earthworms digest micro-organisms is, however, less certain. The crops, gizzards and intestines of earthworms have been examined for large micro-organisms by Aichberger (1914), who found there very few organisms not possessing firm outer coats and no live yeasts, diatoms, desmids, blue-green algae or rhizopods. Moreover, Protozoa appear to form an essential constituent of the diet of at least one species of earthworm, the dung hill and compost inhabiting *E. foetida*. It is apparently unable to grow to sexual maturity in the absence of the motile Protozoa normally so abundant in its environment (Miles, 1963). There are only two records of bacteria being killed out after ingestion by earthworms and both were non-autochthonous forms, *Serratia marcessens* (Day, 1950) and *Escheria coli* (Brüsewitz, 1959), introduced to the soil by inoculation. Day (1950) also found that *Bacillus cereus* var. *mycoides*, in a heavily inoculated soil, decreased in numbers after ingestion by *L. terrestris*, but persisted at low densities in a way suggesting considerable destruction of vegetative cells but not of spores. In general, however, in uninoculated soils, numbers of yeasts and fungi are little changed in passage through the earthworm gut and bacteria and actinomycetes increase exponentially from fore-gut to hind-gut (Table XX).

Earthworm faeces emerge as a saturated paste, poorly aerated but rich in ammonia and partially digested organic matter. The ensuing changes in microbial numbers were first recorded by Stöckli (1928). He found that the total cell count doubled in the first week after the casts were formed and remained at about this level, though with considerable fluctuation, for a further 3 weeks (Fig. 36). Parle (1963a) found no consistent changes in num-

TABLE XX

Numbers of actinomycetes and bacteria in different sections of *L. terrestris* intestine* (from Parle, 1959)

	Fore gut ($\times 10^6$)	Mid gut ($\times 10^6$)	Hind gut ($\times 10^6$)
Actinomycetes	26	358	15,000
Bacteria	475	32,900	440,700

* Means of 5 samples counted by double dilution technique.

bers of actinomycetes or bacteria in ageing casts but yeasts increased and fungi, present almost entirely as spores in the gut, started to germinate in the casts and hyphae were most abundant in casts 15 days old (Fig. 25). These changes in numbers of micro-organisms are in marked contrast with the

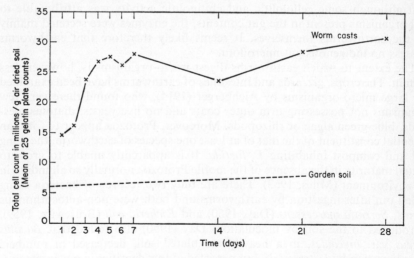

FIG. 36. Total cell counts from earthworm casts of different ages, and garden soils (from Stöckli, 1928).

course of microbial activity shown by the oxygen consumption of casts of increasing age, which declines consistently from the time when the cast material is excreted (Parle, 1963a). When glucose or cellulose is added to casts of different age total oxygen uptake increases but the older casts continue to respire at a lower rate than those produced more recently (Fig. 37). The effect therefore does not seem to arise from the exhaustion of energy supplies or from a decline in the microbial population—it occurs when this is either increasing or stationary—but because an increasing proportion of the population forms resting stages as the casts age. Ruschmann (1953) reported that *Nocardia polychromogenes*, *Actinomyces* spp. and *Streptomyces coelicolor* isolated from worm casts or gut contents are particularly antagonistic to aerobic spore-forming bacteria, and the decline in respiratory exchange in the casts may result from an antibiotic effect of their dense populations of actinomycetes.

Many investigations have shown that the microbial population of casts is generally higher than that of surrounding soil, but it is rarely possible to

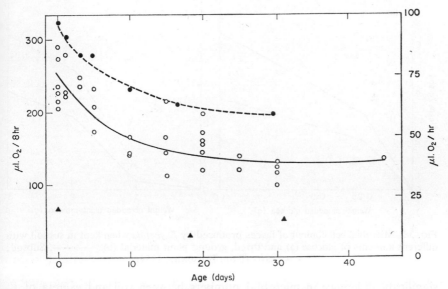

Fig. 37. Left, oxygen uptake in 8 hr by cast material at different ages. o, cast; ▲, soil.

Right, oxygen uptake in 1 hr by cast material of different ages in the presence of excess glucose (•) (from Parle, 1963a).

distinguish how far this arises from selective feeding on materials forming a substrate for microbial activity and how far it arises from changes brought about in the earthworm's intestine. Undoubtedly the size of the increase in the microflora in earthworm faeces depends largely on the amount and type of plant material in the soil ingested (Fig. 38b) but, as has already been shown, the numbers of bacteria and actinomycetes in the ingested material increase considerably in the gut. The size of the increase under field conditions may be assessed from Parle's results. He estimated that the bacteria and actinomycetes were up to 1,000 times more numerous in the gut than in the surrounding soil, and that the oxygen uptake by cast material was still considerably higher than that of the soil after 50 days.

Three workers found fewer or the same number of micro-organisms in casts as in soil, but these apparently anomalous results may be accounted for by the experimental procedures used. All worked with earthworms in containers of prepared soil. Day (1950) found no consistent difference between the bacterial numbers in firmly tamped soil and fresh excreta produced by specimens of *L. terrestris* as they burrowed into it. Under these conditions ingested soil passes through the gut in 11 to 12 hours (Parle, 1963b), which is about twice the rate for worms feeding normally and probably too quick for the bacteria to multiply detectably. Jeanson-Luusinang (1963) also found no

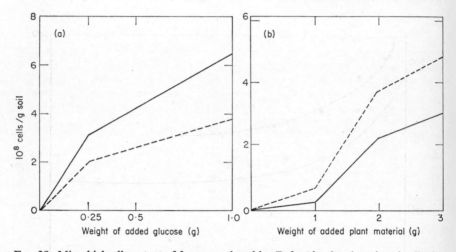

FIG. 38. Microbial cell content of faeces produced by *E. foetida* when kept in subsoil with different amounts of glucose (a) and dried, ground plant material (b). ————, Subsoil; — — —, casts (from Brüsewitz, 1959).

significant difference in microbial numbers between soil and excreta of *L. terrestris* but in this experiment milled lucerne was mixed with the soil, which was kept at field capacity and maintained for 1 month at 18–22° C. Lucerne is a readily decomposed, nitrogen-rich energy source and as it was milled and dispersed in the soil under virtually optimal conditions of moisture, aeration and temperature it is scarcely surprising that ingestion of the medium by earthworms had no further effect on microbial abundance. In the third example glucose was added to the worm cultures and cell counts were lower from casts than from soil (Brüsewitz, 1959) (Fig. 38a). Again with a rich energy source already available in the soil, the increased availability of organic supplies in the gut would be of less significance. Indeed, competitive utilization of the glucose combined with some digestion of the micro-organisms may have contributed to the observed decrease in the population in the ingested soil.

Finally, in pot experiments with various earthworm species, Went (1963) obtained bacterial counts from earthworm faeces intermediate between the low density in the clay soil in which the worms were kept and the high density in alder leaves on which they fed. Alder leaves have an exceptionally high nitrogen content and decompose so fast that earthworm activity would be unlikely to accelerate it appreciably. Although bacterial numbers were higher in rotting alder leaves than in the mixture of leaf and mineral matter comprising the earthworm faeces, the results do not preclude the conclusion that ingestion by earthworms increases the rate of decomposition of materials more resistant to microbial attack.

B. STIMULATION OF MICROBIAL DECOMPOSITION BY EARTHWORM ACTIVITY

It is well established (Tenney and Waksman, 1929; Harmsen and van Schreven, 1955) that simple nitrogen compounds added to nitrogen-poor organic materials are readily incorporated into microbial protein and accelerate the organic materials' decomposition. It would be expected, therefore, that in incorporating plant litter with soil enriched with their nitrogenous excreta, earthworms not only decompose material themselves but stimulate other decomposers. The effect is illustrated in an experiment (Barley and Jennings, 1959) in which grass and clover litter with a nitrogen content of 2·5% and dung pellets were left to decay in cultures of soil with and without young specimens of *A. caliginosa*. The concentration of worms in the cultures, 3 g/kg, was within the range encountered in the field. The cultures were kept moist, well aerated and at 15°C for a period of 45 days, during which their oxygen consumption was recorded and also the rate of ammonium and nitrate accumulation for a further 5 days. The oxygen consumption of the worms alone at 15°C was estimated in a separate experiment (Table XXI).

TABLE XXI

Influence of *A. caliginosa* on the decomposition of herbage litter and dung (from Barley and Jennings, 1959)

Treatment	Oxygen consumption from 15 to 45 days (μl./g of medium)	Log value	Nitrate + ammonium N accumulated in 50 days p.p.m.	Log value
With worms	2600	3·39	129	2·10
Without worms	2190	3·32	105	2·01
Min. sig. diff. ($P=0·01$)	—	0·05	—	0·09

The cultures with worms consumed 410 μl.O_2/g of medium more than those without worms, and it was estimated that 200 μl. of this was consumed by the worms themselves. Table XXI shows that worms increased the rate of decomposition by about one-fifth to one-sixth, due, about equally, to their own

318 J. E. SATCHELL

action as decomposers and to stimulating other decomposing organisms. The temperature, moisture, aeration and supply of relatively easily decomposed organic matter was such as to favour microbial activity even without earthworms, so their activity probably modified the microbial environment less than it would under field conditions.

Composting techniques for vineyard residues also show how earthworms stimulate microbial decomposition. Anstett (1951) incubated grape husks at 25 to 30°C in pots, some of which he inoculated with *E. foetida*. After 5 months the microbial population was 4 to 5 times greater in the inoculated pots. Decomposition of the husks was measured by loss on ignition, which was 75% in the inoculated pots and 86% in the controls at the end of the experiments. The additional decomposition in the presence of *E. foetida* appeared to result mainly from the increased population of micro-organisms, since the

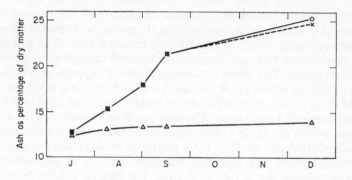

Fig. 39. Loss on ignition of decomposing grape husks in the presence and absence of *Eisenia foetida* (data from Anstett, 1951). △, without worms; ○, with worms; ×, with worms to September 1st, then without.

losses on ignition were the same from pots which contained worms throughout the experiment and from pots from which they were removed after 6 weeks (Fig. 39).

The effect of earthworms on the decomposition of more resistant organic residues, e.g. forest litter, has been little studied but clearly should not be judged by the oxygen consumption and/or excretory output of the worms themselves. On present evidence, conditioning plant remains for microbial decomposition seems to be the most important action of Lumbricidae in the ecosystem.

REFERENCES

Aichberger, R. von (1914). *Kleinwelt*, **6**, 53–88.
Anstett, M. A. (1951). *C. r. hebd. Séanc. Acad. Sci., Paris*, **37**, 262–264.
Archangels'kii, M. P. (1929). *Nauchno-agron. Zh.* **6**, 849–862.
Avel, M. (1929). *Bull. biol. Fr. Belg.* **63**, 149–320.

Bakhtin, P. U. and Polsky, M. N. (1950). *Pochvovedenie*, 487–491.

Barley, K. P. (1959). *Aust. J. agric. Res.* **10**, 171–185.

Barley, K. P. (1961). *Adv. Agron.* **13**, 249–268.

Barley, K. P. (1964). *Aust. Soc. Anim. Prod. Proc.* 5th Biennial Conf., 236–240.

Barley, K. P. and Jennings, A. C. (1959). *Aust. J. agric. Res.* **10**, 364–370.

Barley, K. P. and Kleinig, C. R. (1964). *Aust. J. Sci.* **26**, 290–291.

Bassalik, K. (1913). *Z. GärPhysiol.* **2**, 1–32.

Berthet, P. (1963). *In* "Soil Organisms." (J. Doeksen and J. van der Drift, eds.), pp. 18–31. North-Holland Publ. Co., Amsterdam.

Bocks, S. M., Brown, B. R. and Handley, W. R. C. (1963). *Rep. Forest. Res. Lond.* 1962, 93–96.

Bocock, K. L., Gilbert, O., Capstick, C. K., Twinn, D. C., Waid, J. S. and Woodman, M. J. (1960). *J. Soil Sci.* **11**, 1–9.

Bocock, K. L. (1963). *In* "Soil Organisms." (J. Doeksen and J. van der Drift, eds.), pp. 85–91. North-Holland Publ. Co., Amsterdam.

Bornebusch, C. H. (1930). *Fors. ForsVæs. Danm.* **11**, 1–224.

Bornebusch, C. H. (1953). *Dansk. Skovforen. Tidsskr.* **38**, 557–579.

Boynton, D. and Compton, O. C. (1944). *Soil Sci.* **57**, 107–117.

Brody, S. (1945). "Bioenergetics and growth." Reinhold, New York.

Brown, B. R., Love, C. W. and Handley, W. R. C. (1963). *Rep. Forest. Res. Lond.* 1922, 90–93.

Brüsewitz, G. (1959). *Arch. Mikrobiol.* **33**, 52–82.

Cragg, J. B. (1961). *J. Anim. Ecol.* **30**, 205–234.

Darwin, C. R. (1881). "The Formation of Vegetable Mould through the Action of Worms, with Observations on their Habits." Murray, London.

Davis, J. G. and Slater, W. K. (1928). *Biochem. J.* **22**, 338–343.

Day, G. M. (1950). *Soil Sci.* **69**, 175–184.

Dobson, R. M. and Satchell, J. E. (1956). *Nature, Lond.* **177**, 796–797.

Doeksen, J. (1964). *Jaarb. Inst. biol. scheik. Onderz. LandbGewass.* **256**, 187–191.

Doeksen, J. and Wingerden, C. G. van (1964). *Jaarb. Inst. biol. scheik. Onderz LandbGewass.* **255**, 181–186.

Dutt, A. K. (1948). *J. Am. Soc. Agron.* **40**, 407–410.

Edwards, C. A. and Heath, G. W. (1963). *In* "Soil Organisms." (J. Doeksen and J. van der Drift, eds.), pp. 76–84. North-Holland Publ. Co., Amsterdam.

Emerson, W. W. (1954). *J. Soil Sci.* **5**, 234–250.

Evans, A. C. (1948). *Ann. appl. Biol.* **35**, 1–13.

Evans, A. C. and Guild, W. J. Mcl. (1947). *Ann. appl. Biol.* **34**, 307–330.

Evans, A. C. and Guild, W. J. Mcl. (1948). *Ann. appl. Biol.* **35**, 471–484.

Finck, A. (1952). *Z. PflErnähr. Düng. Bodenk.* **58**, 120–145.

Franz, H. and Leitenberger, L. (1948). *Öst. zool. Z.* **1**, 498–518.

Galoux, A. (1953). *Trav. Stn Rech. Groenendael*, Ser. A. No. 8, 1–235.

Gerard, B. M. (1960). "The biology of certain British earthworms in relation to environmental conditions." Ph.D. Thesis, University of London.

Gerard, B. M. (1964). The Linnean Society of London Synopses of the British Fauna. No. 6. Lumbricidae (Annelida).

Graff, O. (1953). *ForschAnst. Landw., Braunschweig-Völkenrode*, **7**, 5–81.

Grant, W. C. (1955a). *Ecology*, **36**, 400–407.

Grant, W. C. (1955b). *Ecology*, **36**, 412–417.

Gromadska, M. (1962). *Studia Soc. Sci. Torun*, Sec. E. **6**, 179–189.

Guild, W. J. Mcl. (1948). *Ann. appl. Biol.* **35**, 181–192.

Guild, W. J. Mcl. (1955). *In* "Soil Zoology." (D. K. McE. Kevan, ed.), pp. 83–98. Butterworths, London.

Gurianova, O. Z. (1940). *Pochvovedenie*, **4**, 99–107.

Handley, W. R. C. (1954). *Bull. For. Comm. Lond.* No. 23, 1–115.

Harmsen, G. W. and Schreven, D. A. van (1955). *Adv. Agron.* **7**, 299–398.

Haughton, T. M., Kerkut, G. A. and Munday, K. A. (1958). *J. exp. Biol.* **35**, 360–368.

Hess, W. N. (1924). *J. Morph.* **39**, 515–542.

Hoeksema, K. J., Jongerius, A. and Meer, K. van der (1956). *Boor en Spade*, **8**, 183–201.

Hogben, L. and Kirk, R. L. (1944). *Proc. R. Soc. B.* **132**, 239–252.

Hopp, H. (1946). *Soil Conserv.* **11**, 252–254.

Hopp, H. (1947). *Proc. Soil Sci. Soc. Am.* **12**, 503–507.

Hopp, H. and Slater, C. S. (1948). *Soil Sci.* **66**, 421–428.

Iimura, K. and Egawa, T. (1956). *Soil Pl. Fd Nishigahara*, **2**, 83–88.

Jacks, G. V. (1963). *Soils Fertil.* **26**, 147–150.

Jeanson Luusinang, C. (1963). *In* "Soil Organisms." (J. Doeksen and J. van der Drift, eds.), pp. 266–270. North-Holland Publ. Co., Amsterdam.

Joachim, A. W. R. and Pandittesekera, D. G. (1948). *Trop. Agric.* **104**, 119–129.

Johnson, M. L. (1942). *J. exp. Biol.* **18**, 266–277.

Kahsnitz, H. G. (1922). *Bot. Arch.* **1**, 315–331.

Kalmus, H., Satchell, J. E. and Bowen, J. C. (1955). *Ann. Mag. nat. Hist. Ser.* 12 **8**, 795–800.

Kirberger, C. (1953). *Z. vergl. Physiol.* **35**, 175–198.

Kollmannsperger, F. (1955). *Decheniana*, **108**, 81–92.

Konopacki, M. M. (1907). *Bull. Acad. Krakowie*, 357–431.

Korschelt, E. (1914). *Zool. Anz.* **43**, 537–555.

Krüger, F. (1952). *Z. vergl. Physiol.* **34**, 1–5.

Kubiena, W. L. (1953). "The Soils of Europe." Murby, London.

Laverack, M. S. (1960). *Comp. Biochem. Physiol.* **1**, 259–266.

Laverack, M. S. (1961a). *Comp. Biochem. Physiol.* **3**, 136–140.

Laverack, M. S. (1961b). *Comp. Biochem. Physiol.* **2**, 22–34.

Laverack, M. S. (1963). "The Physiology of Earthworms." Pergamon Press, London.

Lawrence, R. D. and Millar, H. T. (1945). *Nature, Lond.* **155**, 517.

Lee, K. E. (1959). *N.Z. Dep. Sci. industr. Res. Bull.* **130**, 1–486.

Lindquist, B. (1941). *Svenska SkogsvFör. Tidskr.* **39**, 179–242.

Lunt, H. A. and Jacobson, G. M. (1944). *Soil Sci.* **58**, 367–375.

Macfadyen, A. (1963). "Animal Ecology: Aims and Methods." 2nd Ed., Pitman, London.

Mamytov, A. (1953). *Pochvovedenie*, **8**, 58–60.

Mangold, O. (1953). *Zool. Jb. Allg. Zool. Physiol.* **63**, 501–557.

Mellanby, K. (1960). *Soils Fertil.*, **23**, 8–9.

Merker, E. (1928). *Naturu. Mus.* **58**, 361–366.

Merker, E. and Braunig, G. (1927). *Zool. Jb.* **43**, 277–338.

Meyer, L. (1943). *Bodenk. PflErnähr.* **29**, 119–140.

Michon, J. (1954). "Contribution expérimentale à l'étude de la biologie des Lumbricidae. Les variations pondérales au cours des différentes modalités du développement postembryonnaire." Ph.D. Thesis, Universitaire de Poitiers.

Michon, J. (1957). *Année biol.* **33**, 367–376.

Miles, H. B. (1963). *Soil Sci.* **95**, 407–409.

Muldal, S. (1950). *Nature, Lond.* **166**, 769–770.
Müller, I. (1943). *Biol. Zbl.* **63**, 446–453.
Nagano, T. (1934). *Sci. Rep. Tohoku Univ.* (Ser. iv) **9**, 97–109.
Needham, A. E. (1957). *J. exp. Biol.* **34**, 425–446.
Nelson, J. M. and Satchell, J. E. (1962). *In* "Progress in Soil Zoology." (P. W. Murphy, ed.), pp. 294–299). Butterworths, London.
Nijhawan, S. D. and Kanwar, J. S. (1952). *Indian J. agric. Sci.* **22**, 357–373.
O'Connor, F. B. (1963). *In* "Soil Organisms." (J. Doeksen and J. van der Drift, eds.), pp. 32–48. North-Holland Publ. Co., Amsterdam.
Parker, G. H. and Parshley, H. M. (1911). *J. exp. Zool.* **11**, 361–363.
Parle, J. N. (1959). "Activities of micro-organisms in soil and influence on these of the soil fauna." Ph.D. Thesis, University of London.
Parle, J. N. (1963a). *J. gen. Microbiol.* **31**, 13–22.
Parle, J. N. (1963b). *J. gen. Microbiol.* **31**, 1–11.
Pomerat, C. M. and Zarrow, M. X. (1936). *Proc. natn. Acad. Sci., U.S.A.* **22**, 270–273.
Ponomareva, S. I. (1950). *Pochvovedenie*, 476–486.
Ponomareva, S. I. (1953). *Trud. pochv. Inst.* **41**, 304–378.
Prosser, C. L., Brown, F. A., Bishop, D. W., Jahn, T. L. and Wulff, V. J. (1950). "Comparative Animal Physiology." Saunders, New York.
Raffy, A. (1930). *C.r. Séanc. Soc. Biol.* **105**, 862–864.
Ralph, C. L. (1957). *Physiol. Zoöl.* **30**, 41–55.
Raw, F. (1959). *Nature, Lond.* **184**, 1661–1662.
Raw, F. (1960). *Nature, Lond.* **187**, 257.
Raw, F. (1961a). *Rep. Rothamsted exp. Stn. 1960*, 156.
Raw, F. (1961b). *Soils Fertil.*, **24**, 1–2.
Raw, F. (1962). *Ann. appl. Biol.* **50**, 389–404.
Reynoldson, T. B. (1955). *N.West. Nat.* 291–304.
Reynoldson, T. B., O'Connor, F. B. and Kelly, W. A. (1955). *Bardsey Observatory Report, 1955.*
Rhee, J. A. van (1963). *In* "Soil Organisms." (J. Doeksen and J. van der Drift, eds.), pp. 55–59. North-Holland Publ. Co., Amsterdam.
Rhee, J. A. van and Nathans, S. (1961). *Neth. J. agric. Sci.* **9**, 94–100.
Richardson, H. L. (1938). *J. agric. Sci.* **28**, 73–121.
Rogers, C. G. and Lewis, E. M. (1914). *Biol. Bull. mar. biol. Lab., Wood's Hole*, **27**, 262–268.
Roots, B. I. (1955). *J. exp. Biol.* **32**, 765–774.
Roots, B. I. (1956). *J. exp. Biol.* **33**, 29–44.
Ruschmann, G. (1953). *Z. Acker-u PflBau.* **97**, 101–114.
Russell, E. J. (1910). *J. agric. Sci. Cambridge* **3**, 246–257.
Russell, E. J. (1950). "Soil conditions and plant growth." 8th ed. Longmans, London.
Saroja, K. (1961). *Nature, Lond.* **190**, 930–931.
Satchell, J. E. (1953). "Studies in earthworms and their relation to soil fertility." Ph.D. Thesis, University of London.
Satchell, J. E. (1955). *In* "Soil Zoology." (D. K. McE. Kevan, ed.), pp. 180–201. Butterworths, London.
Satchell, J. E. (1960). *New Scient.* **7**, 79–81.
Satchell, J. E. (1963). *In* "Soil Organisms." (J. Doeksen and J. van der Drift, eds.), pp. 60–66. North-Holland Publ. Co., Amsterdam.
Satchell, J. E. and Lowe, D. G. (in press) *In* "Progress in Soil Biology," (O. Graff and J. E. Satchell, eds), Vieweg, Brunswick.

Shiraishi, K. (1954). *Tohoku Imp. Univ. Sci. Rep. 4th Ser.* **20**, 356–361.
Slater, C. S. and Hopp, H. (1947). *Proc. Soil Sci. Soc. Am.* **12**, 508–511.
Southern, H. N. (1954). *Ibis*, **96**, 384–410.
Stephenson, J. L. (1930). "The Oligochaeta." Oxford University Press.
Stöckli, A. (1928). *Landw. Jb. Schweiz*, **42**, 1.
Stöckli, A. (1949). *Z. PflErnähr. Düng. Bodenk.* **43–46**, 41–53.
Svendsen, J. A. (1955a). "Studies on the Earthworm Fauna of Pennine Moorland." Ph.D. Thesis, University of Durham.
Svendsen, J. A. (1955b). *Nature, Lond.* **175**, 864.
Svendsen, J. A. (1957a). *J. Anim. Ecol.* **26**, 423–439.
Svendsen, J. A. (1957b). *J. Anim. Ecol.* **26**, 411–421.
Swaby, R. J. (1950). *J. Soil. Sci.* **1**, 195–197.
Tenney, F. G. and Waksman, S. A. (1929). *Soil Sci.* **28**, 55–84.
Teotia, S. P., Duley, F. L. and McCalla, T. M. (1950). *Bull. Neb. agric. Exp. Stn.* **165**, 1–20.
Waters, R. A. S. (1955). *N.Z. Jl Sci. Technol.* **36** A, 516–525.
Went, J. C. (1963). *In* "Soil Organisms." (J. Doeksen and J. van der Drift, eds.), pp. 260–265. North-Holland Publ. Co., Amsterdam.
Wittich, W. (1953). *SchrReihe forstl. Fak. Univ. Gottingen*, **9**, 5–33.
Wolf, A. V. (1938a). *Ecology*, **19**, 346–348.
Wolf, A. V. (1938b). *Ecology*, **19**, 233–242.
Wolf, .A V. (1940). *Physiol. Zoöl.* **13**, 294–308.
Wragg, J. M. and Ball, D. F. (1964). *J. Soil Sci.* **15**, (1), 124–133.

Chapter 10

Arthropoda (except Acari and Collembola

F. RAW

Rothamsted Experimental Station
Harpenden, Herts., England

I. GENERAL ASPECTS

The soil contains a remarkably diverse population of Arthropoda which reaches its greatest complexity and abundance in undisturbed habitats such as forest, woodland, or permanent grassland, in situations where the climate, vegetation and soil type combine to supply a suitable humidity, temperature and food supply. An account of the arthropod fauna of such habitats provides a convenient starting point for discussing the ecological relationships of differing arthropod groups and their effect on various soil processes.

A. TEMPERATE FORESTS (MULL AND MOR)

There have been numerous studies of the soil fauna of forests in temperate regions; indeed our understanding of the part played by the soil fauna in determining the form of the soil organic matter owes much to the pioneer work of forest zoologists and entomologists. One of the earliest studies was that of Diem (1903). Ramann (1911) made a preliminary study of the fauna of some German forests. Pillai (1922) studied the litter fauna of pine woods in Bavaria and Pfetten (1925) in Germany, and Soudek (1928) in Czechoslovakia, made similar studies of the fauna of spruce forests. Ulrich (1933) compared the soil fauna of a spruce forest where the litter decomposed rather slowly with that of a mixed beech/oak forest where the litter decomposed more rapidly. Studies of the soil fauna of Swedish forests were made by Tragardh (1929) followed by more detailed studies by Forsslund (1943). Bornebusch (1930) studied the soil fauna of oak, beech and spruce forests in Denmark. More recent studies are those of Jahn (1946) in Austria and van der Drift (1950) in Holland. Studies of the fauna of forests in the New World include those of Jacot (1936), Lunn (1939), Eaton and Chandler (1942) and Pearse (1946). Grimmet, (1926) investigated the soil fauna of a beech forest and a tawa forest in New Zealand.

The results of Bornebusch's studies (Table 1) illustrate several general features. He showed that the fauna of forest soils consists of communities that are closely associated with, and characteristic of, a particular type of soil and vegetation. The fauna of deciduous forests (oak and beech) with a mull humus formation, i.e. where the organic matter is intimately mixed with the mineral soil, was characterized by the abundance of earthworms, which were estimated to make up 50–80% of the total biomass. The dominant arthropod groups were Diplopoda, esp. Julidae and Glomeridae, Isopoda, esp. *Trichoniscus* spp., and Coleoptera, esp. Carabidae, Staphilinidae and the larvae of Elateridae. In spruce mull, the earthworms were less predominant, forming about 50% of the total biomass. The dominant arthropods were Acari, Diplopoda, larvae of Diptera, esp. Tipulidae, Mycetophilidae and Bibionidae and larvae of Elateridae.

In deciduous forests with a mor humus formation, i.e. where the organic matter forms a discrete layer on the soil surface, earthworms were fewer, usually less than 20% of the total biomass. The dominant arthropod groups were dipteran larvae, elaterid larvae, Diplopoda, Collembola and Acari. In spruce forest mor, earthworms were sparse, Isopoda were absent and Diplopoda rare. Elaterid larvae, chiefly *Athous subfuscus*, and dipteran larvae, chiefly Tipulidae and Mycetophilidae, were the dominant larger arthropods, Collembola were numerous but were far outnumbered by the Acari. Geophilids were numerous and appeared to replace, as predators, the Coleoptera of mull soils.

In general, where earthworms were abundant the leaf litter was incorporated into the soil and decomposed rapidly to give a mull humus formation, characteristic of deciduous forests on moderately drained soils with adequate calcium supply. There the arthropod fauna was dominated by relatively large species which, though not necessarily numerous, formed the greater part of its biomass. By contrast, where earthworms were few the leaf litter accumulated on the soil surface, giving a mor humus formation characteristic of coniferous forests on well-drained soils deficient in calcium. There the arthropod fauna was dominated by vast numbers of small species such as the Acari and Collembola, and the total biomass was usually less than in soils with a mull humus formation. Intermediate stages between these two contrasted types of arthropod community can be found, depending on local conditions of soil, vegetation and climate.

TABLE I

The fauna of forest soil

Weight of fauna in the 10 main localities (g/m²)

Stand	Oak	Beech						Spruce		
Soil	Mull	Mull			Raw Humus			Mull	Raw Humus	
Soil Flora	Mercuri-alis	Asper-ula	Melica	Oxalis	Poly-trichum Type	no flora	no flora	Oxalis	Hylo-comium	Hylo-comium
1. Lumbricidae	61·00	53·10	27·90	5·90	1·45	5·40	1·15	5·05	0·90	1·55
Gastropoda	5·32	4·95	3·98	0·92	—	3·21	1·65	0·16	0·15	—
Enchytraeidae	0·68	1·07	1·09	0·72	0·22	1·56	1·19	0·02	0·13	0·05
Isopoda	0·28	0·15	0·15	0·00	—	0·05	0·01	0·00	—	—
Diplopoda	4·70	7·50	1·87	0·92	—	1·13	0·69	0·36	0·10	—
Acarina	0·06	0·23	0·17	0·21	0·09	0·34	0·67	0·43	0·62	0·45
Collembola	0·10	0·06	0·06	0·08	0·30	0·22	0·28	0·09	0·08	0·14
Diptera	3·10	1·51	1·03	2·00	1·10	7·04	3·35	1·49	4·31	1·03
Elateridae	0·18	0·18	0·58	1·33	0·60	3·48	2·85	0·88	3·71	3·14
Other Insects*	0·55	0·56	0·42	0·45	0·33	0·52	0·28	1·29	1·12	1·12
2. Humivorous animals	14·97	16·21	9·35	6·63	2·64	17·55	10·97	4·72	10·22	5·93
Chilopoda	0·61	1·29	0·20	0·15	0·84	0·51	4·10	0·56	0·74	1·76
Arachnida†	0·06	0·03	0·04	0·07	0·03	0·13	0·09	0·03	0·04	0·07
Staphylinidae	0·11	0·11	0·16	0·14	0·26	0·43	0·24	0·25	0·24	0·45
Carabidae	0·06	0·03	0·11	0·01	0·03	0·00	0·02	0·11	0·08	0·08
3. Rapacious animals	0·84	1·46	0·51	0·37	1·16	1·07	4·45	0·95	1·10	2·36
Total	76·81	70·77	37·76	12·90	5·25	24·02	16·57	10·72	12·22	9·84

* except Staphylinidae and Carabidae   † except Acari   From Bornebusch (1930).

B. Temperate Grassland

Early studies of the arthropod fauna of grassland and cultivated soils were handicapped by lack of suitable methods for extracting the arthropods from soil samples. The Tullgren funnel, that has proved so useful when studying the fauna of forest soils, where there is frequently much surface litter, is less reliable when applied to grassland soils, especially loams and clays. Progress in studying the arthropod fauna of such soils has depended on the development of improved techniques for extracting the fauna from soil samples.

Using an efficient flotation method, Salt, Hollick, Raw and Brian (1948) made a census of the arthropod fauna of a permanent pasture in Cambridgeshire that was used principally for grazing and occasionally cut for hay. Their results, summarized in Fig. 1, illustrate the main features of the arthropod fauna of temperate grassland with mull humus formation.

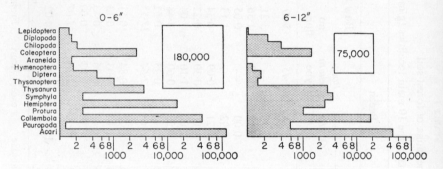

Fig. 1. Soil Arthropods; number per square yard in permanent grassland.

Members of six classes of arthropods (Arachnida, Pauropoda, Diplopoda, Chilopoda, Symphyla and Insecta) were found, representing at least 19 orders, of which 10 were insects. Smaller arthropods were much more numerous than larger ones so the fauna as a whole can be represented as a pyramid with the smallest species such as the Acari, with a density of about 165,000/m^2 at the base and the larger forms such as lepidopteran larvae and Diplopoda with a density of a few hundreds/m^2 at the top. About 70% of the total population was found in the top 6 inches of soil, but some groups, chiefly members of the true subterranean fauna such as the Pauropoda, Protura and, particularly, the Symphyla, were more numerous below 6 inches. In general the smaller forms lived deeper in the soil. This was particularly true for non-burrowing forms such as the Acari and Collembola whose vertical distribution must depend, among other things, on the size distribution of pore spaces at differing levels in the soil.

The information provided by the census on the horizontal distribution of the fauna suggested that a non-random and aggregated distribution, known to be characteristic of some soil species such as wireworms, is probably common to many groups of soil arthropods. Such a distribution may reflect oviposition patterns or that the soil animals aggregate at favourable feeding sites, but much further work on the subject is needed.

The average number of individuals in the top 6 inches of soil was about 1/cc, and about 3/cc where the population was greatest. The size range of soil arthropods is enormous, from specimens such as lepidopteran larvae or large diplopods with a volume of 1 cc or more, to small mites whose volume is probably between 5×10^{-7} and 4×10^{-6} cc. If it is assumed that the volume of an average soil arthropod is about 5×10^{-5} cc and that the top 6 inches of pasture soil contains, on average, 5–10% of air, then the arthropods occupy about 0·5 to 1·0% of the air space.

No comparable census of the arthropod fauna of mor grassland seems to have been made. Macfadyen (1952) made a census of the small arthropods of a Molinia fen in Oxfordshire over a period of one year. His sampling method was not designed to collect the larger arthropods and consequently his data refer chiefly to Acari and Collembola and give an inadequate picture of the abundance or distribution of the other arthropods. Woodlice were abundant, adult and larval Coleoptera and larval Diptera were numerous and several species of Thysanoptera and Hemiptera (Aphididae) were present. Cragg (1961), has given an account of ecological studies of the main animal groups occurring in a series of moorland habitats, ranging from actively growing bog through mixed moor, Juncus moor, Nardus grassland, to limestone grassland on the Moor House National Nature Reserve in the northern Pennines. The main groups of arthropods studied were Acari, Collembola and larval Diptera (Tipulidae), which indicates that in grassland mor, as in forest mor, these are the dominant groups.

C. TROPICAL FORESTS

Information about the arthropod fauna of tropical soils is relatively scanty. Williams (1941) described the ground fauna of a Panama rain forest where he found representatives of seven classes of arthropods, Crustacea, Arachnida, Pauropoda, Diplopoda, Chilopoda, Symphyla and Insecta. The Arachnida, Diplopoda and Insecta were particularly well represented, the latter by members of 15 orders, Thysanura, Collembola, Orthoptera, Isoptera, Neuroptera, Anoplura, Psocoptera, Thysanoptera, Hemiptera, Dermaptera, Trichoptera, Diptera, Coleoptera, Lepidoptera and Hymenoptera. Altogether 289 species were determined, including 67 new species, 20 new genera and one new family and it was estimated that at least 100 more species remained unidentified. The Acari, Collembola and Formicidae accounted for over 80% of all the animals found.

D. TROPICAL GRASSLAND

When compared with that of forests or temperate grassland the arthropod fauna of tropical grassland appears relatively impoverished. Strickland (1947) compared the soil fauna of a cacao plantation in Trinidad with that of a plot of permanent savannah grassland of the same soil type. The grass plot was mown each fortnight except for a small sub-plot where the grass was allowed to grow. Each area was sampled at fortnightly intervals during the last month of the wet season and the first two months of the dry season. In the litter and top 3 inches of soil of the cacao plantation members of 5 classes of arthropods representing at least 16 orders, 75 families and 120 species were found. No diplopods were found in the savannah plot and the members of the other four classes present represented at least 13 orders, 39 families and 70 species. However, the fauna of the savannah plot was not just an impoverished forest fauna because, although the two plots were on the same soil type, only 19 of the identified genera were common to both. This suggested that there was a real difference in the generic composition of the two communities induced by the contrasted environmental conditions resulting from the closed protective canopy of the cacao plot and the exposed grass of the savannah plots. The average population of the cacao plantation was 25,000 arthropods/m^2 in the surface litter and 11,000/m^2 in the top 3 inches of soil compared with 14,000/m^2 in the savannah plot that had been mown and 25,000/m^2 in the savannah sub-plot left unmown during the sampling period. With the onset of the dry season the proportion of the population below 1·5 inches increased on each plot, but this increase was most marked on the mown savannah plot. The smaller numbers found in the mown savannah plot and the more marked depletion of its surface population as the dry season progressed undoubtedly result from the heat and dryness to which the surface soil of such tropical habitats is exposed.

Conversely, a marked increase in the arthropod population of the surface soil as the wet season progressed was observed by Belfield (1956), who studied the vertical distribution of arthropods in the top 18 inches of soil in a grazed field on the Accra plains of Ghana (Fig. 2). Between December and May, as the wet season progressed, the total population of arthropods increased threefold, from 7,100 to 21,500/m^2 due almost entirely to an increase from 2,500 to 15,000/m^2 in the top 6 inches of soil, mostly in the top 2 inches. Below 6 inches, the population changed little. Belfield considered that all the requirements for soil arthropods were present in the upper layers of the soil throughout the year but were not available during the dry season because of drought. With adequate soil moisture, the surface soil developed the richest layer of the fauna.

Similar results were obtained by Salt (1952, 1955), who examined a number of soil samples from pastures and cultivated soil in East Africa. Under elephant grass leys, where the ley protected the surface soil from insolation, the numbers found indicated an arthropod population of about 87,000/m^2 in the top 6 inches of soil compared with about 38,000/m^2 for grazed pastures and about 25,000/m^2 for cultivated soils such as coffee and cassava plantations and fallow ground.

The extraction method used by Salt (1952, 1955) and Strickland (1947) was identical with that used by Salt et al. (1948) for estimating the arthropod population of an English pasture, and Belfield's method was similar. After allowing for modifications in technique which would affect the results, such as the introduction of an extra filtering component by Salt *et al.* (1948) and for the different depths to which samples were taken, the indications are that the arthropod population of tropical pastures is much less than, and probably about half as great as, that of temperate pastures; the most probable cause

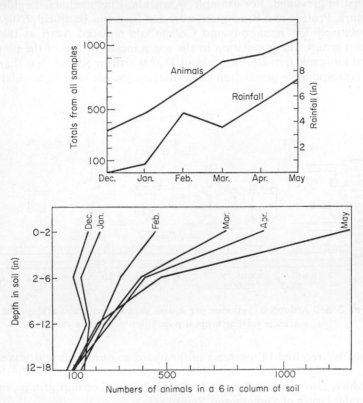

FIG. 2. Soil fauna of West African pasture.
a. Total animals collected in each month, and rainfall.
b. Total animals collected each month at different depths. The figures for the top 2 inches and 2–6 inches are corrected to correspond to 6 inches. From Belfield (1956).

being the effects of insolation. Salt emphasized this difference and suggested that there may be a connection between the meagre arthropod (and earthworm) population of tropical pastures and cultivated soils and the large amount of ligneous material found in the samples he examined.

E. EFFECTS OF CULTIVATION AND MANURING

In general, cultivation greatly decreases the diversity and abundance of the arthropod fauna of the soil. This can be seen by comparing the fauna of the

Cambridgeshire pasture (Fig. 1) with that of the Barnfield mangold plots at
Rothamsted (Fig. 3) which have been cropped with mangolds each year
since 1876. Both are on similar soil types (clay with flints) and were sampled
by the same flotation method. The Barnfield plots contained members of 6
classes of arthropods, as did the permanent grassland. However, fewer
orders were represented and the relative abundance of those present differed
from that in grassland. For example, Araneida, Chelonethida, Lepidoptera,
Thysanura, Protura and Psocoptera were not found in Barnfield; Coleoptera
were relatively less numerous and Collembola replaced Acari as the most
abundant group. The population in the top 8 inches of soil of the plots that
received inorganic fertilizers was about 18,000 arthropods/m^2; less than 10%
of the corresponding population of permanent grassland. The population of

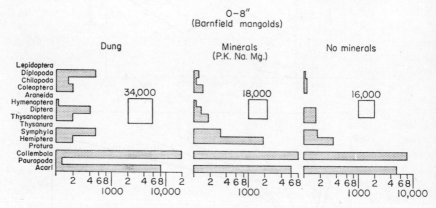

FIG. 3. Soil Arthropods; number per square yard in permanent arable land.
□ = average total arthropod population per square yard.

the plots that received 14 tons/acre of farmyard manure each year was almost
double, with 34,000 arthropods/m^2. Pauropoda were found only in the dunged
plots which also contained a greater proportion of certain groups such as
Diplopoda, larvae of Diptera and Symphyla.

Repeated applications of 14 tons/acre per annum of farmyard manure
have increased the organic matter content of the Barnfield farmyard manure
plot to 2·4% compared with 1·0% for the other plots. However, the difference of 1·4% accounts for only a small proportion of the organic matter that
has been applied. Most of it, particularly in recent years, has been lost from
the soil as energy dissipated by the much greater soil population it has helped
to support, and of which the arthropods form part. Russell (1961) estimated
that the energy dissipated annually in this way from the corresponding farmyard manure plot on the Broadbald wheat field at Rothamsted is 15 times
greater than from the unmanured plot or the plots receiving inorganic
fertilizers. This great difference cannot be accounted for solely by differences
between plots in the number of soil organisms present and evidently reflects

a large luxury consumption of energy by the soil population, particularly micro-organisms, when large quantities of organic matter are available. The situation in the Barnfield plots is no doubt very similar.

II. ARTHROPOD GROUPS

Although the soil contains such a rich and varied arthropod fauna many groups seldom occur in sufficient numbers to have much influence on their habitat. Others are much more important, either because they are more abundant or more widespread or because their activities have a greater effect on the soil, the vegetation or other members of the fauna. The Acari and Collembola, which will be dealt with in the next chapters, are by far the most numerous and widespread of the soil arthropods. Other important groups are the Myriapoda, especially the Chilopoda, Symphyla and Diplopoda, and, among the Insecta, the Isoptera (Termites), Coleoptera and Diptera. Ants (Hymenoptera) may also be important in soil, but they are a particularly diverse group and as their effects on soil have not been studied as much as those of Termites, they are not included in this account.

A. MYRIAPODA

1. Pauropoda

They are extremely small, rarely more than 1–2 mm long, and are seldom found in appreciable numbers in soil unless methods are used that extract the minutest members of the arthropod fauna. They form part of the true subterranean fauna: of the $600/m^2$ found by Salt et al. (1948) in permanent grassland, less than 10% occurred in the top 6 inches of soil. Starling (1944) found $400/m^2$ specimens of *Pauropus carolinensis* in sandy forest soil and $300/m^2$ in loamy soil. Little is known of their feeding habits; Starling considered that *Pauropus* spp. feed on fungi, Verhoeff (1934) considered them predacious. Like the Protura, the Pauropoda are a group of hypogeal arthropods about which little is known but which, because of their small size and relative scarcity compared with other groups such as the Acari and Collembola, presumably have little affect on the biology of soil.

2. Chilopoda

They are primarily carnivorous but some geophilomorph centipedes will occasionally feed on plant tissue. They are predominantly woodland species but are also common in grassland, arable land and, unlike millipedes, in moorland where the geophilomorphs *Brachygeophilus truncorum* (Bergsoe & Meinert) and *Geophilus carpophagous* Leach and the lithobiids *Lithobius variegatus* Leach, *L. calcaratus* Koch, and *L. lapidicola* Meinert, are frequently common. Blower (1955) pointed out that the species frequently found in moorland and heaths are often also frequent in woodland soils tending to mor conditions, whereas the species found in grassland and arable land are those commonly associated with mull soils.

The distribution and activities of centipedes depend largely on their body form and moisture relations. They easily desiccate but, because they are extremely active creatures, they can forage temporarily in dry places that they could not inhabit permanently. The body wall musculature of geophilomorph centipedes enables them to burrow several inches deep in soil. There is some evidence that *Geophilus* spp. move up and down in the soil in response to seasonal changes. Although they desiccate easily, particularly by water loss through the spiracles, their waterproof, hydrofuge cuticle enables them to survive temporary flooding in soil. In contrast, lithobiomorph centipedes are unable to burrow properly. Their waterproof hydrofuge cuticle seems less well developed and, although they differ little from geophilomorph centipedes in their resistance to drought, they are less well able to withstand flooding. Consequently, geophilomorph centipedes are part of the truly hypogeal fauna whereas lithobiomorph centipedes tend to be restricted to sheltered niches on the soil surface, beneath stones, bark, etc., or to a porous litter layer through which they can push their way.

3. Symphyla

They are sometimes considered rare animals but in several surveys of soil arthropods they were the most numerous myriapods present (Salt *et al.*, 1948; Edwards, 1958). Michelbacher (1949) gives a general account of their ecology, and states that they are widely distributed through temperate and tropical regions and occur in both cultivated and uncultivated soils, being particularly abundant in warm moist organic soils. Estimates of their abundance differ widely and may exceed 20,000/m^2, but such differing estimates undoubtedly reflect the efficiency of the sampling methods used as well as the actual abundance of symphyla. Symphyla are part of the true hypogeal fauna and at certain times are commonly found in greatest numbers in the lower soil layers. *Symphylella subterranea* Mich., for example, is rarely found in the top 6 inches of soil and may be most abundant below 12 inches.

Edwards (1958) sampled 415 sites in southern England and found symphylids in 46% of them. Of the various habitats sampled, they were found in 32% of the grassland sites, 26% of the forest litter sites, 44% of the cultivated soils and 53% of the grassland soils. *Symphylella* spp. were more widespread than *Scutigerella* spp. which, however, tended to be more numerous when present, although the average populations of the two genera for each habitat was similar. Loams appeared to be the most favourable soil type, with clay loams and sandy loams intermediate, and sandy loams, sands and clays the least favourable. The greatest populations were found in glasshouse soils (5–88 million/acre), followed by cultivated soils (4–29 million/acre) forest litter (5–12 million/acre), grassland (0·4–7 million/acre) and fallow soil (0·5–4·8 million/acre). These results probably reflect the preference of symphylids for soils with an open texture, good moisture holding capacity and high organic matter content.

Many symphylids make seasonal vertical migrations in soil in response to changes in soil moisture and temperature, and to feeding, moulting and oviposition cycles. Phytophagous species, such as *Scutigeralla immaculata* New-port, will feed on young roots near the soil surface when soil conditions are otherwise unfavourable. Other species may be attracted to the surface soil when it is warm and moist but at other times, or when moulting or laying eggs, they retreat to the lower soil layers. Symphylids feed voraciously, mainly on vege-table material and soil micro-organisms, and some, such as *S. immaculata*, are serious pests of horticultural crops, particularly in glasshouses. They undoubtedly contribute to the breakdown of soil organic matter, particularly in situations such as glasshouses where they may be the dominant group of soil arthropods. In general, however, their contribution to such breakdown may be limited because, although widespread and relatively abundant, they usually form a relatively small part of the total biomass of the soil fauna.

4. Diplopoda

Like Chilopoda, they are predominantly woodland species. They are also common in grassland and arable land where Verhoeff (1934) considered they represented a relict forest fauna.

(a) *Distribution.* Blower (1955) has described the distribution of milli-pedes in Britain and his account illustrates their range of habitat. The species most commonly found in grassland and arable soils are *Blaniulus guttulatus* (Bosc) and *Brachydesmus superus* Latzel; the former species is sometimes sufficiently abundant to become a pest. Other species found in agricultural soils, such as *Cylindroiulus londinensis* var. *cearuleocinctus* (Wood) and *Archeboreoiulus pallidus* (Brade-Birks) tend to be restricted to calcareous soils. As the data from the Barnfield mangold plots showed, (p. 330), repeated applications of farmyard manure favour millipedes.

Blower (1955) distinguished three types of woodland habitat where milli-pedes occur; the surface of the soil, litter and vegetation; the interior of the litter and soil; the subcortical layers of tree stumps, logs, etc., and rotting wood. The Iulids, *Tachypodiulus niger* (Leach) and *Schizophyllum sabulosum* (Linne) are characteristic of the first type of habitat. Many species occur within woodland litter and soil. *Glomeris marginata* Villers, *Cylindoiulus punctatus* (Leach) and *Polydesmus denticulatus* (Latzel) are characteristic of climax oak woodland and *Iulus scandinavius* Latzel and *Ophyiulus pilosus* (Newport) of mixed deciduous woodland. Where litter decomposition is rapid, as in ash woods, *G. marginata* becomes dominant. *Schizophyllum sabulosum* is charac-teristic of coniferous woodland and *C. punctatus* and *L. scandinavius* pre-dominate in deciduous mor. Most species of millipede may be found in sub-cortical habitats. Although millipedes tend to be more plentiful on calcareous soils, only *C. londinensis* Leach and *A. pallidus* (Brade-Birks), of the British species, appear to be truly calcicole.

(b) *Feeding and ecological preferences.* Millipedes are exclusively vege-tarian and feed on plant litter in varying stages of decomposition. They are convenient animals for laboratory experiments so their feeding habits and digestion have been studied in some detail. Lyford (1943) investigated the palatability of leaves of different tree species to *Diploiulus londinensis caeruleocinctus* (Wood) by measuring the leaf area eaten when specimens caged in glass vessels were offered leaves from different tree species. The palatability of leaves from the same tree or from adjacent trees of the same species differed somewhat but not so much as leaves from different tree species. Palatability was correlated with the calcium content of the leaves. However, other factors must affect palatability for the leaves of some trees with high calcium content, such as the black cherry *Prunus serotina* Ehrh whose calcium content of 2·29% was the second highest of the leaves tested, were amongst the least palatable. Moreover, the millipede used for these tests, *D. londinensis caeruleocinctus* (Wood), is one of the calcicole species.

Using the euryoke species *Glomeris marginata* Koch and the stenoke species *Cylindroiulus nitidus* Verk. as test animals, Thiele (1959) investigated the factors likely to account for "calcicole" species such as *C. nitidus* being restricted to plant communities on lime rich soil. Tests done in a choice chamber with substrates at pH 7·5 and 4·0 showed that *G. marginata* preferred the neutral substrate but *C. nitidus* showed no preference. Both species could be maintained on either substrate. Young specimens of *G. marginata* that were fed for 6 months on beech litter from a lime rich habitat increased from 34·8 to 43·8 mg compared with an increase from 36·3 mg to 53·1 mg for similar specimens fed on beech litter from an acid soil. In the same experiment young specimens of *C. nitidus* failed to maintain themselves on either diet, possibly because the substrate tended to dry out. When a satisfactory moisture content was maintained, groups of *C. nitidus* at various stages of development grew equally well on beech litter from lime rich and from lime poor habitats. The palatability of beech litter was unaffected by soaking it in 2% tannin solution, but fresh litter was usually rejected whereas litter that had been weathered for one year was accepted and formed a suitable diet.

These experiments showed that the distribution of the species could not be accounted for by the pH of the substrate or by the characteristics of litter from lime rich and lime poor habitats. Experiments were then done to see if the calcicole species needed certain microclimatic conditions that occurred only on lime rich soils.

The preferred temperature of several species was determined using an apparatus which gave a temperature gradient from $+30°c$ to $+2°c$. The moisture preference of each species was estimated by recording the percentage of occasions that individuals selected the moister region when placed in a choice chamber in which one half was maintained at 75% R.H. and the other at 30–40% R.H. The results, summarized in Fig 4 and Table 2 show that, except for *T. albipes*, the preferred temperatures of the various species differed little and could not account for some of them being restricted to plant communities on calcareous soils. *T. albipes* is known to be restricted to the coolest and moistest parts of deciduous forests and its low preferred temperature could account for this. By contrast, the moisture preferences of the species differed markedly. In particular, stenoke species showed a much greater preference for a high relative humidity than euryoke species of the same genus. *J. scandinavius* was rather exceptional for a euryoke species in showing an unusually marked preference for a high relative humidity.

Because relatively high and uniform atmospheric humidity is characteristic of woodland communities on calcareous soils, but not of other plant com-

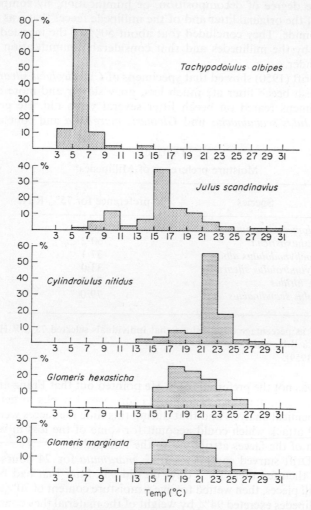

FIG. 4. Temperature preference of Millipedes.

Ordinate=percentage of occasions when Millipedes in a temperature gradient were observed at each temperature. From Thiele (1959).

munities in which euryoke species occur, it was concluded that the moisture requirements of the "calcicole" species was the decisive factor responsible for their "stenoke" distribution. Their temperature preferences were less important in determining their distribution.

(c) *Food consumption and digestion.* Franz and Leitenberger (1948) investigated the chemical changes in leaf litter when it is eaten by millipedes and particularly the extent to which it is humified during passage through the gut. They fed millipedes for several weeks on newly fallen litter and then estimated the degree of decomposition, or humification, by comparing the percentage of the original litter and of the millipede faeces that was insoluble in acetyl bromide. They concluded that about 50% of the ingested material was utilized by the millipedes and that considerable humification occurred in the remainder.

Van der Drift (1950) showed that specimens of *Cylindroiulus silvarum* Mein reared on fresh beech litter ate much less, grew slower and more died than similar specimens reared on beech litter several years old. He got similar results with *Julus scandinavius* and *Glomeris marginata* and concluded that

TABLE II

Moisture preference of Millipedes*

Species	% preference for 75% R.H.
Glomeris marginata	36.4
G. hexasticha	60·2
Tachypodoiulus albipes	37·1
Cylindroiulus silvarum	33·0
C. nitidus	76·2
Julus scandinavius	79·0

* Expressed as percentage of occasions that individuals selected 75% R.H. in preference to 30-40% R.H. when in a choice chamber.

From Thiele (1959).

fresh litter was not the preferred food. He pointed out that Franz and Leitenberger had to continue their experiments for several weeks to get sufficient faeces for chemical analysis and that during this time the faeces were exposed to microbial attack which could account for some of the loss in weight and humification of the faeces attributed to the millipedes.

Van der Drift starved specimens of *G. marginata* for 24 hours to empty the gut and then fed them for 5 days on old oak litter that had been dried, cut into small pieces, then wetted to give a moisture content of 70%. He found that the millipedes excreted 94% by weight of the material they consumed and utilized only 6% of it. The food contained 2·55% nitrogen, 0·35% phosphorus (P_2O_5), and 1·1% calcium (CaO) compared with 2·50% nitrogen, 0·30% phosphorus and 1·0% calcium in the faeces. After allowing for experimental errors, Van der Drift concluded that about 7% of the nitrogen, 20% of the phosphorus and 15% of the calcium was utilized. Analysis by acetyl bromide suggested that little humification had occurred during passage through the gut. Litter consumption was greatest when the temperature was between

17·5 and 22·5°C, which is close to the preferred temperature of *C. marginata* as found by Thiele, and when the moisture content of the litter was about 70%. When expressed as a percentage of the body weight, the amount of litter consumed daily was inversely correlated with size, being relatively about twice as great for small individuals weighing about 52 mg as for large individuals weighing about 190 mg. When expressed as a proportion of the surface area of the individual, the daily litter consumption was roughly constant (Table III).

TABLE III

Litter consumption of *Glomeris marginata* of different sizes
(average values for 30 individuals of each size)

Average live wt (mg.) (w.)	Daily consumption (as % of body wt)	Air dry wt of litter consumed (c.) per ind./5 days	$\dfrac{c.}{w.^{\frac{2}{3}}}$
52·1	66	57·7	4·1
117·7	49	95·8	4·0
190·6	36	113·8	3·4

From van der Drift (1950).

In feeding experiments with *Glomeris hexasticha* Brandt and *Chromatojulus projectus* Verhoeff, Gere (1956) got similar results to van der Drift. In addition, he showed that the amount of litter consumed and the amount utilized depended on its state of decomposition when eaten. Millipedes fed on oak litter from the F_x layer ate less and utilized more than those fed on more decomposed oak litter from the F_1 layer (Table IV).

TABLE IV

Consumption of F_x and F_1 litter by millipedes

Litter layer	Dry wt eaten/day as % of live wt	% excreted	% converted to body tissue	% lost by oxidation
F_x	1	80 to 85	1·7 to 7·4	9·5 to 14·5
F_1	1 to 3	88 to 96	−6·9* to 5·3	0 to 12·1

* Some animals fed on F_1 litter lost weight.
From Gere (1956).

Gere's results can account for some of the difference between van der Drift's results and those of Franz and Leitenberger.

Dunger (1958) studied the chemical changes in leaf litter when it is eaten by different soil animals. His test species included the millipedes *Cylindrojulus teutonicus* Poc., *Glomeris connexa* Koch and *Julus scandinavius* Latz. To

estimate the humic acid content of the food and of the faeces the material
was air dried, finely ground, extracted with 0·5% NaOH over a boiling water
bath for 8 hours, then centrifuged at *c.* 4,000 rev/min. Absorption measurements of the extract were made with a Pulfrich-photometer using Zeiss filters
S47 (465 mμ) and S66 (665 mμ). An arbitrary formula was used to calculate
the total humic acid content and the colour quotient of the extract. Dunger
regarded the difference between the humic acid content of the food and the
faeces calculated by this method as a measure of the humification caused by
the animals. He also regarded the colour quotient (absorption at 465 mμ/
absorption at 665 mμ) as a measure of humification; highly humified material
having a lower colour quotient than less humified material. From the results
it was concluded that changes in the humic acid content of the leaf litter
during passage through the gut depended on its initial state and composition
and did not differ significantly for each of the animal species tested.

In experiments with fresh litter, there was a significant increase in humic
acid content only when nitrogen rich leaves were eaten. A change of colour
quotient indicating an increase of nitrogen rich grey humic acid could be
detected only with leaves that had the highest nitrogen content, i.e. *Sambucus
nigra*. With leaves that had a low nitrogen content and high humic acid content there was a decrease in humic acid content which the lower colour
quotient suggested was due to a partial decomposition of the unstable brown
humic acid.

In experiments with litter that had overwintered naturally, the chemical
changes during passage through the gut were much smaller. Some increase in
humic acid content occurred with nitrogen rich litter such as that from
Fraxinus excelsior and *Alnus glutinosa*. With leaves of some other species
such as *Quercus robbor*, *Acer platanoides* and *Ulmus carpinifolia*, some
decomposition of humic acids occurred.

Changes occurring in fresh litter during passage through the gut closely
resembled those that occurred during natural overwintering which suggested
that the processes were the same and differed only in the rate at which they
occurred.

Some changes in humic acid content could have resulted from microbial
activity after the faeces left the animals but tests after 5 days failed to detect
such changes and only slight changes were detected after much longer periods.

Analyses of the food and the faeces (Table V), showed that the total nitrogen and carbon content of the faeces was always slightly less than that of
the food and that the C/N ratio tended to be lower in the faeces. No change
in total nitrate and nitrite nitrogen and only slight changes in NH_3 nitrogen
were observed. These small changes indicated that relatively little carbon
and nitrogen was utilized. By contrast, between 9 and 37% of the calcium
was utilized.

Bocock (1963) studied digestion and assimilation of food by *G. marginata*
fed for 18 days on ash litter several months old and got similar results to
earlier workers. He estimated that 6·0–10·5% of the dry matter, 43·2% of the
crude fat, 28·4% of the holocellulose, 28·7% of the soluble carbohydrates

and 0·3–0·4% of the nitrogen present in the ash litter was utilized. From these results it was deduced that about 70% of the energy assimilated by *G. marginata* was derived from the holocellulose, 19·5% from the crude fat and 10·5% from soluble carbohydrates. Females and males converted into body tissue 0·29% and 0·45% respectively of the ash litter they consumed.

TABLE V

Chemical analysis of food and faeces of Diplopods

Leaf species	Diplopod species		%N	%NH$_3$	%C	C/N	%Ca
Ulmus	*Cylindroiulus*	l.	2·19	0·16	38·2	17·4	2·3
carpinifolia	*teutonicus*	f.	2·01	0·21	33·5	16·7	2·0
Tilia		l.	2·33	0·28	41·0	17·7	2·2
cordata	*C. teutonicus*	f.	2·18	0·22	35·7	16·4	2·0
	Glomeris connexa	f.	2·33	0·22	34·4	14·8	1·6
Fraxinus		l.	2·59	0·08	41·8	16·1	2·8
excelsior	*C. teutonicus*	f.	2·56	0·19	41·6	16·2	1·9

l=litter; f=faeces; N, NH$_3$, C as % of air dry wt; Ca as % absolute dry wt. From Dunger (1958).

Bocock also recorded that the faeces contained more ammonia and total nitrogen than the food (Table VI).

The increase in ammonia, which could also account for the pH of the faeces of Glomeris being higher than that of the food, may represent animal

TABLE VI

Nitrogen metabolism of *G. marginata*

Test material	Amino nitrogen (μg/g)	Ammonia nitrogen (μg/g)	As % of Total N	Total nitrogen (μg/g)
Food	193	175	2·7	13,600
Uneaten food	86	335	3·2	13,100
Faecal pellets	103	1,385	9·5	15,700

From Bocock (1963).

excretory products or may result from the death and autolysis of micro-organisms in the gut or faeces. Bocock also recorded that there was an increase in lignin as a result of digestion but this may be an artefact or experimental error as a result of estimating lignin as the fraction insoluble in 72% sulphuric acid.

In general it seems that many millipedes eat large amounts of leaf litter of little nutritional value and excrete most of it relatively unchanged chemically but greatly fragmented and so more readily available to micro-organisms.

B. ISOPTERA

Although some termites occur in temperate regions, most species are tropical or sub-tropical. They exhibit a great range of form and social organization and differ greatly in their feeding habits and the type of nest they construct. Some wood feeding species live entirely in galleries excavated within decaying logs or trees; others construct simple protective passages from earth or faeces to connect timbers that they attack. Other species construct earth mounds of varying size and complexity. Some species feed exclusively on wood, others cultivate fungi and many feed on vegetable refuse in varying stages of decomposition. Their importance for soil biology lies

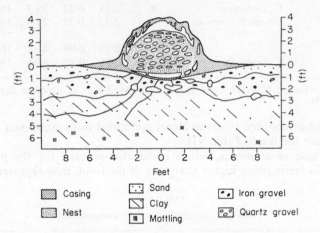

FIG. 5. Structure of a Termite mound.

Relation between mound of *Macrotermes nigeriensis* and the underlying soil. From Nye (1955).

in the extent to which they move and mix soil and organic matter from different horizons and in the extent to which they help to decompose large quantities of organic matter, particularly cellulose.

(a) *Mound building and the soil profile*. The effects of mound building on the distribution and composition of soil mineral and organic matter is well illustrated by Nye's account of mounds of *Macrotermes nigeriensis* Sjost, which are common around Ibadan, Nigeria (Nye, 1955). Mounds (Fig. 5) consisted of an outer casing that was penetrated by irregular channels and made of pellets of coarse red sandy clay, about 1–2 mm in diameter. This casing surrounded the nest which was made of a compact mass of pellets like those of the casing but without the coarse sand fraction. Galleries radiated in all directions from the floor of the nest and indicated the depth and area of soil disturbed while making the mound. They were particularly numerous to a depth of 3 ft below the mound and some went 10 ft deep. The mechanical analysis showed that none of the particles found in the casing exceeded 4 mm and only a small proportion of them exceeded 2 mm, which suggests that the termites were reluctant to manipulate particles larger than 2 mm. In the nest, only a small proportion of the particles exceeded 0·5 mm and the upper limit was 2 mm. It was suggested that this difference in mechanical composition arose because the nest was built mainly from earth that had passed through the termites' bodies. The colour and mechanical composition of the casing and nest suggested that most of the material came from 12–30 inch depth and that the humic surface soil was not used for building material.

The organic carbon content of the casing was somewhat higher than that of the surrounding earth from which it was formed, possibly because of secretions used to cement the particles together, but otherwise it differed little from it in chemical composition. The nest framework and the layers immediately beneath it contained varying amounts of excreta and fungal material and contained more organic carbon than the casing and surrounding profiles. They also had a higher pH, exchangeable Ca and Mg and saturation percentage. There was no sign that calcium carbonate accumulated at the base of the mounds as observed by Griffith (1938) and Milne (1947) in E. Africa and by Pendleton (1942) in Siam. Mounds were built rapidly: they reached up to 2 ft in a month, and a mature mound reaches 5 ft within a year. Abandoned mounds collapse slowly and probably take several years to collapse completely. The proportion of living to abandoned mounds was 1:15. It was estimated that in the Ibadan region at least ½ ton of earth per acre, mainly from below the creep horizon, is deposited on the top soil by termites each year.

Annual crops such as maize grow relatively poorly in soil from termite mounds because it is usually poorer in nutrients and more compact than the surrounding topsoil, although the subsoil beneath the mounds may be richer in nutrients. The most important contribution that mound building termites make to soil changes is the gradual production of a gravel free topsoil. They may also be important in accelerating creep whereby the topsoil is gradually lowered and nutrients released in the subsoil are more accessible to the vegetation.

Holdaway (1933) and Cohen (1933) showed that the mounds of an Australian species *Eutermes* (*Nasutitermes*) *exitiosus* contained 8–25% organic carbon in the outer wall and 44–53% organic carbon in the nest. The ratio of lignin to cellulose was about 4:1, increasing slightly towards the centre of the nest. This compares with a ratio of 1:2 for most wood and suggests that lignin is not digested by this species. The increase in the lignin:cellulose ratio towards the centre of the nest suggests that there had been more prolonged digestion of the material there.

(b) *Feeding and digestion.* Hendee (1935) and Hungate (1941) showed that the species *Zootermopsis* only grows and increases its nitrogen content when it feeds on wood infected by fungi and it seems probable that the fungi are important in fixing nitrogen from soil sources in a form that can be utilized by the termites.

Although termites have no cellulase of their own and many mono- and di-saccharide sugars are readily assimilated, cellulose is the main carbohydrate utilized by termites feeding on wood or plant tissues. Except for the Termitidae, all forms feeding on material containing cellulose have a rich intestinal fauna of flagellates (*Polymastigina* and *Hypermastigina* spp.) that secrete a cellulase. Usually each species of termite has only one species of flagellate but some have more. Hungate (*ibid.*) showed that *in vitro* digestion of cellulose by the intestinal protozoa of *Zootermopsis* produced CO_2, H_2 and simple organic acids, mainly acetic acid. It was thought that the acetic acid is probably absorbed and metabolized by the termite.

Carbohydrate metabolism in Termitidae which lack flagellates is not understood. As they usually ingest a high proportion of humus or fungi when feeding they may not be so dependent on cellulose.

Because they utilize organic residues so effectively and completely, termites can decrease the organic carbon content of soil by accelerating decomposition of organic matter in the upper layers. Where vegetation is abundant they are unlikely to cause a deficit of soil organic matter, but this could happen in arid regions where termites are plentiful and the flora sparse.

C. COLEOPTERA

The Coleoptera, which is the largest order of insects, contains a vast number of species, and beetles have colonized most of the habitats where insects occur. Because of their adaptability and range of structure beetles have extremely differing habits but they predominate on or in the soil as predators or associated with decaying animal or vegetable matter. Table VII illustrates the range of feeding habits of the main groups that may be found on or in the soil.

(a) *Beetle predators and effects of predation*. Some predators such as the Cicindellidae, Carabidae, Histeridae, and Staphylinidae range widely and prey on many other species. Other predators are more restricted in their habitat and prey. For example, the Scydmaenidae and Pselaphidae that occur in litter appear to prey mainly on oribatid mites. The Drilidae, Lampyridae and some sylphid larvae prey on snails and slugs. Other groups such as the Cleridae, Melyridae and Trogositidae and the Rhysophagidae, Cucujiidae and Colydiidae are found mainly in decaying wood where they prey on lignocolous and saprophagous insects.

The effect of predators on the abundance of their prey and the way this can be altered by the use of insecticides is well illustrated by studies of the beetle predators of the cabbage root fly, *Erioischia brassicae* (Bouché).

Wright (1956) observed that on plots where DDT, aldrin or BHC had been broadcast and then mixed into the top 4 inches of soil at 12, 2 or $\frac{3}{4}$ lb/acre cabbages were damaged more by cabbage root fly larvae than those growing on untreated plots. Root and soil samples showed that cabbage root fly larvae and pupae were more abundant on treated plots. The concentration of the insecticide was known to be too low to kill cabbage root fly eggs and larvae directly, but it evidently affected beetles because they were less abundant for 3 months after the insecticides were applied though more were found later. Feeding tests showed that more than 30 species of beetles, chiefly carabids and staphylinids, would eat cabbage root fly eggs, larvae or pupae and that some species, common on brassica plots, such as *Bembidion lampros* (Herbst.) and *Trechus obtusus* F., ate them voraciously. By decreasing the number of predatory beetles without controlling the pest, insecticide treatments increased cabbage root fly damage. Later work showed that beetle species occurred in succession in the crop, some being associated with the open conditions following planting out, others with the more shaded conditions following crop growth. Differences in weather appeared to cause seasonal differences in the extent to which insecticides affected predation.

Hughes and Salter (1959) studied mortality during the immature stages of the first generation of cabbage root fly from 1954–58 and concluded that it was greatest in the egg stage and that on average 15% of the eggs laid produced larvae that became established in host plants, 92% of these larvae survived to pupate and 37% of the pupae produced flies. Mortality during the egg stage was then studied in more detail and a method was developed for estimating the average survival of eggs over short periods by counting the eggs in the soil near different groups of plants at different time intervals, namely 2 and 4 days. It was shown that the egg survival estimated in this way was inversely related to the numbers of predatory beetles, *Bembidion lampros*, caught in pitfall traps during the same period. From this relationship and the daily trap catches of beetles, the egg survival on each day was estimated and then used to estimate the total number of eggs laid each day from the numbers actually counted. In this way it was estimated that predation accounted for more than 90% of the mortality between the time the eggs were laid and larvae hatching from them became established in plants. Weather affected predation by affecting the activity of the predators and the length of time the eggs took to hatch. Heavy rain decreased predation by breaking down the soil crumbs and sealing eggs in the soil where they were less accessible to predators.

This work probably over-estimated the effect of predators and underestimated the direct effect of soil conditions, particularly dryness, because Coaker and Simpson (1962) found that cabbage root fly eggs dried up easily and that, in pot tests, 70% of emerging larvae became established in host plants in soil at field capacity but only 30% became established when the moisture content of the topsoil was 20–30%.

Coaker and Williams (1963) used a serological method to find out which of the species of carabids and staphylinids found on their brassica plots actually preyed on the immature stages of cabbage root fly. Samples of each species were collected throughout the season and their gut contents were tested for cabbage root fly tissue with anti-cabbage root fly serum. Their results,

12+s.b.

TABLE VII

Feeding habits of Coleoptera commonly found in the soil

Family	Predaceous	Necrophagous	Coprophagous	Xylophagous	Fungivorous	Saprophagous	Phytophagous
ADEPHAGA							
Rhysodidae	a & l						
Cicindellidae	a & l						
Carabidae	a & l						occ.
POLYPHAGA							
Histeroidea							
Histeridae	a & l	a & l				a	
Staphylinoidea							
Clambidae							
Ptiliidae						a & l	
Anisotomidae					a & l		
Silphidae	l	a & l				a & l	
Scydmaenidae	a & l				a & l		occ.
Scaphidiidae	a & l				a & l		
Pselaphidae	a & l						
Staphylinidae	a & l						a & l
Scaraboidea							
Passalidae				a & l			
Lucanidae				a & l			
Trogidae		a & l	occ.				
Acanthoceridae							
Geotrupidae			a & l			a & l	a & l
Scarabaeidae			a & l			a & l	a & l

Taxon				
Dascilloidea				
Dascillidae				
Eucenetidae	a & 1			
Buprestoidea				
Buprestidae	1 occ.			
Elateroidea				
Cebrionidae	1			1 occ.
Elateridae				1 occ.
Trixagidae	1			
Eucnemidae		1		
Cantharoidea				
Drilidae				a & 1
Lampyridae				a & 1
Cantharidae				1
Lycidae				1
Cleroidea				
Cleridae				1
Melyridae				1
Trogossitidae				a & 1
Cucujoidea				
Nitidulidae	a & 1	a & 1	a & 1	a & 1
Rhizophagidae		a & 1		a & 1
Cucujidae		a & 1		1 occ.
Other *Clavicornia*	a & 1		a & 1	a & 1
Colydidae		a & 1	a & 1	a & 1
Other *Heteromera*	a & 1	a & 1	a & 1	
Anthicidae		a	a & 1	a
Curculinoidea	a & 1			

l = larvae   a = adults   occ. = occasional

summarized in Table VIII, shows what a complex community of predators was present, for 22 species gave positive reactions and the proportion of individuals that reacted varied greatly. Feeding tests with individual species of carabids showed that the percentage of eggs that they ate during 3 days

TABLE VIII

Predators of cabbage root fly, *Erioischia brassicae* (Bouché)
Results of testing beetle predator smears against anti-cabbage root fly serum

	No. tested	Percentage reacting
Carabidae		
Nebria brevicollis (F.)	178	11·8
Clivina fossor (L.)	91	12·0
Bembidion lampros (Herbst.)	750	20·0
B. quadrimaculatum (L.)	332	18·1
Trechus quadristriatus (Sch.)	104	11·5
T. obtusus Er.	33	4·9
Harpalus aeneus (F.)	365	23·9
H. rufipes (Deg.)	305	14·1
Amara familiaris (Duft.)	181	22·1
Feronia vulgaris (L.)	236	11·4
F. madida (F.)	39	2·7
Agonum viduum (Panz.)	31	3·2
A. dorsale (Pont.)	68	4·4
	Mean	12·3
Staphylinidae		
Oxytelus rugosus (F.)	119	13·5
Xantholinus longiventris Heer	30	20·0
Philonthus succicola Thom.	27	11·4
P. cognatus Steph.	23	4·5
Tachyporus hypnorum (F.)	76	6·6
T. solutus (Er.)	33	3·0
T. obtusus (L.)	38	5·3
Aleochara bilineata Gyll.	556	2·5
A. bipustulata (L.)	115	2·6
	Mean	7·7

From Coaker and Williams (1963).

differed, and that on this basis they could be ranked in order of predator value (Table IX).

The results of the serological and feeding tests were then used in conjunction with field population estimates to assess the predation by carabids and staphylinids on the immature stages of cabbage root fly attacking summer brassicas from April to May 1961 (Table X). The number of meals taken was estimated from the numbers present and the mean percentage reacting with anti-cabbage root fly serum. The mortality inflicted was estimated from tests

TABLE IX

Predator value of carabids measured as the percentage of eggs eaten during 3 days compared with the percentage eaten by *Bembidion lampros*

Species	*Bembidion lampros*	*Bembidion quadrimaculatum*	*Harpalus aeneus*	*Harpalus rufipes*	*Feronia vulgaris*	*Nebria brevicollis*	*Agonum dorsale*	*Clivina fossor*	*Trechus obtusus*
% eggs eaten	72·6	52·5	57·0	16·1	17·9	28·3	37·3	8·9	74·5
Mean predator value	1·0	0·73	0·68	0·23	0·23	0·42	0·49	0·14	1·06

From Coaker and Williams (1963).

comparing survival in the presence and absence of carabid adults. The mortality inflicted by staphylinids was calculated by proportion. In this way it was estimated that carabids and staphylinids accounted for about 60% of the mortality of the immature stages of cabbage root fly.

TABLE X

Comparative predation by carabids and staphylinids on immature stages of *Erioischia brassicae* attacking summer cabbages, April–May 1961

	Estimated nos.	Mean % reacting with anti-CRF serum	Estimated no. of meals taken	Estimated mortality inflicted on CRF
Carabids	11,729	12·3	7209	24%
Staphylinids	26,235	7·7	11,351	34%

(b) *Decomposition of carrion.* Beetles play a prominent part in the decomposition of carrion and it is possible to distinguish a succession of species associated with different stages of decomposition.

In the early stages, when rapid bacterial decomposition and liquefaction occurs, Silphidae, such as the common sexton or burying beetles, *Necro phorus* spp. and the smaller Catopinae, such as *Catops* and *Ptomaphagus* spp. invade the carrion. *Necrophorus* adults are readily attracted by smell to carrion and eventually bury it by excavating the earth beneath. Often a pair of beetles take possession of a carcase by attacking other species or *Necrophorus* individuals present. After mating, and when the carrion is enclosed in a "mortuary cellar", the female *Necrophorus* lays eggs in pockets in the walls of a narrow horizontal passage leading from the "mortuary cellar". The young larvae at first depend on the adults for food but later feed on the carrion themselves. They develop rapidly and pupate in 10–14 days.

When the butyric fermentation stage is reached other beetles associated with decomposition under drier conditions are found, for example, dermestids and clerids. Later still, tenebrionids, a group commonly associated with stored products, may be found.

Bornemissza (1957) studied carrion decomposition under experimental conditions in sclerophyll woodland in Western Australia. He described the succession of arthropods that occurred (Fig. 6) in the carcasses, and showed that the soil fauna played little part in the decomposition, for ants and earwigs were the only members of the usual soil fauna observed to feed on the carrion. Most of the decomposition was brought about by a succession of other arthropod groups. He also showed that when active decomposition occurs the area around and beneath the carrion becomes unfavourable for the normal soil fauna and may remain so for many months before it is slowly re-colonized.

(c) *Decomposition of plant material.* An enormous range of beetles feed on fresh or decomposing vegetable matter on or in the soil. Their feeding habits can be illustrated by those of the super-family Scaraboidea.

The Passalidae is a family of predominantly tropical species whose adults and larvae inhabit decaying wood. The larvae of the Lucanidae, a fairly cosmopolitan family that includes the stag beetles with their striking sexual dimorphism, also inhabit decaying wood as do the larvae of the Acanthoceridae, which is a small family of tropical species.

The Geotrupidae (dor beetles) are predominantly coprophilous although some species such as *Lethrus* are phytophagous and may attack crops. *Geotrupes* is associated with dung pats under which it makes burrows about 18 inches deep. Each burrow is provisioned with dung for its larvae and one egg is laid in the dung in each burrow. The dung-feeding habit also predominates in two of the sub-families of Scarabaeidae—the Aphodiinae and the Coprinae. Species of *Aphodius* are widespread and abundant in dung. One Australian species, however, *Aphodius howitii* Hope, is phytophagous and is a serious pest of pastures in south-west Australia. The Coprinae, which are commonest in the tropics, live almost entirely in dung. They include the genus *Scarabaeus*, which has developed the curious habit of rolling up balls of dung, which are then moved to underground chambers to serve as food for the beetles and larvae. Few eggs are laid and the females guard the nest and tend the larvae till they mature.

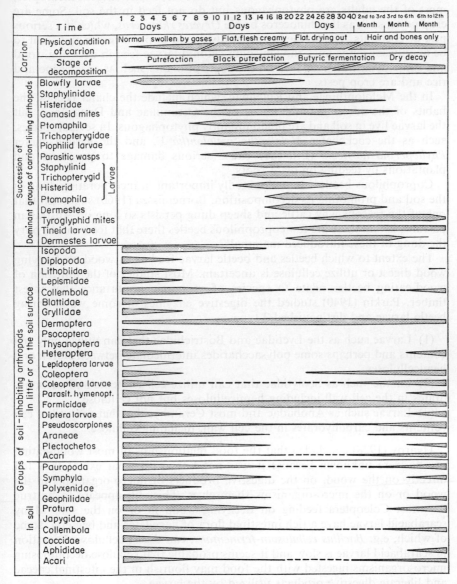

Fig. 6. Arthropod succession in carrion.

Succession of arthropods in carrion (dead guinea pigs) showing almost complete disappearance of soil dwellers while the carrion dwellers are active. Relative abundance within the groups shown by variations in thickness of each band. From Bornemissza (1957).

In the Cetoniinae and Dynastinae, which are also commonest in the tropics, most of the adults are phytophagous but do not feed in the soil. Some are crop pests, such as the rhinoceros beetle *Oryctes rhinoceros*, which is a serious pest of coconuts. The larvae are generally found in plant refuse and seem to be mainly saprophagous, though some cetonid larvae feed in decaying wood and some dynastid larvae feed on the roots of plants such as sugar cane and rice and are crop pests.

In the Melolonthinae and Rutelinae, which include the chafer beetles, the habits of the adults resemble those of the Cetoniinae and Dynastinae, but the larvae live in soil and are predominantly phytophagous. In several species, such as the cockchafer *Melolontha melolontha* F. and the garden chafer *Phyllopertha horticola* (L.), they cause serious damage to grassland and plantations by feeding on plant roots.

Coprophilous beetles are undoubtedly important in incorporating dung in the soil and promoting its decomposition. Bornemissza (1960) suggested that one of the reasons why cattle and sheep dung persists so long on Australian pastures is that there are few coprophilous beetles there that feed on and bury the dung of these introduced mammals.

The extent to which beetles and beetle larvae feeding in wood or decaying wood digest or utilize cellulose is uncertain. Most studies of the nutrition of wood-eating beetles relate to species of economic importance that infest timber. Parkin (1940) studied the digestive enzymes of some wood-boring beetle larvae and distinguished 3 types:

(1) Larvae such as the Lyctidae and Bostrichidae that can utilize only cell contents and perhaps some polysaccharides intermediate between starch and hemicelluloses.

(2) Larvae such as Scolytidae that can utilize cell contents and carbohydrates in the cell wall including hemicelluloses but not cellulose.

(3) Larvae such as Anobiidae and most Cerambycidae that can utilize cell contents and carbohydrates in the cell wall, including cellulose.

Uvarov (1928) concluded that the food relationships of most wood-eating insects were unknown because it was not known to what extent they fed directly on the wood, on the digestive products of micro-organisms in the wood or on the micro-organisms themselves. This still appears to be true for most Coleoptera feeding on decaying wood in or on the soil. Many scarabaeid larvae have a rich intestinal flora of flagellates and bacteria, some of which, e.g. *Bacillus cellulosam-fermentans*, can digest cellulose. Digestion in scarabaeid larvae is slow and it seems probable that cellulose decomposing micro-organisms ingested with the food may flourish in the intestinal caecae and liberate digestive products utilized by the larvae.

D. DIPTERA

The larvae of Diptera parallel the Coleoptera in the variety of species associated with the soil and in the range of their feeding habits (Table XI).

Brauns (1954) gives an account of the main groups of terricolous Diptera larvae.

1. Nematocera

The vast majority of Nematocera larvae associated with soil are saprophagous or secondarily phytophagous. The chief exceptions are the fungivorous and predacious mycetophylid larvae, some cecidomyid larvae that are predacious or coprophagous, and some bibionid larvae that are predacious or coprophagous, and some bibionid larvae, (Scatopsidae) that live in dung.

Larvae of Trichoceridae (winter gnats) and Anisopodidae are common in all kinds of decaying vegetable refuse such as decaying leaves, rotting vegetables and garden refuse. Some occur in decaying fungi, others in rotting wood. They are readily found in earth clamps of root vegetables such as potatoes, turnips and beet when some of the roots have decayed. In such situations they often occur with other saprophagous larvae, such as scatopsids, mycetophylids, borborids and predacious stratiomyid larvae.

As their name suggests, larvae of Mycetophilidae (fungus gnats) feed mainly on fungi. They are common in moist places that encourage fungus growth and where decomposing fruit and vegetable material is plentiful, such as compost, leaf mould and manure. Some occur in rotting wood. Several species of *Sciara* are pests of commercial mushrooms. The adults are attracted to the mushroom beds and oviposit on the mushrooms or the surrounding casing soil. The eggs hatch in a few days and the larvae invade the mushrooms, usually about soil level, and tunnel and feed in them. The larval stage lasts about 3 weeks and pupation may occur in the mushrooms or in the soil. As three or more generations may occur during the "life" of a commercial mushroom bed, enormous populations sometimes build up when no attempt is made to control them. In some species of *Sciara* the larvae are occasionally found in vast numbers that travel as a solid, slow-moving mass rather like a slow-moving column of driver ants.

The larvae of many species of Ceratopogonidae (biting midges) occur in moist or semi-aquatic habitats where decaying organic matter is plentiful. Kettle and Lawson (1952) described the immature stages of 28 British species of *Culicoides*. The major larval habitats were very wet or waterlogged soil and were classified as Bogland, Fresh Water Marsh, Swamp, Mud, Salt Marsh and Dung. Usually several species were found in each habitat with one or two species predominating. Two species, *Culicoides chiopterus* (Meigen) and *C. pseudochiopterus* (Downes & Kettle), were found in dung, even old dry dung pats which is a particularly dry habitat for *Culicoides* larvae. In a given breeding place there were specific differences in the vertical distribution of the larvae. Some species were most numerous in the top inch, others between 1 and 2 inches deep and others were most numerous below 2 inches deep. Such a difference in vertical distribution might account for several closely related species being able to exist in one breeding place.

Larvae of Bibionidae commonly occur in soil. Those of *Bibio* spp. such as *Bibio johannis* L. and *B. marci* L. feed gregariously at the roots of grasses

12*

TABLE XI

Feeding habits of Diptera commonly found in soil

Family	Predaceous	Necro-phagous	Xylo-phagous	Copro-phagous	Fungivorous	Sapro-phagous	Phyto-phagous
Nematocera							
Tipulidae						1	1
Trichoceridae						1	
Psychodidae						1	
Cecidomyidae	occ. 1			occ. 1			
Anisopodidae						1	
Bibionidae						a & 1	
Mycetophylidae	occ. 1				a & 1		
Ceratopogonidae						1	
Chironomidae				occ. 1		1	
Brachycera							
Xylophagidae			1 (?)				
Stratiomyidae	1 (?)						
Rhagionidae	1						
Tabanidae	1						
Therevidae	1						
Asilidae	1						
Empidae	1						
Dolichopodidae	1 (?)						

Cyclorrhapha				
(a) *Aschiza*				
Lonchopteridae	par. 1			
Phoridae	1			
Syrphidae	1 (?) / a & 1			
(b) *Schizophora*				
Agromyzidae	1			
Lonchaeidae				
Sepsidae	1			
Piophilidae				
Psilidae	1			
Sapromyzidae				
Anthomyzidae	1			
Opomyzidae				
Borboridae	par. 1			
Chloropidae	1			
(c) *Calyptratae*				
Calliphoridae	par. 1			
Tachynidae	par. 1			
Muscidae	1			

1 = larvae   a = adults   occ. = occasional   par. = parasitic   ? = probable or doubtful

and arable crops and from time to time have been reported as damaging crops although they are primarily saprophagous. Larvae of Scatopsinae, such as *Scatopse fuscipes* Meigen and *S. notata* L., are common in dung and putrefying organic matter.

Morris (1921–22) has described oviposition in *B. marci*. The females burrow into the soil, using the forelegs to move the soil, and construct a narrow winding burrow ending in a cell in which a regularly arranged mass of eggs is laid. Such egg masses give rise to the characteristic dense aggregations of bibionid larvae sometimes found in soil.

The ecology of the Tipulidae has been studied more than that of most Nematocera with soil-inhabiting larvae because several species, such as *Tipula paludosa* Meigen and *T. oleracea* Meigen are important crop pests.

Coulson (1959) studied the Tipulidae on the Moor House Nature Reserve, Westmorland, and made collections by sweep netting and by using sticky traps. Sixty-six of the 300 or so British species of tipulids were found on the reserve and could be divided into 3 major groups depending on the larval habitats. Sixteen species had completely aquatic larvae and were therefore confined to the distribution of suitable streams. Sixteen species were apparently confined to moorland and 17 species occurred also in terrestrial habitats at low altitudes though not always in precisely the same habitat as on moorland. The tipulid fauna as a whole was related to that of northern Scandinavia for 50 of the Moor House species occur in Denmark, Sweden and or Norway but only 38 occur in France. The larval habitats could be divided into numerous arbitrary groups depending largely on the vegetation, and Tipulidae were most common in the wetter habitats. Relatively few species were found in the better drained habitats.

The peat and alluvial areas of the reserve differed markedly in the tipulid species that occurred in them and these differed in their abundance and seasonal occurrence. The biology of *T. subnodicornis* (Zetterstedt), which occurred only in peat areas, and *T. paludosa* Meigen, which occurred only in mineral soils, was studied in detail, Coulson (1962). The peak emergence period for *T. subnodicornis* was late May and early June and eggs were laid in cavities in the peat by the females entering the cavities to oviposit or inserting the abdomen into them to oviposit. Consequently most eggs were laid more than 1 cm deep. By contrast, *T. paludosa* laid most of its eggs in the top cm. Population estimates showed there was great mortality in the egg and first instar stages, probably because of desiccation, and that 30–50% of the over-wintering larvae died, possibly because of disease or the severe winter climate. In 1955, when there was a drought in late June and early July during the egg and first instar period, *T. subnodicornis* died out or decreased drastically in several habitats on the reserve and only survived in relatively wet places, such as Sphagnum bogs (Table XII), which usually do not support large populations but clearly act as reservoirs where the population can survive the markedly fluctuating conditions associated with high moorlands (Cragg, 1961).

Milne *et al.* (1965) recorded population trends of *T. paludosa* at several farms in Northumberland from 1954–64 by recording the adults caught in light traps from May to November and the larvae recovered by the St. Ives method from standard turf samples in late November to early December. They recorded population crashes in 1955 and 1959 when the rainfall in the study area was unusually low during August and September. They did a field experiment in which eggs and larvae in pots of soil were exposed to con-ditions simulating the 1955 and 1959 rainfall and concluded that the popula-tion crashes of those years were caused by excessive mortality from desiccation during the egg stage.

TABLE XII

Survival of *Tipula subnodicornis* in different habitats on Moor House Nature Reserve, Westmorland

Habitat	No. of fourth instar larvae/m^2		
	1954	1955	1956
Juncus squarrosus moor	168	140	0
Eriophorum moor	70	104	4
Sphagnum bog	17	36	14

From Cragg (1961) based on Coulson (1962).

Larvae of some Cecidomyidae occur in soil, such as those species that feed on the faeces of insect larvae, nematodes and earthworms. Others, like many species of Diptera, pupate in the soil. For example, larvae of the swede midge, *Contarinia nasturtii* (Keiffer), leave their host plant when fully fed and pupate in the soil inside silken cocoons covered with soil particles. Similarly, the Wheat Blossom Midges, *Contarinia tritici* (Kirby) and *Sitodi-plosis mosellana* (Gehin), which infest the ears of wheat, pupate in the soil where those of *C. tritici* can remain viable for 3–4 years and those of *S. mosellana* for at least 13 years. Cocoons of gall-forming Cecidomyidae may also be found in soil. For example, in beech plantations infested with *Mikiola fagi* (Hartig), which forms conspicuous galls on the beech leaves, the upper part of the gall containing the larva falls to the ground, the larva pupates inside it and many such galls may be found in the beech litter.

Larvae of terrestrial Chironomidae may also be abundant in moist beech litter and are quite common in the leaf litter of deciduous forests at high altitudes, but not in coniferous forests.

2. Brachycera

In contrast to the predominantly saprophagous soil-inhabiting Nematocera the soil-inhabiting Brachycera are predominantly predacious.

Larvae of Xylophagidae occur in rotting wood such as decaying logs and tree stumps but, despite their name, they are probably not xylophagous. The form of their mouthparts suggests they are predacious and they probably prey on other insect larvae, small oligochaetes and nematodes living in the decaying wood. Predacious Brachycera larvae are also common in habitats rich in organic matter that support a large population of saprophagous organisms. For example, larvae of Stratiomyidae, Rhagionidae, Asilidae, Empidae and Dolichopodidae occur in habitats such as dung, compost, leaf mould and other decaying vegetable matter where nematoceran larvae and other small invertebrates that they prey on abound. Tabanid larvae are more common in damp habitats such as wet soil bordering ponds and streams where they prey on other insect larvae, small oligochaetes and crustacea.

3. Cyclorrhapha

The *Cyclorrhapha* include some of the most highly specialized Diptera and the habits of those associated with the soil differ widely.

(a) *Aschiza*. The larvae of some *Lonchopteridae* occur among leaf litter and in vegetable refuse and are saprophagous or feed on the faeces of herbivorous mammals. The habits of the Syrphidae are extremely varied. Some are saprophagous and occur in moist organic matter, mud, or dung; others occur in rotting wood. Of the phytophagous Syrphidae, the larvae of *Merodon equestris* (F.), *Eumerus srtigatus* Flor. and *E. tuberculatus* Rond. are pests of bulbs, especially narcissus bulbs and others such as Amaryllis, Galtonia and Scilla. The eggs are laid singly in the soil or at the base of plants, the larvae feed between the bulb scales and usually pupate in the soil but occasionally inside the bulb. Other syrphid larvae (*Microdon* spp.) are scavengers in ant and termite nests and some *Volucella* spp. scavenge in nests of aculeate Hymenoptera. The Phoridae are particularly interesting because in many species the wings are vestigial or absent and adults and larvae may be found in decaying vegetation. Other species occur in ant and termite nests. Some phorid larvae are necrophagous and feed on dead earthworms, snails and decomposing lepidoptera larvae and pupae, others are parasitic in myriapods and diptera larvae, especially Bibionidae and Tipulidae.

(b) *Schizophora*. The larvae of several families are scavengers in decomposing plant or animal material. Larvae of Sapromyzidae scavenge in leaf litter. Larvae of some Lonchaeidae and Borboridae occur in dung or rotting vegetation; larvae of Sepsidae are common in dung and larvae of Piophilidae occur in carrion. The larvae of some other families of Schizophora are phytophagous and include several important crop pests, such as frit fly, *Oscinella frit* (L.) (Chloropidae), carrot fly, *Psila rosae* (F.) (Psilidae) and *Opomyza florum* (F.) (Opomyzidae).

Frit fly, which infests grasses and is a pest of cereals, especially spring oats, has three generations a year and overwinters as larvae mainly infesting the central shoots of grasses. In spring these larvae produce the first generation of flies and they lay their eggs on or near the base of young oat plants or in the soil nearby. Usually about 90% of the eggs are found in the soil. Cunliffe and Hodges (1946) concluded that a greater proportion of the eggs are laid in the soil during dry weather than during wet weather, which suggests that the adults avoid ovipositing in the soil when it is wet. However, subsequent work has not always supported this view though confirming the overall proportion of eggs found in the soil. The eggs hatch in a few days, the larvae tunnel into and feed in the oat shoots and later pupate within the shoots or in the soil. The second generation, which occurs in summer, infests the ears of oats and sometimes wheat but not grasses; and the third generation, which occurs in autumn, oviposits mainly on grasses but occasionally on cereals.

The carrot fly has two generations a year, in spring and in summer. Eggs are laid singly or in small groups in the soil near the base of the host plant, carrots or occasionally celery, and the larvae tunnel into the side roots or taproots of carrot or the roots, crown or leaf bases of celery. When fully fed the larvae leave the plants and pupate in the soil.

Opomyza florum infests grasses and also cereals, especially wheat. It has one generation a year and overwinters in the egg stage in the soil, which is unusual for stem-boring Diptera (cf. wheat bulb fly, *Leptohylemyia coarctata* (Fall.) p. 358). The eggs are laid in the soil in late autumn, close to winter wheat plants or grasses, the larvae hatch in late March and invade the central shoot of the host plant where they feed and pupate. The adults emerge in June but do not oviposit until autumn.

(c) *Calyptratae*. The Calliphoridae includes many species whose larvae are saprophagous in decomposing plant or animal material. For example, larvae of many Calliphorinae and Sarcophaginae occur in carrion. Others are parasitic, such as the cluster fly, *Pollenia rudis* (F.), which parasitizes earthworms of the genus *Allolobophora*; and *Theria muscaria* (Meig.), which parasitizes snails. *P. rudis* oviposits in the soil in autumn and the young larvae penetrate the host and remain in the vesicula seminalis during the winter, before migrating forwards and becoming attached to the prostomium with the spiracles penetrating the body wall. After moulting, the larva penetrates the pharynx, and as a third instar larva it then feeds towards the end end of its host and finally pupates. The life history of *Onesia accepta* Mall., which parasitizes the earthworm, *Microscolex dubius* Fletcher, is similar (Fuller, 1933). Eggs are laid on or in the soil and the larvae find their host and penetrate the body wall. First and second instar larvae need living earthworm tissue, but third instar larvae can live on dead or putrid worms. The tracks made by the larvae burrowing beneath the skin cause constrictions that give the worms a twisted, misshapen appearance.

Several species of Rhinophorinae parasitize the woodlice, *Porcellio scaber* L., *Oniscus asellus* L., *Metaponorthus pruinosus* Brandt. and *Armadillidium vulgare* Lat. (Thompson, 1934). As with *Pollenia* and *Onesia* there is no direct contact between the adult parasite and the host of its larvae, the eggs are laid in crevices in bark, decaying logs or beside stones, where woodlice occur, and the larvae seek out their hosts.

Larvae of the Tachinidae are parasitic on other insects and arthropods, and many are recorded as parasitizing soil-inhabiting arthropods.

Larvae of some of the Muscidae are saprophagous and feed in decaying organic matter; others are carnivorous, such as larvae of *Fannia* spp., which occur in dung and prey on other insect larvae and small oligochaetes. The Anthomyidae includes several important crop pests whose immature stages occur in the soil, such as cabbage root fly, *Erioischia brassicae* (pp. 342–347), and wheat bulb fly, *Leptohylemyia coarctata* Fall. The biology of these species resembles that of the stem-boring Schizophora.

Larvae of wheat bulb fly infest the basal part of the shoots of various grasses such as *Agrostis tenuis*, *Agropyron repens*, *Festuca pratensis*, *Poa pratensis* and *P. trivialis*. They also attack winter wheat, barley and rye. The incidence of the species as a pest of autumn sown cereals, especially winter wheat, depends on its response to certain soil conditions and on farming practice, for the eggs are laid not in the cereal crop but in the soil during the previous summer. The flies, which emerge in June and begin to oviposit 3 or 4 weeks later, prefer bare or sparsely covered soil for oviposition. Development within the eggs is complete in 2–3 weeks and the larvae then go into diapause and the eggs do not hatch until the following January–March. In Britain, wheat bulb fly attacks occur chiefly after summer fallowing on heavy soils and after cropping with sugar beet or potatoes on light soils.

Infestations depend greatly on soil conditions during the oviposition period. In an experiment on fallow land on heavy soil, Raw (1955) found that plots with a rough tilth became more heavily infested than plots with a smooth tilth and that plots cultivated during the oviposition period contained more eggs than undisturbed plots (Table XIII).

TABLE XIII

Effect of soil conditions on wheat bulb fly oviposition
(No. of wheat bulb fly eggs/ft^2)

| | Plots with | |
	Rough tilth	Smooth tilth
Cultivated plots	94	77
Uncultivated plots	78	39

Several factors could account for these results. Wheat bulb flies oviposit in cracks in the soil and both rough tilth and cultivation may give more such oviposition sites than a smooth or uncultivated tilth. If wheat bulb fly eggs are preyed on by beetle predators, as are cabbage root fly eggs (p. 343), those laid in a rough tilth or buried by cultivation may be better protected from predators than eggs laid in more exposed places. Another anthomyid, *Chortophila cilicrura* (Rond.), is strongly attracted to freshly cultivated soil (Miles, 1950) and lays its eggs there. Wheat bulb fly may react similarly.

Eggs laid in arable land become buried and distributed throughout the topsoil by subsequent cultivations. Consequently, when they hatch, larvae may have to travel several inches to reach a host plant. Newly hatched larvae can survive several days without food and sometimes infest plants after travelling more than 12 inches through soil. Much of this movement may be random and in wheat crops more than 50% of emerging larvae usually fail to infest plants. Stokes (1956) showed that larvae can detect and respond to exudates from wheat plants and this no doubt assists larvae to locate host plants. There is some evidence that wheat bulb fly larvae respond to exudates from plants that are unsuitable host plants, and it is not known over what distance the response can occur in soil or how it is affected by soil physical and chemical conditions. It may be that the response, acting in conjunction with random movement, helps to bring the larvae into the root zone and then other stimuli or other chemical substances and responses result in actual host plant penetration.

E. ISOPODA

Woodlice (Oniscoidea, Isopoda), are of particular interest because they are common terrestrial representatives of a Class of predominantly marine or freshwater organisms, the Crustacea. Other Crustacea, such as some copepods, ostracods and amphipods, may be found in specialized terrestrial habitats, such as caves, sea shores, and permanent floating islands of organic debris, but only the terrestrial isopods have become widespread on land. However, they retain many primitive characters of the group and, in particular, lack a waterproof cuticle (cf. millipedes and centipedes) that would enable them to resist desiccation (Fig. 7). Consequently they tend to be restricted to moist habitats and their success in colonizing terrestrial habitats depends more on behaviour patterns that keep them in moist places than on adaptations that make them independent of the environment.

Woodlice are strongly thigmotactic and prefer a saturated atmosphere so they tend to stay in narrow crevices where they crowd together and so decrease water loss. The habit of rolling into a ball helps the Armadillidiidae to conserve water as well as being a defence mechanism. Because they avoid light and move slower and change direction more in moist air than in dry air they tend to remain in dark moist places. However, their reaction to light is reversed if they dry out and then they move about in the light until they enter a moist place and again become photo-negative. Similarly, at night, they respond less to humidity and so forage in drier places until they again become strongly photo-negative after several hours in darkness, which makes them return to shelter by daylight.

Woodlice can restore water loss by absorbing water through the mouth and anus from free water surfaces. In unsaturated air they can also absorb water through the mouth from moist surfaces and so counteract the water lost through the integument. Littoral species, such as Ligia, can tolerate large changes in the osmotic pressure of the blood and some degree of osmotic tolerance probably helps other woodlice to withstand desiccation. Edney (1954) gives a detailed review of the water relations of woodlice. The behaviour patterns that enable them to avoid desiccation have been particularly studied by Cloudsley-Thompson (1952, 1956).

In general, the distribution of the various families reflects their ability, or degree of specialization, to avoid desiccation. Of the British families, the Ligiidae is the most primitive and least adapted to terrestrial life. *Ligia oceanica* is littoral; on rocky shores it occurs in deep narrow crevices just above high-tide level or within reach of sea-spray; on sandy shores it lives under stones or in similar protected places. The Trichoniscidae also require very moist conditions. *Trichoniscus pusillus* is abundant in wet decaying leaves in moist woodlands. The Oniscidae, Porcellionidae and Armadillidiidae are progressively more adapted to drier habitats. *Oniscus asellus*, which is the

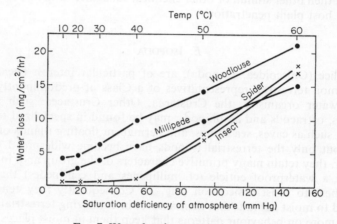

FIG. 7. Water loss in some Arthropods.

Rate of water-loss in dry air at different temperatures, and corresponding saturation deficiencies, from a woodlouse (*Porcellio*), millipede (*Oxidus*), spider (*Lycosa*) and inset (*Pieris* larva). In the woodlouse and millipede the rate of water-loss is proportional to the saturation deficiency of the atmosphere, but in the spider and insect it is negligible below about 30°, the critical temperature at which their epicuticular wax-layers become more porous. Rate of water-loss is expressed in mg/m² of surface area/hr. (After Cloudsley-Thompson, 1955).

commonest woodlouse, is widely distributed, in moist crevices, under stones, bark, decaying logs, etc. *Porcellio scaber*, which is also common, particularly beneath bark, can inhabit somewhat drier places and *Armadillidium vulgare* can tolerate drier conditions than other British species. Like other Armadillidium species, it is restricted to calcareous habitats, such as chalk grassland and has been found in direct sunlight on open, dry, porous surfaces. However, the habitat preferences of woodlice are by no means rigid and it is not uncommon to find species from several families in one habitat.

Woodlice feed mainly on dead and decaying organic matter such as garden refuse and leaf litter. Occasionally they damage plants, especially in glasshouses, where they are difficult to eradicate. They can play a significant part in litter breakdown in woodlands. In their feeding habits, as in their water relations, there are interesting parallels between woodlice and millipedes, but digestion in woodlice does not seem to have been studied in such detail as in millipedes, possibly because woodlice are more omnivorous. Conversely, the water relations of woodlice have been studied in much more detail than in millipedes.

REFERENCES

Belfield, W. (1956). *J. Anim. Ecol.* **25**, 275–287.
Blower, J. G. (1955). *In* "Soil Zoology." (McE. Kevan, ed.), pp. 138–151. Butterworths, London.
Bocock, K. L. (1963). *In* "Soil Organisms." (J. Doeksen and J. van der Drift, eds.), pp. 85–91. North Holland Publ. Co., Amsterdam.
Bornebusch, C. H. (1930). *Forst. ForsVæs. Danm.* **11**, 1–244.
Bornemissza, G. F. (1957). *Aust. J. Zool.* **5**, 1–12.
Bornemissza, G. F. (1960). *J. Aust. Inst. Agric. Sci.* **26**, 54–56.
Brauns, A. (1954). Terricole Dipterenlarven. "Musterschmidt", *Wissenschaftlicher Verlag, Gottingen.*
Cloudsley-Thompson, J. L. (1952). *J. exp. Biol.* **29**, 295–303.
Cloudsley-Thompson, J. L. (1955). *Discovery*, **16**, 248–251.
Cloudsley-Thompson, J. L. (1956). *J. exp. Biol.* **33**, 576–582.
Coaker, T. H. and Simpson, D. A. (1962). *Rep. Nat. Veg. Res. Sta. Wellesbourne* (1961), 50.
Coaker, T. H. and Williams, D. A. (1963). *Ent. exp. & appl.* **6**, 156–168.
Cohen, W. E. (1933). *Australia C.S.I.R.* **6**, 166–169.
Coulson, J. C. (1959). *Trans. R. Ent. Soc. Lond.* **111**, 157–174.
Coulson, J. C. (1962). *J. Anim. Ecol.* **31**, 1–21.
Cragg, J. B. (1961). *J. Anim. Ecol.* **30**, 205–234.
Cunliffe, N. and Hodges, D. J. (1946). *Ann. appl. Biol.* **33**, 339–359.
Diem, K. (1903). *Jb. st. Gall. Naturwiss. Ges.*, 1901–1902, 234–414.
Drift, J. van der (1950). *Tijdschr. Ent.* **94**, 1–168.
Dunger, W. (1958). *Zool. Jb.* **86**, 139–180.
Eaton, J. H. Jr. and Chandler, R. F. Jr. (1942). *Mem. Cornell Univ. agric. Exp. Stn.* No. 247, 1–26.
Edney, E. B. (1954). *Biol. Rev.* **29**, 185–219.
Edwards, C. A. (1958). *Pan-Pacif. Ent.* **25**, 1–11.
Forsslund, K.-H. (1943). *Meddn Stat. Skogförs Anst.* **34**, 1–264.
Franz, H. and Leitenberger, L. (1948). *Osterr. Zool. Z.* **1**, 498–518.
Fuller, M. E. (1933). *Parasitology*, **25**, 342–352.
Gere, G. (1956). *Acta biol. hung.* **6**, 257–271.
Griffith, G. Ap. (1938). *E. Afr. agric. J.* **4**, 70–71.
Grimmett, R. E. R. (1926). *Trans. Proc. N.Z. Inst.* **56**, 423–440.
Hendee, E. C. (1935). *Hilgardia* **9**, 499–525.
Holdaway, F. G. (1933). *J. Coun. sci. ind. Res. Australia* **6**, 160–165.
Hughes, R. D. and Salter, D. D. (1959). *J. Anim. Ecol.* **28**, 231–241.
Hungate, R. E. (1941). *Ann. ent. Soc. Am.* **34**, 467–489.
Jacot, A. P. (1936). *Ecology*, **17**, 359–379.
Jahn, E. (1946). *Bl. Ges. Forst.-u Holzwirtsch* **70**, 65–80.
Kettle, D. S. and Lawson, J. W. H. (1952). *Bull. ent. Res.* **43**, 421–467.

Lunn, E. T. (1939). "The ecology of the forest floor, with particular reference to the microarthropods." Northwestern University Library, Illinois.

Lyford, W. H. (1943). *Ecology*, **24**, 252–261.

Macfadyen, A. (1952). *J. Anim. Ecol.* **21**, 87–117.

Michelbacher, A. E. (1949). *Pan-Pacif. Ent.* **25**, 1–11.

Miles, M. (1950). *Bull. ent. Res.* **41**, 343–354.

Milne, A., Laughlin, R. and Coggins, R. E. (1965). *J. Anim. Ecol.* **34**, 529–544.

Milne, G. (1947). *J. Ecol.* **35**, 192–265.

Morris, H. M. (1921–22). *Bull. ent. Res.*, **12**, 221–232.

Nye, P. H. (1955). *J. Soil. Sci.* **6**, 73–83.

Parkin, E. A. (1940). *J. exp. Biol.* **17**, 364–377.

Pearse, A. S. (1946). *Ecol. Monogr.* **16**, 127–150.

Pendleton, R. L. (1942). *J. Am. Soc. Agron.* **34**, 340–344.

Pfetten, J. V. (1925). *Z. angew. Ent.* **11**, 35–54.

Pillai, S. K. (1922). *Z. angew Ent.* **8**, 1–30.

Ramann, E. (1911). *Int. Mitt. f. Bodenk.* **1**, 138–164.

Raw, F. (1955). *Plant Pathology*, **4**, 114–117.

Russell, Sir E. J. (1961). "Soil Conditions and Plant Growth." 9th Ed. Longmans, London.

Salt, G. (1952). *Bull. ent. Res.* **43**, 203–220.

Salt, G. (1955). *Bull. ent. Res.* **46**, 439–445.

Salt, G., Hollick, F. S. J., Raw, F. and Brian, M. V. (1948). *J. Anim. Ecol.* **17**, 139–150.

Soudek, S. (1928). *Bull. Ecole. sup. Agron. Brno. R. C. S. Fac. Silvicult.* D.8. 24 pp.

Starling, J. H. (1944). *Ecol. Mongr.* **14**, 291–310.

Stokes, B. M. (1956). *Nature, Lond.* **178**, 801.

Strickland, A. H. (1947). *J. Anim. Ecol.* **16**, 1–10.

Thiele, H.-U. (1959). *Z. angew Ent.* **44**, 1–21.

Thompson, W. R. (1934). *Parasitology*, **26**, 378–448.

Tragardh, I. (1929). *Fourth Int. Congr. Ent. Ithaca 1928*, **2**, 781–792.

Ulrich, A. T. (1933). *Mitt Forstwirstch. Forstwiss.* **4**, 283–323.

Uvarov, B. P. (1928). *Trans. ent. Soc. Lond.* **76**, 255–343.

Verhoeff, K. W. (1934). In *Bronn, Klassen und ordnung des Terreiches. V/II/III/1–2 Leiferung*.

Wright, D. W. (1956). *Rep. Nat. Veg. Res. Stn., Wellesbourne* (1955), 47.

Williams, E. C. Jr. (1941). *Bull. Chicago Acad. Sci.* **6**, 63.

Chapter 11

Acari

J. A. WALLWORK

Westfield College, University of London, England

I. INTRODUCTION

Ecological studies on the soil Acari are changing in character at present. The descriptive approach is no longer an end product, but a basis for analyses of functional relationships between the animals and their environment. This analytical approach includes two distinct, but complementary, lines of enquiry. On the one hand, there are investigations of the structure and behaviour of populations in relation to micro-environmental factors, and on the other, considerations of the effects of these populations on the micro-environment, particularly in relation to the circulation of material and energy through the soil/vegetation system. In simpler terms, this involves a study of action and reaction in a complex community.

The present survey illustrates this change in emphasis and is divided into three main sections. The first recognizes the importance of basic information relating to distribution and population fluctuations. The section on feeding habits underlines the fundamental relationships between soil Acari and their biological environment, and introduces the third section in which the role of soil Acari in the processes of energy transfer and organic decomposition is considered.

The references cited include only those studies directly relevant to the lines of discussion presented. More extensive lists are given by van der Drift (1951) and Kühnelt (1961). This review attempts a synthesis of the more recent developments in the ecology of soil Acari. The fact that more than half of the references cited have appeared during the last 5 years is testimony to the rapid expansion occurring in this field.

II. CLASSIFICATION OF ACARI

Before discussing their ecology, some mention must be made of the general characteristics of the main groups of soil Acari. A comprehensive account of acarine morphology and taxonomy is given by Evans *et al.* (1961); the present account is limited to short, simple definitions to assist the general reader.

Throughout this review the interpretation of acarine classification proposed by Evans *et al.* (1961) is adopted. This system divides the Acari into 7 Orders of which 4, namely the Prostigmata, Mesostigmata, Astigmata and Cryptostigmata, are generally represented in the soil fauna. As their names imply, the adult stages of these groups are distinguished basically on the character of the respiratory system. Unfortunately this is not always easily identifiable and definitions must include other, more readily recognizable structural features. The combination of characters outlined below should

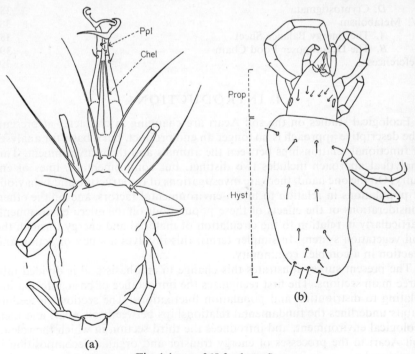

(a)   (b)

Fig. 1 (see p. 365 for legend)

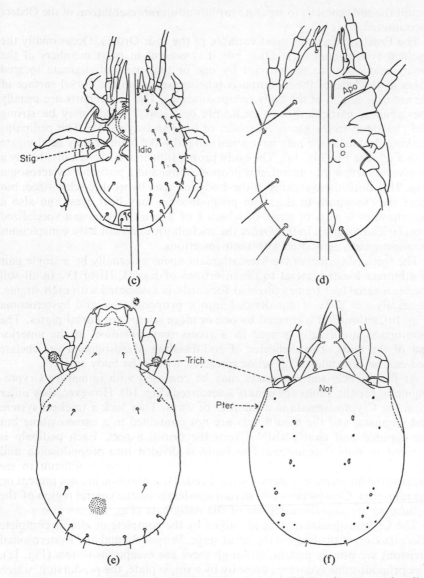

FIG. 1. Representatives of the four orders of soil Acari. (a) Prostigmata, undescribed species from West Africa (× 125). (b) *Rhagidia* sp. (Prostigmata) from Antarctica (× 50). (c) Mesostigmata species, Puerto Rico (× 50). (d) *Rhizoglyphus* sp. (Astigmata) from Britain (× 125). (e) *Tectocepheus* sp. (Cryptostigmata) from Britain (× 125). (f) *Scheloribates* sp. (Cryptostigmata) from Central Africa (× 125).

ppl., pedipalps; chel., chelicerae; prop., propodosoma; hyst., hysterosoma; stig., stigma; idio., idiosoma; apo., coxisternal apodemes; trich., trichobothrium; pter., pteromorph; not., notogaster.

permit the soil ecologist to separate rapidly adult representatives of the Orders encountered.

The Prostigmata is the most variable of the four Orders. Occasionally the tracheal system may be lacking, but it is present in most members of the group, and opens to the exterior by one or two pairs of stigmata located either at the base of the mouthparts (chelicerae) or on the dorsal surface of the anterior region of the body (propodosoma). The mouthparts are usually conspicuous, particularly the chelicerae or "jaws," which may be strong and chelate as in the genus *Rhagidia*, or long and stylet-like. The pedipalps flanking the chelicerae may have a normal palp-like form or may be elongate with a chelate tip (Fig. 1a). The body proper (idiosoma) is often divided by a transverse furrow into an anterior propodosoma and a posterior hysterosoma (Fig. 1b). Both these regions of the body are usually weakly sclerotized, but there are exceptions to this. The propodosoma may bear eyes, and also a maximum of 6 pairs of setae, of which 1 or 2 pairs may have a specialized form (trichobothria). In this Order the trichobothria do not have conspicuous pseudostigmata associated with their insertions.

The tracheal system of the Mesostigmata opens externally by a single pair of stigmata located lateral to the insertions of legs II, III or IV. In all soil species a canal (peritreme), directed forwards, is associated with each stigma. Generally the body is not divided into a propodosoma and hysterosoma (Fig. 1c), although it is covered by one or more sclerotized dorsal plates. The mouthparts are usually housed in a recess (camerostome) at the anterior end of the body. The chelicerae of soil-dwelling Mesostigmata are chelate and can be protruded (Fig. 1c) or retracted within the body cavity.

At first glance, soil Astigmata may be confused with immature Cryptostigmata, for the adults are weakly sclerotized (Fig. 1d). However, they differ from the Cryptostigmata in a number of ways. They lack a tracheal system and stigmata, and the mouthparts are not contained in a camerostome but are exposed and clearly visible from the dorsal aspect. Each pedipalp is reduced to only 2 segments. The body is divided into propodosoma and hysterosoma, although the line of separation is sometimes difficult to see because the integument is weakly sclerotized. Trichobothria are not present on the idiosoma. Conspicuous coxisternal apodemes on the ventral region of the podosoma are also characteristic of the Astigmata (Fig. 1d).

The Cryptostigmata may be identified by the complete or almost complete sclerotization of the body in the adult stage. Propodosomal and hysterosomal divisions are usually present, although there are exceptions to this (Fig. 1e). The propodosoma is covered dorsally by a single plate, the prodorsum, which usually bears sclerotized ridges (lamellae), 4–5 pairs of setae and a pair of trichobothria (pseudostigmatic organs) inserted in specialized pits (pseudostigmata). The hysterosoma is usually covered by a single dorsal plate (notogaster), although sometimes several dorsal sclerites are present. Ventrally, the genital and anal apertures are conspicuous and longitudinal, each covered by a pair of plates. In many groups these apertures are widely separated in a common ventral plate, although in some forms the two regions are contiguous and flanked respectively by lateral aggenital and adanal plates. A tracheal system is usually present, but stigmata are not conspicuous, being located on the lateral region of the podosoma near the insertions of the legs, or on the legs themselves. The mouthparts are housed in a camerostome and are not exposed in dorsal view, as a general rule. Chelicerae are chelate and the pedipalps are simple and 5-segmented. Many Cryptostigmata show development of lateral notogastral wings or pteromorphs (Fig. 1f), which may or may not be hinged to the notogaster proper.

III. DISTRIBUTION AND DYNAMICS

A. GENERAL DISTRIBUTION OF THE ACARI

Cryptostigmata are numerically the most abundant acarine group in most soils. Many of its members require humidity conditions approaching saturation, and their prevalence in soil compared with more exposed habitats above ground reflects this dependence on high humidity. The Prostigmata and Mesostigmata are usually more active; they range freely through the soil and frequently are not restricted to it. Many of them are predators as, for example, the prostigmatid families Bdellidae, Rhagidiidae, Trombidiidae and the mesostigmatid Veigaiidae, Parasitidae, Gamasolaelaptidae and Macrochelidae. The Astigmata are not important elements in the acarine fauna of many soils, and the role of these mites in the soil community has been little studied. The group is more commonly associated with drier situations where some species such as *Acarus siro* L., *Tyrophagus putrescentiae* (Schrank) and *Tyrolichus casei* Oudms., may become serious pests of stored food products. Intensive studies of various soil communities have shown, however, that Astigmata may be locally abundant in pasture and arable soils. Sheals (1957) recorded *Glycyphagus destructor* (Schrank), *Acarus siro*, *Rhizoglyphus echinopus* (F. & R.) and *Tyrophagus castellanii* (Hirst) from old grassland. Similarly *Caloglyphus mycophagus* (Megnin) and members of the Anoetidae are found in soils where anaerobic decomposition is occurring (Karg, 1963). Most of the qualitative and quantitative information about the ecology of soil acarine populations relates to the European fauna, particularly of Scandinavia, so much of it concerns temperate forest and grassland communities. Because of their numerical abundance, soil Cryptostigmata have been studied more extensively than other soil mites, and much of this section deals with their distribution and population dynamics in temperate soils.

Cryptostigmata occur in greatest numbers in forest soils of the mor type (i.e. in which discrete litter, fermentation and humus layers are present). They are particularly numerous in such soils under oak, beech, Douglas fir, hemlock and pine (van der Drift, 1951; Wallwork, 1959; Crossley and Bohnsack, 1960; Evans *et al.*, 1961), where they may represent as much as 75% of the total acarine fauna. They are less abundant in mull humus formations (i.e. in which mixing of humus and mineral soil prevents the formation of distinct organic layers) such as those developed in grassland, in some forest soils developed on limestone under oak or beech, for example, and in fen-land and heathland soils. However, even under these conditions Crypto-stigmata remain the dominant group (Macfadyen, 1952; Sheals, 1957; Engelmann, 1961). Cultivated soils are usually sparsely populated by Crypto-stigmata. Although most ecological investigations have been of forest and grassland soils, the communities of other soil and vegetation types such as *Sphagnum* bog and salt marsh have been studied. As a detailed summary of all these ecological surveys would be too exhaustive to be included in this review, mention will be made of a representative selection.

Several species of Cryptostigmata are widely distributed over the North Temperate region, being present in both the Old and the New World. A list of such species includes *Oppia nova* (Oudms.), *Brachychthonius berlesei* Willm., *Tectocepheus velatus* (Mich.), *Rhysotritia ardua* (C. L. Koch), *Scheloribates laevigatus* (C. L. Koch), *Platynothrus peltifer* (C. L. Koch), *Ceratoppia bipilis* (Herm.) and *Oribatula tibialis* (Nic.). Similarly in other parts of the world *Malacoangelia remigera* Grandj. appears to have a circum-tropical distribution, *Calyptozetes sarekensis* Trgdh. (Arctic) and *Alasko-zetes antarcticus* (Mich.), *Halozetes belgicae* (Mich.) and *Oppia crozetensis* (Richters) (Antarctic) have circum-polar distribution patterns. Despite this fact, many of these species are not ubiquitous in the sense that they occur in every type of soil throughout their geographical range. It is true that some species, for example *Oppia nova*, *Tectocepheus velatus* and *Scheloribates laevigatus*, are usually present in a variety of soil conditions from heathland and forest mor to grassland mull [although the last-named species was not recorded from any of 7 forest soils in Britain investigated by Evans (Evans et al., 1961)]. More often, however, species are much more limited in their distribution, as shown when faunal comparisons between communities reveal variations in species composition. These variations occur not only between communities of different vegetational types such as heathland, bog, grassland and forest, but also on a more restricted scale as, for example, between different forest soils. Thus, in the above-mentioned study by Evans, of the 67 species of Cryptostigmata recovered from 7 forest soils, 26 species were restricted to one or other of these soils. A survey made on two adja-cent pastures in Kentucky, one grazed by sheep and the other by cattle (Wallwork and Rodriguez, 1961), revealed 13 species of Cryptostigmata from sheep pasture compared with only 8 from cattle pasture; furthermore the dominant species in sheep pasture were *Galumna virginiensis* Jacot and *Scheloribates laevigatus*, whereas in cattle pasture *Eupelops* sp. was domi-nant. Studies such as these suggest that micro-environmental factors may affect considerably the species composition of the acarine component of a soil community. Pronounced variations occur when soil Acari from different edaphic and vegetational conditions are compared. Thus *Steganacarus magnus* (Nic.), *Nothrus sylvestris* (Nic.), *Carabodes labyrinthicus* (Mich.), *Fuscozetes fuscipes* (C. L. Koch), *Phthiracarus borealis* (Trgdh.) and *Meso-plophora pulchra* Selln. are more commonly associated with highly organic deposits in forest soils. Species and individuals of Galumnidae are frequently less common in forest soils than in grassland soils; other species associated with the latter are *Oppia minus* (Paoli), *Punctoribates punctum* (C. L. Koch), *Ceratozetes gracilis* (Mich.) and small forms belonging to the genera *Brachychthonius* and *Suctobelba*. However, such characterizations are by no means exclusive and, if anything, tend to oversimplify the natural relationships between the species and its environment.

B. SYNECOLOGY

In an attempt to relate species composition to micro-environment Strenzke (1952) proposed to define groups of species (Synusien) whose distribution is a function of their dependence on a particular combination of micro-environmental factors (moisture content, organic content, pH, salinity, ground cover). The suggestion that certain species always occur with certain other species or their ecological equivalents is implicit in this concept, and has been demonstrated for certain communities (Klima, 1959). However, its general applicability remains to be established. Rajski (1961) investigated the Cryptostigmata of 5 plant associations in the vicinity of Poznan and concluded that a number of synusiae could be defined, namely syn. *Hydrozetes lemnae, Ceratozetes mediocris, Nanhermannia comitalis, Damaeus riparius* and *Chamobates borealis*. These groups apparently represented a community succession paralleling that of the vegetation during the transition from a purely aquatic (fresh-water) condition through meadow to deciduous woodland. Community succession in a *Sphagnum* bog has been studied by Tarras-Wahlberg (1954, 1961) with the definition of a characteristic association of species including *Tectocepheus velatus, Malaconothrus gracilis* van der Hammen, *Nanhermannia nana* (Nic.) and *Nothrus pratensis* Selln. in the hummocks. Hammer (1937) recognized a *Platynothrus peltifer/Melanozetes* sp. community in east Greenland characteristic of wet biotopes (lake bank, bog and moss) and a dry biotope community (fell-fields, heath and grassland) characterized by *Zygoribatula exilis* (Nic.), *Calyptozetes sarekensis* and *Camisia horrida* (Herm.). Haarløv (1942) was able to identify the wet biotope community but not the dry one in north-east Greenland. The fact that such findings may be valid only within a limited geographical area emerges if they are compared with those of Weis-Fogh (1948) from Denmark, who described a wet or moist biotope characterized by *Tectocepheus velatus* and *Scheloribates laevigatus* and a dry community with *Folsomia quadrioculata* (Collembola) and *Variatipes quadrangularis* (Berl.) (Prostigmata) as the characteristic groups. The findings of Forsslund (1943), Karppinen (1955, 1958), Knülle (1957) and Klima (1959) are examples of many similar studies.

The definition of various communities having characteristic species has stimulated attempts to assess the extent of the similarity between them. Several statistical methods are available for this purpose, each of which has its disadvantages. One of the most commonly used is that based on "quotients of similarity" (Franz, 1963). The limited usefulness of the sociological approach has been discussed by Haarløv (1960). Evidently some species can be used as indicators of special environmental conditions. *Platynothrus peltifer*, *Nothrus palustris* C. L. Koch and *Hydrozetes* spp. are associated with wet or moist biotopes; *Pelops acromios* (Herm.), *Phauloppia lucorum* (C. L. Koch), *Dometorina plantivaga* (Berl.), *Pirnodus detectidens* Grandj., *Mycobates parmeliae* (Mich.) and *Camisia horrida* are more common in dry localities (Travé, 1963). Despite these examples, a large number of Cryptostigmata such as *Tectocepheus velatus*, *Scheloribates laevigatus* and *Oppia nova* will tolerate a wide range of ecological conditions and are therefore poor indicators. This is well illustrated by a study of the zonation of Cryptostigmata in 4 alpine vegetation zones in Sweden (Dalenius, 1962). Of the 76 species recorded from all zones, the greatest number (67) occurred in the vegetation belt below the timber line, but more than half of these also occurred in vegetation belts above the timber line. This study contrasts with that of Evans discussed earlier and illustrates the difficulty of making broad comparisons. Only in restricted habitats having a small number of species, such as the intertidal zone, can strong associations be recognized.

C. VERTICAL DISTRIBUTION

The vertical distribution of Acari is well documented and it is generally recognized that species composition varies with depth in the soil. Three distinct ecological zones can be distinguished in any vegetation type, namely (1) the epigeal zone (vegetation zone), (2) hemiedaphic zone (organic layers associated with the surface of the soil) and (3) the euedaphic zone (the deeper mineral strata of the soil). Soil Acari are primarily hemiedaphic, although their distribution may also extend into the other two zones, as with active and tolerant species. Thus, many predatory Prostigmata and Mesostigmata may be found in all three zones; some tolerant Cryptostigmata, such as *Passalozetes* spp., *Scutovertex* spp., *Oribatula tibialis* (Nic.) and *Eremaeus* spp., may be similarly distributed. Again, a number of hemiedaphic species such as *Galumna virginiensis*, *Scheloribates laevigatus*, *Eupelops* spp. and *Diapterobates humeralis* (Herm.) show regular vertical movements into and from the epigeal zone (Wallwork and Rodriguez, 1961; Tarras-Wahlberg, 1961). This activity seems to be correlated with the humidity fluctuations of the epigeal zone. On the other hand, the hemiedaphon is itself heterogeneous and may be sub-divided into the organic strata lying on the surface of mineral soil and the more specialized habitats associated with moss, lichens and bark. Here also, faunal division is largely arbitrary for there is considerable overlap in species distribution (Travé, 1963). The form of the organic deposits in soil influences distribution. A fairly even vertical pattern may be found to a depth of 20 to 30 cm in a mull grassland soil where humus material mixes extensively with mineral soil. In contrast, the fauna of a heath or forest mor is very largely concentrated in the surface organic layers which may vary in total thickness from 1 to 8 cm (Murphy, 1955).

Cryptostigmata in forest soils are usually most numerous in the fermentation layer or, when this is not defined, in a zone of intergradation between litter and humus. The upper parts of litter are frequently subject to extremes of temperature and to desiccation which undoubtedly limit acarine distribution in this region. Deeper organic layers rarely dry out, for even when the moisture decreases appreciably the relative humidity within the soil cavities remains high (Thamdrup, 1939). In these lower layers the diameter of the soil interstices may limit depth distribution of soil Acari. These cavities become smaller with increasing depth (Haarløv, 1960), and as most soil Acari move through these channels it is not surprising to find smaller species becoming relatively more abundant with increasing depth. Some medium- and small-sized species show little or no decided preference for one or other of the organic strata and are frequently found in all layers, except perhaps the upper litter layer. Such species include *Scheloribates laevigatus*, *Oppia nova*, *Suctobelba* spp., *Tectocepheus velatus* and *Brachychthonius* spp. Species showing a preference for the litter layer include the large predatory and trachytoid Mesostigmata and the cryptostigmatid species *Platynothrus peltifer*, *Oribatula tibialis*, *Chamobates* sp. and *Achipteria coleoptrata* (L.) (van der Drift, 1951; Wallwork, 1959; Evans *et al.*, 1961). Many more prefer the more stable conditions of the lower litter layer and the zone of intergradation between litter and humus. Typical of this region are *Hypochthonius rufulus* (C. L. Koch), *Nanhermannia* spp., *Nothrus silvestris*, *Oppia ornata* (Oudms.), *Phthiracarus borealis*, *Rhysotritia* spp., *Belba* spp. and members of the meso- stigmatid families Zerconidae and Digamasellidae. Examples of the few species which prefer the humus layer proper are *Rhysotritia minima* (Berl.), *Rhysotritia ardua* (C. L. Koch), *Suctobelba sarekensis* Forssl. and *Oppia minus*. Deeper still in the lower layers of the humus and in underlying mineral soil *Rhodacarus* sp. (Mesostigmata), small *Oppia* species and immature forms occur sporadically. There is little food in the deeper mineral layers and con- sequently the fauna is impoverished.

It must be remembered that these distribution patterns are not static. Vertical movements occur between one organic stratum and another, and are obviously more frequent among the active predatory Prostigmata and Meso- stigmata than among the more sedentary Cryptostigmata. Nevertheless this activity may also be characteristic of many Cryptostigmata. The diurnal movements of some species between the hemiedaphon and epigeal zone have been mentioned already. Similar short-term movements between different organic layers in the hemiedaphon also occur (Tarras-Wahlberg, 1961) and these may be responses to less favourable temperature conditions in certain parts of the profile. Recent work by Berthet (1964) shows that some of the larger Cryptostigmata may move appreciable distances daily, and that some- times these movements are positively correlated with the moisture content of the litter. This suggests that such behaviour is at least partly controlled by environmental factors. The more thoroughly studied seasonal movements are probably governed in much the same way and may be regarded as long- term extensions of the diurnal phenomenon. On the other hand, seasonal movements may have an antagonistic effect on diurnal movements. Popula- tions normally moving between surface and deeper layers during the diurnal cycle in summer may be restricted to deeper layers during winter and show little or no diurnal vertical movement during this season. This will depend, to a great extent, on local conditions such as the amount of snow cover and temperature variations within the soil profile. In temperate soils the larger species such as *Platynothrus peltifer*, *Oribatula tibialis*, *Chamobates* sp. and *Achipteria coleoptrata* which prefer the litter layer apparently maintain this preference throughout the year, even during hot and cold dry periods, and evidently can tolerate these unfavourable conditions (van der Drift, 1951; Wallwork, 1959). *Nothrus silvestris*, *N. pratensis*, *Scheloribates laevigatus*, *Oppia nova* and many of the medium and smaller forms normally found in litter and fermentation layers during the summer decrease in numbers in these layers during winter, in some localities. This decrease is frequently associated with an increase in numbers in humus and such circumstantial evidence suggests a downward movement from litter to humus during early winter. Van der Drift (1951) and Karppinen (1955) attribute this movement to an avoidance of the dry, cold conditions in litter at this time. Experiments on the temperature preference of *Oppia nova* also support this view (Wallwork, 1960). Lebrun (1964b) has reservations regarding the smaller species, for he could detect no downward movement into the humus layer of an oak mull forest floor at the onset of winter in the species *Suctobelba subtrigona* (Oudms.), *Oppia quadricarinata* (Mich.), *O. ornata*, *O. subpectinata* (Oudms.), *Autogneta willmanni* (Dyrd.), *Tectocepheus velatus* and *Minunthozetes semirufus* (C. L. Koch). Clearly these behaviour patterns can only be explained in the context of the natural conditions to which the particular animals are accustomed. The findings from one locality do not necessarily apply generally, particularly for ecologically tolerant species. Much has still to be learned about the physiological basis of behaviour in the Acari. Experimental work on temperature preferences (Wallwork, 1960; Tarras-Wahlberg, 1961) indicates that various species differ in their reactions to certain temperature conditions, and that these reactions are governed in part by the environmental temperature range naturally encountered by the species. Investigations of humidity preferences have produced similar results (Madge, 1964a, b); thus, litter-dwelling species *Platynothrus peltifer* and *Belba geniculosa* Oudms. showed a preference for high humidity under experimental conditions, whereas *Humerobates rostrolamellatus* Grandj., an arboreal species, initially preferred a low humidity but reversed this response after one-third the initial body weight was lost. These responses are affected by the amount of water in the body and the nutritional state of the animal.

D. LIFE FORMS

Morphological adaptations of certain species to particular ecological zones may lead to the definition of life forms. The correlation between body size and depth distribution, where the diameter of the soil interstices is a limiting factor, has been discussed above. Soil porosity is by no means the only limiting factor in the distribution of soil Acari, and other morphological features associated with improved locomotion and reduction of water loss across the integument have been considered as direct adaptations to particular environmental conditions. Klima (1956) correlated body width of various Cryptostigmata with vertical distribution in the soil, and also considered (1) the functional relationship between the structure of the integument and resistance to desiccation and (2) the colour of the body and the amount of light to which the species is naturally exposed. These correlations formed the basis for a definition of structural classes whereby the species concerned were grouped into euedaphic, hemiedaphic (with its hygrophilous, mesophilous and xerophilous subdivisions distinguished) and epigeal (atmobios) forms. Tarras-Wahlberg (1961) devised similar groupings for the Cryptostigmata from a bog by correlating the form of the pseudostigmatic organ with the environmental moisture gradient. Thus, hygrophilous species such as *Limnozetes ciliatus* (Mich.) and *Trimalaconothrus novus* Selln. have greatly reduced pseudostigmatic organs; in xerophilous and epigeal species such as *Carabodes labyrinthicus*, *Scheloribates laevigatus* and *Phauloppia lucorum* these organs are globular, whereas in the mesophilous species a wide variety of form exists. Reduction of sensillae is quite common among aquatic and semi-aquatic (fresh-water and inter-tidal) Cryptostigmata belonging to the genera *Hydrozetes*, *Ameronothrus*, *Hygroribates* and *Halozetes*. It must be remembered, however, that even in these conditions there are many species which do not appear to be morphologically adapted (Luxton, 1964). This may reflect a lack of knowledge concerning the sensory physiology and behaviour of Acari. The difficulty in applying the concept of life forms to soil Cryptostigmata has been stressed by Märkel (1964) in a study of species distribution in three different sites. Horizontal and vertical distribution of three species associations, *Rhysotritia duplicata*, *Steganacarus spinosus* and *Hermannia gibba*, differed from site to site and appeared to be governed by distribution of food rather than by physical characteristics of the environment.

E. POPULATION FLUCTUATIONS AND PHENOLOGY

Unlike the Mesostigmata and, to a lesser extent, the Prostigmata, soil Cryptostigmata show seasonal fluctuations in population size and age class distribution. Detection of these population changes depends, ultimately, on the efficiency of sampling. Variations in counts occur within series of samples and partly result from the non-random distribution of soil mites. Reliable estimates of population density can be achieved, however, by assessing statistically the degree of aggregation and analysing the sources of variation (Macfadyen, 1952; Hartenstein, 1961; Healy, 1962; Ibarra *et al.* 1965). Population fluctuations are closely related to the length of the life cycle and the number of generations per year of the constituent species. These are influenced in turn by environmental conditions, so that broad geographical variations in fluctuation patterns may be expected. Hammer (1944) recorded maximum populations of mites and Collembola in Greenland during the summer, at a time when temperate mite populations are at a minimum. Unfortunately there is little information about fluctuations in tropical soils where precipitation may be an important factor.

In general, populations of Cryptostigmata in the European and North American habitats studied are greatest during the autumn and winter months (October to February) and least during the summer (July to August). This applies to forest soils (Evans, 1955; Wallwork, 1959), fenland soil (Macfadyen, 1952) and uncultivated grassland (Sheals, 1957) with only minor variations depending on variations in local climatic conditions (Fig. 2). The autumn/ winter population peak is largely produced by the appearance of larval and protonymphal stages; adults are generally more abundant during late

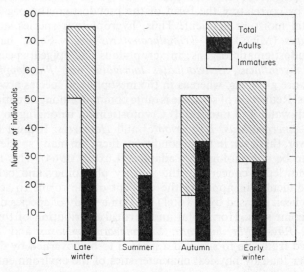

FIG. 2. Seasonal fluctuations in density and age class distribution of the Cryptostigmata of a hemlock-yellow birch forest floor at Imp Lake, Michigan, U.S.A.

summer and early autumn when, presumably, the eggs are laid from which winter immatures will develop. This would certainly seem to be true of the humus populations and because many litter-dwelling species move down into humus at the onset of winter, changes in humus populations at this time will form a significant part of the total population change in the profile as a whole. However, a small number of species live predominantly in the litter throughout the year. In contrast to those in humus, litter populations of these species evidently are greatest in spring and early summer (Lebrun, 1964a). Furthermore, the life cycles of all species are not synchronized; one, two or even three generations may be produced in a year, depending on the species and the climatic conditions. Observations on laboratory cultures have demonstrated that the life cycles of many Cryptostigmata are relatively long (Grandjean, 1950; Pauly, 1956; Sengbusch, 1958). Lebrun (1964a) combined this approach with age class distribution data from samples of field populations to determine the phenology of Cryptostigmata, taking account of climatic factors and species tolerance. He suggested that *Nothrus silvestris, Chamobates incisus* van der Hammen, *Rhysotritia ardua* (C. L. Koch), *Platynothrus peltifer* and *Euzetes globulus* (Nic.) have only one generation per year, whereas *Oppia nova, Autogneta willmanni, Nanhermannia elegantula* Berl., *Steganacarus magnus, Minunthozetes semirufus, Parachipteria willmanni* van der Hammen, *Phthiracarus piger* (Scop.) and *Damaeus onustus* C. L. Koch, may have two generations per year under the same conditions. *Carabodes marginatus* (Mich.), *Chamobates cuspidatus* (Mich.) and *Oribatella quadricornuta* (Mich.) are examples of species which could produce 3 generations per year. *Tectocepheus velatus* and *Oppia subpectinata* are also included in the latter group for they are highly adaptable to local conditions, and may produce 3–5 generations per year when conditions are favourable. They may also produce fewer than this, for Haarløv (1960) and Murphy and Jalil (1964) have suggested two generations per year for *T. velatus*. Under more exacting climatic conditions, such as the long, cold winters and hot summers occurring in parts of North America, most species may produce only one generation per year, as indicated in Fig. 2.

IV. FEEDING HABITS

An understanding of the feeding habits of soil Acari is necessary before the role of these organisms in the energetics of the soil community can be analysed critically. Soil presents a large and varied assortment of ecological niches and it is not surprising that the Acari show a corresponding variety of feeding habit. The extent to which Acari exploit these niches is still not fully known, largely through lack of information about natural feeding habits. Attention has been focused on this problem in recent years, and whereas much has been learned from studies on laboratory cultures, these observations cannot be applied indiscriminately to field populations. Generalizations based on the structure of mouthparts must also be treated cautiously. Direct observation of natural feeding activity is difficult because of the small size of the mites and their cryptic behaviour, although the habits of some Acari, such as wood-boring Cryptostigmata, make this possible. In most instances reliable information on feeding habit is obtained from gut content analyses of large samples taken directly from the field. Information can be obtained from such analyses by using differential staining techniques to identify lignin, cellulose and chitin components. The more conspicuous fungal hyphae and spores can be identified without staining (Fig. 3). Occasionally it is possible to determine feeding habit by identifying characteristic lesions in litter fragments. This method has been used to discriminate between the feeding activity of Diptera larvae, earthworms and small arthropods on small litter samples (Edwards and Heath, 1963). It may also be applied to leaf- and wood-boring mites, although it is unlikely that it could be used generally at the specific level for soil-inhabiting forms.

The feeding habits of selected groups of soil Acari are given in Tables I

13—s.b.

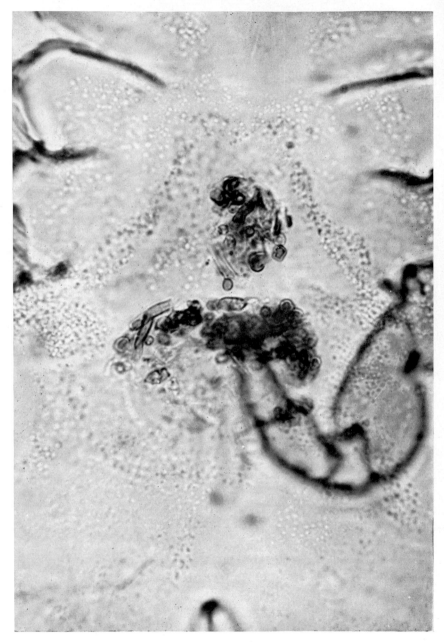

FIG. 3. Contents of the mid-gut of a cryptostigmatid tritonymph taken on Macquarie Island. Fungal spores and hyphae surrounded by a fluid or semi-fluid material can be identified (× 500).

TABLE I

The feeding habits of selected groups of soil Acari belonging to the
orders Prostigmata, Mesostigmata and Astigmata*

Group	Carnivore	Herbivore/Decomposer			
	Predator	Plant detritus	Moss and lichens	Wood	Fungi and algae
Prostigmata					
Bdellidae	×				
Trombidiidae	×				
Tydeidae	(×)				×
Rhagidiidae	×				
Eupodidae	(×)				(×)
Erythraeidae					
Erythraeus	×				
Balaustium	×	×			
Scutacaridae	(×)				×
Pyemotidae					×
Tarsonemidae					×
Mesostigmata					
Macrochelidae	×				
Veigaiidae	×				
Parasitidae	×				
Zerconidae	(×)	×		×	×
Digamasellidae	(×)				
Uropodidae					
Uropoda		(×)			
Fuscuropoda	×	×			(×)
Trachytidae		×	×		×
Rhodacaridae	(×)				
Astigmata					
Glycyphagidae					×
Acaridae					
Histiogaster				(×)	×
Rhizoglyphus		×			(×)
Schwiebea				(×)	(×)
Caloglyphus					(×)
Anoetidae		×			×

* Symbols in parentheses denote unconfirmed or conflicting reports.

and II. As information on feeding behaviour accumulates it is becoming
more difficult to generalize about these habits at the familial, generic and
specific levels, and consequently several different kinds of behaviour may
occur within these levels. The soil-dwelling Prostigmata and Mesostigmata
are largely represented by predatory forms. Astigmata feed mainly on liquids
or plant detritus in an advanced stage of decomposition in the soil. Cryptostigmata have generally been considered as fungal feeders, although the data

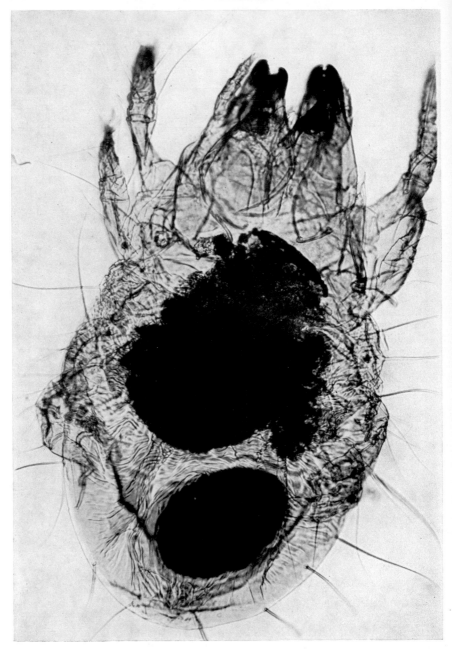

FIG. 4. Tritonymph of a cryptostigmatid mite (*Hermannia* sp. ?) taken from lenticel of fallen yellow birch twig at Imp Lake, Michigan, U.S.A. Black cork material from the lenticel is present in the gut (× 125).

given in Table II indicate a wide range of feeding habit. Each of these groups
will be considered separately.

A. PROSTIGMATA

Predatory Prostigmata, with their stylet-like mouthparts adapted for
piercing and sucking, probably form an important trophic link in the soil
community between soft-bodied Astigmata and immature Cryptostigmata on
which they feed, and the larger carnivorous arthropods. Predatory activities
of a number of common families, such as the Bdellidae, Cheyletidae, Rhagidiidae and Trombidiidae, are well established (Baker and Wharton, 1952).
The Tydeidae have also been considered as predators on eggs and small
arthropods in the soil (Baker and Wharton, 1952), although Karg (1963)
was not able to observe predatory activity in cultures and concluded from his
observations and examinations of mouthparts that they are fungal feeders.
Some confusion surrounds the feeding habits of the Eupodidae. Kühnelt
(1961) considers them to be mainly predatory, whereas Evans *et al.* (1961)
suggest that they are fungal feeders. The family contains a number of phytophagous species which are agricultural pests in certain countries (Baker and
Wharton, 1952). Very little is known of the feeding of some of the smaller
soil-dwelling prostigmatids such as the Scutacaridae, Pyemotidae and
Tarsonemidae. Many of them may be introduced accidentally into the soil
by other invertebrates, for they are known to be parasitic or phoretic on larger
arthropods, such as insects. They are considered to be fungal feeders, although
they may occupy a niche similar to that of the phoretic Mesostigmata, such
as *Macrocheles muscaedomesticae* (Scop.), which feed on insect eggs and small
nematodes. The family Erythraeidae contains aggressive predators, common
examples of which belong to the genera *Erythraeus* and *Balaustium*. In contrast to other Erythraeidae the genus *Balaustium* has a wide range of feeding
habit (Newell, 1963), some species being active predators of scale insects,
thrips and other insects associated with vegetation, others being phytophagous on green leaves or on pollen.

B. MESOSTIGMATA

Many of the predatory Mesostigmata are large, active mites with mouthparts adapted for piercing, sucking and tearing (Figs 5 and 7). Representatives of the genera *Veigaia, Pergamasus, Parasitus, Gamasolaelaps* and *Macrocheles* are commonly present in many forest soils. *Veigaia* spp. are known to
feed in culture on proturans, collembolans and pauropods (Hurlbutt, 1964),
and have also been observed to attack cryptostigmatid mites (Wallwork,
1957). *Veigaia mitis* (Berl.) feeds by piercing the integument of the prey,
inserting the two chelicerae which move forwards and backwards simultaneously or alternately, and imbibing the body fluids. The action of the
chelicerae probably serves to macerate the body tissues of the prey and also
to assist in the imbibition process. Some of the large, viviparous mesostig-
matids, such as *Pergamasus* spp., feed on their own young in culture, in

addition to Collembola, insect larvae and the nymphs of *Parasitus* sp. and *Gamasolaelaps* sp.. The genus *Macrocheles* is frequently found in rather specialized habitats, such as dung and compost, where its members live phoretically with certain Diptera and Coleoptera. *M. muscaedomesticae*, phoretic on the house fly, feeds on eggs and first-instar larvae of this dipteran.

Fig. 5. Mouthparts of a predatory mesostigmatid mite from Puerto Rico (specimen from collection of Dr. Maldonado Capriles) (× 125).

Wallwork and Rodriguez (1963) have demonstrated that the feeding rate of this mite is related to the amount of ammonia in the substrate, and that the feeding response (i.e. puncturing of eggs) will continue as long as the concentration of ammonia remains above a threshold, despite the fact that the mite may be completely engorged. This species has also been shown to feed on the nematode *Rhabditella leptura*, Collembola and various Astigmata. It is probable that these organisms, together with insect eggs, form the diet of at least some of the macrochelids of pasture and forest soils. The Zerconidae and Digamasellidae may be predators (Wallwork, 1957), although small

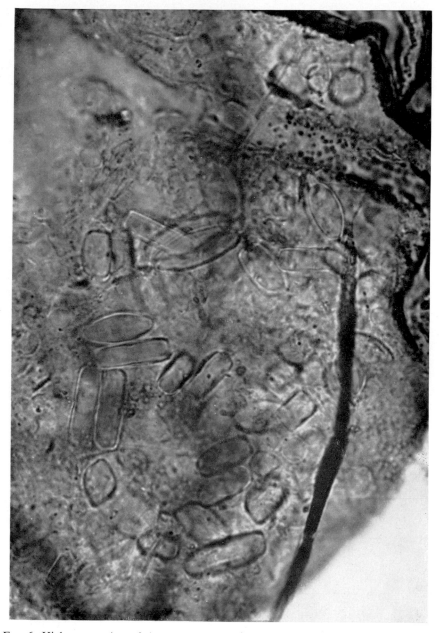

FIG. 6. High power view of the cerotegument of tritonymph of *Halozetes* sp. (Cryptostigmata) from Macquarie Island, showing diatoms adhering to body surface (× 500).

in size and less active than the larger forms. More information is needed on their feeding habits. Many of these predatory forms are also considered to be carrion feeders (Kühnelt, 1961), but this requires confirmation. Another group of Mesostigmata, the Uropodina, contains a number of fungal-feeding mites (Evans *et al.*, 1961). These are slow moving and not adapted to a predatory habit, although one member of this group, *Fuscuropoda marginata* (C. L. Koch), which has been considered coprophagous (Kühnelt, 1961), has been shown to be a predator of the astigmatid mite *Caloglyphus myco-phagus* (Rohde, 1959).

C. ASTIGMATA

The feeding habits of the soil-dwelling members of this group of mites are not well known, although it is probable that they feed on plant detritus, fungi, algae and the liquified products of putrefaction processes (Karg, 1963). The Glycyphagidae are mainly fungal feeders, and the same appears to be true of the *Histiogaster* species found in the galleries of wood-boring beetles. Members of this last-named genus apparently have a wide range of feeding habit, and have also been recorded as carrion-feeders (Woodring, 1963), a habit also shown by the anoetid genus *Histiosoma*. Karg (1963) considers many of the Anoetidae to be filter feeders on liquids rich in micro-organisms. As far as other soil-dwelling species are concerned, *Rhizoglyphus* species feed on decaying plant material, *Caloglyphus* species on carrion, although they may also be fungivorous; *Schwiebia talpa* Oudms. has been recovered from beneath the bark and in cavities in hemlock and yellow birch twigs lying on the forest floor (Wallwork, 1957), and although the feeding habits of this species have not been established with certainty, it may feed on fungi and the woody products of fungal decay in this situation. In general, it would seem that soil Astigmata require for their maintenance organic material in an advanced stage of decay, low oxygen concentration, and a plentiful supply of moisture.

D. CRYPTOSTIGMATA

Cryptostigmata may be an important element in the decomposer food-chain in the soil community on account of their feeding habits. Many species feed on soil fungi and bacteria and it has been suggested that the mites may control the growth of these organisms (Engelmann, 1961). Evidently the relationship is not a simple one, for mites also help to disseminate fungal spores. A great many Cryptostigmata are unspecialized feeders, and indeed, restriction to one type of food is rare in these soil forms. The emphasis hitherto placed on fungal food arises partly because hyphae and spores are easily identified in gut contents, whereas plant material in an advanced stage of decomposition is not. Results of feeding experiments made by Hartenstein (1962) on 20 species indicate that about half of them preferred fungi as food, whereas the others preferred decomposing plant material. This lack of specificity of many species has been noted commonly in observations on cultures

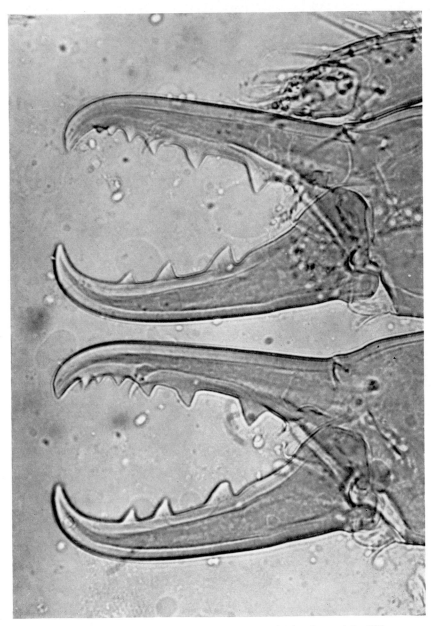

FIG. 7. Cheliceral digits of *Gamasolaelaps* sp. (Mesostigmata) (× 500).

TABLE II

The feeding habits of selected groups of soil Cryptostigmata

Group	Herbivore	Decomposer			Microphyte	
	Green plants	Plant detritus	Wood	Carrion	Moss and lichen	Fungi and algae
Hypochthonius				×	×	×
Liochthonius		×		×		×
Eniochthonius		×				×
Camisia		×			×	×
Nothrus						
silvestris		×			×	×
palustris					×	
Platynothrus		×				
Nanhermannia		×			×	×
Mesoplophora						
pulchra			×			×
Phthiracarus		×	×			×
Steganacarus						
magnus		×	×			
Rhysotritia						
ardua		×	×			
Euphthiracarus					×	
Hermannia		×	×			
Liacarus		×	×			×
Adoristes						
ovatus		×				×
Ceratoppia			×			×
Hermanniella		×	×			
Carabodes		×	×			×
Cepheus			×		×	
Tectocepheus						
velatus		×				× ?
Belba		×		×		×
Oppia nova		×			×	×
Oppia spp.			×			×
Oribatula						
tibialis						×
Scheloribates	×	×	×		×	×
Achipteria	×	×			×	×
Fuscozetes						
fuscipes		×				×
Peloribates	×	×	×	×		×
Protoribates		×	×			
Ceratozetes		×	×			×
Eupelops	×	×				
Galumna (s.l.)	×	×	×		×	×

and gut contents (Forsslund, 1939; Riha, 1951; Schuster, 1956; Wallwork, 1957; Woodring and Cook, 1962), and is illustrated by data presented in Table II.

Some tentative conclusions may be drawn from these findings. Species

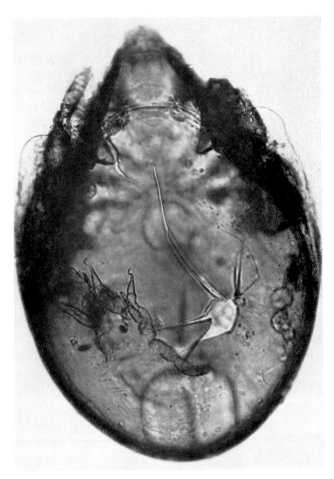

FIG. 8. *Scheloribates perforatus* Wallw. showing development of larva inside shell of the adult (× 125).

predominantly fungivorous under natural and artificial conditions include *Ceratoppia bipilis* (Herm.), *Adoristes ovatus* (C. L. Koch), *Belba* spp., *Belba kingi* Hartenstein, *Oribatula tibialis*, *Oribatula minuta* (Banks), *Scheloribates laevigatus*, *Ceratozetes gracilis* (Mich.) and *Galumna elimata* (C. L. Koch). Sustained feeding on plant fragments will only occur, generally, if these fragments are undergoing wet decomposition. Such food material is suitable for many Cryptostigmata including *Liochthonius* sp., *Nothrus silvestris*, *Nothrus biciliatus* (C. L. Koch), *Platynothrus peltifer*, *Camisia* spp., *Phthiracarus* spp., *Hermannia* sp., *Liacarus xylariae* (Schranck), *Carabodes* spp., *Oribatella* sp., *Fuscozetes fuscipes* (C. L. Koch), *Peloribates* sp., *Protoribates lophotrichus* Berl. and *Eupelops* sp. Feeding preference is frequently related to the stage of decomposition of the plant material. Thus, *Achipteria* sp. will feed on the epidermal layer of dry hemlock needles and may prefer this food to highly decomposed plant remains. Similarly, *Eupelops* sp. and *Peloribates* sp. will feed on parenchyma of dry leaves. Whether or not populations can subsist indefinitely on this food source is not known. A number of species, including *Scheloribates laevigatus*, *Achipteria* sp. and *Eupelops* sp. are known to feed on living green plant material (Wallwork, 1957; Woodring, 1963), although this may not be an important part of the diet under natural conditions, for reproduction apparently does not occur in cultures using this food source. However, one instance has been reported recently (Wallwork, 1965) of a galumnoid mite, *Orthogalumna terebrantis* Wallw., from Uruguay feeding exclusively, at least in the nymphal stages, on living parenchyma of leaves of the water hyacinth, *Eichhornia crassipes*. The adult is active on the surface of leaves and the water surrounding the plant. The leaf is probably entered by the larva or protonymph cutting a hole in the epidermis and invading the parenchyma. A cylindrical burrow is excavated by the feeding of the three nymphal stages which develop *in situ*. After the final ecdysis the adult cuts through the epidermis and emerges. At the other extreme are species feeding only on plant material in an advanced stage of decay. These forms include the adults of many of the small species belonging to the genera *Brachychthonius*, *Oppia* and *Suctobelba*, as well as *Eniochthonius pallidulus* (C. L. Koch), *Tectocepheus velatus* and the immature stages of many of the larger species. The apparent absence of solid food in the gut of *Hypochthonius rufulus*, *Oppia* spp. and *Suctobelba* spp. may be due to these mites feeding on liquified organic material in the soil. On the other hand, many Cryptostigmata are coprophagous, particularly in the larval and nymphal stages. This habit is common among immature forms of typical wood-feeding species belonging to the genera *Steganacarus* and *Rhysotritia*, as well as in adults of *Oppia* spp., *Scheloribates laevigatus* and *Galumna formicarius* (Berl.) which are associated with these xylophages in certain situations (Wallwork, 1957). Many species feeding on liquid, semi-liquid or faecal material no doubt ingest fungal hyphae and spores associated with this material. This probably occurs in *Liochthonius* sp., *Tectocepheus velatus*, *Oppia* spp. and *Hypochthonius rufulus*. Under certain conditions *Peloribates* sp., *Hypochthonius rufulus*, *Belba* spp. and *Liochthonius* spp. have been observed to feed on carrion (Riha, 1951; Wallwork, 1957), although it is not known to what extent this forms part of the natural diet. Several instances have been given of predation by *Oribella castanea* (Herm.), *Scheloribates laevigatus* and *Galumna* sp. These appear to be isolated records, for predation is not usually associated with the slow-moving Cryptostigmata. However, it is possible that eggs of other animals, such as insects and Collembola, may provide a source of food.

A number of species, including *Scheloribates laevigatus, Galumna virginiensis, Tectocepheus velatus* and *Eupelops* sp. ingest the eggs of anoplocephalid cestodes (Rajski, 1960). Sometimes the eggs are crushed, sometimes they are swallowed whole and may continue development in the mites.

Some soil Cryptostigmata prefer woody tissue as food. These include *Mesoplophora pulchra, Steganacarus magnus, Rhysotritia* spp., *Liacarus* sp., *Carabodes* sp., *Cepheus* sp., *Hermannia* sp., *Hermanniella* sp., *Oppia* spp., *Scheloribates* sp. and *Galumna* sp. Decided preferences are found within this group of xylophages. Some species feed on the woody vascular elements of leaves (*Hermannia* sp., *Phthiracarus borealis*), others, such as *Mesoplophora pulchra* and *Steganacarus diaphanum* Jacot consume softened, decomposing woody fibres of twigs lying on the surface of, or embedded in, the soil. A more specialized habit is shown by those mites which actually burrow into bark and heart wood of fallen twigs. *Steganacarus magnus* and *Rhysotritia ardua* may be confined to this restricted habitat in certain localities, for investigations of their burrows (Wallwork, 1957) have revealed complex formations consisting of a main channel containing the adult, and side branches occupied by immature forms. Other wood-borers are not so restricted and may spend only a part of their life cycle under these conditions as, for example, *Cepheus latus* C. L. Koch, which may become a wood-borer as an adult, although this stage is apparently not an obligate xylophage, for it may be encountered ranging freely through the soil (Wallwork, 1957). An extreme case of specialized feeding habit is provided by the mite illustrated in Fig. 4, which is tentatively identified as a tritonymph belonging in the genus *Hermannia*. It has been taken frequently from lenticels of fallen yellow birch twigs (Wallwork, 1957). All nymphal stages occur there, but no adults. Without exception, analysis showed the gut filled with corky material from the lenticel (Fig. 4). In conclusion, the distribution of three wood-borers in fallen twigs of yellow birch and hemlock is given in Table III. It may be noted from the Table that two of the three species most frequent in heart wood of yellow birch (*Steganacarus magnus* and *Rhysotritia ardua*) also occur in hemlock, but are restricted there to the bark region. This observation emphasizes the impossibility of rigidly defining the feeding habits of Acari. For most species with a wide range of habit, compensation may occur, and the emphasis on any one particular food source will vary with the soil type and locality.

In addition to these qualitative aspects of nutrition, quantitative variations during the life cycle also affect the trophic status of a species. The feeding rate of a given species may not be constant throughout the life cycle. Later immature forms may feed almost continuously, as would be expected of the growing stages, except during the pre-ecdysial quiescent periods. This point is well illustrated by Murphy and Jalil (1964) who found that 30% of the tritonymphs of *Tectocepheus velatus* had food in the gut, compared with only 17 to 22% of adults and other immatures. Studies of this kind show that feeding rate may decline sharply with age once the adult stage has been reached. This phenomenon varies with the species. Adults of *Oppia nova* and *Rostrozetes* sp. continue feeding, whereas in *Galumna elimata, Scheloribates laevigatus* and *Ceratozetes cisalpinus* Berl. the feeding rate decreases considerably after a few weeks (Woodring, 1963). These considerations are of paramount importance when assessing population metabolism and community energy flow, because they emphasize the significance of the feeding habits of the later nymphal stages. Similarly, the adults of most species must be regarded as the main dispersive stage, because of their greater mobility.

The above remarks have been concerned mainly with the kinds of food material ingested by mites. The proportion of this ingested material which is assimilated and utilized for growth and energy requirements is unknown.

TABLE III

The distribution of 3 species of wood-boring Cryptostigmata in twigs of yellow birch and hemlock undergoing wet decomposition*

| Species | Yellow birch | | | Hemlock | | |
	In bark	Under bark	In heart wood	In bark	Under bark	In heart wood
Steganacarus magnus	+	+	+ + +	+ + +	+	−
Rhysotritia ardua	+	−	+	+ +	−	−
Hermannia sp. (nymph)	+ +	+	−	+	−	−

* High, medium and low frequencies denoted (+ + +), (+ +) and (+) respectively.

Very little information exists about the efficiency of the digestive system in the Cryptostigmata, although work has been started by Engelmann (1961) using radioactive tracers. Analyses of faecal pellets (Schuster, 1956) suggest that much of the ingested material passes out of the gut without much change in its chemical composition. Easily digested substances such as proteins, carbohydrates and lipoids are probably assimilated, but hemicelluloses, cellulose and lignin apparently are not chemically degraded by the enzyme systems of the mite. The possibility that some Cryptostigmata may possess gut symbionts that can digest these substances has been suggested (Hartenstein, 1962; Woodring, 1963), although more evidence is needed to confirm this. Another possibility is that Cryptostigmata may digest the micro-organisms on the surface of fungal hyphae, spores and plant debris, and that these materials merely act as carriers for the more digestible sources of nutriment.

V. METABOLISM

A. THE ENERGY BALANCE SHEET

The numerical abundance of the Acari in many soil types naturally leads to a consideration of their biological effects, in particular their contribution to total soil metabolism. Here again the Cryptostigmata are singled out for special emphasis because their great numbers and feeding habits give them a certain significance in the decomposer food-chain of some soil communities. To investigate this significance it is necessary to establish not only population densities and feeding habits, but also to know how much energy is assimilated into the body, and what proportions of this assimilated energy are (1) used in metabolism, and (2) stored in the body, ultimately to be passed on to a different trophic level. The construction of an energy balance sheet of this kind is difficult, for measurements of rates of feeding, assimilation and metabolism must be made in the laboratory under controlled experimental conditions. These laboratory data have to be extrapolated to natural situations, taking account of population fluctuations and temperature variations in the habitat over a given period of time. This laboratory work presents several difficulties because the mites are so small, but with the development of special techniques for measuring rates of oxygen consumption with micro-respirometers, and rate of assimilation by radioactive tracers, considerable progress is now being made in this field (Engelmann, 1961; Macfadyen, 1963; Berthet, 1963).

The biological activity of a natural population is expressed, for purposes of comparison, in relation to the size of the population. In much purely descriptive ecological work, population size of soil mites is stated in terms of numbers of individuals. Numbers give poor estimates of the biological activity of a population in animals the size of soil mites; biomass is a much more reliable guide, and energy values per unit biomass are even more realistic. This leads to another difficulty, namely that whereas mites are not too small to be counted accurately, they are frequently too small to be weighed accurately. This difficulty may be met by assuming that most of the dry weight of the animal is in the exoskeleton, so that there is a linear relationship between dry weight and surface area of the body. Engelmann (1961) has demonstrated that this relationship is established for a number of terrestrial arthropods, and has calculated the dry weight of individual mites from the regression formula:

$$\text{Log weight } (\mu g) = 1 \cdot 32 \ (\text{log length} + \text{log width } [\mu]) - 5 \cdot 87.$$

The assumption on which this regression is based is evidently valid for the adults of many hard-bodied Cryptostigmata, but the relationship may be less direct for gravid females of some of the larger species (which may contain as many as 20 mature or nearly mature eggs) and immature forms, particularly tritonymphs where, theoretically at least, dry weight may be more a function of volume than of surface area. Furthermore, in using this method to calculate metabolism it must also be assumed that the exoskeleton is metabolically active (F. Raw, personal communication), and this may not be true in adult Cryptostigmata.

The amount of food assimilated by an organism in a given period of time can be determined if the amounts consumed and egested are known. The amount of food consumed under natural conditions is difficult to measure

and is obviously affected by a number of variables including, for Cryptostigmata, moisture content of food, its state of decomposition and environmental temperature. An indirect method of estimating consumption has been
suggested by van der Drift (1951) from studies on the feeding rates of the
diplopod *Glomeris marginata*. This method is based on the assumption that
there is a definite relationship between feeding rate and body weight so that:

$$\text{Food consumed} = \sqrt[3]{(\text{body weight})^2} \times \text{constant}.$$

According to this relationship the relative feeding rate (i.e. feeding rate per
unit weight) decreases with increasing body weight. Evidence from feeding
studies on Cryptostigmata indicates that the relative feeding rate decreases
with increasing body weight and that the absolute feeding rate of the nymphal
forms, particularly the tritonymphs, is higher than that of the adults. This
would affect the constancy of the above relationship. Balogh (1958) has
discussed other limitations of the method. On the other hand, the direct
weighing method using differences in weights ingested and egested as estimates of assimilation is also subject to errors because of the small amounts
of materials involved. Engelmann (1961) obtained more reliable estimates of
assimilation by using yeast labelled with radioactive glycine ^{14}C as the food
source. He calculated that the food assimilated by the Cryptostigmata of a
grassland soil was equivalent to 8% of their body weight per day; expressed
in terms of the whole population (biomass: 54 mg/m^2) for one year, this
amounted to about 20% of the food ingested.

The next item on the balance sheet, metabolic estimates, can be calculated
by indirect or direct methods. Engelmann (1961) calculated respiration rates
of several species of Cryptostigmata indirectly, where technical difficulties
prevented direct estimations. The method assumed a linear relationship
between log body weight and log respiration which, for the data used, could
be expressed by the equation:

$$\text{Log respiration } (\mu l\ 10^{-3}) = 0.85\ (\text{log weight in } \mu g) + 0.44.$$

By using the results obtained by this regression technique in conjunction
with direct respirometric estimates made at 25°C, and by correcting them for
temperature conditions of the habitat, Engelmann calculated that the yearly
expenditure of energy on respiration by the whole population under natural
conditions was about 96% of the total energy assimilated into the body during
that period.

Respiration rates can be used as a reliable index of metabolic activity.
When combined with calorimetric studies, they provide a basis for comparing
the contribution of individual trophic groups to total soil metabolism. For
detritus-feeding forms, such comparisons help to explain their importance in
decomposition processes. Despite the variability in the results obtained by
direct respirometry, this approach promises to be more reliable than the
indirect method. Berthet (1963) determined the oxygen consumption of
several species of Cryptostigmata from a forest soil. Although results for

individuals of the same species differed greatly, he was able to demonstrate the influence of temperature and body weight on respiration rate. Thus, oxygen consumption of *Platynothrus peltifer* and *Parachipteria willmanni* remained relatively constant at 15°C and was 0·222 mm³ and 0·176 mm³ respectively per individual per day. Measurements at different temperatures indicated a linear relationship between the log oxygen consumed and temperature which only held within the range 5–15°C. Above this range, the oxygen consumption was lower than expected and the relationship assumed a sigmoid form. This characteristic was apparently not taken into consideration by Engelmann. Within the range 5–15°C a relatively constant temperature coefficient of approximately 4 was calculated for 16 common species. An exponential relationship between body weight and oxygen consumption was described for individuals of *Steganacarus magnus* at 15°C, and as a result of these studies Berthet postulated a general relationship between oxygen consumption, temperature and body weight, expressed by the equation:

$$Y = 18·059 + 0·7W - 0·487Z$$

where $Y =$ log oxygen consumed/individual/day in 10^{-3} mm³

$W =$ log body weight in μg and

$Z = \dfrac{1}{T_{abs}} . 10^4.$

Methods such as these can be extended to determine energy flow and transfer within and between different trophic levels in the soil community. Without data on differential mortality rates, the efficiency of energy transfer from one level to another must be based on assumptions until further developments provide more precise estimates. The preceding discussion has been concerned exclusively with the energetics of the decomposer level, for it is with this level that the very large majority of soil Acari are identified. The little work done on the energy relations of predatory mites by Engelmann (1961) and Macfadyen (1963) indicates that these forms may make a significant contribution to energy circulation in the community. A detailed energy balance sheet cannot be given for the Cryptostigmata at present, although the results surveyed briefly above do give indications of the picture emerging from these studies. It seems that much of the energy ingested is not assimilated into the body, but is egested with the faeces. Thus, the Cryptostigmata are wasteful feeders from this point of view (Macfadyen, 1963). Much of the energy assimilated into the body is used in respiration and only a relatively small amount is incorporated into the standing crop biomass.

B. The Decomposer Food Chain

Finally we turn to the role of the acarine decomposers in breakdown processes occurring in the soil. The overwhelming importance of decomposers in some situations has been demonstrated by Macfadyen (1963), who calculated that this group attracted considerably more of the energy flow than the herbivore/carnivore food chain in a meadow soil. There is further evidence that the decomposer fraction is well represented in a variety of soil types, although the small-sized decomposers, of which the Cryptostigmata form a prominent part, predominate in mor-type soils (Macfadyen, 1963). Cryptostigmata have a low metabolic rate compared with other small-sized decomposers such as Collembola. Berthet (1963) calculated that the metabolism of these mites accounts for only 1·8% per annum of the total soil metabolism in a forest soil. He also found that the mites of the litter layer, although fewer and having a smaller biomass than those in the lower organic layers, made an appreciably greater contribution to soil metabolism than the latter, a fact he attributed to higher respiration rates of litter inhabitants during the summer months.

The impression gained from these quantitative studies is that the Cryptostigmata play only a minor role in the direct decomposition and chemical degradation of litter material. It is clear from the results of feeding studies that most of the detritus-feeding Acari prefer decomposing plant material or fungi. Their contribution to primary breakdown of fresh litter may be studied using the litter-bag technique, in which litter is contained in bags of varying mesh sizes to exclude certain faunal groups, and then placed on the surface of, or embedded in, the soil. Using this approach, Edwards and Heath (1963) and van der Drift (1963) concluded that the Cryptostigmata are of little importance in primary decomposition. On the other hand, Crossley and Witkamp (1964) were able to demonstrate a successional development of the mites in litter bags, characterized by an initial invasion by large numbers of individuals belonging to a small number of species, followed by an increase in species diversity as decomposition proceeded, and a reduction in the number of individuals per species. Most Cryptostigmata would seem to be associated more with the later stages of decomposition, and even here their effect appears to be small. Before making any final assessment, however, there are two important points to be borne in mind. First, most determinations of metabolic rate and food assimilation have been made on adult mites. Now the nymphal stages, at least of the Cryptostigmata, appear to be the important feeding stages in the life cycle, and it is possible that they have a higher metabolic rate than the adults. These weakly chitinized immatures are also more vulnerable to predators, and may participate more than the adults in the transfer of material and energy to higher trophic levels in the community. When more information is available about the biological activity of these immature forms, the assessment of the metabolic contribution of the Cryptostigmata to total soil processes may well need revision. Berthet (1963) has shown that nymphal Cryptostigmata may contribute as much as 70% to the total metabolism of the whole group during a year. Second, the long-term metabolic role of these mites must be considered. Many forest soils provide unsuitable conditions for the larger and metabolically more active decomposers, and under such conditions the slow but continuous decomposition of plant material may be maintained appreciably by the activity of detritus-feeding mites. However, we know little of these long-term effects in which soil micro-organisms such as Protozoa and bacteria may also be important.

On the other hand, many authors have stressed the indirect importance of the detritus-feeding mites in litter decomposition. In many ways, that cannot be determined quantitatively at present, these mites assist the decomposition processes by promoting the growth and distribution of micro-organisms (see Fig. 6) and fungi (Fig. 3), and by transporting the products of decomposition to the lower layers and root zones of the soil profile. The relationship between the mites and fungi is complex. Some forest soils having dense fungal mats do not support large populations of Cryptostigmata, which suggests antagonism between the two groups of organisms, although it may result from differential reaction to some environmental factor such as low relative humidity. In other situations, the feeding of fungivorous mites may control the growth of fungi and may lead ultimately to more vigorous fungal growth, by preventing overcrowding. Mites play an important part in the dissemination of fungal spores, which may adhere readily to the surface of the body or be transported in the gut of the mites. Xylophagous species may be particularly important in this respect. Although the symbiotic relationship between mites and micro-organisms requires confirmation, the two groups may be associated in the decomposition process, for there is evidence that litter or decomposing material may be more susceptible to microbial activity after it has passed through the gut of the mites (Ghilarov, 1963; Kühnelt, 1963). The "wasteful" feeding behaviour of the Cryptostigmata may in fact be quite the reverse (Macfadyen, 1961). The comminution of organic material by their mouthparts may be important in the physical breakdown of litter, thus exposing a greater surface area to microbial activity and leaching (Crossley and Witkamp, 1964). The importance of the Cryptostigmata in the transportation of organic material in an advanced stage of decay to deeper layers of the soil profile is established from identification of characteristic faecal pellets. A study by Jongerius (1963) on the humus components of three different profiles defines this activity in quantitative terms. According to these findings, the Cryptostigmata play a more prominent part in the vertical transportation of organic material in a mor profile than in a mull type and, in the former, the volume of mite excrements is appreciable in the root zone at a depth of 7 to 12 cm, whereas the excrements of larger decomposers are localized in the upper regions of the profile. The Cryptostigmata appear then to be important in the deep mixing of organic material. In contrast, the larger decomposers are more effective in surface mixing.

REFERENCES

Baker, E. W. and Wharton, G. W. (1952). "An Introduction to Acarology." Macmillan, New York.
Balogh, J. (1958). *Acta zool. hung.* **4**, 89–114.
Berthet, P. (1963). *In* "Soil Organisms." (J. Doeksen and J. van der Drift, eds.), pp. 18–31. North-Holland Publ. Co., Amsterdam.
Berthet, P. (1964). *J. Anim. Ecol.* **33**, 443–449.

Crossley, D. A. and Bohnsack, K. K. (1960). *Ecology*, **41**, 785–790.

Crossley, D. A. and Witkamp, M. (1964). *C. r. 1er Congr. Int. d'Acarologie* (1963); *Acarologia*, **6** (h. s.), 137–146.

Dalenius, P. (1962). *K. Fysiogr. Sällsk. Handl.* **32**, 105–129.

Drift, J. van der (1951). *Tijdschr. Ent.* **94**, 1–168.

Drift, J. van der (1963). *In* "Soil Organisms." (J. Doeksen and J. van der Drift, eds.), pp. 125–133. North-Holland Publ. Co., Amsterdam.

Edwards, C. A. and Heath, G. W. (1963). *In* "Soil Organisms." (J. Doeksen and J. van der Drift, eds.), pp. 76–84. North-Holland Publ. Co., Amsterdam.

Engelmann, M. D. (1961). *Ecol. Monogr.* **31**, 221–238.

Evans, G. O. (1955). *In* "Soil Zoology." (D. K. McE. Kevan, ed.), pp. 55–61. Butterworths, London.

Evans, G. O., Sheals, J. G. and MacFarlane, D. (1961). "The Terrestrial Acari of the British Isles." Vol. I. British Museum of Natural History.

Forsslund, K. H. (1939). *7th Int. Congr. Ent. Berlin* (1938), **3**, 1950–1957.

Forsslund, K. H. (1943). *Meddr. St. Skogföslksanstalt*, **34**, 1–283.

Franz, H. (1963). *In* "Soil Organisms." (J. Doeksen and J. van der Drift, eds.), pp. 345–367. North-Holland Publ. Co., Amsterdam.

Ghilarov, M. S. (1963). *In* "Soil Organisms." (J. Doeksen and J. van der Drift, eds.), pp. 255–259. North-Holland Publ. Co., Amsterdam.

Grandjean, F. (1950). *Bull. Mus. Hist. nat. Paris*, **22**, 224–231.

Haarløv, N. (1942). *Meddr. Grønland*, **128**, 1–71.

Haarløv, N. (1960). *Oikos*, Suppl. **3**, 1–176.

Hammer, M. (1937). *Meddr. Grønland*, **108**, 1–53.

Hammer, M. (1944). *Meddr. Grønland*, **141**, 1–210.

Hartenstein, R. (1961). *Ecology*, **42**, 190–194.

Hartenstein, R. (1962). *Ann. ent. Soc. Am.* **55**, 202–206.

Healy, M. J. R. (1962). *In* "Progress in Soil Zoology." (P. W. Murphy, ed.), pp. 3–9. Butterworths, London.

Hurlbutt, H. (1964). *C. r. 1er Congr. Int. d'Acarologie* (1963); *Acarologia*, **6** (h. s.), 150–152.

Ibarra, E., Wallwork, J. A. and Rodriguez, J. G. (1965). *Ann. ent. Soc. Am.* **58**, 153–159.

Jongerius, A. (1963). *In* "Soil Organisms." (J. Doeksen and J. van der Drift, eds.), pp. 137–148. North-Holland Publ. Co., Amsterdam.

Karg, W. (1963). *In* "Soil Organisms." (J. Doeksen and J. van der Drift, eds.), pp. 305–315. North-Holland Publ. Co., Amsterdam.

Karppinen, E. (1955). *Ann. Zool. Soc.* "Vanamo", **17**, 1–80.

Karppinen, E. (1958). *Ann. Zool. Soc.* "Vanamo", **19**, 1–43.

Klima, J. (1956). *Oikos*, **7**, 227–242.

Klima, J. (1959). *Nat. Tirol.* 197–208.

Knülle, W. (1957). *Z. Morph. Ökol. Tiere*, **46**, 397–432.

Kühnelt, W. (1961). "Soil Biology." Faber and Faber, London.

Kühnelt, W. (1963). *In* "Soil Organisms." (J. Doeksen and J. van der Drift, eds.), pp. 333–341. North-Holland Publ. Co., Amsterdam.

Lebrun, P. (1964a). *Bull. Acad. r. Belg. Cl. Sci.* **5**, 370–392.

Lebrun, P. (1964b). *Bull. Soc. R. ent. belg.* **100**, 69–77.

Luxton, M. (1964). *C. r. 1er Congr. Int. d'Acarologie* (1963); *Acarologia*, **6** (h.s.), 172–182.

Macfadyen, A. (1952). *J. Anim. Ecol.* **21**, 87–117.

Macfadyen, A. (1961). *Ann. appl. Biol.* **49**, 216–219.

Macfadyen, A. (1963). *In* "Soil Organisms." (J. Doeksen and J. van der Drift, eds.), pp. 3–17. North-Holland Publ. Co., Amsterdam.

Madge, D. S. (1964a). *Acarologia*, **6**, 199–223.

Madge, D. S. (1964b). *Acarologia*, **6**, 566–591.

Märkel, K. (1964). *C. r. 1er Congr. Int. d'Acarologie* (1963); *Acarologia*, **6** (h. s.), 158–170.

Murphy, P. W. (1955). *In* "Soil Zoology." (D. K. McE. Kevan, ed.), pp. 99–124. Butterworths, London.

Murphy, P. W. and Jalil, M. (1964). *C. r. 1er Congr. Int. d'Acarologie* (1963); *Acarologia*, **6** (h. s.), 187–197.

Newell, I. M. (1963). *J. Parasit.* **49**, 498–502.

Pauly, F. (1956). *Zool. Jb.* **84**, 273–328.

Rajski, A. (1960). *Wiad. Parazyt.*, **7**, 39–42.

Rajski, A. (1961). *Poznan Soc. Friends of Science*, **25**, 1–160.

Riha, G. (1951). *Zool. Jb. (Systematik)*, **80**, 407–450.

Rohde, C. J. (1959). *Ecology*, **40**, 572–579.

Schuster, R. (1956). *Z. Morph. Ökol. Tiere*, **45**, 1–33.

Sengbusch, H. G. (1958). *Naturwissenschaften*, **20**, 498–499.

Sheals, J. G. (1957). *J. Anim. Ecol.* **26**, 125–134.

Strenzke, K. (1952). *Zoologica*, **37**, 1–172.

Tarras-Wahlberg, N. (1954). *Oikos*, **4**, 166–171.

Tarras-Wahlberg, N. (1961). *Oikos*, Suppl. 4, 1–56.

Thamdrup, H. M. (1939). *Acta jutl.* Suppl. 11, 1–82.

Travé, J. (1963). *Vie et Milieu*, Suppl. 14, 1–267.

Wallwork, J. A. (1957). "The Acarina of a hemlock-yellow birch forest floor." Thesis, University of Michigan.

Wallwork, J. A. (1959). *Ecology*, **40**, 557–563.

Wallwork. J. A. (1960). *Proc. zool. Soc. Lond.* **135**, 619–629.

Wallwork, J. A. (1965). *Acarologia*, **7**, 758–764.

Wallwork, J. A. and Rodriguez, J. G. (1961). *J. Econ. Ent.* **54**, 701–705.

Wallwork, J. H. and Rodriguez, J. G. (1963). *In* "Advances in Acarology." (J. A. Naegele, ed.), Vol. I, pp. 60–69. Cornell University Press, Ithaca.

Weis-Fogh, T. (1948). *Natura. jutl.* **1**, 139–270.

Woodring, J. P. (1963). *In* "Advances in Acarology." (J. A. Naegele, ed.), Vol. I, pp. 89–111. Cornell University Press, Ithaca.

Woodring, J. P. and Cook, E. F. (1962). *Acarologia*, **4**, 101–137.

Chapter 12

Collembola

W. G. HALE

City of Liverpool College of Technology,
Liverpool, England

I. INTRODUCTION

The Collembola are usually given the status of an Order in the Sub-Class Apterygota (Insecta). Imms (1936) considers that they are best regarded as an offshoot from the base of the early Symphylan stock, but stresses the remoteness of the group from the main evolutionary line of the Insecta. Ewing (1942), Wygodzinsky (1943), Jeannel (1949), Paclt (1954) and Ross (1955) give more recent assessments of the taxonomic position of the group, but, for the most part, agree with the conclusions of Imms.

While it is generally considered that the group retains rather primitive features, Gisin (1943), Delamare-Deboutteville (1950) and Paclt (1956) have suggested that many of these are adaptations to life in the soil; Delamare-Deboutteville points out that the persistence of primitive characteristics is typical of soil-living groups, and attributes this to the stability of the soil as an environment. Gilyarov (1949) suggests that aerial habitats were first colonized by insects via the soil.

Numerically the Collembola usually take second place only to the Acari in the air-breathing fauna of the soil, and on occasions (Stockli, 1943, 1946), they have been found to be even more numerous than the mites. Collembola actually living in the soil spaces seldom exceed 3 mm in length, but the surface and litter forms may reach a length of 6–7 mm.

II. SYSTEMATICS

The classification of Collembola is essentially due to Borner (1906), although great advances have been made in the taxonomy at the specific level during the past two decades. Such are these advances that in some cases, e.g. the Onychiuridae (Gisin 1952), where species groups exist, present workers are unable to make comparisons with much of the published data. It is important that ecologists should adopt the narrow species concept of Gisin, as further study of the biology of the genus *Onychiurus* (Hale, 1965a, b, c) has provided additional justification for it. J. P. C. Rowland (personal communication) has obtained further evidence in the form of the chromatographic separation of ninhydrin-positive substances in the *O. armatus* species group, where clear differences occur in 5 species of the group.

The keys of Stach (1947–1960) and Gisin (1960) are the most widely used for purposes of identification, and the latter author supplements his key by monthly additions and corrections in the form of leaflets entitled "Summarische Nachtrage zu 'Collembolenfauna Europas'".

Collections are normally preserved in 70% alcohol, to which a little glycerol is added to prevent accidental desiccation. For specialized taxonomic purposes the best results are obtained by fixing in Gisin's fixative (Gisin, 1960) for two days before mounting. Temporary mounts can be made in lactophenol; permanent preparations are best made either in Goto's modification of polyvinyl lactophenol or using the method recommended by Gisin (1960).

III. GEOGRAPHICAL DISTRIBUTION

Some species of Collembola, e.g. *Isotomurus palustris* (Muller, 1776) have a world-wide distribution, and in general Collembola have a more extensive distribution than the species of any other insect group. Probably this is due to two factors: first, they are easily dispersed by air or water currents or on the feet of birds; and, second, they are of great antiquity. Arthropods closely related to Collembola have been found in lower Devonian deposits in Scotland, whereas the first pterygote insects are from the upper Carboniferous. Salmon (1941) suggests a north European origin for Collembola, followed by an extension of the range in three directions: into Africa, North America and Australasia; and while the present-day distribution supports this hypothesis, it should be remembered that transportation by man has now greatly complicated, if not entirely masked, the original picture.

IV. LIFE CYCLES

At high altitudes and in arctic or sub-arctic climates, Collembola have only one or two generations a year. Agrell (1941) records two generations in

Folsomia quadrioculata (Tullberg, 1871) in arctic Sweden, and the present writer, working on an area which experiences a sub-arctic climate in the northern Pennines, has found that most species have only one, or at the most two, generations a year (Hale, 1965b). At lower altitudes, and in more temperate climates, some species have several generations a year. Folsom (1916) records 3–4 generations in *Hypogastrura armata* (Nicolet, 1841) and Britt (1951) records a maximum of 12 generations a year in the same species kept in the laboratory at 24°C. The latter author indicates that the life span is about 2 months in *H. armata*, but that overwintering individuals live for about a year. Ripper (1930) records a life span of 5–10 months for Collembola of the genus *Hypogastrura*.

Even at high temperatures some species are limited to a single generation a year; this has been shown by Agrell (1941) in *Tomocerus vulgaris* (Tullberg, 1871) and by Bellinger (1954) in *T. flavescens* (Tullberg, 1871). Members of the Sminthuridae, even under sub-arctic conditions, tend to have more than one generation a year; Davidson (1934) records 4 generations during one year in *Sminthurus viridis* (Linné, 1758) under field conditions.

Estimates of the numbers of eggs laid by Collembola vary greatly. South (1959) records that a single female *Entomobrya multifasciata* (Tullberg, 1871) can lay up to six batches during a single period of laying, and each of these batches may contain up to 50 eggs. Under sub-arctic conditions probably fewer than 100 eggs are laid by most species of Collembola during the lifetime of a single female (Hale, 1965b).

While sexual reproduction is the normal method in most Collembola (Mayer, 1957), parthenogenesis is important in some species. Handschin (1928) referred to the possibility of parthenogenesis in Collembola, and suggested that the periodic appearances of large numbers of a single species might be considered as circumstantial evidence for it. Isolation of adult females of various species by Strebel (1932, 1938), Falkenhan (1932), Schaller (1953) and Mayer (1957) resulted in no young individuals being produced. In only one case, recorded by Lindemann (1950), in *Orchesella villosa* (Geoffroy, 1764), did an isolated female produce eggs which subsequently developed, and Mayer (1957) explains this by suggesting that spermatophores were introduced to the culture with the food. Subsequent to this, good evidence for parthenogenesis has been provided: in *Onychiurus parthenogeneticus* (Choudhuri, 1958) parthenogenesis is the normal form of reproduction, and males apparently do not exist in this species (Choudhuri, 1958); a form of parthenogenesis has been recorded in other members of the Onychiuridae by Hale (1965a, 1965b). Goto (1960) and Marshall and Kevan (1962) have demonstrated facultative parthenogenesis in *Folsomia candida* (Willem, 1902).

The study of life histories of Collembola often involves laboratory culturing; the method described by Goto (1961) has proved most efficient for this.

V. FOOD

Whilst the identification of the gut contents of Collembola presents many problems, attempts have been made to determine the natural foods of these insects. Strebel (1928) records decaying plant material, fungal mycelia, spores, dipteran pupae, other Collembola, parts of decaying earthworms and their own cast cuticles from the intestine of individuals of *Hypogastrura purpurescens* (Lubbock, 1867). Poole (1959) concluded, from gut analyses, that the larger species of Collembola fed mainly on soil fungi, whereas the smaller forms appeared to feed directly on the humus. No evidence has been found which suggests that different species of Collembola have different food preferences, and, in fact, the contrary seems to be the case: Agrell (1940) found the gut contents of one species to consist entirely of fungal mycelia in one area, and of amorphous detritus in another area.

The laboratory experiments of Dunger (1956) have shown that while Collembola were able to feed on fresh leaves, and conditioning of the leaves by micro-organisms was not a necessary preliminary, leaves which had been attacked by micro-organisms were eaten more readily. Schaller (1950) also found a preference for decaying leaves in *Tomocerus flavescens* and *Orchesella flavescens* (Bourlet, 1839). The variety of food material taken into the gut, and the preference for leaves attacked by micro-organisms, suggests that particles may be ingested, and apparently taken as food, because of the fungal mycelia, or other micro-organisms, that they contain. This is supported by observations of the present writer: after putting Collembola in to culture jars, which contain a mixture of plaster of Paris and powdered charcoal, it can be seen that after only a few hours their intestines contain particles of charcoal, and examination of the faecal pellets also reveals the presence of plaster of Paris. Often, too, yeasts appear to be passed through the gut unchanged. When the eggs hatch, the first instar individuals begin to feed immediately and often their intestines appear as black lines, the lumen being filled with particles of charcoal. Clearly neither the charcoal nor the plaster of Paris is ingested because of its nutritive value, but more probably because of the fungal mycelia growing over the surface; thus, everything that is taken into the gut of Collembola must not be regarded as food.

I. Healey (personal communication) has found that food preference experiments done in laboratory cultures provide little useful information. Probably this is a result of the unnatural conditions in the laboratory and the poor sensory equipment of the Collembola involved (*Onychiurus procampatus* Gisin, 1956), for this type of experiment. However, it was found that very high growth rates occurred when *O. procampatus* was fed on *Mortierella isabellina*, *Trichoderma viride* and *Phoma* sp.

VI. SAMPLING AND EXTRACTION TECHNIQUES

Numerous methods have been used to remove Collembola from soil samples, and to date the most efficient methods are the high gradient cylinder of Macfadyen (1961) and the flotation method of Raw (1955). The latter method has the disadvantage of being suitable only for mineral soils, but Hale (1964) devised a similar method for use with organic soils.

For quantitative work, the present writer has found a sample unit size of

10^{-3} m^2 to be most convenient. In most soil types this gives between 20 and 200 Collembola per core, which is a convenient number for counting and identification in a single session. On grassland areas between 15 and 30 such units taken on each sampling occasion give a standard error of the mean of about 5% of the value of the mean.

VII. HORIZONTAL DISTRIBUTION

Glasgow (1939), Macfadyen (1952, 1957), Raw (1956), Hughes (1962), Kaczmarek (1960), Haarlov (1960) and Poole (1961) have all found that microarthropods tend to be aggregated in the soil.

Glasgow (1939) took samples in pairs, so that the edge of one sample touched the edge of the other. Comparing the variance between pairs with the variance within pairs, the former was found to be much the greater, indicating an aggregated population; this was shown in 4 species: *Onychiurus armatus* (Tullberg, 1869), *not* sensu Gisin, 1952; *O. ambulans* (Linné, 1758); *Tullbergia quadrispina* (Borner, 1901); and *T. krausbaueri* (Borner, 1901). Macfadyen (1952) found indications of aggregations in *Folsomia quadrioculata* from comparison of paired samples, but concluded that there was a very uniform distribution of microarthropods within each plant type examined. Kacsmarek (1960) defined the degree of aggregation by the percentage of samples in which the number of individuals was less than the mean, whilst Haarlov (1960) and Poole (1961) detected aggregation by the use of the coefficient of dispersion (Salt and Hollick, 1946).

The sizes of aggregations of Collembola have been estimated by Glasgow (1939); *Onychiurus armatus* aggregations were found to be between 3 inches (7·6 cm) and 12 inches (30·5 cm) in diameter, while in *O. ambulans*, *Tullbergia quadrispina* and *T. krausbaueri* the diameter was greater than 12 inches (30·5 cm).

Poole (1961) has attempted to show that aggregations of Collembola are not related to egg clusters, by comparing the egg batch sizes of different species with their coefficients of dispersion; the coefficient varies inversely with the egg batch size in all three cases. Comparison with data obtained by the present writer (Hale, in press) shows no clear correlation, and apparently aggregations may arise from gregariousness, egg batches, or the coming together of individuals at a food source. Swarming of Collembola on snow and water surfaces, as described by Davies (1932) and Paclt (1956), is probably a result of active gregariousness. Haarlov (1960) contends that the better the locomotory organs are developed, the less aggregated is the distribution of the species of Collembola in question, but the present writer has found no evidence to support this.

VIII. VERTICAL DISTRIBUTION

Macfadyen (1957) has commented upon the fact that life tends to be concentrated where two phases meet, because of the photosynthetic demands of the plants which form the primary food source. From the point of view of the soil microarthropods this has been demonstrated by Glasgow (1939), Agrell (1941), Gisin (1943), Nielsen (1949), Schaller (1949), van der Drift (1951), Murphy (1953), Bellinger (1954), Kuhnelt (1955) and Poole (1961), who have all shown that the highest densities occur in the upper layers of the soil. Other authors have correlated the depth distribution and size of microarthropods with the structure of the soil in which they have been collected. Schimitscheck (1938), Stockli (1946), Weis-Fogh (1948), Kuhnelt (1950),Macfadyen (1952), Elton and Miller (1954), Haarlov (1955, 1960), Murphy (1955) and Klima (1956) have considered microarthropods in relation to soil structure, and have shown that the highest densities occur where the pore spaces are largest. According to Haarlov (1955) the cavity size decreases with depth in mineral soils, and here again the results show high densities in the upper layers of soil.

It has been shown in both mites and Collembola that changes in vertical distribution of different species occur throughout the year (Volz, 1934; Agrell, 1934; Jacot, 1936, 1940; Glasgow, 1939; Baweja, 1939; Strickland, 1947; Belfield, 1956; Schweizer, 1956; Stockli, 1957). In most cases this is interpreted as a vertical migration during periods of adverse climatic conditions in the upper layers of the soil, although it could, of course, be due to differential mortality. Frenzel (1936) and Dhillon and Gibson (1962) found no evidence of seasonal changes in distribution, and Leuthold (1961) has suggested the possibility of a diurnal rhythm in vertical movement.

IX. SEASONAL VARIATIONS IN NUMBERS

Before the work of Glasgow (1939), population studies of Collembola had been directed mainly at describing the fluctuations in large groups of species. Glasgow showed that different species reached maximum and minimum numbers at different times of the year, and thus the discrepancies (Table I) resulting when the work of different authors was compared could be explained. Table I summarizes the knowledge of the times of occurrence of peak numbers of microarthropods, with particular reference to Collembola. Most workers found an autumn peak, with low numbers in summer, although under arctic conditions Agrell (1941) and Hammer (1944) obtained summer peaks, as did Stockli (1957) in Switzerland and Poole (1961) in Wales. Bellinger (1954) found maxima at different times of the year in different species, and in this way these results compare with those of Glasgow (1939).

Since all work on the seasonal fluctuations of Collembola has been limited to two years or less, it has been found difficult to demonstrate a regular annual cycle.

X. COLLEMBOLA AS INDICATORS OF SOIL CONDITIONS

Gisin (1943) has suggested that different species of Collembola occur in soils of different degrees of acidity and quotes *Odontella armata* (Axelson,

1903) as typically basophil and *O. lamellifera* (Axelson, 1903) as strictly acidophil. Although some species are restricted to acidic or basic soils, this is not generally so, and many species, e.g. *Friesia mirabilis* (Tullberg, 1871), are equally common on acidic peats and base-rich soils.

TABLE I

Summary of data on the seasonal distribution of Collembola and other microarthropods

Author	Group	Peak populations			
		Spring	Summer	Autumn	Winter
Thompson (1924)	Total Arthropods	—	—	—	×
Edwards (1929)	Total Arthropods	—	—	Oct.	—
Ionescu (1932)	Protura	—	—	Oct.	Jan.
Frenzel (1936)	Mites and Collembola	×	—	Oct.	Jan.
Ford (1937)	Collembola	—	—	—	Dec.–Feb.
Baweja (1939)	Collembola	—	—	Nov.	—
Glasgow (1939)	Collembola	April	—	Oct.	Dec.
Agrell (1941)	Collembola	—	× (Arctic)	—	—
Hammer (1944)	Mites and Collembola	—	× (Arctic)	—	—
Weis-Fogh (1948)	Mites and Collembola	—	—	×	—
Strenzke (1949)	Collembola	—	July	—	Dec.
Schaller (1949)	Collembola	—	—	Oct./Nov.	Jan.
Macfadyen (1952)	Mites and Collembola	—	—	—	Jan./Feb.
Sheals (1957)	Collembola	—	—	Oct.	Dec.
Stockli (1957)	Mites and Collembola	—	×	—	—
Poole (1961)	Collembola	—	Aug.	—	Feb.
Dhillon and Gibson (1962)	Mites and Collembola	May	—	Sept.	—
Milne (1962)	Collembola	May/June		—	Dec.
Hale	Collembola	April/May (sub-arctic)	—	Nov./Dec. (sub-arctic)	

× = Season but no month given; Spring = March to May; Summer = June to August; Autumn = September to November; Winter = December to February.

As Davies (1928) and Agrell (1941) have shown, probably the most important single factor governing the distribution of Collembola is humidity, and thus it is possible that Collembola may be used as indicators of the soil water conditions. Murphy (1955) and Hale (1963) have shown that changes in populations of Collembola appear to be governed by physical factors which bring about changes in the water content of the habitat, and thus the species composition of a population can be related to the water content of the soil. In the case of eroding moor (Hale, 1963), this can be summarized in the following way, where soil types are indicated by their location and vegetation cover:

Bare → *Eriophorum* → *Eriophorum* → Mixed → Hummock → Hagg
peat *angustifolium* *vaginatum* moor top lip

Hydrophil fauna ————————→ Mesophil fauna ·————————→ Xerophil fauna
Isotoma antennalis *Folsomia brevi-* *Tetracanthella*
(Bagnall, 1940) *cauda* *wahlgreni*
Agrell, 1939 Linnaniemi,
Friesea mirabilis 1911
(Tullberg, 1871)
Isotoma sensibilis
(Tullberg, 1876)
———————————————— Increasing population density ————————————→
———— Decreasing water content ————————→

XI. POPULATION DENSITIES

Published estimates of population densities vary greatly, and a summary of the available information is given in Table II. Glasgow (1939) has estimated that in some soils Collembola constitute up to 80% of the total numbers of animals, but, because of size differences, this is clearly no indication of their relative importance.

When the microdistribution of Collembola is considered, the specialized fauna associated with the hagg lip, on peat moorland, has afforded the highest densities yet recorded (Cragg, 1961; Hale, 1963). The maximum population density recorded by the present writer, from this area, was $230,000 \pm 28,400/$ m^2, on 4 December, 1961; this figure was obtained from 15 sample units each 10^{-3} m^2 in surface area and 3 cm deep.

XII. BIOMASS AND GENERAL METABOLISM

Although Collembola constitute a large numerical proportion of the fauna of most soil types, they constitute only a small percentage of the total biomass. From data obtained by the present writer, Cragg (1961) has compared the biomass and respiration of Collembola with other groups of the moorland soil fauna, and with two of the sites studied by Bornebusch (1930). These data are summarized in Table III. From this it can be seen that with regard to biomass and general metabolism the Collembola form a relatively unimportant part of the fauna of Limestone grassland and *Juncus squarrosus* grassland. However, on *Calluna* moor Collembola play a greater part in the general metabolism. Biomass figures for mixed moor, obtained by the present writer, are little below those for Limestone grassland, i.e. about 0·4 g/m², and Cragg (1961) has estimated that on this soil type Collembola account for 1·4% of the total biomass. Thus it appears to be on mixed moor that Collembola are of most importance on upland soils (from the point of

TABLE II

Estimates of population densities from different soil types

Author	General habitat type	Vegetation and/or soil type	Density in thousands/m²
van der Drift (1951)	Forest soil	*Fagus* mor	0·7
Poole (1961)		*Pseudosuga* litter	40·0*
Forsslund (1945)	Heath	*Vaccinium*	15·0
Glasgow (1939)	Grasslands	*Dactylis*	27·0*
Salt *et al.* (1948)		Pasture soil	43·0
Weis-Fogh (1948)		Sandy soil	8·5
Schaller (1949)		Limestone grassland	15·9 and 25·0
Dhillon and Gibson (1962)		Loam on boulder clay	33·0*
Hale (1966)		Limestone grassland	53·0* (1960)
			42·0* (1961)
		Alluvial grassland	44·0* (1960–61)
		Juncus squarrosus	21·0*
Strenzke (1949)	Fen	*Phragmites*	20·0
Macfadyen (1952)		*Molinia*	25·0*
		Deschampsia	24·0*
		Juncus subnodulosus	7·2*
Hale	Moorland	*Calluna* litter	35·0*
Milne (1962)		Bracken	15·5* (1956)
			17·7* (1957)

* Mean for 12 months (one year).

Note: only figures quoted in the literature after 1939 are given, as data collected before this date give very low estimates of population densities because of inefficiencies in the extraction methods used.

view of total metabolism). The figures quoted for Bornebusch (1930) seem much too high. Biomass figures of the order of ten times those recorded from the Moor House National Nature Reserve (W. G. Hale, unpublished) are claimed for populations fifty times smaller, when suitable corrections are made to convert the Bornebusch weighings of preserved material to live weights (see Nielsen, 1949).

Cragg (1961) points out that it is dangerous to make too detailed a comparison between the estimates of metabolic activity because the respiratory rates of animals under natural conditions are not known. Even so, it is clear that Collembola play a smaller part in the total soil metabolism than is suggested by the theoretical example for a meadow soil, constructed by Macfadyen (1957). In this example, Collembola account for 6·4% of the total biomass and 15·2% of the total metabolism in calories. Cragg (1961)

TABLE III

A comparison of biomass (live weight) and respiration for two of the Bornebusch (1930) sites and two sites from Moor House, Westmorland (1840 ft O.D.). Modified from Cragg (1961)

Site and population density	Collembola		Total fauna	
	g/m^2	Respiration (mg $O_2/m^2/hr$ at 13°C)	g/m^2	Respiration (mg $O_2/m^2/hr$ at 13°C)
Limestone grassland 80,000/m^2	0·6 (0·3%)	1·1 (2·0%)	189·7	54·9
Juncus squarrosus 12,000/m^2	0·1 (0·1%)	0·3 (0·3%)	78·0	107·0
Quercus mull Bornebusch (1930). Site 10 493/m^2	5·2 (5·8%) (0·10)	9·6 (25·5%) (0·19)	90·1 (76·8)	37·7 (17·7)
Spruce raw humus Bornebusch (1930). Site 8 2302/m^2	6·8 (13·6%) (0·14)	20·0 (22·9%) (0·41)	50·0 (9·84)	87·4 (7·09)

Note: The data from Bornebusch (1930) have been corrected according to Nielsen (1949) and others; the original data appear below in brackets. While the corrections for "Total fauna" are probably more accurate than the original data, consideration of the population densities involved suggests that the original data are more nearly accurate for Collembola. The figures for respiration of Collembola are of the same order of magnitude as those obtained by I. Healey (personal communication) using the Cartesian diver.

has pointed out that this largely results from the relative absence of earthworms and enchytreids in Macfadyen's example. However, Macfadyen (1963) allows for earthworms and enchytreids in the analysis of the biomass and metabolism of a grassland habitat, and again quotes a high figure (13·4%) for the relative metabolic activity of Collembola. This figure is probably too high because of the method used for determining the weights of individual Collembola, and then calculating the total biomass by assuming a population of individuals all equivalent to adults in weight.

Calculations made by the present writer from weights of individuals of known instar, have shown that a population of 40,000 Collembola/m^2 is equivalent to a biomass of about 280 mg/m^2, and I. Healey (personal communication) quotes a figure of 350 mg/m^2 for a population density of 40,000/m^2 on *Pteridium* moorland. These figures are appreciably less than those used by Bornebusch (1930), Macfadyen (1957, 1963) and others in the estimation of metabolic activity in Collembola.

A further point is that because of the small percentage biomass of Collembola they can form only a relatively unimportant potential source of food for predators, and a relatively insignificant quantitative part of the total food web on most soils.

XIII. THE EFFECT OF CLIMATE ON THE CONTRIBUTION TO THE SOIL TURNOVER

Apart from their metabolic activities during life, Collembola, like any other soil animals, contribute to the general soil turnover on dying, with the breakdown of the body by soil micro-organisms. Thus, where several generations occur each year, this type of contribution is greater than where few generations occur. In the sub-arctic climate of the northern Pennines only one, or at most two, generations occur each year, and metabolism is accelerated by higher temperatures and retarded by lower temperatures. Clearly, then, the annual contribution of Collembola at high altitudes is in this way smaller than in areas having a milder climate.

While many soil animals living under sub-arctic conditions are active at low temperatures, this is particularly noticeable in the Collembola, where there is apparently no diapause (at least in the Arthropleona), and most species are fully active just above freezing point (Kuhnelt, 1950). Choudhuri (1961) and South (1959) found threshold temperatures of about 4°C, below which no egg development occurred. The latter author also found that in the field, *Entomobrya multifasciata* laid only when the temperature exceeded 5°C, and laying ceased when temperatures fell below this level. The present writer (Hale, 1965b), working with Collembola collected from 2,000 ft O.D. in the northern Pennines, found that eggs would develop in a temperature as low as 2°C, and that some individuals laid eggs at temperatures not exceeding 3°C. While Choudhuri and South worked on Collembola from low-lying areas, the work of the present writer relates to Collembola living normally in a sub-arctic climate; it thus appears possible that there is a physiological mechanism allowing high-altitude forms to carry out biological processes at a temperature below those at which it is possible for the same processes to be carried out at lower altitudes, in a relatively warmer climate. It is thus possible that while contributing relatively little to the soil by way of decaying animal remains, Collembola contribute relatively more to the soil turnover at high altitudes than other groups, by remaining active at low temperatures.

XIV. THE ROLE OF COLLEMBOLA IN SOIL FORMATION

In the living state, Collembola contribute to the soil in two different ways. First, they remove from it material which is ingested into the gut and, second, they produce faecal pellets which are added to the soil. Collembola have been recorded taking into their guts a variety of materials already described, and

15+S.B.

their partial breakdown by Collembola may be an important factor in their being made more readily available to other decomposers. Stockli (1950), Dunger (1956, 1958) and Schuster (1956) have drawn attention to this aspect of soil formation by Collembola and mites and have considered their role in humus formation. Poole (1959) has suggested that Collembola play an important part in the dissemination of fungi, and in the breakdown of the faeces of larger arthropods. J. Doeksen (personal communication) and P. L. Hitchen (personal communication) have demonstrated the presence of a bacterium (*Bacillus* sp.) which breaks down chitin in the intestine of Collembola. Collembola eat their own cuticles, and it is possible that they ingest chitinous material in the form of remnants of other arthropods. In this way Collembola may play an important role in making chitinous material available again in the soil.

Zachariae (1963) has concluded that the contribution of Collembola to the mechanical and chemical breakdown of the soil is insignificant in forest soils. The weight of evidence suggests that this is, in fact, not so. In addition to what has already been said, there is the evidence of what has been termed by Muller (1879, 1884) "insect mull" soils. Probably the best known of these is the Alpine pitch rendzina of Kubiena (1953, 1955), where the A_1 and A_2 horizons are largely of coprogenous origin, with the presumed collembolan faeces forming a layer up to 30 cm deep. Schaller (1950) has calculated that populations of Collembola of the order of $100,000/m^2$ produce 183 cc of faeces annually, which is equivalent to a layer 0·2 mm deep. However, this disregards breakdown by leaching and biological activity which, under the climatic conditions prevailing in the northern Pennines, would occur relatively quickly. G. Zachariae (personal communication) has expressed the opinion that the Alpine pitch rendzina has been produced not by Collembola but by Enchytraeidae. However, since no distinction can at present be made between the faecal pellets of the two groups, this cannot be regarded as established.

Kubiena (1955) has described how a coprogenous soil (Peat moder) can be derived from undecomposed peat, if the water table is lowered. While it is possible that Enchytraeidae may be responsible to a large extent for the formation of coprogenous soils, the density of mites and Collembola together exceeds that of Enchytraeidae in many areas, e.g. mixed moor (Cragg, 1961), so it seems reasonable to assume that they play at least an equal part in the accumulation of faecal material in such a situation.

On peat soils, the relative importance of Collembola is increased by the absence of earthworms and millipedes. According to van der Drift (1951), Kubiena (1955) and Blower (1956) millipedes are largely responsible for the formation of "mull-like moder" in some forest soils.

While on the face of it Collembola may not appear to be of great importance in the general soil turnover, it may be that in the comminution of plant residues and in their activity in raw humus they play an indispensible role; this aspect of the activity of Collembola in the soil should be carefully assessed in future work on the feeding activities of the group.

REFERENCES

Agrell, I. (1934). *Ent. Tidsk.* **55**, 181–248.
Agrell, I. (1940). *Ent. Meddr.* **22**, 12–13.
Agrell, I. (1941). *Opusc. ent.* Suppl. **3**, 1–236.
Baweja, K. D. (1939). *J. Anim. Ecol.* **8**, 120–161.
Belfield, W. (1956). *J. Anim. Ecol.* **24**, 275–287.
Bellinger, P. F. (1954). *Bull. Conn. agric. Exp. Stan.* **583**, 1–67.
Blower, J. G. (1956). *Int. Congr. Soil Sci.* **3**, 169–176. Paris.
Bornebusch, C. H. (1930). *Forst. ForsVæs. Danm.* **11**, 1–224.
Borner, C. (1906). *Mitt. naturh. Mus. Hamb.* **23**, 147–188.
Britt, N. W. (1951). *Trans. Am. microsc. Soc.* **70**, 119–132.
Choudhuri, D. K. (1958). *Proc. R. ent. soc. Lond.* (B) **27**, 855–159.
Choudhuri, D. K. (1961). *Proc. zool. Soc. Beng.* **16**, 97–117.
Cragg, J. B. (1961). *J. Ecol.* **49**, 477–506.
Davidson, J. (1934). *Bull. Coun. sci. ind. Res., Melb.* **79**, 1–66.
Davies, W. M. (1928). *J. exp. Biol.* **6**, 79–86.
Davies, W. M. (1932). *Nature, Lond.* **130**, 94.
Delamare-Deboutteville, C. (1950). *Bull. Mus. Hist. nat. Marseille,* **8**, 177–182.
Dhillon, B. S. and Gibson, N. H. E. (1962). *Pedobiologia,* **1**, 189–209.
Drift, J. van der (1951). *Tijdschr. Ent.* **94**, 1–168.
Dunger, W. (1956). *Zool. Jb. Abt. Systematik,* **84**, 75–99.
Dunger, W. (1958). *Z. Pfl-Ernähr. Düng. Bodenk.* **82**, 174–193.
Edwards, E. E. (1929). *Ann. appl. Biol.* **16**, 299–323.
Elton, C. and Miller, R. (1954). *J. Ecol.* **42**, 460–496.
Ewing, H. E. (1942). *Proc. ent. Soc. Wash.* **44**, 75–98.
Falkenhan, H. H. (1932). *Z. wiss. Zool.* **141**, 524–580.
Folsom, J. W. (1916). *Proc. U.S. natn. Mus.* **50**, 477–525.
Ford, J. (1937). *J. Anim. Ecol.* **6**, 98–111.
Forsslund, K. H. (1945). *Meddn. St. SkøgsförsAnst.* **34** (5), 341–364.
Frenzel, G. (1936). "Untersuchungen über die Tierwelt des Weisenbodens." Jena.
Gilyarov, M. S. (1949). "Osobennosti pocvy kak sredy obitanija i jeje znacenije v evoljuciji nasekomych." Moscow and Leningrad.
Gisin, H. (1943). *Revue suisse Zool.* **50**, 131–224.
Gisin, H. (1952). *Mitt. schweiz. ent. Ges.* **25**, 1–22.
Gisin, H. (1960). "Collembolenfauna Europas." *Mus. Hist. Nat.,* Geneva.
Glasgow, J. P. (1939). *J. Anim. Ecol.* **8**, 323–353.
Goto, H. E. (1957). *Scott. Nat.* **69**, 1–10.
Goto, H. E. (1960). *Nature, Lond.* **188**, 958–959.
Goto, H. E. (1961). *Entomologist's mon. Mag.* **96**, 138–140.
Haarlov, N. (1955). *In* "Soil Zoology." (D. K. McE. Kevan, ed.), pp. 167–178. Butterworths, London.
Haarlov, N. (1960). *Oikos,* Suppl. 3.
Hale, W. G. (1963). *In* "Soil Organisms." (J. Doeksen and J. van der Drift, eds.), pp. 406–413. North-Holland Publ. Co., Amsterdam.
Hale, W. G. (1964). *J. Anim. Ecol.* **33**, 363–369.
Hale, W. G. (1965a). *Rev. Ecol. Biol. Sol.* **1**, 501–510.
Hale, W. G. (1965b). *Pedobiologia,* **5**, 146–152, 161–177.
Hale, W. G. (1965c). *Pedobiologia,* **5**, 228–243.
Hale, W. G. (1966). *Pedobiologia,* **6**, 65–99.

Hammer, M. (1944). *Meddr. Grønland*, 108 (2), 1–42.
Handschin, E. (1928). *Schr. phys. -okon. Ges. Königsb.* **65**, 124–154.
Hughes, R. D. (1962). *In* "Progress in Soil Zoology." (P. W. Murphy, ed.), pp. 51–55. Butterworths, London.
Imms, A. D. (1936). *Trans. Soc. Br. Ent.* **3**, 1–32.
Ionescu, M. A. (1932). Contributiuni la studiul faunei frunzarului (patura de frunze moarte) de fag. Cercetari statistice, oecolodisce si sistematice in padurile de fag de la Sinaia si de pe valea. Prahovei. Bucharest.
Jacot, A. (1936). *Ecology*, **17**, 359–379.
Jacot, A. (1940). *Q. Rev. Biol.* **15**, 28–58.
Jeannel, R. (1949). *In* "Traite de Zoologie." (P. P. Grassé, ed.), **9**, 3–17, 21–23. Paris.
Kaczmarek, W. (1960). *Ekol. pol.* (A) **8**, 50–64.
Klima, J. (1956). *Oikos*, **7**, 227–242.
Kubiena, W. L. (1953). "The Soils of Europe." T. Murby & Co., London,
Kubiena, W. L. (1955). *In* "Soil Zoology." (D. K. McE. Kevan, ed.), pp. 73–82. Butterworths, London.
Kuhnelt, W. (1950). Bodenbiologie. Mit besonder Berucksichtigung der Tierwelt, Verlag Herold, Vienna.
Kuhnelt, W. (1955). An introduction to the study of soil animals. *In* "Soil Zoology." (D. K. McE. Kevan, ed.), pp. 3–22. Butterworths, London.
Lindemann, W. (1950). *Revue suisse Zool.* **57**, 353–428.
Leuthold, R. (1961). *Z. angew. Ent.* **49**, 1–50.
Macfadyen, A. (1952). *J. Anim. Ecol.* **22**, 65–77.
Macfadyen, A. (1957). "Animal Ecology, Aims and Methods." Pitman, London.
Macfadyen, A. (1961). *J. Anim. Ecol.* **30**, 171–184.
Macfadyen, A. (1963). *In* "Soil Organisms." (J. Doeksen and J. van der Drift, eds.), pp. 1–17. North-Holland Publ. Co., Amsterdam.
Marshall, V. G. and Kevan, D. K. McE. (1962). *Can. Ent.* **94**, 575–586.
Mayer, H. (1957). *Zool. Jb.* **85**, 501–570.
Milne, S. (1962). *Pedobiologia*, **2**, 41–52.
Muller, P. E. (1879). *Tidskr. Skovbr.* **3**, 1–124.
Muller, P. E. (1884). II. *Tidskr. Skovbr.* **7**, 1–232.
Murphy, D. H. (1955). *In* "Soil Zoology." (D. K. McE. Kevan, ed.), pp. 157–166. Butterworths, London.
Murphy, P. W. (1953). *J. Soil Sci.* **4**, 155–193.
Murphy, P. W. (1955). *In* "Soil Zoology." (D. K. McE. Kevan, ed.), pp. 99–124. Butterworths, London.
Nielsen, C. O. (1949). *Nat. Jutland.* **2**, 1–131.
Paclt, J. (1954). *Zool. Anz.* **153**, 275–281.
Paclt, J. (1956). "Biologie der primar flugellosen Insekten.' 'Gustav Fisher Verlag, Jena.
Poole, T. B. (1959). *Proc. zool. Soc. Lond.* **132**, 78–82.
Poole, T. B. (1961). *Pedobiologia*, **1**, 113–137.
Raw, F. (1955). *In* "Soil Zoology." (D. K. McE. Kevan, ed.), pp. 341–346. Butterworths, London.
Raw, F. (1956). *J. Anim. Ecol.* **25**, 15–21.
Ripper, W. (1930). *Z. angew. Ent.* **16**, 3:546–584.
Ross, H. H. (1955). *Ent. News*, **66**, 197–208.
Salmon, J. T. (1941). *Trans. R. Soc. N.Z.* **70**, 282–431.

Salt, G. and Hollick, F. S. J. (1946). *J. exp. Biol.* **23**, 1–46.

Salt, G., Hollick, F. S. J., Raw, F. and Brian, M. V. (1948). *J. Anim. Ecol.* **17**, 139–150.

Schaller, F. (1949). *Zool. Jb. Abt. Systematik.* **78**, 363–293.

Schaller, F. (1950). *Zool. Jb. Abt. Systematik.* **78**, 506–525.

Schaller, F. (1953). *Z. Morph. Okol. Tiere,* **41**, 265–277.

Schimitscheck, E. (1938). *Z. angew. Ent.* **24**, 216–247.

Schuster, R. (1956). *Z. Morph. Okol. Tiere,* **45**, 1–33.

Schweizer, J. (1956). *Ergebn. wiss. Unters. schweiz. Natn Parks,* **5**, 215–377.

Sheals, J. G. (1957). *J. Anim. Ecol.* **26**, 125–134.

South, A. (1959). The taxonomy and biology of the British species of Entomobrya (Collembola). Thesis: University of London.

Stach, J. (1947–1960). "The Apterygotan Fauna of Poland in Relation to the World Fauna of This Group of Insects." 8 volumes. Krakow.

Stockli, A. (1943). *Schweiz. landw. Mh.* **18**, 159–172.

Stockli, A. (1946). *Verh. naturf. Ges. Basel,* **91**, 1–18.

Stockli, A. (1950). *Z. PflErnahr. Dung. Bodenk.* **45**, 41–53.

Stockli, A. (1957). *Landw. Jb. Schweiz 6* (n.s.), 571–595.

Strebel, O. (1928). *Z. wiss. Insekt Biol.* **23**, 135–143.

Strebel, O. (1932). *Z. Morph. Okol. Tiere.* **25**, 31–153.

Strebel, O. (1938). *Konowia,* **17**, 272–291.

Strenzke, K. (1949). *Arch. Hydrobiol.* **42**, 201–203.

Strickland, A. H. (1947). *J. Anim. Ecol.* **16**, 1–10.

Thompson, M. (1924). *Ann. appl. Biol.* **11**, 349–394.

Volz, P. (1934). *Zool. Jb. Abt. Systematik,* **66**, 153–210.

Weis-Fogh, T. (1948). *Nat. Jutlandica,* **1**, 139–277.

Wygodzinsky, P. (1943). *Revta Ent. (São Paulo),* **14**, 516–521.

Zachariae, G. (1963). *In* "Soil Organisms." (J. Doeksen and J. van der Drift, eds.), pp. 109–124. North-Holland Publ. Co., Amsterdam.

Chapter 13

Mollusca

P. F. NEWELL

Rothamsted Experimental Station*
Harpenden, Herts., England

I. INTRODUCTION

Some representatives of most of the major phyla of marine animals, including Mollusca, succeeded in colonizing the land, often it is believed, *via* freshwater. There are many terrestrial species of molluscs and some are abundant, but their diversity is small compared with the marine forms; consequently most standard works (see References) deal mainly with marine molluscs. This account summarizes the salient features of the biology of terrestrial snails and slugs with the emphasis on their ecology.

The nomenclature of snails and slugs has often been revised. For uniformity Ellis's nomenclature in the 1951 census of British non-marine Mollusca has mostly been used for snails and Quick's (1960) for slugs. However, *Cepaea nemoralis* (L.) is used in preference to the name *Helix nemoralis*, and *Agriolimax agrestis* (L.) has been changed to *A. reticulatus* (Müller) because *A. agrestis* has been definitely recorded only from Norfolk. The generic name *Agriolimax* has been used in preference to *Deroceras*, which appears in the American literature.

Figure 1 relates the number of terrestrial families of Mollusca in the 1951 British census to Thiele's stirps or super-families (Thiele, 1931–35), and shows that most British terrestrial families belong to the stylommatophoran group

* Now at Westfield College, University of London, England.

of pulmonates. Many of the modifications to the basic marine molluscan pattern they show are associated with the transition to land and include the development of a lung, internal fertilization, large yolky eggs and various physiological and behavioural methods of water conservation; these are features that also occur in many littoral gastropods.

Morton (1955, 1958), reviewing the origins and evolution of the pulmonates, reaffirmed the view that those unspecialized Basommatophora, the Ellobiidae and Chilinidae, are the most primitive families and share many features with an ancestral group of pulmonates from which terrestrial Stylommatophora could have arisen.

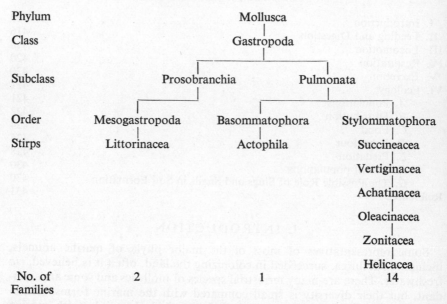

FIG. 1. An outline classification of British land mollusca based on Thiele, 1931–1935. Number of families taken from Ellis, 1951.

Of the non-pulmonate (operculate or prosobranch) land snails only *Pomatias elegans* (Müller) and *Acme fusca* (Montagu) occur in the British Isles, but in some tropical areas, such as Jamaica, about half of all species present on the island are operculate snails (Hunter, 1955). These operculate snails are thought to have been derived from marine snails similar to periwinkles (Littorinidae) which they closely resemble.

There are two main groups of land pulmonates, namely, snails and slugs, and there can be little doubt that slugs have been derived from fully-shelled pulmonates, perhaps along two distinct lines. The families Testacellidae and Limacidae, which include all slugs with a reduced external or internal shell, have probably been derived from a group of snails with reduced, thin shells similar to the Glass-snails, *Hyalinia* sp. The Arionidae include slugs with no true shells and are thought to have been derived from a group of snails, similar to *Helix*, by the complete loss of the shell.

Most snails and slugs can be identified from external characters and often, as with snails, by their shells alone, though sometimes colours and texture of shells alter with age and weathering, and some species have many colour varieties (Cain and Williamson, 1958). Some species have to be identified by

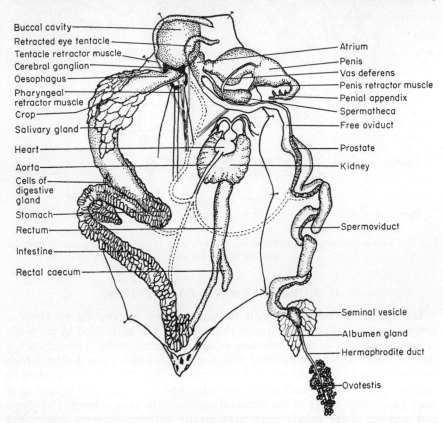

Buccal cavity
Retracted eye tentacle
Tentacle retractor muscle
Cerebral ganglion
Oesophagus
Pharyngeal retractor muscle
Crop
Salivary gland
Heart
Aorta
Cells of digestive gland
Stomach
Rectum
Intestine
Rectal caecum

Atrium
Penis
Vas deferens
Penis retractor muscle
Penial appendix
Spermatheca
Free oviduct
Prostate
Kidney

Spermoviduct

Seminal vesicle
Albumen gland
Hermaphrodite duct
Ovotestis

FIG. 2. General anatomy of a slug, *Agriolimax reticulatus*, with the animal dissected so that the mantle lies to the right. The blood vascular system is not shown but dotted lines indicate the sites that the main branches supply. The genitalia, and particularly the shape of the atrium, penis and penial appendix are most important features for their identification.

dissection of the genitalia. Many snails live in well-defined habitats; the plants in the area and the precise locality of collection are often valuable aids to identification. Ellis (1926) gives keys for identifying most British snails and slugs, Morton and Machin (1959) give a field key to common British snails and Barnes and Weil (1944) give one for slugs. Quick's "British Slugs" (1960) is an excellent specialist's book for identifying slugs. Figures 2 and 3 show the general anatomy of a slug and a snail.

15*

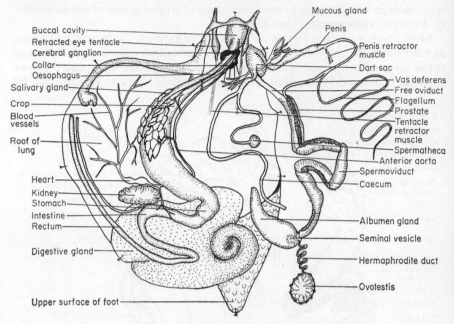

FIG. 3. General anatomy of a snail, *Helix aspersa*, with the animal dissected so that the mantle lies to the left.

II. FEEDING AND DIGESTION

The structures associated with feeding of land gastropods all show a common pattern. They consist of a radula and a jaw embedded in the walls of the anterior end of the alimentary canal, the buccal cavity. The radula is a strip of tough membrane covered with teeth, rather like a wood rasp, which are continuously being replaced at the posterior end. This rasp is worked to and fro over a bar of hard tissue, the odontophore, which supports it as it tears away small pieces of the material on which the animal feeds. The shape and number of the radula teeth vary greatly between different genera but usually carnivorous species, such as *Testacella* slugs, have relatively few, long teeth whereas typical herbivorous browsers, such as *Helix aspersa* Müller, have many, small, regularly arranged ones. Most species have a single chitinized mandible, or jaw, embedded in the upper portion of the anterior end of the buccal cavity.

The small particles of food, scraped off by the radula, are passed into the gut where digestive enzymes secreted by the digestive gland act on them. There are at least 30 enzymes in the gut-extracts of *Helix pomatia* L. and *H. aspersa*, of which two-thirds are carbohydrases (Holden, Pirie and Tracey, 1950; Holden and Tracey, 1950). Both lipases and proteinases are present in small amounts. Most of a minced and washed tobacco leaf lamina preparation was digested by these enzymes leaving a residue of cuticle, vessels and chlorenchyma sludge.

Myers and Northcote (1958) reported abundant carbohydrases and "significant lipase activity" but little proteinase activity in gut extracts of *H. pomatia*. Undoubtedly most of these enzymes come from the hepatopancreas, or digestive gland, of the snail, but there has been much controversy about the source of cellulase and chitinase enzymes.

Cellulose digesting bacteria in the gut of ruminants do not produce a free cellulose; the enzyme is bound to the surface of the bacteria (Kitts and Underkofler, 1954). Gut extracts of snails contain a free cellulase whose activity does not alter with storage (Holden and Tracey, 1950). This suggests that if bacteria are responsible for the free cellulase in gut extracts they cease to produce enzymes when isolated; moreover, as the cellulase activity was unaltered by centrifuging the extracts to remove bacteria the cellulase was probably secreted by the hepatopancreas of the snail. Strasdine and Whitaker (1963) later showed that the hepatopancreas of *H. pomatia* contained only few bacteria and that after the snail emerged from hibernation its protein content decreased greatly while enzymatic protein in the gut juice in the form of cellulase and chitinase increased (Table I); thus supporting the view expressed above. Tribby and Carmichael (1935) demonstrated a cellulase in gut extracts of the slug *Limax flavus*, L.

TABLE I

Properties of digestive juice homogenates of hepatopancreas and intestine from hibernating snails (A) and feeding snails (B) (Strasdine and Whitaker, 1963)

| | | Average values/snail | | | Specific activity | | |
		Protein (mg)	Cellulase units	Chitinase units	Cellulase units/mg protein	Chitinase units/mg protein	Cellulase/ chitinase ratio
Digestive juice	A	122	320	10·2	2·63	0·084	31
	B	206	541	15·7	2·63	0·076	34
Hepatopancreas	A	160	49·6	1·5	0·31	0·010	31
	B	95	45·2	1·6	0·47	0·016	30
Intestine	A	8·2	9·2	0·25	1·12	0·030	37
	B	11·4	13·3	0·40	1·17	0·032	37

Strasdine and Whitaker (1963) also found that when snails were fed briefly after emergence from hibernation, and then starved for 5 days the volume of their digestive juice increased and had almost the same concentration of protein, cellulase and chitinase as the smaller quantity of juice produced by snails starved only for one day (Table II).

This again conflicts with the idea that the cellulase and chitinase came solely from bacteria which are unlikely to produce it in the same amounts per unit volume of extract in starved and unstarved snails, and the fact that the hepato-pancreas lost protein suggests the enzymes were produced there.

However, two types of cellulose-digesting bacteria occur in the gut of *H. pomatia* (Florkin and Lozet, 1949), so probably snails digest cellulose by cellulases from the bacteria in the gut as well as by their own cellulases.

TABLE II

Properties of digestive juice of snails deprived of food after a brief post-hibernation feeding* (Strasdine and Whitaker, 1963)

| Period without food (days) | Mean volume (ml) | Mean concentration | | | | Mean ratio, cellulase/ chitinase |
		Protein mg/ml	Helicorubin units/ml	Cellulase units/ml	Chitinase units/ml	
1	0.42 ± 0.05	267 ± 15	67.3 ± 8.5†	981 ± 82	24.2 ± 1.9†	38.8 ± 3.3
2	0.58 ± 0.05	221 ± 15	66.6 ± 9.2	784 ± 82	22.2 ± 1.6	35.1 ± 2.8
3	0.65 ± 0.05	241 ± 15	71.9 ± 5.5	890 ± 82	23.2 ± 1.6	38.4 ± 2.8
Combined averages		243 ± 9	68.6 ± 3.8	885 ± 47	23.1 ± 1.0	37.3 ± 1.7

* The body weights of the snails were adjusted to 15·3 g.

† Mean and standard error estimate of 3 samples; all other averages estimated from 4 samples.

III. LOCOMOTION

Slugs and snails crawl by muscular waves, which appear like a series of dark bands and pass from back to front on the lower surface of the foot. These dark bands correspond to contracted areas of the foot not in contact with the substrate; the wider, lighter, areas are in contact with the surface. Lissmann (1945) gives a very clear account of the crawling mechanism in *H. aspersa* and *H. pomatia*. Any one point on the anterior end of the foot

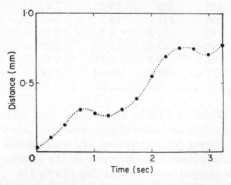

FIG. 4. Forward motion of mucous glands on the sole of the foot of *Helix pomatia*, normal crawling vertically upwards. (Redrawn from Lissmann, 1945.)

moves at an irregular speed. The distance moved by any easily identifiable point on the snail's foot, such as a large mucous gland, plotted against unit time shows only a short interval when any point is stationary, and forward

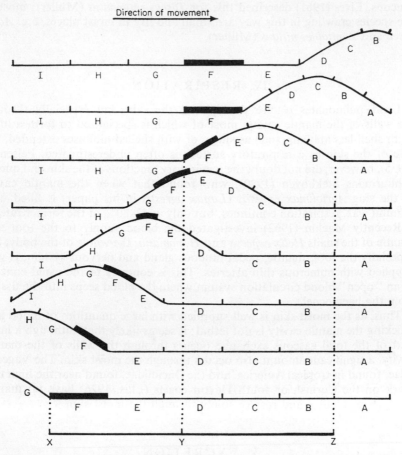

FIG. 5. Diagram showing lifting, contraction and expansion of a portion of the foot of *Helix* during the passage of a pedal wave. (Redrawn from Lissmann, 1945.)

A given part, section F, is overtaken from the rear by a pedal wave. It is then lifted, contracted and carried forward and makes contact with the surface in a position anterior to that which it formally occupied. The distance moved forward by the passage of any wave is represented by the line XY and is the difference in length between the contracted portion, YZ, and the uncontracted portion, XZ.

movement continues after the wave has passed (Fig. 4). The animal loses some forward motion which is greatly exaggerated when it is crawling vertically on a well-lubricated surface. Figure 5 shows the vertical displacement and forward movement of a fixed point when a wave passes through.

All gastropods have many mucous glands in the foot which lubricate its surface as it moves across the ground, leaving dried trails as evidence of snail and slug activity. A few land snails are peculiar in that they progress not by waves of contraction along the foot, but by cilia beating in the secreted mucous. Elves (1961) described this for *Discus rotundatus* (Müller): most of the species crawling in this way are small and live in moist places, e.g. *Acme fusca* and *Zonitoides nitidus* (Müller).

IV. RESPIRATION

Land pulmonates respire through all the skin, but especially through the walls of the mantle cavity, most of which is specialized to form a lung. With shell-less animals, such as slugs, or with shelled molluscs extended, the role of the skin as a respiratory surface is often underestimated. Pelseneer (1935), however, did not doubt the respiratory functions of the skin and quotes Schuurmans Stekhoven (1920), who found that when the mantle cavity of the slug *Agriolimax agrestis* (*Limax agrestis* in his paper) is filled with paraffin wax, respiration continues, but only at 43–80% of the former rate.

Recently Machin (1962) investigated the blood supply to the foot and mantle of the snails *Helix aspersa* and *H. pomatia*; the whole of the body, but especially the foot, mantle, pedal mucous gland and nervous system, is well supplied with numerous thin arteries. This is contrary to the usual concept of an "open" blood circulation system where the blood seeps into the tissues from the haemocoel.

Thus, as the moist skin is well supplied with large quantities of blood and blocking the mantle cavity is not lethal; it seems likely that, although a large part of the total gaseous exchange occurs through the walls of the mantle cavity, a significant amount also occurs through the moist skin. The Vagenulidae, found in tropical America, and the Oncidiidae, found near the high tide mark on the Cornish or south Devon coasts (Ellis, 1926) have no mantle cavity, are sluglike, and respire solely through the moist skin.

V. EXCRETION

The nitrogenous waste products of metabolism are excreted, in a solid form, as insoluble uric acid, in a manner comparable to that of birds and reptiles. All land gastropods have a single kidney that filters the nitrogenous waste from the blood in the pericardium and opens externally by a short duct, near the anus in pulmonates and to the rear of the mantle cavity in prosobranchs. Pericardial glands, developed from the thickened pericardial epithelium, are accessory excretory organs. The kidney resorbs water and some inorganic salts and excretes the uric acid *via* the kidney duct to the outside. Urine formation in pulmonate molluscs has recently been studied by Martin, Stewart and Harrison (1965).

VI. ECOLOGY

A. POPULATIONS

Methods of assessing populations are easiest for those molluscs that occur on the surface of the soil, for which random quadrats can often be used. However, as mentioned earlier, molluscs are extremely sensitive to micro-environmental conditions and usually aggregate. For example, *Helix aspersa* will be found in crevices and under some large stones, *Cepaea nemoralis* often on the stems of stinging nettles (*Urtica dioca* L.) and the stems of hogweed (*Heracleum* sp.). These animals will sometimes become active after rain and crawl over vegetation. Counting the numbers in a square yard or the numbers collected after dark (Barnes, 1944) may not then give a true estimate of the total population, but only of those active on the surface. Similarly, the numbers of slugs caught in metaldehyde traps in the field depends on the activity of the animals (Thomas, 1944). Webley (1964) recently showed that the numbers of slugs caught by this type of trap is related to the average night temperature and the age of the bait; most slugs are caught on a warm night with a fresh bait. Such difficulties have dogged population studies of slugs.

Other soil animals are sampled by taking soil cores with a standard sampling tool to a known depth, extracting them by flotation or by a Tüllgren funnel. Such extraction methods are impracticable for routine estimation of slug populations which are usually small compared with those of soil arthropods and may be aggregated (South 1965) and so give variable results. Taking larger soil samples greatly increases the labour of sampling. Separating slugs from soil by hand is inefficient and time-consuming (Bruel and Moens, 1958), and a flotation technique has recently been devised by South (1964).

Another method of estimating populations is to release a known number of marked animals onto a known area and then to calculate the total population by the proportion of marked slugs recaptured (Lincoln, 1930; Jackson, 1939). The population present at the time of sampling is given by the equation,

$$p = \frac{a \times c}{b}$$

where p = population present, a = number released, b = number recaptured and c = number of unmarked captures.

This technique is easy with snails whose shells can be painted different colours with a quick-drying cellulose acetate paint, but slugs cannot be marked in this way because of their slimy skin. However, they can be labelled by feeding them on lettuce plants grown in a solution containing the radioactive isotope of phosphorus, ^{32}P, so that the plants contain about 4 μc of ^{32}P (Newell, 1963). These marked animals are then randomly released into the field (they remain identifiable for at least 1 month), and a series of random samples of the population are made at regular intervals. Assuming that marked and unmarked slugs are equally likely to be captured, the field population can be calculated. Modern refinements of the release and recapture technique depend on marking individuals each time they are captured thus allowing emigration, immigration, birth and death rates to be estimated. At present this method is useful only for assessing population sizes, because individuals that have been recaptured only once cannot be distinguished from those that have been recaptured many times. Other radioactive isotopes were used as markers by Moens *et al.* (1965).

Trapping techniques for estimating populations of all land gastropods are probably the easiest to use on a large scale. However, before they can give precise estimates the relationship between the actual populations, the proportion active during any trapping period and the trapping efficiency must be established. Recent work at Rothamsted shows that, in July, most *A. reticulatus* slugs in an outdoor microplot are active on the surface during warm nights.

B. DISTRIBUTION

When collecting snails or slugs in the field it is soon noticed that some sites contain more species, and individuals, than others. Boycott (1934), in his classical paper on the habitats of British land mollusca, considers that lime and moisture are the co-dominant ecological factors that determine distribution. Earlier, Atkins and Lebour (1923) observed that many more species, and individuals, occur in soils with higher pH values with more available calcium than in the more acid soils (Fig. 6). They also noticed that those

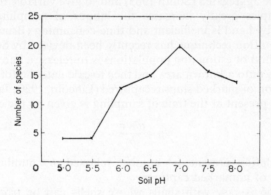

FIG. 6. Graph showing the distribution of the numbers of snail species related to soil pH. (Redrawn from Atkins and Lebour, 1923.)

species of snails with hyaline shells occurred in habitats with a wide range of soil pH, whereas those with large calcareous shells are restricted to habitats with a high soil pH. Owen (1965) found that the tropical snail *Limicolaria martensiana* (Smith) grew to a larger size on calcium-rich volcanic ash soils than those on calcium-scarce ferallitic soils. Soil acidity, or alkalinity, probably has little direct effect on the distribution of slugs or snails. The essential factor, as far as the animal is concerned, is the supply of calcium

ions in food plants, and the seeming relationship between soil pH and distribution of slugs and snails occurs because plants growing on acid soils contain little calcium. Thus, the efficiency with which their food plants can extract
calcium from the soil, rather than soil pH, may influence the distribution of
some land molluscs. This is certainly so with *Achatina fulica* Férussac, which
forms large populations in tea plantations in Ceylon, where the soil is very
acid, solely because the tea plant, on which it feeds selectively, extracts
calcium ions from the soil and so concentrates them. In his review of this
subject Robertson (1941) concludes that, although most snails prefer calcareous habitats, where they can colonize the more acid habitats their shells
are thinner and smaller.

Carrick (1942) showed that population density of *Agriolimax reticulatus*,
measured by the amount of damage caused to potato crops, is more closely
correlated with the moisture content than the soil pH. Howitt (1961) showed
that irrigation increased the size of the slug population in an orchard undersown with a grass-clover ley. Stephenson (1965) also showed that slug
damage to a potato crop was increased by irrigation. Moisture is particularly
important during the egg-laying period because the water content of the eggs
depends on the moisture in the surrounding soil and eggs can be killed by
drought (Table III). The adult slugs lay their large, albumen-coated eggs in a
moist, humid, sheltered environment in the soil, or under decaying plant
litter (Carrick, 1938).

TABLE III

Oviposition record for 5 sexually mature *A. reticulatus* slugs on soil
at each of 5 different saturation percentages at laboratory temperatures
(Arias and Crowell, 1963)

Observations (one day intervals)	No. of eggs laid at a saturation percentage of				
	10	25	50	75	100
1st	0	0	32	41	0
2nd	0	0	48	72	0
3rd	0	45	62	36	0
4th	0	0	0	51	41
5th	0	56	23	0	0
Totals	0	101	165	200	41

Egg development, which is greatly influenced by temperature (Fig. 7), was
described by Arias and Crowell (1963) for *Agriolimax reticulatus*. Carrick
(1942) also found that this slug and its eggs could withstand prolonged exposure to cold, two adults surviving $-5°$c for 2 hours. Mellanby (1961)
showed that *A. reticulatus* moves and feeds, apparently normally, at $0·8°$c
and is not completely immobilized even at $0°$c, but *Arion hortensis* Férussac
and *Milax budapestensis* (Hazay) both become inactive at temperatures above
this. Carrick (1942) also found that all *A. reticulatus* died after only 1 hour at

35°c, and 80% after 4 hours at 30°c; one individual survived 30°c for 10 hours.

Both Carrick (1942) and Arias and Crowell (1963) described the resistance of nearly fully-developed eggs to cold; Carrick found that they could survive several days at 0°c and Crowell that 1,000 eggs were alive after 7 months at 4°c. When these eggs were returned to room temperatures hatching started within 24 hours. This tolerance to cold (newly fertilized eggs are less tolerant) probably explains the small mortality during exceptionally cold winters, such as that of 1962–63 in the United Kingdom. Both slug and snail eggs are laid in the soil, usually in the top 6 inches. The soil temperatures during the 1962–1963 winter at 4 inches at both Reading and Sittingbourne did not drop below

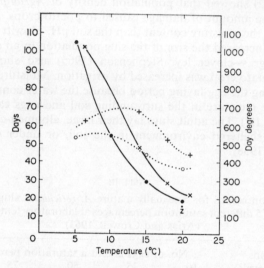

Fig. 7. Incubation of the eggs of *Agriolimax reticulatus* at constant temperatures. x = Data from Bachrach and Cardot (1924), o = Carrick (1942) and z = Arias and Crowell (1963). (Redrawn and slightly altered from Carrick, 1942.)
————, Constant temperature curve; ············, day degree curve.

about −2°c for more than 2 days (Hurst and Lenz, 1963). Thus, if either eggs or adults were below 4 inches in the soil they would have survived.

C. FOOD

The food of land gastropods seems to include every category of edible material. Some species, such as the slugs *Agriolimax reticulatus, Arion hortensis* and *Arion fasciatus* (Nilsson), will feed on many plants, e.g. chickweed, *Stellaria media* (L.) Vill., black bindweed, *Polygonum convolvulus* L., groundsel, *Senecio vulgaris*, L., horseradish, *Armoracia rusticana*, Gaertn., Mey. and Scherb., and the dandelion, *Taraxacum officinale*, Weber. Most snails and slugs in captivity thrive on lettuce. Garden and farm crops, such as beans and other legumes, brassicas, beet, potatoes, carrots, wheat, chrysanthemums and lettuces are often attacked. The slugs that attack underground storage organs, such as potatoes and carrots, are often different species from those feeding on leaves and stems of plants. It may be of interest to note here that damage to winter wheat crops by *A. reticulatus*, feeding on the seed embryo below the surface of the soil, is greatly lessened when the seed bed is compacted after sowing, which presumably hinders the slugs burrowing through the soil and finding the wheat seeds.

Some snails and slugs eat algae and lichens on the surface of trees and decaying wood, and tracks cleared of algae often show on the trunks of beech trees. Others feed on dead or decaying plants found on compost heaps, in gardens, or leaf litter layers under hedges or in woodland; such animals include the snails *Helix aspersa* and *Cepaea nemoralis* and the slugs *Arion ater* (L.) and *Limax maximus* L. Fungi seem especially favoured as food by land molluscs, particularly slugs, and Taylor (1907) mentions *Milax sowerbii* (Férussac), *Arion subfuscus* (Draparnaud) and several species of *Limax* as being particularly partial to this food. Some species are omnivorous and Taylor (1914) mentions several species of *Oxychilus* snails that will feed on other snails when kept in the same box, and *Arion hortensis*, *Milax budapestensis* and *Agriolimax reticulatus* will all feed on other individuals when crowded. *Arion ater* will feed on almost any meat or carcass, and carnivorous slugs of the genus *Testacella* will enter the burrows of earthworms and feed on the worms and also other species of slugs (Barnes and Stokes, 1951).

D. BEHAVIOUR

The distribution of molluscs in any one habitat is governed by many factors of which the presence, or absence, of moisture (p. 423), calcium (p. 422) and shelter and food (p. 424), are the most important. Snail and slug populations are not uniformly distributed within broadly suitable sites, probably because of various micro-climatological and micro-topographical features of the habitat which, in turn, may be linked to the micro-distribution of such foodstuffs as algae, lichens and fungi. Such animals include Door-shells (*Clausilia* sp.), Chrysalis-snails (*Pupilla* sp.) and the Bulins (*Ena* sp.) which are mainly found in crevices and on tree trunks that are covered in mosses and lichens.

Ecologists are interested to discover the environmental factors that influence the distribution and the behaviour of the animals while they are active. The experimental and physiological background for such ecological work has been well summarized by Fraenkel and Gunn (1940) and Carthy (1958), but much work described deals only with laboratory experiments (Frandsen, 1901; Crozier and Frederighi, 1925; Crozier and Libby, 1925; Dainton, 1954a, b). Field studies, using information from laboratory experiments, have recently been described for littoral prosobranchs (*Littorina* sp.) by Newell (1958) and Evans (1961), and show that these marine animals orientate in their habitats by using environmental cues. Evans (1961) showed that winkles visually oriented to the shoreline, and the capability of the *Littorina* eye to form images has been confirmed by Newell (1965).

Land mollusca probably orientate similarly. Looped tracks are described by Frandsen (1901) for *Limax maximus*, and Taylor (1907) records that the snails *Helix aspersa, Cepaea nemoralis* and the slugs *Limax maximus* and *L. flavus* all show "homing" behaviour; that is they go on foraging excursions and then return to the same crevice, or home. Experiments of this kind are much easier with snails than with slugs because their shells can be painted with identification marks. Barnes and Stokes (1951) marked the external shell of *Testacella* slugs and found that the furthest distance travelled on the surface was about 7 ft in 5 hours; none of their results suggest a homing response, although some slugs stay on the surface for only a very short time,

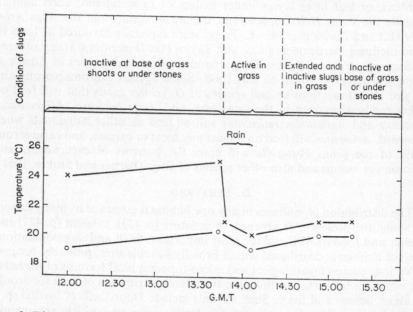

FIG. 8. Diagrammatic summary of field observations made in showery, warm weather. (Redrawn and slightly altered from Dainton, 1954a, b.)
—x—x—, Grass temp., —o—o—, ground temperature under grass.

making it difficult to distinguish between emergence on to the surface halfway round a feeding trail and emergence at the beginning of a feeding trail, that is, identification of the home would be difficult.

Newell (1966) used a high-speed flash and a ciné camera to study the nocturnal surface activity of *Agriolimax reticulatus* introduced into a strange environment. Not all the animals returned home, but those that did spent a greater proportion of their time on the surface feeding than those that emerged and returned to different parts of the plot.

Dainton (1954a) described a mechanism by which slugs are stimulated to activity on the soil surface (Fig. 8). Below 21°C slugs became active only when it became colder, whereas above 21° c they were stimulated to move only by rising temperatures. This could have a definite survival value by protecting them from prolonged exposure to hot conditions. A diurnal activity rhythm at fairly constant laboratory temperatures was also described. (Small fluctuations in temperature and other environmental factors are noted but not considered.) These rhythms persist for 2 or 3 days. It was concluded that activity is not influenced by humidity although the duration of activity may be shortened at low humidities, and the animals containing much water can crawl further than those partly desiccated. *A. reticulatus* could be stimulated to activity until it had lost about 25% of its original weight, the loss being mainly from hydrated muco-proteins secreted during locomotion.

Machin (1962, 1964a, b, c) recently found with *Helix pomatia* and *H. aspersa* that, although mucus loss and crawling are not correlated, mucus loss and water content of the animal are; an animal with a large water content lost much mucus and one with a small one lost little mucus during crawling. The blood seems to act as a water reservoir while these animals crawl. In his study of water loss by evaporation he demonstrated that the shell affects evaporation in active animals. The air flow over a model snail shell in a wind tunnel showed that animals lost most water when facing into the wind, least when facing down wind and intermediate amounts when facing across the wind. The shell slows the air flow over the mantle and head region, and so lessens the water loss, especially when the animal faces down wind. That moist-skinned animals resist desiccation by having a surrounding layer of relatively static air is also shown by the fact that mucus drops lose water by evaporation at the same rate as do drops of distilled water. Later work (Machin, 1965) amplified this and showed that the amount of water lost from the animal is related to the quantity of mucus produced and not to diffusion of water through the snail's skin.

The water lost through evaporation from slugs must vary little either with position to the wind or with their activity, or inactivity, on an exposed site. Active and inactive snails, however, lose water at very different rates for in harsh conditions a dried mucus, or even a heavy calcareous epiphragm (as in *H. pomatia*), is secreted into the mouth of the shell and the snail becomes sealed into it. A snail without an epiphragm lost 8 times as much water as one with an epiphragm (Machin, 1962). Even half an epiphragm greatly lessened water loss (Table IV).

The body weight of both slugs and snails fluctuates with changes in body water content (Howes and Wells, 1934a, b). Water is taken up over the whole body surface of slugs and when dehydrated animals crawl on a moist surface they absorb water through their skins (Dainton, 1954a). This absorption is facilitated by the hydrophilic property of hydrated mucus, which tends to spread a drop of water as an even film all over the body, thus giving it a large absorptive area. The rate water enters through the skin of snails was estimated by immersing them in water with the mouth ligatured and correcting for the amount needed to hydrate the mucus present. Snails can thus increase their weight by 30% in one hour (Machin, 1962).

TABLE IV

The effect of the epiphragm upon water loss from inactive *Helix aspersa* (Machin, 1962)

	90 h wt. loss (mg/24 h)	24 h wt. loss (mg/24 h)	41 h wt. loss (mg/24 h)	Mean wt. loss (mg/24 h)
Shell filled with distilled water	245	252	247	248
1 No epiphragm	6·8	4·3	7·0	
2 No epiphragm	15·9	7·5	6·8	8·1
3 Half epiphragm	0·6	1·1	1·4	
4 Half epiphragm	0·9	0·8	1·3	1·0
5 Complete epiphragm	1·1	0·6	1·8	
6 Complete epiphragm	0·6	0·5	1·3	1·1
7 Attached by epiphragm to glass slide	1·2	0·5	1·2	1·0

E. PREDATION

Sometimes predators affect distribution within a habitat. For example, thrushes eat the polymorphic land snail *Cepaea nemoralis*. In some extremely interesting papers Cain and Sheppard (1950) and Sheppard (1951, 1952) show that shell colour is an important factor in determining the amount of predation, and therefore the survival of *C. nemoralis* (Table V). Cain and Sheppard (1950) found a relationship between the ratio of the banded varieties and different colours and the habitat in which *C. nemoralis* lives. In a beech wood with a predominantly even, brown-coloured litter more brown and pink colours and fewer yellows were eaten than in short, grazed, grass downland sites. The selective value of any of these shell colours alters throughout the year with the changing colour of the background. Table V records the colours of *C. nemoralis* shells found on thrushes' anvils during a period when the habitat colour changed from brown to green and shows that browns and pinks are selected against, to the advantage of the yellows; in the winter and autumn the converse would be true. In general, habitats with a uniform colour have a population with a small proportion of banded snails whereas in non-uniformly coloured habitats, such as hedgerows, a large proportion of individuals are banded. A similar polymorphism was reported by Owen (1963, 1965) for the snail *Limicolaria martensiana*. Dense populations have all colour forms whereas in sparse populations the streaked form predominates. These snails are undoubtedly being used as food by other animals and so are being selected against, but the predators have not been fully studied.

Many other animals feed on snails and several have been tried for biological control of land molluscs. In Britain several species of mice will feed on snails, and Demelow (1963) showed that hedgehogs, *Erinaceus europaeus* L., will feed on many species of slugs and snails. Beetles such as *Carabus violaceus* L. will kill the snail *Helix aspersa* and the slugs *Arion hortensis*, *Agriolimax reticulatus* and *Milax gagates* (Draparnaud) (Moore, 1934; Tomlin, 1935). Carabid beetles, *Tefflus* sp., and drilid beetles, *Drilus* sp., Indian glow-worm larvae, *Lamprophorus tenebrosus* (Walker), and predatory snails, such as *Gonaxis kibweziensis* (E. A. Smith), are described by Mead (1961) as having been used for the biological control of *Achatina fulica*. At least 400 species in the dipterous family Sciomyzidae feed exclusively on non-operculate aquatic

TABLE V

Shells found on thrush anvils in Ten Acre Copse (Sheppard, 1951)

Date	Pink and brown	Yellow	Total	% Yellow
April 19	0	1	1	
April 21	2	0	2	
April 22	1	1	2	41·7
April 25	2	1	3	
April 26	2	2	4	
April 28	1	0	1	
May 1	2	1	3	22·2
May 2	4	1	5	
May 4	2	0	2	
May 5	3	0	3	11·1
May 8	3	1	4	
May 11	3	1	4	
May 12	2	0	2	12·5
May 16	2	0	2	
May 17	1	0	1	
May 20	4	0	4	0
May 22	2	0	2	
May 28	2	0	2	
May 30	1	1	2	11·1
June 3	2	0	2	
June 5	11	1	12	

or terrestrial snails or on slugs. The ecological significance of this group in limiting the numbers of slugs and snails has not yet been assessed but it could be considerable, when one fly larva feeds on more than one animal, as for example *Tetanocera elata* (Meig.), which killed 4 to 9 slugs before pupating (Berg, 1961; Knutson, 1962; Knutson and Berg, 1963; Knutson, Stephenson and Berg, 1965).

F. SIZE OF POPULATIONS

Slugs and snails are very abundant in some habitats. Weber (1954) recorded 750 snails (*Achatina*) in an area 50 × 75 ft; that is, 7,500 snails/acre, a considerable biomass, bearing in mind the enormous size of this snail. Lewis and La Follette (1942) record 129 ± 9 *Helix aspersa* per tree in citrus plantations in January and 248 ± 13 per tree in summer. Assuming that the trees were spaced at 20 ft intervals, which gives a tree density of 364 trees/acre, then the summer snail population would be between 90,000 and 95,000 and the winter population between 46,500 and 50,000 snails/acre. In a barley stubble undersown with grass and clover I estimated that there were 72,000 ± 25,000 *A. reticulatus* per acre, and Thomas (1944) mentions a population of 600,000/acre *A. reticulatus* in a wheat crop that was badly damaged. Drift (1951) gives an average density of 14 *Arion subfuscus* per metre square in a beech forest (= 5,600/acre).

G. THE POSSIBLE ROLE OF SLUGS AND SNAILS IN SOIL FORMATION

Soil animals are widely considered to be important in disposing of litter and to affect the crumb structure by passing soil through their guts; which in turn influences the aeration and water retaining capacity of the soil. Inasmuch as snails and slugs also feed on vegetation and produce partially digested plant material and mucus they also may have a similar function. The large numbers of land molluscs in some soils may modify their soil environment. Like earthworms, they produce mucoproteins both with their faeces and during crawling, which may bond small soil particles together to form a well-defined soil crumb structure. Ghilarov (1963), in his survey of current Russian work on the interrelations between soil invertebrates and micro-organisms, says that there are more bacteria and actinomycetes in earthworm castings than in the surrounding soil. When assessing the role of soil invertebrates in the breakdown of litter he states that decomposition is 2 to 5 times greater when they are present than when they are not. However, bacteria are also important in modifying the plant food of soil invertebrates. Cellulose is usually only assimilated after it is digested by the cellulase-secreting bacteria of the gut flora. (Snails, and possibly slugs, secrete their own cellulases; p. 417.)

In an attempt to determine the relative importance of soil animals in decomposing surface litter, Bornebusch (1930) measured their respiration rates and expressed his results in μg/oxygen consumed/h per m² of soil. Although this method can be criticized on several important points (Drift, 1951), it does give some clues to the relative respiration rates of the main groups of isolated soil animals. This suggests that in some soils, especially oak mulls, the gastropods are the third largest consumers of oxygen after earthworms and millipedes. The role of earthworms in relation to soil fertility and soil structure is summarized by Satchell (1958). The evidence that earthworms do affect soil structure under laboratory conditions is good, but the mechanism by which soil particles aggregate to produce water-stable soil structures is not clear. However, gut secretions producing colloids, and bacterial colonies which flourish in the casts and produce mucoid substances, seem to be the main cement producing agents. Some slugs, e.g. *Milax budapestensis* (Stephenson, 1963), ingest soil, and all snails and slugs not only produce faeces that contain a large proportion of partially digested organic matter but also secrete mucus when crawling. These materials may be important sources of cementing mucoids in habitats with a large gastropod population, either directly or indirectly by providing habitats suitable for the multiplication of bacteria or actinomycetes.

REFERENCES

Arias, R. O. and Crowell, H. H. (1963). *Bull. Sth. Calif. Acad. Sci.* **62**, 83–97.
Atkins, W. R. G. and Lebour, M. V. (1923). *Scient. Proc. R. Dubl. Soc.* **17**, 233–240.
Bachrach, E. and Cardot, H. (1924). *C.r. Séanc Soc. Biol., Paris,* **91**, 260–262.
Barnes, H. F. (1944). *Ann. appl. Biol.* **31**, 160–163.
Barnes, H. F. and Stokes, B. M. (1951). *Ann. appl. Biol.* **38**, 540–545.
Barnes, H. F. and Weil, J. W. (1944). *J. Anim. Ecol.* **13**, 140–175.
Berg, C. O. (1961). *Proc. 9th Int. Congr. Ent.* (*1960*), **1**, 197–202.
Bornebusch, C. H. (1930). *Forst. ForsVæs. Danm.* **11**, 1–224.
Boycott, A. E. (1934). *J. Ecol.* **22**, 1–38.
Bruel, W. E. van den and Moens, R. (1958). *Parasitica,* **14**, 135–147.
Cain, A. J. and Sheppard, P. M. (1950). *Heredity, Lond.* **4**, 275–294.
Cain, A. J. and Williamson, M. H. (1958). *Proc. malac. Soc. Lond.* **33**, 72–86.
Carrick, R. (1938). *Trans. R. Soc. Edinb.* **LIX**, 563–597.
Carrick, R. (1942). *Ann. appl. Biol.* **29**, 43–55.
Carthy, J. D. (1958). "An Introduction to the Behaviour of Invertebrates." Allen & Unwin, London.
Crozier, W. J. and Frederighi, H. (1925). *J. gen. Physiol.* **7**, 151–169.
Crozier, W. J. and Libby, R. L. (1925). *J. gen. Physiol.* **7**, 421–427.
Dainton, B. H. (1954a). *J. exp. Biol.* **31**, 165–187.
Dainton, B. H. (1954b). *J. exp. Biol.* **31**, 188–197.
Demelow, E. J. (1963). *Proc. zool. Soc. Lond.* **141**, 291–309.
Drift, J. van der (1951). *Tijdschr. Ent.* **94**, 1–168.
Ellis, A. E. (1926). "British Snails." Oxford University Press.
Ellis, A. E. (1951). *J. Conch. Lond.* **23**, 171–244.
Elves, M. W. (1961). *Proc. malac. Soc. Lond.* **34**, 346–355.
Evans, F. (1961). *Proc. zool. Soc. Lond.* **137**, 393–402.
Fischer, P. H. (1950). "La Vie et Mœurs des Mollusques." Payot, Paris.
Florkin, M. and Lozet, F. (1949). *Archs. int. Physiol.* **57**, 201–207.
Fraenkel, G. S. and Gunn, D. L. (1940). "The Orientation of Animals." Clarendon Press, Oxford.
Fransden, D. (1901). *Proc. Am. Acad. Arts Sci.* **37**, 185–228.
Fretter, V. and Graham, A. (1962). *Ray soc. Publs.* **144**.
Ghilarov, M. S. (1963). *In* "Soil Organisms" (J. Doeksen and J. van der Drift, eds.), pp. 255–259. North-Holland Publ. Co., Amsterdam.
Holden, M., Pirie, N. W. and Tracey, M. V. (1950). *Biochem. J.* **47**, 399–407.
Holden, M. and Tracey, M. V. (1950). *Biochem. J.* **47**, 407–414.
Howes, N. H. and Wells, G. P. (1934a). *J. exp. Biol.* **11**, 327–343.

Howes, N. H. and Wells, G. P. (1934b). *J. exp. Biol.* **11**, 344–351.
Howitt, A. J. (1961). *J. econ. Ent.* **54**, 778–781.
Hunter, W. R. (1955). *Glasg. Nat.* **17**, 173–183.
Hurst, G. W. and Lenz, Y. (1963). *Agric. Memo.* 83, Meteorological Office, Bracknell.
Jackson, C. H. N. (1939). *J. Anim. Ecol.* **8**, 238–246.
Kitts, W. D. and Underkofler, L. A. (1954). *J. agric. Fd. Chem.* **2**, 639–645.
Knutson, L. V. (1962). *Cornell Plantns.* **17**, 59–63.
Knutson, L. V. and Berg, C. O. (1963). *Proc. R. ent. Soc. Lond.* (A) **38**, 45–58.
Knutson, L. V., Stephenson, J. W. and Berg, C. O. (1965). *Proc. malac. Soc. Lond.* **36**, 213–220.
Lewis, H. C. and La Follette, J. R. (1942). *J. econ. Ent.* **35**, 359–362.
Lincoln, F. C. (1930). *Circ. U.S. Dep. Agric.* No. **118**.
Lissmann, H. W. (1945). *J. exp. Biol.* **21**, 58–69.
Machin, J. (1962). "The water relations of snail integument." Ph.D.Thesis, London.
Machin, J. (1964a). *J. exp. Biol.* **41**, 759–769.
Machin, J. (1964b). *J. exp. Biol.* **41**, 771–781.
Machin, J. (1964c). *J. exp. Biol.* **41**, 783–792.
Machin, J. (1965). *Naturwissenschaften*, **52**, 18.
Martin, A. W., Stewart, D. M. and Harrison, F. M. (1965). *J. exp. Biol.* **42**, 99–123.
Mead, A. R. (1961). "The Giant African Snail: A Problem in Economic Malacology." Chicago University Press.
Mellanby, K. (1961). *Nature, Lond.* **189**, 944.
Moens, R., Francois, E., Riga, A. and Bruel, W. E. van den (1965). 17th Symp. Phytopharm. (in press).
Moore, L. H. (1934). *J. Conch. Lond.* **20**, 85.
Morton, J. E. (1955). *Proc. zool. Soc. Lond.* **125**, 127–168.
Morton, J. E. (1958). "Molluscs." Hutchinson, London.
Morton, J. E. and Machin, J. (1959). *Fld. Stud.*, **1**, 57–71.
Myers, F. L. and Northcote, D. H. (1958). *J. exp. Biol.* **35**, 639–648.
Newell, G. E. (1958). *J. mar. biol. Ass. U.K.* **37**, 229–239.
Newell, P. F. (1963). *A.R.C. 822/63.*
Newell, P. F. (1965). *J. Anim. Behaviour,* **13**, 579.
Newell, G. E. (1965). *Proc. zool. Soc. Lond.* **144**, 75–86.
Newell, P. F. (1966). *Med. biol. Illust.* **16**, 146–159.
Owen, D. F. (1963). *Science*, N.Y. **140**, 666–667.
Owen, D. F. (1965). *Proc. zool. Soc. Lond.* **144**, 361–382.
Pelseneer, P. (1906). "Mollusca." Part 5 of "A treatise on zoology". (E. R. Lankester, ed.). Black, London.
Pelseneer, P. (1935). "Essai d'éthologie zoologique d'après l'étude des Mollusques." Palais des Académies, Bruxelles.
Quick, H. E. (1960). *Bull. Br. Mus. nat. Hist.* **6**, 103–226. Zoological series.
Robertson, J. D. (1941). *Biol. Rev.* **16**, 106–133.
Satchell, J. E. (1958). *Soils Fertil.* **21**, 209–219.
Schuurmans Stekhoven, J. H. (1920). *Tijdschr. ned. dierk. Vereen.* **18**, 1–43.
Sheppard, P. M. (1951). *Heredity,* **5**, 125–134.
Sheppard, P. M. (1952). *Heredity,* **6**, 233–238.
South, A. (1964). *Ann. appl. Biol.* **53**, 251–258.
South, A. (1965). J. Anim. Ecol. **34**, 403–417.
Step, E. (1945). "Shell Life." Warne, London.

Stephenson, J. W. (1963). *Rep. Rothamsted exp. Stn.* 1962, 158.

Stephenson, J. W. (1964). *Rep. Rothamsted exp. Stn.* 1964, 151.

Stephenson, J. W. (1965). *Eur. Potato J.* **8**, 145–149.

Strasdine, G. A. and Whitaker, D. R. (1963). *Can. J. Biochem. Physiol.* **41**, 1621–1626.

Taylor, J. W. (1894–1914). "Monograph of the Land and Freshwater Mollusca of the British Isles." Taylor, Leeds.

Thiele, J. (1931–1935). "Handbuch der systematischen Weichtierkunde." Fischer, Jena.

Thomas, D. C. (1944). *Ann. appl. Biol.* **31**, 163–164.

Tomlin, J. R. le B. (1935). *J. Conch.* **20**, 165.

Tribby, W. W. and Carmichael, E. B. (1935). *Proc. Soc. exp. Biol. med.* **33**, 42–44.

Weber, P. W. (1954). *Proc. Hawaii ent. Soc.* **15**, 363–367.

Webley, D. (1964). *Ann. appl. Biol.* **53**, 407–414.

Chapter 14

The Importance of Antibiotics and Inhibiting Substances

DAVID PARK

*Department of Botany, Queen's University
Belfast, Northern Ireland*

I. INTRODUCTION

This article surveys the probable effects of inhibiting substances upon the biology of micro-organisms, mainly fungi and bacteria, in soil. Antibiotics in the defined sense (Waksman, 1945) include only those substances produced by micro-organisms, an artificial distinction in this context, and the wider term is preferred here so as to include substances of probable activity in soil from all sources. Parts of this discussion deal with antagonisms, and in some of the examples there is no proof that inhibiting substances mediate the antagonistic phenomena. However, antagonisms have the same significance biologically; moreover, most investigated antagonisms are produced by inhibiting substances (Park, 1960).

II. EXISTENCE IN SOIL

Evidence for the presence in soil of substances inhibitory to micro-organisms is of two sorts: direct, involving specific detection by isolation, bioassay or chromatography; and indirect, from observations of the effects produced on selected micro-organisms. Various authors have demonstrated specific antibiotics to be present in soil that has been inoculated with organisms known to produce the antibiotics, and lists of references on this topic are given by Brian (1949, 1957). Most of such work has been done with sterilized soil, either additionally supplemented with energy-rich materials, or unsupplemented except for the increase in nutrients that normally occurs as a result of sterilization. In either case, such work is of little relevance to normal soil conditions, in which the over-all level of nutrients is low and the population large and varied. Much greater difficulty has attended the identification of antibiotics in unsterilized soil; most attempts being unsuccessful, although some workers, e.g. Gregory *et al.* (1952), have shown anti-microbial activity without being able to identify the antibiotic. An outstanding exception is the work of Wright (1952), who demonstrated that gliotoxin could be produced in amounts detectable by paper chromatography in unsterilized but heavily-supplemented soil. The significance of this work has since been extended by the discovery (Wright, 1956) that small local substrata, e.g. seed coats, may in unsterilized normal soil provide conditions for the production of detectable amounts of antibiotics by a fungus resident as inoculum in the soil.

Although the evidence for the presence of specific antibiotics in soil under normal conditions is thus scanty, there exists more data bearing on the existence in soil of unidentified substances inhibitory to micro-organisms. Greig-Smith (1912) described bacteriotoxic substances which he called the agricere. From the sub-surface layers of soil, Newman and Norman (1943) extracted inhibiting substances that were held partly responsible for the differences between surface and sub-surface microbial populations. Bublitz (1954) and Winter (1955) have extracted inhibiting substances from soil litter and from raw humus, both being materials of unusually low microbial activity. More recently, lignin and chemically related substances present in soil have been demonstrated to be toxic to micro-organisms and have been implicated as a possible cause of inhibition in soil (Lingappa and Lockwood, 1960, 1962). There is thus direct evidence that there may be present in soils substances able to inhibit microbial development. There is, however, little conclusive data on the amounts of such substances in soil, and on the sort of levels that would be necessary under soil conditions to result in inhibition of microbial growth and activity. This knowledge would be necessary before one could accept these substances as being responsible for the effects recorded by indirect methods.

The indirect methods for observing inhibitory phenomena, and thus inferring the presence of inhibiting substances in soil, involve placing test organisms, usually fungi, in or in contact with soil and comparing their germination, growth or morphological development, with control sets. Owing to the opacity of soil the observation of microbial structures in direct contact with it is difficult, and most methods involve some carrier medium to facilitate subsequent observation of the exposed test organisms. The carrier medium may incidentally entail some separation of organism from soil. Neilson-Jones (1941) and Jackson (1958a) used a layer of agar on the surface of a layer of soil, making observations on the upper surface. Jefferys and Hemming (1953) buried in soil slabs of agar which were later removed, washed, and seeded for test. Chinn (1953) incorporated test spores in a thin layer of agar supported on a glass slide which could, after burial in soil, be lifted for observation. Dobbs and Hinson (1953) separated fungus spores from soil during the period of exposure by using a layer of Cellophane, and Kerr (1958) used a similar method to observe the effects of soil on growing mycelium. Data provided by such methods agree together and give a picture of most soils inhibiting fungal germination and growth, often producing morphological peculiarities in growing hyphae, and, by some methods, causing death and lysis of structures. However, the results of methods involving carrier media must be evaluated with some caution since, first, the carriers may necessitate diffusion, possibly differential, of substances between soil and test organisms; second, the carriers may provide nutrients to one or other of the test organisms or soil microbial population; and, third, even inert additions to soil, e.g. clean glass (Dobbs and Hinson, 1953), may result in behaviour not found in normal soil. Lingappa and Lockwood (1961) have critically analysed the drawbacks of such carrier medium methods of testing for soil toxins, and demonstrate convincingly that it is possible for agar or Cellophane to act as enrichment media and to allow the activity of sections of the normal soil microbia that are able, within the period of the test, to produce toxic substances as a direct result of the presence of the carrier medium. While this evidence does not disprove the existence in soils of inhibiting substances, it indicates that methods of this type are inappropriate for the detection of the normal presence in soil of such substances. The methods may, however, be used to indicate the presence in soils of organisms able to produce inhibiting substances under appropriate conditions.

Methods not involving carrier media have been used. Park (1955) added spores directly to the soil surface and later obtained some of them for subsequent observation by means of glass slides pressed onto the inoculated surface. Data obtained by such direct contact methods give general agreement with those from carrier media methods. Lingappa and Lockwood (1961) also confirm by direct contact methods that the failure of fungal spores to germinate in natural soils is a fact and not an artefact of carrier media methods, but they suggest that the surface of the spore, or materials exuded from it, may act as a nutrient supplement simulating antagonistic organisms in the environment to produce inhibiting substances in consequence of the spores' presence in the soil. Convincing evidence for this mechanism has more recently been presented by these authors (Lingappa and Lockwood, 1964). These authors were unable to demonstrate fungitoxicity in any extracts from the toxic soil. Some of these findings may be related to those of Jackson (1959), whose unsterilized extracts from soil showed toxicity, but if subjected to any of a variety of sterilization treatments showed no toxicity. Jackson's interpretation was that sterilization removed toxicity, but Lingappa and Lockwood's data could be used to argue that the sterilized extracts had remained non-toxic, while the unsterilized extracts had developed toxicity on testing.

There is then no conclusive evidence that normal mature soils contain effective concentrations of inhibiting substances. Much of the evidence suggests that such substances do exist and are effective, and this is supported by the very low level of activity of micro-organisms in the normal mature soils, but none of this evidence is sufficiently critical to be regarded as adequate proof. What is known is that inhibiting substances may locally exist in effective concentration in special situations, and that in the soil more generally inhibiting substances may at least develop quickly under suitable conditions of stimulation.*

III. PROPERTIES OF THE SOIL TOXICITY

The properties of specific antibiotics have been investigated in some detail in connection with possible therapeutic value, and in relation to soil biology they have been reviewed by Brian (1949, 1957). There is a small number of antibiotics that could, under specified conditions of pH, etc., remain active in soil for effective periods, but most are likely to be adsorbed by soil colloids or otherwise inactivated fairly quickly in soil. Antibiotics of this sort, therefore, may require a specific range of conditions under which to be effective. The more general soil fungistasis on the other hand appears to be effective under a wide range of conditions, and it is of most interest to examine the recorded general properties of this toxicity.

The toxicity of soil for fungi can be counteracted by the proximity of living roots (Kerr, 1956; Jackson, 1957) and by the addition to soil of energy sources for microbes (Neilson-Jones, 1941; Dobbs and Hinson, 1953), the more readily available energy sources having the greatest effect (Jackson, 1960). These facts have led some workers to suppose that the inhibition is caused by nutrient deficiency or competition for nutrients, but Park (1956, 1960) and Lingappa and Lockwood (1961) have shown that the arguments are inadequate.

The inhibitory effect disappears when the soil is sterilized by heat or by exposure to chemical disinfectants (Neilson-Jones, 1941; Dobbs and Hinson, 1953; Park, 1955; Jackson, 1960; Hack and Williams, 1960), and it has been argued from this that the inhibiting substances are thermolabile and sensitive to chemicals. This conclusion is not necessarily true. As already stated, Jackson (1959) showed that all tested forms of sterilization prevented the demonstration of inhibition in normally toxic extracts, and the lack of toxicity may be a function of the state of sterility rather than an effect of the mechanism of sterilization. Partial sterilization may similarly remove or reduce the inhibition (Martin and Aldrich, 1952; Stover et al., 1953). A possible explanation for this situation comes in part from the statement of Dobbs et al. (1960) that the inhibiting substance in soil is volatile or of limited stability, particularly where oxygen is available. Dobbs (1960) has stated that small particles of soil lose their inhibiting property when exposed to air for short periods. It is of interest in this connection that Bilai (1956) has raised the possibility of the existence of volatile antibiotics. Such instability could explain the effect of sterilization, if the normal state were one in which the toxins present were continually diminishing owing to their instability, their level in soil being maintained by a balanced production by some of the organisms in the soil; given these conditions, sterilization, even without

---

* The considerations discussed in this section are reviewed in detail by Lockwood, J. L. (1964). This article appeared too late for it to be appraised in this chapter, but should be regarded as an authoritative account of this aspect of the topic.

assuming any direct destruction of inhibiting substances, could result in their disappearance without the means of replacement. This hypothetical relationship could help to explain an important anomalous property of the inhibiting factor in soil, namely that attempts to isolate it (Dobbs et al., 1960; Jackson, 1959; Lingappa and Lockwood, 1961) or even to demonstrate its presence in extracts or filtrates (e.g. Bamberg, 1930; Tveit and Wood, 1955; Barton, 1961) have frequently failed when the extracts have been cell-free: this would be expected with a substance of limited stability. While rapid lability and continual replacement of the inhibiting substance in soil is hypothetical, it may be noted that the operation in pure culture of an autogenic inhibiting system with these properties has been demonstrated (Park, 1961).

Summarizing, mainly from the works of Neilson-Jones (1941), Dobbs and Hinson (1953), Park (1955), Jackson (1958a, 1959) and Dobbs et al. (1960), a list of the more important properties of the general inhibitory factor of soil can be made. It is of biological origin, is volatile or unstable in air or water at normal temperatures, or is produced best under microaerobic conditions, is not a very large molecule, and is water-soluble and filterable through paper. It is lost after Sterimat filtration or on sterilization by ultra-violet rays, by heat, or by chemicals. The toxicity is temporarily overcome by energy rich materials, and is less marked in acid soils. Under some test conditions the substance is fungistatic, not fungicidal, but under others can cause lysis of cells.

IV. ORIGIN IN SOIL

Substances in soil known to be inhibitory to micro-organisms may have their origin in a number of different sources. It is to be expected that higher plants produce inhibiting substances, since they have the capacity chemically to exclude entry of many potentially parasitic micro-organisms. Several investigations have confirmed that green plant parts contain inhibiting substances and that some of these may remain active on their removal from the plant (Kavanagh, 1947; Hughes, 1952; Topps and Wain, 1957; Nickell, 1959). Roots may also exude into their environment inhibiting substances that may accumulate in soil and there remain effective (Desai, 1946; Stiven, 1952; Naumova, 1953; Buxton, 1957a, b; Woods, 1960). Toxins may be liberated into the soil by decomposition of higher plant parts, or may even be produced there during decomposition (Winter and Willeke, 1952; Winter, 1955; Börner, 1960). A soil animal has been cited as the cause of one specific fungal antagonism in soil (Timonin, 1961a, b). Here an hemipterous insect living on banana roots in soil proved able to reduce the local soil population of *Fusarium oxysporum* f. *cubense*, the cause of the serious Panama disease of the banana plant.

Probably most of the toxicity of soil for micro-organisms comes from the micro-organisms themselves. The emphasis on searches for specific antibiotics from soil micro-organisms reflects this relationship. Moreover, the fact that the toxicity disappears on sterilizing the soil and can be re-introduced

16+S.B.

by re-inoculating with a small amount of normal soil (Neilson-Jones, 1941; Park, 1955), strongly suggests its microbial origin. The work described in the previous section shows that the inhibiting factors in different soils have general properties in common, indicating a general phenomenon of a widespread nature, a conclusion reached by several workers prominent in this field (e.g. Dobbs and Hinson, 1953; Jefferys and Hemming, 1953; Jackson, 1958b). Moreover, the level of fungitoxicity at a site commonly varies with variations in the level of its general microbial activity (Jackson, 1958a, b; Dobbs et al., 1960). In addition, just as the soil toxicity can be restored to sterilized soil by a small inoculum of normal soil, so may it be by inoculation with individual micro-organisms (Katznelson, 1942; Lockwood, 1959), and in this respect any of a number of species may be effective (Park, 1957a, b; Weltzien, 1959).

Stover (1954) has argued that a high level of toxicity developing in flooded soils has a non-biological origin. His evidence does not support this conclusion, however, and Hollis (1948), Mitchell and Alexander (1960) and Newcombe (1960), investigating closely similar situations, all conclude that the increased toxicity in the flood-fallowed soil has a biological origin.

There are several possible origins for substances in soil inhibitory to microorganisms, and in different soils different sets of factors may operate; but while specific substances may be produced by particular organisms, and may be effective under some conditions, the evidence suggests that there is a common inhibitory phenomenon that is a function of the previous general microbial activity in the soil, and which may be produced by several or many species inhabiting the soil.

V. BIOLOGICAL SIGNIFICANCE IN SOIL

In a settled and mature soil there is little microbial activity and the soil has a predominating population of inactive propagules and a residual background inhibition (Park, 1960). When decomposable material is added to such a soil, a succession of events begins in which antagonisms and inhibitions play a large part. The background inhibition is diluted in the immediate vicinity of the amendment, and spores in contact with it are thereby allowed to germinate (Park, 1956). Of the four properties of a successful competitive saprophyte listed by Garrett (1956), the three likely to be of greatest advantage in the initial colonization phase are rapid germination, rapid growth and enzyme production, and antibiotic production. The first two will enable an organism to obtain a large proportion of a newly presented substratum: antibiotic production may, in this relatively simple situation, with very few organisms present, help the producer to exclude other micro-organisms for a time. It was in respect of just such a situation that Wright (1956) demonstrated antibiotic production in non-sterile soil by a colonizing fungus resident in that soil. Regarding Garrett's fourth criterion, that of tolerance for antibiotic substances, it should be pointed out that species occupying this niche of early colonization may have a relatively low tolerance of inhibiting substances, and thus be dependent on obtaining early entry to a substratum. Barton (1960, 1961) has shown that it is sensitivity to antagonism that restricts *Pythium mamillatum* to the role of pioneer colonizer. It is the subsequent colonizers of a substratum that need to be tolerant of those inhibiting substances produced by the organisms previously and contemporaneously active. These later colonizers must, of course, also be capable of utilizing the continually diminishing and decreasingly available energy sources. However, as argued by Park (1960), with these later organisms the first three of the above mentioned criteria might be of smaller importance than the fourth, which, with an increasing level of inhibiting substances in the substratum, will become of greater significance. At a relatively late stage in the colonization process, with fewer and more refractory materials available, and microbial activity less intense, the level of inhibiting substances in the substratum may decrease, depending on their degree of lability. This could allow late colonizers to be successful, although possessing a low tolerance for inhibiting substances and therefore a low apparent competitive saprophytic ability in some tests. Thus *Rhizoctonia solani* and *Armillaria mellea* both appear as early colonizers, in fact as parasites of still living plants, and may also be saprophytically active in soil in the later stages of decomposition (Blair, 1943; Rao, 1959; Garrett, 1960). Garrett (1960) has discussed how this type of biphasic development may be regarded as exhibiting two forms of escape from the intense antagonism characteristic of the middle stages of utilization of substrata.

Following its period of activity in a substratum in soil, or subsequent to its addition to soil from outside, a micro-organism may or may not survive there. One of the factors controlling this is the level and type of inhibiting substances in the soil, and the tolerance of the micro-organism to them. These will vary with the soil, with the organism, and with the local conditions. Waksman and Woodruff (1940) showed that some micro-organisms not already in the soil die out when added to it. Katznelson (1940a, b) presented data supporting this conclusion, but by altering the local soil conditions he was able to get survival and even increase of the added organisms. Kubiena and Renn (1935) found that exposure of soil to aerial laboratory contamination had no effect on the soil population, and they stated the general principle that a soil determines its own microbial population. However, Park (1958) records the survival in soil of an added non-indigenous soil fungus. The differences here may depend on whether the species has previously had the opportunity of reaching that particular soil, and of being tested against the local inhibiting substances.

Hawker (1957) lists four attributes contributing to survival in an habitat and, with respect to soil, two of these are relevant to inhibiting substances. One has significance in a positive way ("ability to alter the environment in a direction unfavourable to other organisms") and has been discussed already; the other ("escape from an unsuitable habitat") has significance in a negative way and can be considered further. Garrett (1950, 1956) has discussed how some micro-organisms have during evolution exchanged tolerance to the inhibiting influence of antagonism for tolerance to that of host resistance, concurrent with the parasitic existence. The more highly specialized parasites have escaped further along this route, and, in general, are found to be less tolerant of soil antagonism, having a lower competitive saprophytic ability (e.g. Anwar, 1949; Butler, 1953a, b). Thus, there appears to be an antithesis between the two tolerances; this may be partly explained by the fact that organisms with demanding requirements can, in the presence of organisms with more simply satisfied requirements, survive only if the latter are inhibited or prevented from competing successfully. Parasites generally have more demanding requirements.

Just as some organisms evade exposure to antagonism by the evolution of tolerance to host resistance, others evade it by developing a tolerance to extremes of physical and chemical conditions, and occupying the early stages in the formation of mature soil (Brown, 1958).

Inhibiting substances may influence the direction of evolution in the reverse direction to that just described, namely towards an increased tolerance. There are records (Wiltshire, 1932; Christensen and Davies, 1940; Miller, 1946; Brown and Wood, 1953; Bistis, 1959) of saltants or mutants appearing in inhibited colonies, and possessing increased tolerance to the inhibiting influence. Goodlow et al. (1950) and Goodlow et al. (1952) describe sequences of autogenic evolution directionally determined by inhibitory substances. In addition to influencing the direction of evolution, inhibiting substances of microbial origin may influence the rate of evolution by increasing the incidence of saltation in inhibited cultures (Isaac and Abraham, 1959).

In addition to their influence on the evolution of individual species, inhibiting substances help to determine the evolution of community structure. Nissen (1954) added antibiotics to soils and subsequently isolated soil fungi able to utilize these inhibitory substances as sole carbon source. Just as inhibiting substances of a green plant may determine the local population of its pathogens (Turner, 1960), so Newman and Norman (1943) found that the development of distinctive microbial populations in surface and sub-surface soils, while influenced partly by the substrata presented, was largely determined by the antagonisms developing. These two workers also illustrated in soil a phenomenon of general ecological significance, namely the edge effect (Elton, 1958), by showing that the surface soil with its bigger variety of niches, bore a bigger variety of species; this effect was also shown by England and Rice (1957). The edge effect depends partly upon the fact that an antagonism shown by one species for another is not absolute but depends on the local environment. In part the principle put forward by Brown (1922), that an organism is less susceptible to inhibiting substances when its energy for growth is great, is applicable here, and the effect of inhibiting substances may be greater at the limit of range of an organism (Hawker, 1957). Thus, micro-organisms may be eliminated from the soil matrix but still survive in infected organic material in the soil (Stover, 1953; Venkata Ram, 1953; Macer, 1961). Apparently anomalous results are of the sort where, in the more homogeneous conditions of culture, one organism is inhibitory to another organism and eventually eliminates it; whereas eradication or even inhibition is not exhibited in the soil with its variety of habitats (Sanford and Broadfoot, 1931; Slagg and Fellows, 1947; Isaac, 1953; Wood and Tveit, 1955) and may be related to the edge effect and the greater chances of escape from antagonism in a more varied habitat. Not only can nutritional status of the habitat exert an effect on antagonistic relationships, but so may temperature also. Griffiths and Siddiqi (1961) investigated a soil antagonism shown above 10°C but not below. This example gives further illustration to the general principle that the more varied the habitat the greater the opportunities for escape or evasion of inhibition. In this context relatively small variations may result in markedly different outcomes, as is illustrated by the work of Keynan et al. (1961), who demonstrated that cellulose presented to a soil as Cellophane film was colonized by a particular soil fungus, but if presented as filter paper was colonized by a particular soil bacterium. On analysis, the situation was found to be caused by an antagonism between the two organisms. It is clear then that caution must be exercised in respect of any claim that one organism is antagonistic to a second organism, unless specific conditions are stated. Such a claim cannot be accepted in an absolute sense otherwise the recipient would have become extinct.

Exposure of an organism to inhibiting substances to which it is sensitive may in certain circumstances assist in its survival. Dobbs and Hinson (1953) suggest that in the absence of colonizable substrata any inhibition of spores is favourable to their survival, in the same way that in the absence of the host, obligate parasites like *Plasmodiophora brassicae* survive longest under conditions least favourable for germination (Bremer, 1924). The principle appears to apply best to ecologically obligate parasitic fungi of low competitive saprophytic ability, in which a temporary reduction of soil inhibition, allowing a consequent increase in general microbial activity with a subsequent intensification of inhibiting influences, tends to reduce the numbers of the pathogen (Garrett, 1938), and some methods of biological control depend upon such an increase in general microbial activity (Millard and Taylor, 1927; King et al., 1934; Stover et al., 1953; Baker, 1957). Similarly, the rhizosphere effect, which involves greater activity of soil micro-organisms in the region of the root, may protect against parasites of low competitive saprophytic ability owing to the increase in antagonism (Lochhead et al., 1940; Timonin, 1940, 1941; Agnihothrudu, 1955). In this context it can be pointed out that the rhizosphere effect itself is a result of the root's influence in counteracting the general soil fungistasis in its vicinity (Kerr, 1956; Jackson, 1957). This leads in the first place to a population quantitatively different from that of the soil, and then secondarily to the qualitative differences.

The principle applied above to the reduction in numbers of soil micro-organisms of low competitive saprophytic ability may also apply to less specialized parasites. Newcombe (1960) found that high levels of carbon dioxide inhibited chlamydospore formation in *Fusarium oxysporum* f. *cubense*, but allowed conidial germination to take place. This was not inimical to survival in pure cultures, but only in the mixed culture conditions of soil when there was no colonizable material present. Chinn and Ledingham (1961) consider a similar situation in which they differentiate between "antagonism" and "germination lysis," terms they apply to antagonism in the inactive and active phases respectively. In their experiments, stimulation followed by the consequent intensified antagonism resulted in a decrease of *Helminthosporium sativum* conidia in soil.

Garrett (1955) has pointed out the difficulties in deliberately applying the foregoing principles to methods of biological control. It has for long (e.g. Daines, 1937) been accepted that there are difficulties in the way of successfully inoculating soil with an antagonist to a pathogen. This difficulty is itself a function of the general inhibitory influence of the soil. Even where the antagonist is a normal member of the soil population or even of the host root itself (Kerr, 1961), there exists the difficulty of holding its population at levels higher than that normally obtaining. The reasons for these difficulties are readily understood in the light of what has been written.

Any successful method of biological control of a soil-borne pathogen must depend on the correct adjustment of the environment so that the appropriate antagonistic relationships are brought into play. Some naturally-resistant plant varieties secrete individual inhibiting substances from their roots which result in a biologically protective microbial population (Timonin, 1940, 1941; Buxton, 1957a). In some hosts an infection of the roots with a mild pathogen may result in a synergistic secretion of inhibiting substances (Perry, 1959) that protects against infection by a more serious pathogen (Bega, 1954; Buxton and Perry, 1959). Similarly, mycorrhizal roots are said (Harley, 1959) to be less susceptible to infection than non-mycorrhizal roots of the same plant. It might be easier to establish artificially and maintain such mild infections than to maintain an antagonist in soil or in the rhizosphere.

Most of the few effective and practicable methods of artificial biological control (Garrett, 1946) depend upon alteration of the soil environment by the addition of fairly large amounts of decomposable organic matter, but it is usually difficult to maintain any prolonged change in the composition of the soil population by this method since the added material fairly quickly disappears (Humfeld and Smith, 1932; Dawson *et al.*, 1945; Dunleavy, 1955), and also the relative abundance of the organisms in soil tends by antagonistic balance to be buffered as already described, and may even be controlled by balanced chains of parasites and hyperparasites such as that described by Klement and Király (1957). A possible method for biological control, by which a concentration of effective antagonists may practicably be built up on local organic material in soil about the suscept, depends upon the facts demonstrated by Wright (1956), in which the seed coat can allow favourable conditions for the production of substances inhibitory to pathogens. The practicability of the method had previously been suggested by Simmonds (1947) and by Slykhuis (1947).

Attempts to alter deliberately the natural balance of micro-organisms in soil present the same sort of dangers that face workers concerned with the control of higher plant and animal populations, whereby a treatment may set off a chain of events which finally results in the opposite of the desired effect (Odum, 1954). Gibson *et al.* (1961) have described how a method of control of *Rhizoctonia solani* causing damping-off of tree seedlings subsequently gave an increase in *Pythium* spp. in the soil with an eventual *increase* in damping-off. A study of the often complex interactions in soil and a better understanding of the nature and effects of inhibiting influences in soil might enable the effects of treatments to be explained, if not forecast, with more accuracy than is at present possible.

REFERENCES

Agnihothrudu, V. (1955). *Naturwissenschaften*, **12**, 373.
Anwar, A. A. (1949). *Phytopathology*, **39**, 1005–1019.
Baker, K. F. (1957). *In* "The U.C. System for Producing Healthy Container Grown Plants," pp. 332. Calif. Agric. Exp. Stn. Extension Service.
Bamberg, R. H. (1930). *Phytopathology*, **20**, 140.
Barton, R. (1960). *In* "The Ecology of Soil Fungi." (D. Parkinson and J. Waid, eds.), pp. 160–167. Liverpool University Press.
Barton, R. (1961). *Trans. Br. mycol. Soc.* **44**, 105–118.
Bega, R. (1954). *Phytopathology*, **44**, 482.
Bilai, V. I. (1956). *Microbiology, Moscow*, **25**, 458–465. Abstract in *Rev. appl. Mycol.* **38**, 186.
Bistis, G. N. (1959). *Mycologia*, **51**, 440–452.
Blair, I. D. (1943). *Ann. appl. Biol.* **30**, 118–127.
Börner, H. (1960). *Bot. Rev.* **26**, 393–424.
Bremer, H. (1924). *Landw. Jb.* **59**, 673–685.
Brian, P. W. (1949). *In* "Symp. Soc. exp. Biol." Vol. III, pp. 357–370.
Brian, P. W. (1957). *Symp. Soc. gen. Microbiol.* **VII**, 168–188.
Brown, J. C. (1958). *J. Ecol.* **46**, 641–664.
Brown, W. (1922). *Ann. Bot.* **36**, 285–299.
Brown, W. and Wood, R. K. S. (1953). *Symp. Soc. gen. Microbiol.* **III**, 326–336.
Bublitz, W. (1954). *Naturwissenschaften*, **21**, 502–503.
Butler, F. C. (1953a). *Ann. appl. Biol.* **40**, 284–297.
Butler, F. C. (1953b). *Ann. appl. Biol.* **40**, 298–304.
Buxton, E. W. (1957a). *Trans. Br. mycol. Soc.* **40**, 145–154.
Buxton, E. W. (1957b). *Trans. Br. mycol. Soc.* **40**, 305–317.
Buxton, E. W. and Perry, D. A. (1959). *Trans. Br. mycol. Soc.* **42**, 378–387.
Chinn, S. H. F. (1953). *Can. J. Bot.* **31**, 718–724.
Chinn, S. H. F. and Ledingham, R. J. (1961). *Can. J. Bot.* **39**, 739–748.
Christensen, J. J. and Davies, F. R. (1940). *Phytopathology*, **30**, 1017–1033.
Daines, R. H. (1937). *Am. Potato J.* **14**, 85–93.
Dawson, R. E., Dawson, V. I. and McCalla, T. M. (1945). *Neb. agric. Exp. Sta. Res. Bull. 155*.
Desai, S. V. (1946). *Sci. Rept. Indian agric. Res. Inst.* 1944–45, **57**.
Dobbs, C. G. (1960). *In* "The Ecology of Soil Fungi." (D. Parkinson and J. Waid, eds.), p. 180. Liverpool University Press.
Dobbs, C. G. and Hinson, W. H. (1953). *Nature, Lond.* **172**, 197–199.
Dobbs, C. G., Hinson, W. H. and Bywater, J. (1960). *In* "The Ecology of Fungi." (D. Parkinson and J. Waid, eds.), pp. 130–147. Liverpool University Press.

Dunleavy, J. (1955). *Phytopathology*, **45**, 252–258.

Elton, C. S. (1958). "The Ecology of Invasions by Animals and Plants." Methuen, London.

England, C. M. and Rice, E. L. (1957). *Bot. Gaz.* **118**, 186–190.

Garrett, S. D. (1938). *Ann. appl. Biol.* **25**, 742–766.

Garrett, S. D. (1946). *Soil Sci.* **61**, 3–8.

Garrett, S. D. (1950). *Biol. Rev.* **25**, 220–254.

Garrett, S. D. (1955). *Ann. appl. Biol.* **42**, 211–219.

Garrett, S. D. (1956). "Biology of Root Infecting Fungi." Cambridge University Press, London.

Garrett, S. D. (1960). *Ann. Bot.* **24**, 275–285.

Gibson, I. A. S., Ledger, M. and Boehm, E. (1961). *Phytopathology*, **51**, 531–533.

Goodlow, R. L., Mika, L. A. and Braun, W. (1950). *J. Bact.* **60**, 291.

Goodlow, R. J., Tucker, L., Braun, W. and Mika, L. A. (1952). *J. Bact.* **63**, 681.

Gregory, K. F., Allen, O. N., Riker, A. J. and Petersen, W. H. (1952). *Am. J. Bot.* **39**, 405–415.

Greig-Smith, R. (1912). *Zentbl. Bakt. ParasitKde*, **34**, 224–226.

Griffiths, E. and Siddiqi, M. A. (1961). *Trans. Br. mycol. Soc.* **44**, 343–353.

Hack, J. and Williams, P. H. (1960). *Ann. appl. Biol.* **48**, 236–244.

Harley, J. L. (1959). "The Biology of Mycorrhiza," Leonard Hill, London.

Hawker, L. E. (1957). *Symp. Soc. gen. Microbiol.* **VII**, 238–258.

Hollis, J. P. (1948). *Phytopathology*, **38**, 761–775.

Hughes, J. E. (1952). *Antibiotics Chemother.* **2**, 487–491.

Humfeld, H. and Smith, N. R. (1932). *J. agric. Res.* **44**, 113–120.

Isaac, I. (1953). *Ann. appl. Biol.* **40**, 623–629.

Isaac, I. and Abraham, G. H. (1959). *Can. J. Bot.* **37**, 801–814.

Jackson, R. M. (1957). *Nature, Lond.* **180**, 96–97.

Jackson, R. M. (1958a). *J. gen. Microbiol.* **18**, 248–258.

Jackson, R. M. (1958b). *J. gen. Microbiol.* **19**, 390–401.

Jackson, R. M. (1959). *In* Rep. Rothamsted Exp. Stn. 1958, pp. 71–72.

Jackson, R. M. (1960). *In* "The Ecology of Soil Fungi." (D. Parkinson and J. Waid, eds.), pp. 168–176. Liverpool University Press.

Jefferys, E. G. and Hemming, H. G. (1953). *Nature, Lond.* **172**, 872–873.

Katznelson, H. (1940a). *Soil Sci.* **49**, 21–35.

Katznelson, H. (1940b). *Soil Sci.* **49**, 283–293.

Katznelson, H. (1942). *Can. J. Res.* **20C**, 169–173.

Kavanagh, F. (1947). *Adv. Enzymol.* **7**, 461.

Kerr, A. (1956). *Aust. J. biol. Sci.* **9**, 45–52.

Kerr, A. (1958). *Trans. Br. mycol. Soc.* **41**, 14–16.

Kerr, A. (1961). *Trans. Br. mycol. Soc.* **44**, 365–371.

Keynan, A., Henis, Y. and Keller, P. (1961). *Nature, Lond.* **191**, 307.

King, C. J., Hope, C. and Eaton, E. D. (1934). *J. agric. Res.* **49**, 1093–1107.

Klement, Z. and Király, Z. (1957). *Nature, Lond.* **179**, 157–158.

Kubiena, W. and Renn, C. E. (1935). *Zentbl. Bakt. ParasitKde II*, **91**, 367–291.

Lingappa, B. T. and Lockwood, J. L. (1960). *Phytopathology*, **50**, 644.

Lingappa, B. T. and Lockwood, J. L. (1961). *J. gen. Microbiol.* **26**, 473–485.

Lingappa, B. T. and Lockwood, J. L. (1962). *Phytopathology*, **52**, 295–299.

Lingappa, B. T. and Lockwood, J. L. (1964). *J. gen. Microbiol.* **35**, 215–227.

Lochhead, A. G., Timonin, M. I. and West, P. M. (1940). *Scient. Agric.* **20**, 414–418.

Lockwood, J. L. (1959). *Phytopathology*, **49**, 327–331.

Lockwood, J. L. (1964). *A. Rev. Phytopath.* **2**, 341–362.

Macer, R. C. F. (1961). *Ann. appl. Biol.* **49**, 165–172.
Martin, J. P. and Aldrich, D. G. (1952). *Proc. Soil Sci. Soc. Am.* **16**, 201–203.
Millard, W. A. and Taylor, C. D. (1927). *Ann. appl. Biol.* **14**, 202–216.
Miller, J. J. (1946). *Can. J. Res.* **24C**, 118–212.
Mitchell, R. and Alexander, M. (1960). *Bact. Proc.*, *U.S.A.*
Naumova, A. N. (1953). *Mikrobiologiya*, **22**, 281–287. Abstract in *Soils & Fert.* **17**, 256.
Neilson-Jones, W. (1941). *J. agric. Sci.* **31**, 379–411.
Newcombe, M. (1960). *Trans. Br. mycol. Soc.* **43**, 51–59.
Newman, A. S. and Norman, A. G. (1943). *Soil Sci.* **55**, 377–391.
Nickell, L. G. (1959). *Econ. Bot.* **13**, 281–318.
Nissen, T. V. (1954). *Nature, Lond.* **174**, 226–227.
Odum, E. P. (1954). "Fundamentals of Ecology," W. B. Saunders and Co., Philadelphia, Pennsylvania, U.S.A.
Park, D. (1955). *Trans. Br. mycol. Soc.* **38**, 130–142.
Park, D. (1956). *Int. Congr. Soil Sci.* **III**, 23–28. Paris.
Park, D. (1957a), *Trans. Br. mycol. Soc.* **40**, 283–291.
Park, D. (1957b). *Trans. Br. mycol. Soc.* **40**, 358–364.
Park, D. (1958). *Ann. Bot. N.S.* **22**, 19–35.
Park D. (1960). *In* "The Ecology of Soil Fungi." (D. Parkinson and J. Waid, eds.) pp. 148–159. Liverpool University Press.
Park, D. (1961). *Trans. Br. mycol. Soc.* **44**, 377–390.
Perry, D. A. (1959). *Trans. Br. mycol. Soc.* **42**, 388–396.
Rao, A. S. (1959). *Trans. Br. mycol. Soc.* **42**, 97–111.
Sanford, G. B. and Broadfoot, W. C. (1931). *Scient. Agric.* **2**, 512–528.
Simmonds, P. M. (1947). *Scient. Agric.* **27**, 625–632.
Slagg, C. M. and Fellows, H. (1947). *J. agric. Res.* **75**, 279–293.
Slykhuis, J. T. (1947). *Can. J. Res.* **25C**, 155–180.
Stiven, G. (1952). *Nature, Lond.* **170**, 712–713.
Stover, R. H. (1953). *Nature, Lond.* **172**, 465.
Stover, R. H. (1954). *Soil Sci.* **77**, 401–414.
Stover, R. H., Thornton, N. C. and Dunlap, V. C. (1953). *Soil Sci.* **76**, 225–238.
Timonin, M. I. (1940). *Can. J. Res.* **18C**, 444–456.
Timonin, M. I. (1941). *Soil Sci.* **52**, 395–408.
Timonin, M. I. (1961a). *Pl. Soil*, **14**, 323–334.
Timonin, M. I. (1961b), *Can. J. Bot.* **39**, 695–703.
Topps, J. H. and Wain, R. L. (1957). *Nature, Lond.* **179**, 652–653.
Turner, E. M. C. (1960). *Nature, Lond.* **186**, 325–326.
Tveit, M. and Wood, R. K. S. (1955). *Ann. appl. Biol.* **43**, 538–552.
Venkata Ram, C. S. (1953). *Phytopathology*, **43**, 482.
Waksman, S. A. (1945). "Microbial Antagonisms and Antibiotic Substances," The Commonwealth Fund, New York.
Waksman, S. A. and Woodruff, H. B. (1940). *Soil Sci.* **50**, 421–427.
Weltzien, H. C. (1959). *Naturwissenschaften*, **15**, 456–457.
Wiltshire, S. P. (1932). *Ann. Bot.* **46**, 343–351.
Winter, A. G. (1955). *Z. PflErnähr. Düng. Bodenk.* **69**, 224–233.
Winter, A. G. and Willeke, L. (1952). *Naturwissenschaften*, **9**, 45–46.
Wood, R. K. S. and Tveit, M. (1955). *Bot. Rev.* **21**, 441–492.
Woods, F. W. (1960). *Bot. Rev.* **26**, 546–569.
Wright, J. M. (1952). *Nature, Lond.* **170**, 673–674.
Wright, J. M. (1956). *Ann. appl. Biol.* **44**, 561–566.

15*

Soil Micro-Organisms and Plant Roots

D. PARKINSON

Department of Biology, University of Waterloo
Waterloo, Ontario, Canada

I. INTRODUCTION

As a root grows through soil it alters the soil conditions in its immediate vicinity in a number of ways and in doing so has important effects on the diverse microbial population of the soil. The active root exudes, particularly from a region just behind the root tip, organic and inorganic substances which usually enhance microbial activity although some exuded materials may operate against certain micro-organisms. Sloughed-off root cells, presumably derived in young roots mainly from the root cap, provide substrates for microbial development. Carbon dioxide, oxygen and water tensions in the root region must be considerably different from those in the soil distant from the roots and must affect microbial activity in the root region. Other phenomena include the tendency for the pH of the soil adjacent to roots to be nearer neutrality than that of the soil distant from roots; also the redox potential of the soil adjacent to roots is lower, presumably as a result of root exudates, than that in the general soil. Recently it has been shown (Barber, 1962) that, under certain conditions, it is possible that there may be a concentration of inorganic nutrients in the immediate vicinity of roots.

These factors must all operate in one way or another to effect the now highly documented numerical and physiological stimulation of micro-organisms in the root region—a region which comprises the most studied group of soil microhabitats.

Interest in this group of microhabitats stems from the discoveries in the nineteenth century of spectacular associations of soil micro-organisms and plant roots—legume nodules, mycorrhizas and pathogenic associations. The descriptions of such associations focused attention on the soil-root interface as an important zone of microbial activity. However, this attention was initially concentrated on the possibility of inoculating non-legumes with nitrogen-fixing bacteria, and although these studies were unproductive they nevertheless demonstrated microbial stimulation in the environs of roots. In 1904 Hiltner defined the zone of enhanced microbial development round roots as the rhizosphere (the soil immediately influenced by plant roots), but it was not until a quarter of a century later that detailed studies on the rhizosphere microflora were begun (Starkey, 1929a, b, c).

Thus it has been appreciated that soil micro-organisms exhibit a range of relationships with the roots of higher plants. These may be considered as:

(1) symbiotic (e.g. mycorrhizal associations, legume nodules);
(2) parasitic (where the causal organisms range from unspecialized to highly specialized forms);
(3) less clearly defined relationships grouped together as rhizosphere and root surface phenomena.

It is not proposed to deal with the symbiotic and parasitic associations in this chapter in view of the admirable and detailed accounts which are already available (Harley, 1959; Garrett, 1956; Hallsworth, 1958). It may be considered that many of these associations represent highly evolved types of root-microbe inter-relation, and it is the function of this chapter to consider the less intimate, less specific relations of soil micro-organisms and plant roots.

Although the initial descriptions of increased microbial activity in the rhizosphere were based on studies of soil bacteria, numerous workers (Starkey, 1931; Katznelson, 1946; Hadfield, 1960; Henderson and Katznelson, 1961) have since shown that various other groups of soil micro-organisms (viz. fungi, actinomycetes, algae, protozoa and nematodes) are also stimulated in the root region. It has been generally demonstrated, however, that soil bacteria are the most influenced of the soil microflora in the root region. The stimulus of roots on microbial development in the soil (the rhizosphere effect) has been assessed by comparing the numbers of micro-organisms in unit weight of rhizosphere soil with those in unit weight of soil distant from the roots—thus giving the well-known R/S values.

From the early work of Starkey (1931) and others on rhizosphere phenomena it soon became evident that the numbers of micro-organisms increased with increasing proximity to the roots. Measurable rhizosphere effects have been detected at various distances from plant roots—up to 5 mm from the roots of tomatoes (Rovira, 1953), up to 16 mm from lupin roots (Papavisas and Davey, 1961)—but it is not possible to generalize on the extent of the rhizosphere, being, as it is, dependent on the metabolic state of the plant and the nature of the soil (in general it appears that the poorer the soil the more pronounced the rhizosphere effect). The maximum stimulating effects of plant roots on soil micro-organisms were shown to operate at the root surface (Starkey, 1931; Katznelson, Lochhead and Timonin, 1948; Webley, Eastwood and Gimingham, 1952).

Together with the demonstrations of enhanced microbial development in the root region and of the fact that this enhancement decreased with increasing distance from the roots, there arose a multiplicity of terms—a result of the desire by various workers to recognize zones in the root region. Terms such as "histosphere," "rhizosphere" and "edaphosphere" (Perotti, 1926); inner and outer rhizospheres (Gräf, 1950; Poschenreider, 1930) are examples of such terminology. Clark (1949), in an attempt to emphasize the importance of the root surface, introduced the term "rhizoplane" (defined as the external surfaces of plant roots and closely adhering particles of mineral soil and organic debris); but although it has been used by American and Canadian workers it has not found general acceptance. More recently both Harley (1948, 1959) and Garrett (1955, 1956) have considered the whole range of microbial associations with plant roots, and in so doing have suggested that the root region may be thought of as comprising the rhizosphere and the root surface. This commendably simple concept has been adopted in the account given here.

II. THE ROOT REGION

A. RHIZOSPHERE

Numerous studies have indicated that in this zone there is not only an increase in microbial numbers but also in their physiological activity (as indicated by oxygen uptake measurements, rate of reduction of substances such as methylene blue, rate of utilization of glucose and amino acids, rate of nitrification) as compared with the situation in the soil distant from plant roots. Starkey (1929a, b or c) demonstrated that both numbers and activity of micro-organisms in the rhizosphere reached a maximum at the time of maximum vegetative development of the higher plants, the plant exerting slight effects during its early growth period, and the rhizosphere effect decreasing after maturity subsequent to degeneration and death of the roots. After death of the roots microbial numbers again increase as a result of the active saprophytic colonization of the dead root material.

1. Methods of study

Progress in rhizosphere studies has been considerably hampered by the lack of efficient techniques for the isolation and enumeration of certain of the active components of the rhizosphere microflora. The soil dilution plate technique has been used predominantly for both qualitative and quantitative rhizosphere studies (e.g. Starkey, 1929a, b or c; Timonin, 1940a; Timonin and Thexton, 1951; Webley, Eastwood and Gimingham, 1952; Katznelson, 1960; Papavizas and Davey, 1961). This technique is generally admitted as suitable for the study of rhizosphere bacteria, although it must be remembered that such plating procedures are selective and only allow the isolation of a small proportion of the bacteria present in a population (Starkey, 1958). The use of the soil dilution plate technique for studies of rhizosphere fungi may be more severely criticized (Parkinson, 1957; Parkinson and Moreau, 1959), since it does little more than allow the assessment of the sporing capacity of species which were presumably previously active in the rhizosphere soil and gives little clue to the vital problem of how much active mycelium is present in the rhizosphere. Added point to this criticism comes from the consideration of several workers (Agnihothrudu, 1955; Parkinson, 1957) that the rhizosphere is a zone in which fungi are present mainly as mycelium, whereas in the soil distant from roots they are present mainly as spores, and therefore the use of soil dilution plates for comparing fungal populations of rhizosphere and non-rhizosphere soil may lead to gross inaccuracies. In addition to this the calculated R/S values for fungi must have little meaning because of the filamentous growth form of these organisms —what is the significance of a statement which tells us that there are 5×10^5 fungi per gram dry weight of rhizosphere soil? Surely little or none. Any estimate of the amounts of fungi in a microhabitat must be given in terms of length or weight of mycelium per unit weight or volume of soil.

The Rossi-Cholodny buried slide technique has been applied for rhizosphere studies, and has yielded information on the development of microorganisms in the root region (Starkey, 1938; Stille, 1938), but it has several disadvantages. It is rarely possible to identify the micro-organisms seen on stained Rossi-Cholodny slides, therefore the technique is of little value in studies on the qualitative nature of the rhizosphere microflora. Their use in quantitative investigations, applying the technique described by Jensen (1936), has two major objections. First, the burial of glass slides in soil may in itself allow stimulated microbial development because of the condensation of water on the glass and the consequent overcoming of the general fungistasis in the soil near the buried slides (Dobbs and Hinson, 1953). Second, it is exceedingly difficult to relate the numbers of bacterial cells and lengths of fungus mycelium observed on buried slides to any weight or volume of soil (rhizosphere or non-rhizosphere). However, the use of the Rossi-Cholodny technique has enabled investigators to see clusters of bacteria in the root region, to see abundant fungus mycelium, and to see the abundant growth of bacteria around root hairs.

Direct observations on rhizosphere soil have been only rarely performed but Linford (1940, 1942), using glass observation boxes, demonstrated the concentration of micro-organisms in the root region of seedlings. Krassilnikov (1958) described a method in which plants were grown on glass plates which were mounted in such a way that the roots spread over the glass leaving their "imprints" on the glass. To facilitate microscopic observation, microscope slides were placed on the inner surface of the glass plate and removed after different intervals for study (stained or unstained). Using this technique profuse microbial (bacteria, actinomycetes and fungi) development and also isolated colonies were observed on the surfaces of roots, between root hairs and at some distance from them.

Particular attention has recently been paid to the methods for studying the fungal component of rhizosphere microfloras, and several techniques have been developed. A modification of the Chesters' immersion tube technique (Chesters, 1940, 1948) was shown to be useful in studying rhizosphere fungi (Parkinson, 1957; Chesters and Parkinson, 1959). This modification aimed at isolating fungi present in rhizospheres as actively growing mycelium; but it is now considered that this method, which is subject to all the criticisms which can be levelled at the technique from which it was derived, is of only limited applicability. Direct soil plating (Warcup, 1950) has been used for qualitative studies on rhizosphere fungi (Parkinson, 1957; Chesters and Parkinson, 1959; Čatská, Macura and Vágnerova, 1960); however, this technique suffers from most of the defects of the soil dilution plate technique—probably its only merit is that it is easily and rapidly performed. Recently the development of soil-washing methods (Parkinson and Williams, 1961; Watson, 1960), which attempts to rid the soil of the majority of the fungal spores which it contains prior to the plating of soil particles, have provided possible methods for studying the nature of fungi present in rhizosphere soil as hyphae. This possibility has yet to be explored.

For quantitative assessments of rhizosphere fungi the impression slide technique devised by Brown (1958) has been used (Parkinson, 1958). In this technique, freshly sampled roots with their adhering rhizosphere soil were laid on microscope slides which had been thinly coated with adhesive material (nitrocellulose in amylacetate). The rhizosphere soil stuck to this adhesive material when the roots were carefully removed. Impression slides of the soil distant from roots were made simply by pressing adhesive-coated slides against a freshly exposed soil profile. After staining the impression slides were observed under the microscope and the frequency of occurrence, lengths and types of mycelium present from rhizosphere and non-rhizosphere soil could be compared. However, here again, as with the Rossi-Cholodny slides, one is faced with difficulties in recording the data obtained—once again it is not known from what amount (weight or volume) of soil the observed mycelium has been derived.

It seems likely that attention will become more directed onto the Jones and Mollison (1948) technique, or some modification of it, as a useful means of making quantitative determinations of bacterial numbers and amounts of fungus mycelium in known weights of rhizosphere and non-rhizosphere soils.

2. Bacteria in rhizospheres

In studying the nature, distribution and activities of complex populations it is necessary, under ideal circumstances, to study the whole population and to evaluate the interactions between the various components of the population. In reality this is rarely possible, and in the case of microbial populations of rhizospheres many investigators have regretfully confined themselves to one component of this complex situation for detailed study. In doing so important microbial interactions may be missed—for it is realized that, being as it is a zone of enhanced microbial activity, the rhizosphere may well be a group of microhabitats in which antagonistic and associative phenomena are pronounced.

It is, in fact, the bacterial component of rhizosphere microfloras which has been most studied, the fungi having been studied regularly but not so intensively, and the other groups of soil organisms only irregularly. In the excellent detailed reviews already available (Katznelson, Lochhead and Timonin, 1948; Clark, 1949; Blair, 1951; Starkey, 1958; Krassil'nikov, 1958) accounts are given of the large amount of work done on rhizosphere bacteria. The account of this group given here is, therefore, brief.

Many studies have been concerned with comparing the qualitative natures of bacterial populations in rhizosphere and non-rhizosphere soil. However, only rarely have attempts been made to classify bacteria isolated from rhizosphere soil into genera and species—in general the bacteria isolated have been classified into morphological, physiological or nutritional groups. Many bacteriologists, although recognizing the desirability for "absolute" identification of isolates from soil and rhizospheres, feel that this is an impossibility because of the great plasticity of bacteria, and Cowan (1962), in discussing the difficulties (and futility?) of classifying bacteria, has emphasized that "micro-organisms are not static units but show continuous adaptation to their environment." He has suggested that the bacteria make up a spectrum of gradually merging forms, and this concept has been applied to bacterial populations of rhizospheres (Brisbane and Rovira, 1961). These workers compared three methods of classifying bacteria—division on associated characters, identification using Skerman's key (Skerman, 1959), and by means of the Affinity Index. In studying a random sample of rhizosphere bacteria (43 from 318 bacteria) they considered that this sample formed a spectrum rather than a series of groups.

From the large number of investigations on bacteria in rhizospheres which are discussed in the review papers mentioned above, certain general facts have emerged. It is generally agreed that Gram-negative non-spore-forming bacteria are stimulated to develop in rhizosphere soil—*Agrobacterium radiobacter* being a case in point; also, over recent years, species of *Pseudomonas* have been shown to be abundant in the root region, and have been shown to constitute between 40 and 50% of the bacterial population of some rhizospheres (Vagernerova *et al.*, 1960; Rouatt and Katznelson, 1961). Mycobacteria and Corynebacteria have also been regularly reported as forms stimulated in rhizospheres. In contrast to these examples of stimulation there are reports that *Bacillus* species are present less frequently in rhizospheres than in soil distant from plant roots (Clark, 1940; Krassil'nikov, Kriss and Litvinov, 1936; Lochhead, 1940), although within this genus *Bacillus brevis*, *B. circulans* and *B. polymyxa* were reported by Clark (1940) to "constitute more important fractions of the *Bacillus* population in the rhizoplane than they do in soil." Clark (1940) also showed that Gram-positive cocci were depressed in development in the rhizosphere, where they accounted for only 12% of the isolates (whereas in the soil distant from roots they represented 40% of the isolates).

As has been stated previously, it is generally accepted that microbial activity in rhizospheres is greater than that in the non-rhizosphere soil. Thus, it is perhaps to be expected that studies on rhizosphere bacteria have indicated that such physiological groups as motile forms, chromagenic forms, ammoni-fiers, denitrifiers, gelatin liquefiers, forms giving an acid or alkaline reaction with glucose-peptone media, and aerobic cellulose-decomposing forms are present in larger numbers in rhizospheres than in the general soil. However, nitrifying organisms, anaerobic cellulose decomposing forms and nitrogen-fixing anaerobes (e.g. *Clostridium* spp.) have been recorded as being depressed in rhizospheres.

As might be expected, interest has tended to centre on the role of two of the best-known genera of soil bacteria—*Azotobacter* and *Rhizobium*, both nitro-gen-fixing organisms—in rhizospheres. In the case of *Azotobacter* a good deal of conflicting evidence has been presented. Allison (1947) and Allison, Gaddy and Armiger (1947) showed that there was little or no development of *Azotobacter* in the root region. However, Krassil'nikov (1958) cited a number of examples of the stimulation of *Azotobacter* in the root region of crop plants grown in Russian soils. Krassil'nikov (1958) showed that in the lucerne–cotton crop rotation system in Central Asia (3 years lucerne; 6–9 years cotton), *Azotobacter* increased under lucerne but decreased under cotton. He concluded that certain Angiosperm species enhanced the growth of *Azotobacter* in soil, some species suppressed it, other species had no effect.

Clark (1948) concluded that there was no evidence that the rhizosphere was a favourable zone for the development of *Azotobacter*, and in the follow-ing year (Clark, 1949) he gave a detailed account of the studies on the role of this organism in rhizospheres up to that date. Recently Katznelson and Strzelczyk (1961) investigated the rhizosphere bacteria of 17 crop plants, and showed that counts of *Azotobacter* were very low in both rhizosphere and non-rhizosphere soil. It has been concluded (Katznelson and Strzelczyk, 1961) that these low numbers were caused not by the suppression of *Azotobac-ter* but by the antagonistic effects of various active soil micro-organisms, against which *Azotobacter* could not compete (Zagallo and Katznelson, 1957; Rovira, 1956a; Macura, 1958). Strzelczyk (1961) showed that rhizo-sphere soil contained greater numbers of micro-organisms which were antagonistic to *Azotobacter* than did soil distant from plant roots.

In the case of species of *Rhizobium*, the nodule bacteria of Legumes, it has been known for some time that exudates from legume roots stimulate the development of these bacteria in the legume rhizospheres (West, 1939; Wilson, 1940; Purchase and Nutman, 1957). Before nodule formation begins, *Rhizobium* spp. together with other groups of micro-organisms multiply in legume rhizospheres, and in this early stage of root growth (3–10 days after seed germination) rhizosphere populations of 10^6–10^9 *Rhizobium* spp./ml of rhizosphere soil have been recorded (Purchase and Nutman, 1957). This represented a rapid build-up of this group of bacteria in the rhizosphere (Nutman, 1958). Krassil'nikov and Korenyako (1944) demonstrated that certain Gram-negative non-sporing bacteria could inhibit the development of various species of *Rhizobium* in the rhizosphere of clover, and Hely, Bergersen and Brockwell (1957) suggested that antagonistic reactions with other rhizo-sphere organisms could operate against Rhizobia in legume rhizospheres.

Hely *et al.* (1957) thereby explained the failure of nodulation in legumes in some Australian soils (yellow podzolics). Vincent (1958) presented evidence which indicated that this antagonistic phenomenon must be delicately balanced.

The stimulation of *Rhizobium* spp. is not confined to legume rhizospheres, although non-legumes generally have less effect. In the continued absence of legumes the population of *Rhizobium* spp. in the soil may decline and disappear (Vincent, 1954; Krassil'nikov, 1958); this depends on the nature of the non-legume crops and on the length of time the soil is left fallow.

The fact that different groups of soil bacteria have differing nutritional requirements was exploited by Lochhead and his co-workers (1938–1955) for the characterization of individual organisms and of bacterial populations. In the technique devised by Lochhead *et al.*, the initial isolation of bacteria was onto a non-selective medium (soil extract agar), from which selected colonies were tested for their ability to grow on a range of variously supplemented media: glucose–nitrate–mineral medium (basal medium), basal medium + amino acids, basal medium + amino acids + vitamins, basal medium + yeast extract, basal medium + yeast extract + soil extract.

The comparative application of this method of characterization to bacterial populations of rhizosphere soil and non-rhizosphere soil has been found to demonstrate differences between these populations. It was consistently found that amino acid-requiring bacteria made up a higher proportion of the rhizosphere microflora than of the general soil microflora (Lochhead and Rouatt, 1955); and that rhizosphere contained a higher proportion of bacteria with simple nutritional requirements (i.e. able to grow on the unsupplemented basal medium) and a lower proportion of bacteria requiring yeast extract than did the soil distant from plant roots.

3. Factors affecting bacterial distribution in rhizospheres

In general it appears that various soil treatments (e.g. organic or inorganic fertilizers) do not greatly affect bacterial numbers in rhizospheres (Clark, 1940; Clark and Thom, 1939; Hulpoi, 1936; Katznelson and Richardson, 1948; Obraztsova, 1936; Timonin, 1940a). The effects of such treatments may operate directly on the soil microflora or on the growth rate of the higher plants. Manurial treatments of soil produce large increases in the general soil microflora, but have no similar effect on the microflora of the root region. Thus, the rhizosphere seems to be a zone buffered against changes in the soil; it is under the primary influence of the root. However, Hildebrand and West (1941) showed that manurial treatments which control the incidence of root rot of strawberries also affected the relative incidence of nutritional groups in the rhizosphere.

Liming was reported (Obraztsova, 1936) to cause a 25% increase in bacterial numbers in rhizospheres. Also Rovira (1961) showed that amelioration of a krasnozem (pH 4·8) with CaO and CaO plus minerals caused great increases in the numbers of *Rhizobium* spp. in rhizospheres of red clover. This observation gives some explanation of the well-known phenomenon that liming allows nodulation of legumes in "problem" soils.

The effects of soil moisture have been irregularly studied (probably because of the technical difficulties involved in growing plants under constant and known water regimes). Clark and Thom (1939) showed that over a moisture range of 12 to 20% the R/S values did not vary (R/S=9) but at 24·5% moisture the R/S value fell to 4·5. Timonin (1940) noted that there were increased rhizosphere populations in soils where the moisture content was at 30% of the total moisture holding capacity than where the moisture content was at 60% m.h.c. Clark (1948) also showed that microbial numbers were higher round roots taken from drier as compared with wetter soils. In studying the effects of individual environmental conditions, care must be taken to grow the test plants under controlled conditions and to be able to control the variable which is being examined. It is not certain how these criteria have been fulfilled in the case of studies of the effects of different soil moisture contents on the development of rhizosphere microfloras.

Numerous workers have attempted to study the specific effects of different crop plant species on the soil microflora, to investigate whether the rhizosphere populations of different crop plant species vary from one to another. The most pronounced effects of this type have been shown in comparisons of legume rhizosphere microfloras with those of non-legume species (the former supporting larger rhizosphere populations in which *Rhizobium* spp. may be an important component). However, it does not as yet appear possible to make any real generalizations on the detailed effects of individual crop plant species on soil bacteria. Lochhead (1959) states that ". . . although there is some suggestion that certain crops exert their effects in different degrees. This subject demands much more attention before the specific influence of crops can be well assessed."

4. Fungi in rhizospheres

The amount of attention given to fungi in rhizospheres has been much less than that accorded to the bacteria. Since the work of Starkey (1929a, b, c) the frequent general studies on rhizosphere micro-organisms have usually included data of R/S values for fungi—values which have indicated that fungi increase in rhizospheres much less than do bacteria (previous comments in this chapter suggest that the application of methods for assessing amounts of mycelial development of fungi in soil and rhizospheres may require this concept to be changed). However, until recently relatively few qualitative studies on rhizosphere fungi had been made. Thom and Humfeld (1932), working with corn grown in different soils, reported that on acid to neutral soils species of *Trichoderma* predominated in the rhizosphere, whereas in alkaline soils biverticillate species of *Penicillium* (particularly of the *P. luteum* group) predominated. Katznelson and Richardson (1948) reported that in soils bearing strawberries species of *Fusarium*, *Aspergillus* and *Penicillium* were frequently isolated but from the rhizospheres of the strawberry plants *Cladosporium*, *Chaetomium*, *Rhizoctonia* and unidentified species were present. This picture could be altered by applying different soil treatments. Reviewing the work done on micro-organisms associated with plant roots Clark (1949) wrote ". . . it remains unsettled whether certain species of fungi are preferentially encouraged by plant roots." Certainly it has been shown that different varieties of the same species (differing in susceptibility to disease) may preferentially stimulate the development of certain fungi, and this phenomenon will be discussed subsequently in connection with the relations of rhizosphere micro-organisms to soil-borne pathogens. In general it still remains to be conclusively demonstrated whether or not certain species of non-pathogenic fungi make the rhizosphere their main locus of activity.

Attempts to classify fungi from rhizosphere and non-rhizosphere soil by the nutritional group method (cf. bacteria) have been rare (Atkinson and Robinson, 1955; Thrower, 1954), although a considerable amount of work has been done on the nutritional requirements of mycorrhizal fungi (Harley, 1959). Thrower (1954) reported trends for fungi similar to those observed for bacteria—a higher percentage of fungi capable of maximum growth on simple media and with amino acids in rhizosphere than in non-rhizosphere soil, and lower proportions of isolates with complex nutritional requirements. The extensions of this type of work may well provide much valuable information on rhizosphere fungi.

A renewal of interest in rhizosphere fungi over the last decade has naturally led to an increase in the general information available, but in these studies little qualitative differences have appeared between the fungi in rhizosphere and non-rhizosphere soil (Webley, Eastwood and Gimingham, 1952; Gomolyako, 1956, 1957, 1958; Khalabuda, 1958; Peterson, 1958; Chesters and Parkinson, 1959; Čatská, Macura and Vágnerova, 1960; Papavizas and Davey, 1961). Many of these studies have involved the detailed investigation of fungi in the rhizospheres of plants at various stages in the development of the roots (Peterson, 1958; Chesters and Parkinson, 1959; Čatská et al., 1960), and have shown that the qualitative nature of the rhizosphere mycoflora changes with increasing age of the roots—similar changes not being observed in non-rhizosphere soil. In general, it has been shown that during the initial phases of root development in the rhizospheres (of a range of plants) Phycomycetes predominate, particularly members of the Mucoraceae, with *Penicillium* species also being frequently isolated. With increasing age of the roots this population has been shown to change, genera of the Tuberculariaceae, Dematiaceae and sterile dark fungi increasing in frequency of occurrence. The explanation for these effects (Chesters and Parkinson, 1959) has been based on the possibly predominant effect of root exudates in the production of the rhizosphere effect in the initial stages of root growth (hence the "sugar fungi" would be the preferentially affected group) whereas in the rhizospheres of older roots dead root material is an important cause of the rhizosphere effect (hence the change in mycoflora).

The tendency to treat the rhizosphere as a uniform microhabitat has been criticized (Chesters and Parkinson, 1959). The fact that root exudates are liberated, at least in the early stages of root growth, particularly from certain areas of the roots (Pearson and Parkinson, 1961), means that from this view-point alone the rhizosphere environment will vary from point to point on a root. Sampling from specific regions of the rhizosphere (i.e. rhizosphere soil at the root tip, the crown of the root, and a zone intermediate between tip and crown) has shown (Chesters and Parkinson, 1959) that the phenomenon described earlier, of the change in qualitative nature of the rhizosphere myco-flora with changing root age, begins first in the crown zone and last in the tip zone of roots.

5. Initiation of rhizosphere effect

The initiation of the rhizosphere effect with bacteria, unlike that with the fungi, has also received considerable recent attention. Timonin (1940a), using plating techniques, recorded the stimulation of bacteria round seedling roots, and Linford (1942), using direct observation, reported the large accumula-tions of bacteria round newly developed roots of various plant species. Metz (1955) also demonstrated that when seeds germinate in non-sterile soil, bacteria produce mantles of growth about the roots and root hairs (an effect he reported to be more pronounced round roots of the Cruciferae than the Gramineae). Wallace and Lochhead (1951) demonstrated that plant seeds support characteristic microfloras (with a high percentage of chromogenic forms) and suggested that the rhizosphere microflora represented an inter-mediate group between the seed coat and soil microfloras. That even in the rhizospheres of very young wheat plants (2 to 3 days old) there was a shift towards a population of amino acid requiring bacteria and actively metaboliz-ing forms was reported by Rouatt (1959). At this young stage R/S values of about three were recorded, thus showing that the establishment of rhizosphere microfloras occurs almost as soon as the root grows into, and therefore influences, the soil with its population of micro-organisms.

Seeds, in the process of germination, liberate metabolically reactive sub-stances; hence the initial stimulation of soil micro-organisms may begin in the spermatosphere (Brian, 1957a). However, numerous workers (e.g. Osborne and Harper, 1951; Ferenczy, 1956; Ark and Thompson, 1958; Bowen, 1961) have shown that seed coats or seed coat diffusates may contain anti-microbial substances, and consequently may adversely affect the develop-ment of micro-organisms in the spermatosphere. However, in relation to the crop plants studied, the probability has been suggested of a development of the seed coat microflora into the rhizosphere, although some workers have put forward the view that the general soil population is a more important source of rhizosphere-inhabiting bacteria (Isakova, 1939; Shilova, 1955; Vagnerova et al., 1960).

Gyllenberg (1957) has reported that the bacterial flora of rhizospheres, once it is established in the seedling stage, remains qualitatively similar (but quan-titatively increasing) from the seedling stage to maturity although qualitatively different from the bacterial flora of the soil distant from the roots. After maturity, the rhizosphere bacterial population changes, a population similar to that in the non-rhizosphere soil developing. Rouatt (1959) in his work on the initiation of rhizosphere effects, states that the effects noted in the rhizo-spheres of young plants (i.e. a stimulation of amino acid requiring bacteria, ammonifying, denitrifying, cellulose-decomposing and starch and gelatin hydrolyzing organisms) are maintained, and in some cases exaggerated, as the plants grow older. However, it has been stressed (Lochhead, 1958) that as roots age the situation regarding micro-organisms in rhizospheres becomes complicated because of the superimposition of associative and antagonistic reactions between micro-organisms (e.g. amino acid, growth factor and antibiotic production, competition for energy sources, oxygen and space).

As yet there is little information available on the initiation of the rhizosphere effect on soil fungi. Timonin (1940a) investigated the nature of fungi in the rhizospheres of seedlings of a number of crop plants but failed to demon-strate any significant differences between these populations and those of the soil distant from roots. This problem requires further study using techniques designed for the isolation of organisms present in the rhizosphere in an active mycelial state (Parkinson, 1965).

6. The role of root exudates

It is generally agreed that the exudation of organic compounds by roots constitutes a major factor in the stimulation of microbial growth in the rhizo-sphere. As yet little is known on the physiological processes involved in the release of these organic materials by plant roots.

Since the work of Knudson (1920) there have been many demonstrations that exudation from roots occurs, but most of the work on root exudates has been done since 1950. The nature of root exudates has been demonstrated to be varied; carbohydrates, amino acids, vitamins, organic acids, nucleotides, flavonones and enzymes have been identified in root exudates together with substances such as saponins, glycosides and hydrocyanic acid which have toxic effects on micro-organisms.

Exudation of these materials from roots is affected by environmental conditions. Katznelson, Rouatt and Payne (1954, 1955) showed that tem-porary wilting of plants caused an increased release of amino acids from their roots. Rovira (1959) showed that under high light and temperature conditions there was increased exudation and that this was greatest during the first few weeks of growth.

It appears (Pearson and Parkinson, 1961; Schroth and Snyder, 1961) that the root tip is the zone where exudation is particularly important. However, Frenzel (1960) has indicated that the exudation of certain amino acids occurs at the root tip whilst that of other amino acids occurs in the root hair zone. This possibility has potentially important consequences on the ecology of micro-organisms in rhizospheres.

The study of root exudates has been in two main directions. First, there has been the analysis (qualitative and quantitative) of different groups of com-pounds in the exudates. This has involved, as an essential prerequisite, the growing of plants in considerable numbers under conditions of strict sterility (the presence of micro-organisms in such systems leads to drastic changes in the results obtained, a result of the metabolism of the micro-organisms). Second, there has been the use of collected exudates in model systems—the growth of pure and mixed cultures of micro-organisms in media with and without the addition of root extracts or root exudates (Chan and Katznelson, 1961, 1962) and the construction of "artificial" rhizospheres in natural soil (Timonin, 1941; Rovira, 1956b; Rivière, 1958) are two examples of this type of approach.

There are a considerable number of reports on the effects of root exudates on soil fungi, and factors have been demonstrated in root extracts which are capable of stimulating mycelial growth (Kerr, 1956), stimulating spore germination (Barton, 1957; Coley-Smith, 1960; Jackson, 1957, 1960; Schroth and Snyder, 1961; Buxton, 1962), and attracting zoospores of *Phytophthora* (Bywater and Hickman, 1959; Zentmyer, 1961). On the other hand it has been shown that the root exudates of certain plants contain substances inhibitory to spore germination and mycelial growth (Schönbeck, 1958; Buxton, 1962).

The possible role of exudates in aiding disease resistance was suggested by Timonin (1941), and Buxton (1957) showed, in working with pea varieties differing in susceptibility to the wilt pathogen *Fusarium oxysporum* f. *pisi*, that the root exudates from the wilt-resistant variety inhibited the germination of spares of the pathogen (mycelial growth was not affected), whereas root exudates from wilt-susceptible plants had no such effect; in fact they stimulated spore germination. Buxton (1958) also showed that after several sub-cultures of *F. oxysporum* f. *pisi* on a growth medium containing root exudates from the resistant pea variety, there was increased pathogeneity of the fungus towards the resistant variety.

7. The effects of foliar sprays

Recently attention has been directed to the effects of chemical sprays (fungicidal and insecticidal) on the soil microflora.

Such chemicals may operate in one or more of three possible ways on the soil microflora. First, in any spray programme, frequently a good deal of the chemical material becomes directly incorporated into the soil. Second, chemical materials may be absorbed by the leaves and translocated to other plant parts, in the process of which the metabolism of the plant may be altered and its "rhizosphere effect" changed. Third, the chemicals applied to the leaves may be translocated, and "exuded" from the roots into the rhizosphere and may exert direct effects on the rhizosphere microflora.

Hallek and Cochrane (1958) showed that the application of Bordeaux mixture to the leaves of bean plants led to an increased level of copper and reduced bacterial numbers in the rhizosphere of these plants. Davey and Papavizas (1961) similarly showed that streptomycin applied to the leaves of coleus plants was translocated (either itself or some by-product) and the rhizosphere microflora was qualitatively, but not quantitatively altered (Gram-negative bacteria being suppressed).

Vrany, Vancura and Macura (1962) studied the effects of applying a variety of substances (inorganic phosphate, antibiotics, growth regulators and urea) to leaves and found that the root exudates and rhizosphere microfloras could be markedly altered by such treatments. A number of workers have studied the effects of foliar treatments of urea: Ramachandra-Reddy (1959) showed that treatment of rice plants produced quantitative changes in the bacterial actinomycete and fungus components of the rhizosphere microfloras and Horst and Herr (1962) noted that urea treatment of corn leaves led to an increase in the rhizosphere of actinomycetes antagonistic to *Fusarium roseum* f. *cerealis* during the first week after application.

The fact that foliar applications of certain chemicals caused marked qualitative and quantitative changes in rhizosphere microfloras indicates that this is a potentially important experimental means of studying the ecology of micro-organisms in the root region and of attempting control of root-infecting micro-organisms.

B. ROOT SURFACE

Taking a strict view of the root surface as a group of microhabitats, much of the data obtained before the work of Harley and Waid (1955a, b), which will be considered later, is not strictly valid because the technique applied (the dilution procedure described below) allowed only the plating of superficial root cells contaminated with rhizosphere soil. In other words, much of the work done using this method allows a consideration of micro-organisms in the rhizoplane but not the root surface alone.

Taking this strict view of the root surface there have been, as yet, few studies of micro-organisms in this region. Of these the majority have concerned the fungi, although studies on bacteria on root surfaces and in rhizoplanes of a range of crop plants have been made (Katznelson, 1960) and have in fact demonstrated that fungal and bacterial numbers may be lower in rhizoplanes of certain crop plants than in the rhizosphere soil. In view of the foregoing comments the main emphasis in this section will be on studies of fungi on root surfaces.

1. Methods of study

Until the mid-1950's, the use of the dilution plate method also predominated in the study of root surface micro-organisms. Here the procedure, used by numerous workers, has involved, first, the preparation of a suspension of rhizosphere soil, then the transfer of the crudely washed root system to a known volume of sterile water containing an abrasive agent (sterile sand or glass beads). The shaking of the root in such a system causes the active removal of the outer cell material from the roots, and this material becomes suspended in the sterile water. From this suspension of root cells further dilutions are prepared, and samples of the suitable dilutions plated in the usual way. This technique has been shown to have two main defects—first, as stated earlier, when used for the isolation of fungi it allows the selective isolation of spores, and second, it does not allow accurate isolations from the root surface (what in fact is prepared in the suspension of root cells is a mixture of root surface material and remnants of rhizosphere soil which have not been removed from the roots).

The fact that a careful washing procedure is necessary to remove all the soil particles and loosely adhering material from roots was clearly demonstrated by Harley and Waid (1955a, b), and this work has pointed the way to a more critical examination of micro-organisms (particularly fungi) on root surfaces. The simple serial washing of roots with sterile water, and the subsequent plating of segments of washed root described by Harley and Waid (1955a, b) is, in fact, similar in principle to methods described by earlier workers (Chesters, 1948; Kurbis, 1937; Simmonds, 1930; Simmonds and Ledingham, 1937; Robertson, 1954). The efficiency of this washing technique can easily be tested by incorporating samples of the various washing waters separately into nutrient agar in petri dishes, and by counting the numbers of colonies which develop thereon (such testing is an essential preliminary to any study of root surface micro-organisms using this technique).

In most of the studies using the root washing-segment plating technique, the size of the washed root segments which have been plated has been quite large (in relation to the size of the organisms to be isolated). Thus Peterson (1958) and Čatská et al. (1960) plated 5 mm segments whilst Harley and Waid (1955a, b), Stenton (1958), Sewell (1959) and Parkinson and Clarke (1961) used 2 mm segments. Even a 2 mm segment of root may harbour more than one species (frequently several species of fungi are isolated from a single 2 mm root segment) and when this occurs, then fast growing forms may overgrow slower growing species and therefore prevent the isolation of the slower growing forms.

The sequential plating of root segments has been used by various workers (e.g. Harley and Waid, 1955a, b,) to obtain information on the possible zonation of fungi in the root systems of plants. Some of the results obtained in this way will be discussed subsequently.

In an attempt to allow the plating of smaller units of root material than the segments previously described, and in view of the difficulties in cutting segments of root smaller than 1 mm, other techniques have been devised. Stover and Waite (1953) developed a technique involving the physical maceration of roots (in a Waring blender) and the plating of samples of diluted macerate into nutrient agar. Although this technique was primarily developed for the isolation of *Fusarium* spp. from roots, it has been applied in more general studies. For many roots this technique allows the isolation of increased numbers of species, but for some roots it allows the liberation of antibiotic substances from the root tissues and these inhibit microbial development (Harley, 1960; Clarke and Parkinson, 1960). Hence this method, which allows the dispersion of small fragments of root material in a nutrient medium, must be used with caution.

A similar technique was developed by Warcup (1959) in which small pieces of root were fragmented using sterile needles, the fragments being dispersed in nutrient agar. Once again this technique must be used with caution because of the danger of releasing anti-microbial substances.

With all the techniques described, if applied to the isolation of fungi from roots, measures must be taken to cut down the amount of bacterial development. In many cases, the simple expedient of removing excess water from the roots with sterile filter paper before plating segments on to acidified agar is sufficient. However, if this is not so, then anti-bacterial substances (e.g. streptomycin) must be incorporated into the nutrient agar.

As has been indicated, the plating of washed root segments has been widely used for the isolation of fungi from roots. However, when fungi develop from such plated segments it is frequently impossible to say whether these organisms have grown from the root surface or from the interior of the root. In an attempt to investigate the degree of penetration of root tissues by fungi, Waid (1956) developed a root dissection technique in which washed roots were cut into 2 mm segments which were then dissected into outer cortical material and inner cortex plus stele. These portions of root material were then separately plated. This technique enabled Waid (1957) to investigate the distribution of fungi within senescent roots of rye-grass, and has since been used in studies on the rate of penetration of plant roots by non-pathogenic fungi (Taylor, 1962).

The isolation of fungi developing within plant roots may also be accomplished by killing the fungi developing on root surfaces using surface sterilizing agents (such as mercuric chloride, silver nitrate, and calcium hypochlorite), thus allowing fungi within the root tissues to emerge on to the nutrient isolating medium. This technique, which has long been standard practice for the isolation of pathogenic fungi, has rarely been applied for studies on non-pathogenic micro-organisms developing within plant roots.

It should be remembered that the isolation of a fungus from a root segment or fragment does not indicate the complete permeation of that plated tissue by the fungus—in fact only a small portion of the root appears to be colonized by fungi. This has been indicated by direct microscopic observation of roots stained with dyes (such as cotton blue). Such studies form an important complement to the studies involving isolation of fungi and have provided valuable information on the amount and type of fungal growth on and in plant roots.

2. Nature of root surface populations

Since the development of an easy yet efficient washing technique (Harley and Waid, 1955a, b) a number of investigations have been made on fungi growing on root surfaces and within roots of a number of plant species. The majority of these investigations have concerned crop plants, e.g. wheat, barley, red clover and flax (Peterson, 1958, 1961), peas (Stenton, 1958), dwarf bean, barley and cabbage (Parkinson, Taylor and Pearson, 1963), garlic, onion and leek (Parkinson and Clarke, 1961, 1964), whilst only a few have concerned plants growing in more natural situations, e.g. beech (Harley and Waid, 1955a, b), ling (Sewell, 1959) and ash (Kubikova, 1963).

Probably the most interesting feature of the data obtained in these investigations is that although a wide range of fungi may become intimately associated with plant roots, only a very restricted number of species appear to be isolated from apparently healthy plant roots with high frequency. These species, e.g. *Fusarium* spp., *Cylindrocarpon* spp., *Rhizoctonia* spp., *Gliocladium* spp., *Mortierella* spp., sterile mycelia (particularly dark forms), certain Penicillia (particularly *P. lilacinum*) and, for certain plants, *Trichoderma viride* are for the most part (*T. viride* being an exception) forms which are not isolated with a high frequency from the soil distant from the growing roots. So, at the root surface a selective effect of the growing root is apparent (an effect not seen for the fungi in the rhizosphere soil).

Fusarium oxysporum, frequently isolated from the surfaces of apparently healthy roots, is a species containing a number of varieties which are important specific pathogens producing wilt diseases. It seems likely that we have a situation where these varieties of *F. oxysporum* are capable of growth on and in roots of a wide range of plant species but are capable of disease production in only one species. No work has yet been done on the varietal characterization of the *F. oxysporum* isolates from healthy roots.

Work with plants growing under natural conditions has shown that frequently sterile dark mycelial fungi are important members of the root surface mycoflora. Sewell (1959) investigated *Calluna* roots growing through a podzol—where the fungus flora of the various horizons was characteristic. He found that the species isolated from these roots were much affected by the horizon in which the roots were growing.

Direct observation of roots (see above) has revealed the presence of hyphae traversing the roots. Where the roots are active the hyphae appear in many cases to be widely separated, but in older roots (where dead cortical cells are present) there is frequently much more mycelium present—presumably operating in the decomposition of the moribund root material.

Little is known regarding the role of the root surface fungi; some workers consider that they have a passive role (absorbing root exudates) with little or no effect on the physiology of the roots. However, some workers have taken the view that the colonization of roots by fungi must affect the metabolism of the root cells, and the view that certain root surface fungi (e.g. *Fusarium oxysporum*) act as mycorrhizal organisms has been put forward (Dorokhova, 1953; Bilai, 1955; Khruscheva, 1960).

3. The development of fungi on root surfaces

Stenton (1958) showed that young roots as they grow through the soil present a "virgin ecological niche" for soil micro-organisms. The day-to-day build-up of populations of fungi on plant roots has been followed in a number of crop plant species (Parkinson, Taylor and Pearson, 1963), and from these studies certain basic facts have emerged.

Prior to emergence of the primary root, substances (e.g. amino acids) are liberated from the seed; this liberation of metabolically reactive substances is continued from the root after its emergence. The possible role of such substances, first in releasing fungal spores from the fungistatic factors operating in soil, and then allowing their germination and subsequent growth along a diffusion gradient of root exudates to the growing root, has been demonstrated (Jackson, 1960). This effect of the root exudates appears to be non-selective for, from the study by Parkinson, Taylor and Pearson (1963), it seems that almost any soil fungus will grow onto plant roots; however, many of these species can be regarded as casual colonizers which cannot compete with the typical root surface forms and therefore have a limited life on root surfaces. Thus, during the first 2 or 3 days of root development, a wide range of species of fungi can be isolated from the roots (each in low frequency), but after 5 days the dominance of a small number of typical root surface forms can be seen. It appears, however, that colonization of roots by fungi does not occur until the emergent root is about one day old; after this lag period colonization begins, but the root tip region of the actively growing root remains uncolonized during the whole period of active root growth. Once a stable population of typical root surface forms has become established it appears to be maintained up to the time of senescence of the root system, the relative incidence of the individual species altering little. In some plants (Taylor and Parkinson, 1965) *Cylindrocarpon radicicola* tends to assume a more important role with increasing age of the roots.

With increasing age of plant roots there is, however, an increasing amount of penetration of fungi into the root tissues (as demonstrated by root dissection and surface sterilization). Waid (1957) demonstrated this in decomposing rye grass roots, and Taylor (1962) has shown in dwarf bean roots that little penetration of roots by the root surface fungi occurs in the first 40 days of root growth. After this there is a progressive penetration, first of the cortex and then the stele, with *Cylindrocarpon radicicola* and sterile dark forms being the dominant penetrating organisms (Parkinson, 1965).

Speculation has, as for the bacteria (see earlier), been made as to the origin of the fungi colonizing plant roots particularly in the early stages of root development. The possible sources of fungi are either the seed coat or the soil. It appears that for crop plants the fungi present on the seed surface, under normal circumstances, play little or no part in the colonization of the roots (Peterson, 1959; Parkinson and Clarke, 1964), and it is the soil which is the source of the root surface fungi. These fungi must, presumably, grow through the rhizosphere onto the root surface. Because of this it might be anticipated that the rhizospheres of even young plants would contain fungi such as *Fusarium* spp., *Cylindrocarpon* spp., *Gliocladium* spp. and the other typical root surface forms in high frequency, but this has not been shown to be the case by the isolation methods used for rhizosphere studies. The application of methods more suitable for the isolation of active fungi may reveal their presence. It has been suggested (Taylor and Parkinson, 1961) that the colonization of roots by fungi is brought about by successive lateral colonization from the soil, longitudinal growth down the root from any one point of colonization being, for the most part, restricted in extent. This gives further point to the problem of tracing the path of growth of the root surface forms from the soil distant from the roots on to the root surface.

4. Factors affecting the development of fungi on roots

The effect of soil type on the development of fungal populations on root surfaces was described by Peterson (1958). Working with plants of red clover and wheat grown in acid and alkaline soils he showed that *Fusarium* spp. predominated on roots from the acid soil whereas *Cylindrocarpon* spp. predominated on roots from the alkaline soil. Parkinson and Clarke (1961) substantiated this observation with work on leek seedlings. Further investigations on the effect of soil pH (Taylor and Parkinson, 1964) on the development of root surface fungi, where a single soil was adjusted to a range of pH levels (between pH 3·2 and 8·5) by additions of either calcium hydroxide or aluminium sulphate and dwarf bean plants then grown in each of the pH conditions, showed that the occurrence of *Fusarium* spp. on root surfaces was not markedly affected by different soil pH levels. *Cylindrocarpon radicicola*, on the other hand, showed considerably increased frequency of occurrence with increasing soil pH. In this amended soil system *Penicillium* spp. and *Trichoderma viride* were the dominant colonizers at the lowest pH value (pH 3·2). In the case of *Fusarium* spp. particularly, it would appear that soil pH is not the sole factor operating in natural soils; factors such as abundance of available inoculum and the competitive ability of the available strains will be important also.

The effect of the light regime under which plants are grown in relation to root colonization by non-pathogenic fungi was discussed by Harley and Waid (1955b). Working with beech seedlings grown in experimental frames, different shading treatments were allowed by covering the frames with different layers of butter muslin. Isolation of fungi from tap roots and lateral roots grown in light regimes varying from 25·1 to 3·8% daylight showed that at the highest light intensity *Trichoderma* sp. was the dominant organism on both types of root (with *Gliomastix* sp. an important associated form). At the lowest light intensity a *Penicillium* species dominated the tap root isolates, whilst *Rhizoctonia* sp. was the most frequent isolate from the lateral roots. The condition of the experimental plants receiving most light was much better than that of plants grown at the lower light intensities, and Harley and Waid (1955b) conclude that "the condition of the host plant is a major factor in determining the nature of the surface population of the root system," but it is not certain how far interaction between micro-organisms influences the composition of this population.

Rouatt and Katznelson (1960) studied the effect of light intensity on the bacterial flora of wheat roots, using greenhouse conditions and two light intensities (1,000 and 300 ft candles respectively) for growing the experimental plants, temperature and soil moisture content being constant for both groups of plants. Total numbers of bacteria, of methylene blue reducing forms, glucose fermenting forms and ammonifiers were much greater on the roots of plants grown under the higher light regime, also the percentage of amino acid requiring bacteria was more than double that for roots grown at the lower light regime. Using the same growth conditions together with plant growth room culture at 1,200 and 300 ft candles, Peterson (1961) studied the effect of light intensity on the development of fungi on the root surfaces of wheat and soybean. He found, however, no appreciable effect of this factor on the fungi colonizing the primary roots of the experimental plants despite the marked differences in the development of the experimental plants under the different light conditions.

The effects of different soil moisture and temperature conditions have received little study, although these factors have regularly been studied in relation to root disease fungi. Preliminary investigations on the effect of soil temperature (Taylor and Parkinson, 1964) on the development of fungi on roots of dwarf bean seedlings grown at 15, 20 and 25°c indicated decreased numbers of isolates of fungi with decreasing temperature. *Fusarium oxysporum* and *Gliocladium* spp. increased markedly in frequency of occurrence on roots with increasing soil temperature.

The effect of soil moisture content, as stated earlier, is notoriously difficult to study because of the difficulties of maintaining constant and known moisture regimes throughout the soil mass permeated by the roots under study. Data provided by Taylor and Parkinson (1964), where seedlings of dwarf beans were grown in soil at 30, 50 and 70% of the moisture holding capacity, indicated that under the lowest moisture conditions the root surface mycoflora was dominated by *Penicillium* spp. (species which rapidly disappeared with increasing soil moisture content); on the other hand *Fusarium oxysporum*, *Cylindrocarpon radicicola* and *Gliocladium* spp. increased in frequency of occurrence on roots grown under the higher moisture regimes.

The soil environment may affect the incidence of fungi on plant roots in different ways—through its effect on the growth and vigour of the higher plant, through comparable effects on the fungi concerned in root colonization, and through its effect on the plant-fungus relationship (Taylor, 1962). The data obtained by studying the effects of varying single environmental factors are notoriously difficult to interpret but at least they serve to stress the need to use controlled and defined conditions when conducting comparative experiments on the nature of the root surface mycofloras of different plants.

It has been stated earlier that from studies of the root surface fungi of a range of plant species it has become apparent that only a restricted number of species of fungi are regularly associated with plant roots—*Fusarium* spp., *Gliocladium* spp., *Cylindrocarpon* spp., *Mortierella* spp., sterile mycelial forms, with *Trichoderma viride*, *Penicillium* spp., *Rhizoctonia* spp., *Pythium* spp., and *Phoma* spp. important in certain species and not in others. However, in view of the foregoing comments on the effects of soil environmental factors, it is difficult to compare the various sets of data from which the above generalization has been drawn. Peterson (1961) grew wheat and soybean plants under constant environmental conditions and demonstrated that *Phoma* spp. were frequently isolated from the wheat roots but not from soybean roots. Parkinson *et al.* (1963) studied the development of the root surface mycofloras of seedlings of barley, dwarf bean and cabbage grown under constant environmental conditions, and showed that for dwarf bean and barley seedlings *Fusarium* spp., *Cylindrocarpon* spp. and *Gliocladium* spp. were the important root surface fungi, whereas for cabbage seedlings *Trichoderma viride* and *Penicillium lilacinum* were the dominant members of the developing root surface mycoflora. The amount of fungus material supported by the dwarf bean roots was greater than that supported by barley roots and these more than the cabbage roots; the rates of development and total root surface area of the three plant species also varied.

Once again interpretation of these data is difficult without more precise information regarding the environmental conditions operating at the root surface—is the effect of plant type on the nature of the root surface mycoflora simply a reflection of the nature of the root exudates of the different plant species? Certainly it has been shown that the factors governing the nature of root surface mycofloras are bound up with living roots growing in soil—comparisons with fungi associating themselves with dead roots and inert material (e.g. nylon thread) buried in soil show very marked differences with those obtained from living roots (Parkinson and Pearson, 1965).

C. Effects of Micro-organisms in the Root Region

From the foregoing comments it is clear that the root region (rhizosphere and root surface) represents a group of microhabitats where, as a result of the environment developed by the growing roots, microbial numbers and activity are greater than in the soil distant from the roots. It hardly seems conceivable that the development of such a population of micro-organisms on and round healthy roots will not affect both the development and the physiology of the roots; however, until recently little information has been available on such phenomena.

1. Effects on root development

The best examples of rhizosphere micro-organisms affecting the morphology of plant roots are probably those of the curling legume root hairs prior to infection by *Rhizobium* spp. and of the forking of roots which may precede mycorrhizal infections. Rovira and Bowen (1960) showed that, for subterranean clover grown in sand and agar, the presence of the general rhizosphere microflora brought about a reduction in root hair production and general root growth. However, Pantos (1956) had found that for wheat plants growing in sterile sand culture the addition of various bacteria isolated from wheat rhizosphere soil caused increased growth of both tops and roots of the experimental plants, *Agrobacterium radiobacter* bringing about a 65% increase in growth as compared with the control plants. Detailed studies on a range of plants (Bowen and Rovira, 1961) viz. *Phalaris*, subterranean clover, tomato and radiata pine, grown in sand (plus nutrients) and agar and inoculated with soil suspensions prepared from sterile and non-sterile soil showed that the presence of micro-organisms caused decreased primary root growth, decreased total root growth and decreased production of secondary roots.

Once again they showed a marked reduction in root hair production in subterranean clover in the presence of soil micro-organisms, although for tomato and *Phalaris* this reduction was only slight.

The mechanism bringing about these effects is not known. Certainly micro-organisms are capable of producing growth substances (e.g. auxins), and Brian (1957) examined 25 fungal species of β-indolylacetic acid production and found nearly all capable of this if provided with tryptophane (a compound found in the root exudates of some plants). In fact, β-indolylacetic acid seems to be a common minor metabolic product of fungi and bacteria, its operation as a stimulator or inhibitor of growth depending on the concentration with which it is applied. The curling phenomenon of legume root hairs has been shown to be an effect of β-indolylacetic acid produced by the rhizosphere Rhizobia (Nutman, 1958). Whether such growth substances produced by the general rhizosphere microflora are bringing about the phenomena described in relation to general root development has not been demonstrated.

2. Effects of antibiotic production

Another important group of metabolic products of micro-organisms are the antibiotics. Many soil organisms when grown under pure culture conditions have been shown to be capable of antibiotic production in organic matter under natural conditions (Wright, 1956a, b). In natural conditions (i.e. soil) it is assumed that antibiotic production enhances the competitive capacity of the producer in substrate colonization. For such antibiotic production to be effective in the soil there must be a supply of energy-rich materials available to allow their synthesis; the root region (with the availability of energy-rich materials as root exudates or dead root cells) would appear as a likely site for antibiotic production.

The possibility that antibiotics, if produced in the root region, might be taken up by plant roots, transported through the plant and act in a systematic capacity against certain pathogens (bacterial and fungal), has attracted the attention of various workers (Pramer, 1954; Crowdy and Pramer, 1955; Brian, 1960). However, if this production of antibiotics occurs in the root region, it has been shown likely that they may have important, deleterious effects on root physiology. Even at low concentrations a number of fungal, actinomycete and bacterial antibiotics have been shown to repress root growth (Norman, 1960a) or to injure root cells and cause a leakage of solutes from the irreversibly injured roots (Norman, 1959, 1960a, b), this latter effect being caused by several polypeptide antibiotics.

3. Effects on nutrient availability

Lipman (1935) pointed out that in the rhizosphere the soil plays an important role in plant nutrition, but that in the rhizosphere, because of their increased activity, soil micro-organisms may have marked effects (favourable or unfavourable) on the assimilation of nutrients by roots. However, until relatively recently, little work has been done on this problem, presumably because of technical difficulties involved in growing plants under sterile conditions for long periods and in assessing variations in availability (i.e. increase or decrease) of the nutrient being studied. Preliminary data provided by such workers as Gerretsen (1937, 1948), Leeper and Swaby (1940), MacLachlan (1941, 1943), Timonin (1948) and Bromfield and Skerman (1950) showed that certain micro-organisms are able to affect the availability to higher plants of certain nutrient requirements (e.g. Mn and PO_4) and that certain of these micro-organisms, because of their metabolic activities in the root region, could be the cause of certain mineral deficiency diseases.

Gerretsen (1937) and Timonin (1948) both studied the problem of Mn deficiency in oats and showed that the presence of grey speck disease in oat crops is not necessarily an expression of Mn deficiency in the soil but is also associated with the presence of certain bacteria which can oxidize Mn and render it unavailable to the oat roots. Timonin (1950) showed that, in addition to bacteria, a number of fungi are capable of oxidizing Mn salts (i.e. species of *Helminthosporium*, *Curvularia*, *Periconia*, and *Cephalosporium*), and Bromfield and Skerman (1950) added species of *Cladosporium*, *Trigschemia* and *Pleospora* to this list.

Gerretsen (1948) also approached the problem of phosphate uptake by plants, and demonstrated that some rhizosphere bacteria are capable of solubilizing insoluble phosphate. This has been subsequently demonstrated by numerous other workers (i.e. Sperber, 1958; Katznelson and Bose, 1959; Louw and Webley, 1959; Katznelson, Peterson and Rouatt, 1962). However, few workers (e.g. Gerretsen, 1948; Pikovskaia, 1948; Krassil'nikov and Kotelev, 1956) have demonstrated an increased uptake of phosphate after the addition of phosphate-dissolving bacteria to plants growing in sterile soil to which insoluble phosphate has been incorporated.

In the case of ectotrophic mycorrhizal associations with beech roots, the role of the fungal sheath around such roots in controlling phosphate uptake has been elegantly elucidated (Harley, 1959).

Attention has been directed on to the availability of organic materials in the soil to plant roots, presumably stimulated by the demonstrations that some plants are able to absorb and utilize amino acids (Ghosh and Burris, 1950; Birt and Hird, 1956), and that even proteins may be absorbed by roots (McLaren, Jensen and Jacobson, 1960).

In discussions on the utilization of organic compounds in higher plant nutrition, the role of enzymes produced by the root cells is often raised, the invertase and phosphatase activity of roots being well known (Brown and Robinson, 1955; Burstrom, 1941; Rogers, Pearson and Pierre, 1940). However, in dealing with plants growing under natural conditions it is impossible to make estimates of the enzyme activity of the plant roots alone—enzymes of microbial origin must also be taken into account. Estermann and McLaren (1961) studied the distribution of phosphatase, invertase and urease activity between barley roots and the micro-organisms in the root region of the barley plants. They demonstrated that the phosphatase and invertase activity of the root zone could be attributed in the main to enzymes of the root,

17+s.b.

whereas urease activity could be attributed solely to the micro-organisms in the root region.

The use of radio-isotopes of important nutrients has allowed a more critical approach to the problem of increased or decreased nutrient uptake by roots in the presence of root region micro-organisms. The studies on the effect of ectotrophic mycorrhizas on nutrient uptake are a classic example of this (Harley, 1959; Melin and Nilsson, 1950; Morrison, 1962a, b). There appears to have been little use, as yet, of this powerful experimental tool in analysing the effects of the general root region microflora on nutrient uptake. Subba-Rao, Bidwell and Bailey (1961) studied the effects of various fungi naturally found in the root regions of several tomato varieties on the uptake by the tomato roots of radioactive phosphate, sulphate, bicarbonate and glucose. It was demonstrated that a *Fusarium* sp. suppressed the uptake by roots of tomato varieties Bonny Best and Geneva 11 of all the nutrients used, whereas *Trichoderma viride* suppressed the uptake of inorganic ions but increased the uptake of glucose by roots of tomato varieties Moscow and Loran Blood.

4. Effects on root infection fungi

It should be remembered that any population of micro-organisms in the root region may contain, as well as saprophytes, potential parasites. If such parasites become established in the rhizosphere, they have every chance of invading the plant root system—their degree of success will then depend on the resistance of the root system. However, for a pathogen to successfully establish itself as a member of a rhizosphere microflora, it must be able to compete effectively with the saprophytes of that microflora for nutrients.

The fact that the root region is a group of microhabitats where microbial numbers and activity are enhanced, a zone where, presumably, associative and antagonistic reactions are proceeding at a higher level than in most other soil microhabitats, has led many workers to think of the rhizosphere as the first line of defence of the plant root system against attack by plant pathogens.

It has been shown that, in some cases, the presence of a rhizosphere microflora may prevent infection. Muller-Kogler (1938) showed that *Ophiobolus graminis* could penetrate the roots of many Angiosperms growing in sterile soil, these plants being immune from infection when grown in natural soil. Garrett (1939) obtained infection of roots of wheat seedlings by ascospores of *O. graminis* in sterile sand but not in unsterile sand.

The role of *Trichoderma viride* as an antagonist of various other soil fungi has been quoted in relation to resistance of flax to various wilt-producing organisms (Timonin, 1941) and in relation to the *Fomes annosus* root disease of pines (Rishbeth, 1950, 1951a, b).

However, much more work is required on the possibilities of altering rhizosphere populations in such a way as to eliminate various soil-borne pathogens from the root region (the possibility of foliar applications as a means of effecting such manipulations of rhizosphere microfloras has already been mentioned).

III. CONCLUSION

In recent years there has been a welcome change of emphasis in studies on micro-organisms in the root region—a change in the direction of studying the effects of these micro-organisms on the higher plants. Powerful techniques are now available for such studies, but new techniques and ideas are required to attack the complex group of microhabitats which comprise the root region.

Basic detailed and critical ecological data (i.e. the species complement and amount of microbial material present) for root regions is sparse, due largely to the application, by many workers, of unsuitable techniques for isolation and enumeration of micro-organisms (particularly the fungi). However, it is apparent that much reliable data in this field of study is now being obtained.

In an attempt to reduce the complexity of the root region to manageably experimental proportions it is probable that the use of simple model or artificial systems more amenable to critical biochemical and microbiological analysis will increase. From the synthesis of data from such systems might emerge a detailed picture of the mechanisms of microbial interactions in the root region and of the effects of specific organisms and groups of organisms on root physiology and development. At all events, it is certain that success in elucidating the plant-microbe inter-relationship in the root region can only come by a combined microbiological-physiological-biochemical attack on this complex problem.

REFERENCES

Agnihothrudu, V. (1955). *Naturwissenschaften*, **42**, 515–516.
Allison, F. E. (1947). *Soil Sci.* **64**, 413–429.
Allison, F. E., Gaddy, V. L. and Armiger, W. H. (1947). *Soil Sci.* **64**, 489–497.
Ark, P. A. and Thompson, J. P. (1958). *Pl. Dis. Reptr.* **42**, 645–651.
Atkinson, R. G. and Robinson, J. B. (1955). *Can. J. Bot.* **33**, 281–288.
Barber, S. A. (1962). *Soil Sci.* **93**, 39–49.
Barton, R. (1957). *Nature, Lond.* **180**, 613.
Bilai, V. I. (1955). *In* Report of Conference on Plant Mycotrophy, p. 128. U.S.S.R. Acad. of Sci. Moscow.
Birt, L. M. and Hird, F. J. R. (1956). *Biochem. J.* **64**, 305–311.
Blair, I. D. (1951). Lincoln Coll. N.Z. Tech. Publ. **5**.
Bowen, G. D. (1961). *Pl. Soil*, **15**, 155–165.
Bowen, G. D. and Rovira, A. D. (1961). *Pl. Soil*, **15**, 166–188.
Brian, P. W. (1957a). *Symp. Soc. exp. Biol.* pp. 166–182. Cambridge University Press, London.
Brian, P. W. (1957b). *In* Microbial Ecology Symposium, pp. 168–188, *Soc. gen. Microbiol.* No. **VII**. Cambridge University Press, London.
Brian, P. W. (1960). *In* "The Ecology of Soil Fungi." (D. Parkinson and J. S. Ward, eds.), pp. 115–129. Liverpool University Press.
Brisbane, P. G. and Rovira, A. D. (1961). *J. gen. Microbiol.* **26**, 379–392.
Bromfield, S. M. and Skerman, V. B. (1950). *Soil Sci.* **69**, 337–348.
Brown, J. C. (1958). *Trans. Br. mycol. Soc.* **41**, 81–88.

474 D. PARKINSON

Brown, R. and Robinson, E. (1955). *In* "Biological Specificity and Growth." (E. G. Butler, ed.), pp. 93–118. Princeton University Press.
Bürstrom, H. (1941). *Lantbr.-Högsk. Annlr.* **9**, 264–285.
Buxton, E. W. (1957). *Trans. Br. mycol. Soc.* **40**, 145–154.
Buxton, E. W. (1958). *Nature, Lond.* **181**, 1222–1224.
Buxton, E. W. (1962). *Ann. appl. Biol.* **50**, 269–282.
Bywater, J. and Hickman, C. J. (1959). *Trans. Br. mycol. Soc.* **42**, 513–524.
Čatská, V., Macura, J. and Vágnerova, K. (1960). *Folia Microbiol., Praha,* **5**, 320–330.
Chan, E. C. S. and Katznelson, H. (1961). *Can. J. Microbiol.* **7**, 759–767.
Chan, E. C. S. and Katznelson, H. (1962). *Proc. Int. Conf. Microbiol.* VIII B., 13. 4, p. 53.
Chesters, C. G. C. (1940). *Trans. Br. mycol. Soc.* **24**, 352–355.
Chesters, C. G. C. (1948). *Trans. Br. mycol. Soc.* **30**, 100–117.
Chesters, C. G. C. and Parkinson, D. (1959). *Pl. Soil,* **11**, 145–156.
Clark, F. E. (1940). *Trans. Kans. Acad. Sci.* **43**, 75–84.
Clark, F. E. (1948). *Proc. Soil Sci. Soc. Am.* (1947), **12**, 239–242.
Clark, F. E. (1949). *Adv. Agron.* **1**, 241–288.
Clark, F. E. and Thom, C. (1939). *Trans. Int. Soc. Soil Sci.* (Comm. 3), A, pp. 94–100.
Clarke, J. H. and Parkinson, D. (1960). *Nature, Lond.* **188**, 166–167.
Coley-Smith, J. R. (1960). *Ann. appl. Biol.* **48**, 8–18.
Cowan, S. T. (1955). *J. gen. Microbiol.* **12**, 314.
Cowan, S. T. (1962). *Symp. Soc. gen. Microbiol.* **12**, pp. 433–455.
Crowdy, S. H. and Pramer, D. (1955). *Chem. Ind.* 160–162.
Davey, C. B. and Papavizas, G. C. (1961). *Science,* **134**, 1368–1369.
Dobbs, C. G. and Hinson, W. H. (1953). *Nature, Lond.* **172**, 197–199.
Dorokhova, N. A. (1953). *Agrobiologiya,* **5**, 51–62.
Estermann, E. F. and McLaren, A. D. (1961). *Pl. Soil,* **15**, 243–260.
Ferenczy, L. (1956). *Acta biol. hung.* **6**, 317–323.
Frenzel, B. (1960). *Planta,* **55**, 169–207.
Garrett, S. D. (1939). *Ann. appl. Biol.* **26**, 47–55.
Garrett, S. D. (1955). *Trans. Br. mycol. Soc.* **38**, 1–9.
Garrett, S. D. (1956). "Biology of Root-infecting Fungi." Cambridge University Press, London and New York.
Gerretsen, F. C. (1937). *Ann. Bot. Lond.* **1**, 207–230.
Gerretsen, F. C. (1948). *Pl. Soil,* **1**, 51–81.
Ghosh, B. T. and Burris, R. H. (1950). *Soil Sci.* **70**, 187–203.
Gomolyako, N. I. (1956). *Zh. Mikrobiol.* **18** (3), 12.
Gomolyako, N. I. (1957). *Zh. Mikrobiol.* **19** (4), 8.
Gomolyako, N. I. (1958). *Zh. Mikrobiol.* **20** (3), 3.
Gräf, G. (1950). *Zentd. Bakt. ParasitKde* Abt. II, **82**, 44–69.
Gyllenberg, H. (1957). *Can. J. Microbiol.* **3**, 131–134.
Hadfield, W. (1960). *Nature, Lond.* **185**, 179–180.
Halleck, F. E. and Cochrane, V. W. (1950). *Phytopathology,* **40**, 715–718.
Hallsworth, E. G. (ed.). (1958) "Nutrition of the Legumes." Butterworths, London.
Harley, J. L. (1948). *Biol. Rev.* **23**, 127–158.
Harley, J. L. (1959). "Biology of Mycorrhiza." Leonard Hill Books, London.
Harley, J. L. (1960). p. 49. *In* "The Ecology of Soil Fungi." (D. Parkinson and J. S. Waid, eds.). Liverpool University Press.
Harley, J. L. and Waid, J. S. (1955a). *Trans. Br. mycol. Soc.* **38**, 104–118.

Harley, J. L. and Waid, J. S. (1955b). *Pl. Soil*, **7**, 96–112.

Hely, F. W., Bergersen, F. J. and Brockwell, J. (1957). *Aust. J. agric. Res.* **8**, 24–44.

Henderson, V. E. and Katznelson, H. (1961). *Can. J. Microbiol.* **7**, 163–167.

Horst, R. K. and Herr, L. J. (1962). *Phytopathology*, **52**, 423–427.

Hildebrand, A. A. and West, P. M. (1941). *Can. J. Res.* C, **19**, 183–198.

Hiltner, L. (1904). *Arb. dt. LandwGes.* **98**, 59–78.

Hulpoi, N. (1936). *Arch. Mikrobiol.* **7.5**, 579–583.

Isakova, A. A. (1939). *Dokl. Akad. Nauk. SSSR.*, *nov. ser.* **25**, 317.

Jackson, R. M. (1957). *Nature, Lond.* **180**, 96–97.

Jackson, R. M. (1960). *In* "Ecology of Soil Fungi." (D. Parkinson and J. S. Waid, eds.). pp. 168–176 Liverpool University Press.

Jensen, H. L. (1936). *Proc. Linn. Soc. N.S.W.* **55**, 145–154.

Jones, P. C. T. and Mollison, J. E. (1948). *J. gen. Microbiol.* **2**, 54–69.

Katznelson, H. (1946). *Soil Sci.* **62**, 343–354.

Katznelson, H. (1960). *In* "The Ecology of Soil Fungi." (D. Parkinson and J. S. Waid, eds.), pp. 192–201. Liverpool University Press.

Katznelson, H. and Bose, B. (1959). *Can. J. Microbiol.* **5**, 79–85.

Katznelson, H., Lochhead, A. G. and Timonin, M. I. (1948). *Bot. Rev.* **14**, 543–587.

Katznelson, H., Peterson, E. A. and Rouatt, J. W. (1962). *Can. J. Bot.* **40**, 1181–1186.

Katznelson, H. and Richardson, L. T. (1948). *Scient. Agric.* **28**, 293.

Katznelson, H., Rouatt, J. W. and Payne, T. M. B. (1954). *Nature, Lond.* **174**, 1110–1111.

Katznelson, H., Rouatt, J. W. and Payne, T. M. B. (1955). *Pl. Soil*, **7**, 35–48.

Katznelson, H. and Strzelczyk, E. (1961). *Can. J. Microbiol.* **7**, 437–446.

Kerr, A. (1956). *Aust. J. biol. Sci.* **9**, 45–52.

Khalabuda, T. V. (1958). *Zh. Mikrobiol.* **20** (2), 11.

Knudson, L. (1920). *Am. J. Bot.* **7**, 371–379.

Krassil'nikov, N. A. (1958). "Soil Microorganisms and Higher Plants." Academy of Sciences of the U.S.S.R., Moscow. (Translated by the Israel Program for Scientific Translations, 1961).

Krassil'nikov, N. A., Kriss, A. E. and Litvinov, M. A. (1936). *Mikrobiologiya*, **5**, 270–286.

Krassil'nikov, N. A. and Korenyako, A. I. (1944). *Mikrobiologiya*, **13**, 39–44.

Krassil'nikov, N. A. and Kotelev, V. V. (1956). *Dokl. Akad. Nauk. SSSR.*, CX, No. 5.

Khruscheva, E. R. (1960). *Izvestya Akad. Nauk. SSSR Biol.* **2**, 220–239.

Kubikova, J. (1963). *Trans. Br. mycol. Soc.* **46**, 107–114.

Kürbis, W. P. (1937). *Flora, Jena*, **131**, 129–175.

Leeper, G. W. and Swaby, R. J. (1940). *Soil Sci.* **49**, 163.

Linford, M. B. (1940). *Phytopathology*, **30**, 348–349.

Linford, M. B. (1942). *Soil Sci.* **53**, 93–103.

Lipman, J. G. (1935). *Proc. 3rd Int. Congr. Soil Sci.*

Lochhead, A. G. (1940). *Can. J. Res.* C, **18**, 42–53.

Lochhead, A. G. (1958). *Trans. R. Soc. Can.* Third Series, LII, Section V, 17–24.

Lochhead, A. G. (1959). *In* "Plant Pathology Problems and Progress 1908–1958." (C. S. Holton *et al.*, eds.), pp. 327–338. University of Wisconsin Press.

Lochhead, A. G. and Rouatt, J. W. (1955). *Proc. Soil Sci. Soc. Am.* **19**, 48–49.

Louw, H. A. and Webley, D. M. (1959). *J. appl. Bacteriol.* **22**, 227–233.

MacLachlan, J. D. (1941). *Scient. Agric.* **22**, 201–207.

MacLachlan, J. D. (1943). *Scient. Agric.* **24**, 86–94.
Macura, J. (1958). *Folia biol.* Praha, **4**, 274.
McLaren, A. D., Jensen, W. A. and Jacobson, L. (1960). *Pl. Physiol.* **35**, 549–556.
Melin, E. and Nilsson, H. (1950). *Physiologia*, **3**, 88–92.
Metz, H. (1955). *Arch. Mikrobiol.* **23**, 297–326.
Morrison, T. M. (1962a). *New Phytol.* **61**, 10–20.
Morrison, T. M. (1962b). *New Phytol.* **61**, 21–27.
Müller-Kögler, E. (1938). *Arb. biol. R.A.* **22**, 271.
Norman, A. G. (1959). *Proc. Soil Sci. Soc. Am.* **23**, 368–370.
Norman, A. G. (1960a). Proc. 7th Int. Congr. Soil Sci. II, 531–535.
Norman, A. G. (1960b). *Proc. Soil Sci. Soc. Am.* **24**, 109–111.
Nutman, P. S. (1958). *In* "Nutrition of the Legumes." (E. G. Hallsworth, ed.), pp. 87–107. Butterworths, London.
Obratsova, A. A. (1936). *Izv. Akad. Nauk. SSSR.* No. 1, 255.
Osborn, E. M. and Harper, J. L. (1951). *Nature, Lond.* **167**, 685–686.
Pantos, G. (1956). *Agrokemia Talajt*, **5**, 351–358.
Papavizas, G. C. and Davey, B. C. (1961). *Pl. Soil*, **14**, 215–236.
Parkinson, D. (1957). *Pedologie*, **7**, 146–154.
Parkinson, D. (1965). *In* "Plant Microbes Relationships," pp. 69–75. Publishing House of the Czechoslovak Academy of Sciences, Prague.
Parkinson, D. and Clarke, J. H. (1961). *Pl. Soil*, **13**, 384–390.
Parkinson, D. and Clarke, J. H. (1964). *Pl. Soil*, **20**, 166–174.
Parkinson, D. and Pearson, R. (1965). *Nature, Lond.* **205**, 205–206.
Parkinson, D., Taylor, G. S. and Pearson, R. (1963). *Pl. Soil*, **19**, 332–349.
Parkinson, D. and Moreau, R. (1959). *Annls. scient. Univ. Besançon*, **3**, 85–92.
Parkinson, D. and Williams, S. T. (1961). *Pl. Soil*, **13**, 347–355.
Pearson, R. and Parkinson, D. (1961). *Pl. Soil*, **13**, 391–396.
Perotti, R. (1926). *Proc. int. Soc. Soil Sci.* **2**, 146–161.
Peterson, E. A. (1958). *Can. J. Microbiol.* **4**, 257–265.
Peterson, E. A. (1959). *Can. J. Microbiol.* **5**, 579–582.
Peterson, E. A. (1961). *Can. J. Microbiol.* **7**, 2–6.
Pikovskaia, R. I. (1948). *Mikrobiologiya*, **17**, 362–370.
Poschenreider, H. (1930). *Zentbl. Bakt. ParasitKde* II, **80**, 369–378.
Pramer, D. (1954). *Ann. appl. Biol.* **40**, 617–622.
Purchase, H. F. and Nutman, P. S. (1957). *Ann. Bot., Lond.* **21**, 439–454.
Ramachandra-Reddy, T. K. (1959). *Phytopath. Z.* **36**, 256–259.
Rishbeth, J. (1950). *Ann. Bot., Lond.* **14**, 365–383.
Rishbeth, J. (1951a). *Ann. Bot., Lond.* **15**, 1–21.
Rishbeth, J. (1951b). *Ann. Bot., Lond.* **15**, 221–246.
Rivière, J. (1958). *Annls. Inst. Pasteur, Paris* **95**, 231–234.
Robertson, N. F. (1954). *New Phytol.* **53**, 253–263.
Rogers, H. T., Pearson, R. W. and Pierre, W. H. (1940). *Proc. Soil Sci. Soc. Am.* **5**, 285–291.
Rouatt, J. W. (1959). *Can. J. Microbiol.* **5**, 67–71.
Rouatt, J. W. and Katznelson, H. (1958). *Bact. Proc.* 58–59.
Rouatt, J. W. and Katznelson, H. (1960). *Nature, Lond.* **186**, 659–660.
Rouatt, J. W. and Katznelson, H. (1961). *J. appl. Bact.* **24**, 164–171.
Rovira, A. D. (1953). *Aust. Conf. Soil Sci.* **1**, 1–7.
Rovira, A. D. (1956a). *J. appl. Bact.* **19**, 72–79.
Rovira, A. D. (1956b). *Pl. Soil*, **7**, 209–217.

Rovira, A. D. (1959). *Pl. Soil*, **11**, 53–64.
Rovira, A. D. (1961). *Aust. J. agric. Res.* **12**, 77–83.
Rovira, A. D. and Bowen, G. D. (1960). *Nature, Lond.* **185**, 260–261.
Schönbeck, F. (1958). *Naturwissenschaften*, **45**, 63–64.
Schroth, M. N. and Snyder, W. C. (1961). *Phytopathology*, **51**, 389–393.
Schroth, M. N. and Snyder, W. C. (1962). *Phytopathology*, **52**, 751.
Sewell, G. W. F. (1959). *Trans. Br. mycol. Soc.* **42**, 343–353.
Shilova, E. I. (1955). *Vest. Leningr. gos. Univ. No. 1*, 43.
Simmonds, P. M. (1930). *Phytopathology*, **20**, 911–913.
Simmonds, P. M. and Ledingham, R. J. (1937). *Scient. Agric.* **18**, 49–59.
Skerman, V. B. D. (1959). "A Guide to the Identification of the Genera of Bacteria." Williams & Wilkins, Baltimore.
Sperber, J. I. (1958). *Aust. J. agric. Res.* **9**, 778–781.
Starkey, R. L. (1929a). *Soil Sci.* **27**, 319–334.
Starkey, R. L. (1929b). *Soil Sci.* **27**, 355–378.
Starkey, R. L. (1929c). *Soil Sci.* **27**, 433–444.
Starkey, R. L. (1931). *Soil Sci.* **32**, 367–393.
Starkey, R. L. (1938). *Soil Sci.* **45**, 207–249.
Starkey, R. L. (1958). *Bact. Rev.* **22**, 154–172.
Stenton, H. (1958). *Trans. Br. mycol. Soc.* **41**, 74–80.
Stille, B. (1938). *Arch. Mikrobiol.* **9**, 477.
Stover, R. H. and Waite, B. H. (1953). *Phytopathology*, **43**, 700–701.
Strzelczyk, E. (1961). *Can. J. Microbiol.* **7**, 507–513.
Subba-Rao, N. S., Bidwell, R. G. S. and Bailey, D. L. (1961). *Can. J. Bot.* **39**, 1759–1764.
Taylor, G. S. (1962). "Studies on Fungi Associated with Roots of Certain Crop Plants." Ph.D. thesis, University of Liverpool.
Taylor, G. S. and Parkinson, D. (1961). *Pl. Soil*, **15**, 261–267.
Taylor, G. S. and Parkinson, D. (1964). *Pl. Soil*, **20**, 34–42.
Taylor, G. S. and Parkinson, D. (1965). *Pl. Soil*, **22**, 1–20.
Thom, C., and Humfeld, H. (1932). *Soil Sci.* **34**, 29–36.
Thrower, L. B. (1954). *Aust. J. Bot.* **2**, 246–267.
Timonin, M. I. (1940a). *Can. J. Res.* C, **18**, 307–317.
Timonin, M. I. (1940b). *Can. J. Res.* C, **18**, 444–455.
Timonin, M. I. (1941). *Soil Sci.* **52**, 395–413.
Timonin, M. I. (1948). *Proc. Soil Sci. Soc. Am.* **11**, 284–292.
Timonin, M. I. (1950). *Scient. Agric.* **30**, 324–325.
Timonin, M. I. and Thexton, R. H. (1951). *Proc. Soil Sci. Soc. Am.* **15**, 186–189.
Vágnerova, K., Macura, J. and Čatská, V. (1960). *Folia microbiol., Praha*, **5**, 298–310.
Vincent, J. M. (1954). *Proc. Linnaean. Soc. N.S.W.* **79**, iv–xxxii.
Vincent, J. M. (1958). *In* "Nutrition of the Legumes." (E. G. Hallsworth, ed.), pp. 108–123. Butterworths, London.
Vrany, J., Vancura, V. and Macura, J. (1962). *Folia microbiol., Praha*, **7**, 61–70.
Waid, J. S. (1956). *Nature, Lond.* **178**, 1477–1478.
Waid, J. S. (1957). *Trans. Br. mycol. Soc.* **40**, 391–406.
Wallace, R. H. and Lochhead, A. G. (1951). *Soil Sci.* **71**, 159–166.
Warcup, J. H. (1950). *Nature, Lond.* **168**, 117–118.
Warcup, J. H. (1959). *Trans. Br. mycol. Soc.* **42**, 45–52.
Watson, R. D. (1960). *Phytopathology*, **50**, 792–794.

Webley, D. M., Eastwood, D. J. and Gimingham, C. H. (1952). *J. Ecol.* **40**, 168–178.
West, P. M. (1939). *Nature, Lond.* **144**, 1050–1051.
Wilson, P. W. (1940). "The Biochemistry of Nitrogen Fixation." University of
   Wisconsin Press.
Wright, J. M. (1956a). *Ann. appl. Biol.* **44**, 461–466.
Wright, J. M. (1956b). *Ann. appl. Biol.* **44**, 561–566.
Zagallo, A. C. and Katznelson, H. (1957). *J. Bact.* **73**, 760–764.
Zentmyer, G. A. (1961). *Science*, **133**, 1595–1596.

Chapter 16

The Decomposition of Organic Matter in the Soil

ALAN BURGES

Hartley Botanical Laboratories*
University of Liverpool, England

I. INTRODUCTION

In most natural vegetation, the amount of organic matter in the soil system remains approximately constant from one year to another, despite large seasonal additions from falling leaves and other parts of plants. This means that in any community which has reached relative stability, a rough estimate of the amount of material being decomposed can be obtained by estimating the annual litter fall and annual death of roots. The task of estimating the litter fall has been investigated by a number of workers and many of the difficulties have been overcome, but when one tries to estimate what amount of dead root material is added to the soil system annually many additional difficulties are encountered and, as yet, no satisfactory techniques have been developed. Similarly, a considerable amount is known about the succession of organisms responsible for the decomposition of litter on the soil surface but there is a dearth of satisfactory evidence about the organisms involved in root decomposition. Very few studies are available which attempt to combine information relating to the succession of organisms concerned in the decomposition with the biochemical changes which take place between leaf fall and the final mineralization of the leaf tissue.

II. THE NATURE AND THE AMOUNT OF LITTER

The litter production in forests has recently been admirably reviewed by Bray and Gorham (1964), who have summarized a great deal of information relating to the amounts of litter produced in different forests throughout the world. Most estimates of litter fall depend on catching the litter in some suitable container, but the choice of the container presents many difficulties. Except in very dense forests, there is often a risk that material which has

---

* Present address: The New University of Ulster, Coleraine Northern Ireland.

16*

fallen into the container may subsequently be blown out, so that many workers have chosen relatively deep containers. Interference by animals varies from exploration by monkeys and accidental destruction by larger animals to the eating of certain portions of the litter by foraging mammals and smaller animals. There is often considerable difficulty in providing a suitable container which does not seriously affect the moisture relations of the litter and thus affect its composition, either by leaching or by microbial spoilage. Because of practical difficulties, the area covered by the sampling container must be relatively small in relation to the forest as a whole and this presents certain statistical difficulties. These are not very great when it comes to considering the fall of relatively small leaves, but in determining the amount of larger material falling, other methods must be used. Most investigations have been concerned primarily with the smaller components of the litter, and usually this is divided into crude fractions such as leaves, bud scales, flowers, fruit and bark fragments.

The general litter production in the stable forest is often surprisingly constant. Bray and Gorham, for instance, found in four successive years values for leaves, etc., of 2·8, 3·2, 3·2 and 3·1 metric tons/ha. On the other hand, the fall of branches or stems is, as one would expect, very erratic. Comparable figures for stems, including bark, were 0·6, 3·2, 0·5 and 0·8 metric tons/ha. The amounts produced vary very greatly from one form of vegetation to another. Bray and Gorham have assembled a very extensive table of annual production of leaf and other litter from very many plant communities throughout the world. In alpine and arctic forests, leaf litter may be as low as 0·5 metric tons/ha/yr, whereas in mature secondary forest in Ghana 7 and in a mixed forest in the Congo 8·5 metric tons/ha/yr have been recorded. Total litter fall is usually about one and a half times the leaf litter.

When one examines the seasonal distribution, this varies very much with the type of vegetation and the climate. Even where one is considering the same species, as, for instance, in plantations of *Pinus sylvestris*, there may be a month or more difference between the peak of litter fall in, say, England and Germany. Furthermore, different sections of the litter fall at different times. In a broad-leafed deciduous forest, which produces its major fall of leaves over a very short period in the autumn, there is also a substantial part of the litter falling at other times of the year. It may begin with a fall of bud scales early in spring and be followed by flowering parts in summer. Although the total amounts of these may not appear to be very great, they may have an important effect on the organisms living in the litter and upper layers of the soil because of their high concentration of nutrients. In cool, temperate climates, the marked autumnal litter fall is also associated with very marked seasonal climatic changes. Both of these are associated with an increased activity of the litter and soil organisms. In evergreen forests where there may be several peaks of litter fall throughout the year, one finds similar peaks in activity of the soil organisms.

In addition to what might be regarded as the normal litter coming from the vegetation, there is often a considerable amount of material which is secondary in nature. Many animals attacking the vegetation produce a considerable amount of frass which at times can become a conspicuous feature of the litter. Where large populations of animals occur, their excreta can also be a significant part of the added organic matter.

Carlisle, Brown and White (1966a) gave a detailed account of litter fall in an oak woodland, and examined in detail many aspects of litter fall and the chemical constitution of the various components. They also studied the effect of *Tortrix* attack on the quantity and nature of the litter produced. Table I gives detailed information of the amounts of the various components. Examination of Table I gives a good measure of the complexity of the biological problems involved in litter decomposition. Most of our information at present available has been concerned with the decomposition of leaves and, to a smaller extent, of branches. The successional patterns associated with the decomposition of these two very different substrates are correspondingly very different. It would not be unreasonable to anticipate that additional successional patterns are involved for each of the fractions of the litter dealt with in Table I.

The amount of root material added annually to the soil is difficult to estimate. Table XX of Bray and Gorham (1964) shows that the net production of below-ground parts is usually about two-thirds the weight of leaves produced in temperate forests, whereas in tropical forests the below ground production is nearer to one-third of the leaf production.

III. INITIAL INVASION OF TISSUES

Many investigations of the decomposition of litter have been restricted to studying the changes which take place in leaves after they have fallen to the ground; however, it is clear from a number of studies that considerable changes occur in the leaf before it is shed and, in many cases, a considerable microbiological population is already well established on the leaf before it dies. Some of the organisms are clearly parasitic and invade the living leaf tissues. Others are purely superficial and are able to live on material which is either exuded or which diffuses from the leaf. Little has been done towards investigating the organic matter which is available to micro-organisms growing on the leaf surface. Recently, Carlisle *et al.* (1966b) have shown that rainwater which had passed through the canopy of an oak woodland contained a considerable amount of dissolved organic matter. In August about 70% of the organic matter was carbohydrate, mainly melezitose, glucose and fructose. About 90 kg/ha of carbohydrate came down in the throughfall during the year. Presumably much of this organic matter was initially on the leaf surface. The presence of large amounts of organic material on foliage is often associated with insect attack. Melezitose, a trisaccharide, occurs in the honey dew of aphids and inositol is associated with scale insects.

In recent years there has been a tendency to use the term "phyllosphere" to describe the region around the leaf and to refer to a phyllosphere flora. The organisms which are found most commonly on leaf surfaces are ones

TABLE I

The mean dry weight of litter (kg/ha oven (105°C) dry weight) falling throughout the year (1963–64) in a sessile oak woodland (Table III from Carlisle et al., 1966a)

	Tree leaves			Male flowers	Bud scales	Acorns and peduncles*	Twigs (<40 cm long)	Branches (>40 cm long)	0·2–0·6 mm materials (insect frass, dust, etc.)	0·6 mm miscellaneous materials (lichen, litter bark, etc.)	Totals
	Oak	Birch	Others								
June 1963	21·15	0	0	128·74	79·93	0	82·34	0	30·25	2·10	344·51
July	16·71	0	0	2·53	10·92	0	41·27	0·37	4·69	14·43	90·92
August	37·62	0	0·83	1·42	13·88	0	67·19	22·57	3·85	15·66	162·19
September	228·22	2·25	0	1·20	16·74	46·04	133·90	7·92	5·46	13·07	455·63
October	1362·07	4·72	2·84	0·37	14·37	2·65	290·70	226·78	5·40	8·39	1918·29
November	421·99	0	1·05	0·89	15·05	3·08	56·03	98·34	6·60	20·88	623·91
December	5·40	0	0	0	0·56	0	4·48	3·33	1·05	2·03	16·85
January 1964	0·71	0	0·02	0	0·43	0	53·44	0	1·20	2·84	58·64
February	10·17	0	0·01	0	0·26	0	3·76	1·31	0·83	1·83	18·17
March	1·41	0	0	0·02	0·63	0	0·21	0	1·95	4·93	9·15
April	4·04	0	0	0	1·82	0	7·62	40·27	1·45	3·85	59·05
May	5·33	0	0	14·55	37·19	0	6·96	14·69	8·94	12·82	100·48
Total	2114·82	6·97	4·75	149·72	191·87	51·77	747·90	415·58	71·67	102·83	3857·79
	(±233·64)	(±3·61)	(±6·07)	(±39·56)	(±18·96)	(±34·35)	—	—	(±7·03)	(±28·77)	—

95% confidence limits in parenthesis.

* No ripe seed. All aborted peduncles and cupules.

which can make rapid use of simple organic substances. The surface flora often consists mainly of yeast-like fungi such as *Pullularia*, and *Cladosporium*. They have only a limited capacity for decomposing the more complex carbohydrates but are able to grow very readily on simple hexoses and pentoses, as well as on the simpler polysaccharides and substances such as pectins. Even under relatively dry conditions, extensive populations of such fungi build up on the leaf surfaces. In moister climates, the surface flora becomes very much richer, both in numbers of individuals and in species. The most extensive growths, such as the Sooty moulds are often associated with insect injury and the formation of honey dew or other sugary secretions.

In recent years, considerable evidence has accumulated to change the traditional picture of leaf physiology. It was earlier considered that very little material came out from the leaf tissues so long as the leaf was alive, although it had been established that if the leaf became senescent, there appeared to be a withdrawal of both organic and mineral material from the leaf prior to it being shed. Work by a number of authors has recently established that there are considerable losses of both organic matter and mineral matter from the leaf. As Stenlid (1958) has pointed out, too little regard has been paid to this phenomenon. The most detailed study available is that of Carlisle, Brown and White (1966b). They collected and analysed both the incident rain and the throughfall. Their results showed that inorganic nitrogen and phosphorus were removed from the precipitation as it passed through the canopy, but that considerable quantities of other elements were released. When Carlisle and his colleagues examined the total addition of materials to the soil, they found that 17% of the nitrogen, 37% of the phosphorus, 72% of potassium and 97% of the sodium came down in the throughfall and not in the litter.

It is important to remember that many plants do not have the clear deciduous pattern which is often regarded as characteristic of temperate regions and on which so much ecological discussion has been based. Under natural conditions, plants such as grasses have nothing comparable to leaf fall in the way that a deciduous tree such as oak or beech has; instead, the leaf tissue and stem dies *in situ* and under damp conditions a major part of the decomposition occurs while the tissue is still attached to the plant. Webster (1956, 1957) has shown that the moribund tissue of *Dactylis* is invaded first by the primary saprophytes *Cladosporium, Epicoccum, Alternaria, Leptosphaeria* and *Pleospora* which advance up the stem as the new leaves unfold, and different saprophytic fungi are associated with different nodes. This seems to be related to the differences in water content of the tissues. Subsequently when the stems collapse, different fungi make their appearance on the stems. Comparable results were obtained by Frankland (1966) in her study of the decomposition of *Pteridium* petioles. Here again under natural conditions invasion and considerable decomposition would seem to occur before the petioles become incorporated with the litter proper. When one comes to consider the decomposition of twigs and branches as distinct from the decomposition of leaves, again a considerable part of the decomposition may occur

before the tissue has fallen to the ground. In tropical rain forests, very extensive disintegration of branch systems may be brought about by fungi and
white ants before any substantial branch fall occurs, so that often the dead
tree has lost the bulk of its branch system before the trunk finally falls to
the ground.

During an investigation of the decomposition of pine litter (Kendrick and
Burges, 1962), it was shown that the parasites *Coniosporium*, *Lophodermium*
and *Fusicoccum* occurred very widely on the needles while they were still alive,
although usually the infections were relatively light and would not normally
have been classed as disease infections of any importance. The behaviour of
the parasites differs considerably. In *Pinus sylvestris*, if the needles die, the
activity of *Conopsporium* decreases and by the time the needles are shed, the
parasite has ceased its activity. *Lophodermium*, on the other hand, remains
quite active and, 6 months after the needles have fallen to the ground,
sporulates extensively and then dies away. *Fusicoccum* differs still again. In
the living needle, the areas of *Fusicoccum* mycelium are relatively small but
there is an extensive development of the fungus at the time that the needle
dies and falls, followed by the heavy production of spores 3 to 5 months later.
An examination of a number of other leaf parasites shows a comparable
range in behaviour. Most non-parasitic forms such as *Pullularia* often show
a great burst of activity immediately following the death of the leaf and its
fall to the ground. Once the fallen leaves become part of the litter, invasion
by characteristic litter species is very rapid and the parasitic and saprophytic
species associated with the leaf on the trees are fairly rapidly displaced.

IV. DECOMPOSITION PROCESSES IN THE LITTER

There is an extremely wide range of types of litter. Much of our knowledge
is influenced by work in Western Europe, where it has become customary
to regard the two extreme types, mor and mull, as characteristic of two essentially different patterns of decomposition. In mor humus there is normally a
substantial litter layer which remains relatively undisturbed. Successive leaf
falls bury the previous material so that a stratified litter layer is produced
with the most recently fallen material at the surface and the oldest and most
decomposed at the base of the litter. Therefore the sequence from the top of
the litter to the surface of the mineral soil can be used to study the succession
which occurs during the decomposition. Although the animal populations
in such litter may be very large indeed in terms of the numbers of individuals,
the organisms themselves are small and cause no significant movement of the
decomposing plant tissues. In a characteristic mull condition, incorporation
of the fallen material into the soil is very much more rapid. Often this is
brought about by the action of earthworms (*Lumbricus*) or other animals.
The fallen plant material may be cut up and removed into the burrows or
smaller leaves may be dragged down whole. Except for brief periods of the
year immediately following leaf fall, it is usually impossible to distinguish
clearly any junction between the fallen litter and the mineral soil. All

intermediate conditions between a characteristic mor and mull exist and a number of terms such as "moder" have been introduced for intermediate types.

Many reasons have been advanced to explain why in one place mor and in another mull should develop. At times where general conditions are such that they would appear to be on the borderline between mull and mor formation, it would seem that the presence or absence of earthworms may be decisive.

One factor of extreme importance in relation to litter is the length of time that an individual leaf may take between leaf fall and final decomposition. In cool, temperate conditions and particularly in conifer forests, years are involved. Kendrick (1959) has shown that a period of over 9 years is needed before the needles of *Pinus sylvestris* are sufficiently decomposed to become no longer recognizable as individual needles. In typical mull soil, leaves of oak may take 8 or 9 months before complete disintegration, whereas in moist forests of the warm temperate or tropical regions, a leaf may disintegrate in a matter of weeks after falling to the ground.

The nature of mull and mor humus has been discussed in very considerable detail by Handley (1954), who has suggested that a critical feature of mor humus is that phenolic materials in the leaf tissue tan the protein and form a protective coating over the cellulose of the leaf, thus inhibiting rapid decomposition. Handley's general hypothesis is in accordance with a great deal of field observation which suggests that mor formation is normally associated with a vegetation relatively rich in phenolic compounds and of low base content which gives rise to a relatively acid litter layer. Such litter does not support large numbers of bacteria or earthworms.

Invasion by the characteristic litter fungi appears to occur relatively rapidly. The total number of species in the initial invasion is usually small and most workers report only about half a dozen species as being abundant in the initial stages. At times (Kendrick and Burges, 1962) one can distinguish clearly between species which form superficial networks of hyphae (*Sympodiella* and *Helicoma*) and others which form extensive internal mycelia (*Desmazierella*). The extent of invasion by individual species varies considerably and is often determined by the previous history of the tissue concerned. Some of the parasitic species which have invaded the living leaf often form well-defined marginal zones to the areas they have invaded. This is particularly marked in the invasion by *Lophodermium*. When the litter fungi commence their activity, they often spread fairly rapidly until they reach one of the zones of demarcation caused by *Lophodermium*. Extension of the mycelium is then inhibited and the tissues on the other side of the demarcation zone may be invaded by a different species. In mor litter, there may be a fairly prolonged period, sometimes even as much as 6 months, between the initial invasion and sporulation, as happens in the Delamere Forests, where extensive sporulation of *Desmazierella*, *Sympodiella* and *Helicoma* occurs 6 to 8 months after the needle has fallen to the ground.

When attempts are made to isolate the fungi concerned in the initial invasion, many colonies of fungi such as *Penicillium* and *Trichoderma* are obtained, although direct microscopic examination of the leaf tissues suggests that the bulk of the hyphae seen belong to genera which have dark coloured mycelium. Characteristic spore-producing structures of *Penicillium* and *Trichoderma* do occur, but it is difficult to gain any accurate measure of the importance of these species in terms of their biochemical activity from the small number of fruiting structures observed.

In many of the situations examined, the initial phase of invasion by fungi is replaced by a period of fairly intense animal activity. In pine litter, this is associated with the occurrence of large populations of oribatid mites, although undoubtedly other members of the litter fauna are also very active. Some of the species occurring in pine litter are shown in Table II. The litter fauna feed both on the fungi and on the leaf tissue. Examination of faecal pellets of mites would indicate that they tend to graze indiscriminately on fungi, infected leaf tissue and uninfected tissue. After the first grazing of the fungus-covered leaves, there is often an intermediate period associated with the dryer summer conditions in which mite populations in the upper litter layers are much smaller and fungal growth is much less apparent. Subsequent leaf fall and onset of moister conditions in autumn and winter lead to a second burst of microbial activity which is again followed by extensive animal activity. By this time, the older leaves have become more deeply incorporated in the litter and are less subjected to moisture fluctuations. The seasonal fluctuations of microbiological and animal activity in these areas also becomes less marked.

Histochemical investigations of the leaves during the phases which have just been described indicate that most of the simpler carbohydrates, such as starch and pectins, disappear within a few weeks after the leaves have fallen to the ground. Decomposition of a considerable proportion of the cellulose walls is associated with the growth of many of the dark-coloured fungi and with the presence of *Trichoderma*.

Extensive invasion by the hyphae of basidiomycetes does not usually occur until the leaf litter is sufficiently compressed to remain moist for quite long periods. Extensive development of fungi then takes place, so that the individual leaves often become matted together by wefts of fungal hyphae, many of which bear obvious clamp connections or can at times be associated directly with fruiting bodies of basidiomycetes. Both in pine forests in Europe and in some dipterocarp forests in the Tropics, basidiomycete invasion of leaves may be purely internal, but there are connections between mycelia developed in one leaf *via* rhizomorphs to mycelia in adjacent leaves. This commonly occurs with *Marasmius androsaceus* in Europe and with other species of *Marasmius*, or what appear to be related fungi, in the tropics. Field observations on litters of different types indicate that the depth of the matted fungal zone in mor litter is determined primarily by the micro-climate of the litter rather than by the chemical nature of the components of the litter or the species involved.

At the stage at which there is extensive microbial development, there is a fairly rapid loss of both cellulose and lignin. This is accompanied by considerable activity on the part of the soil fauna, which often completely destroy the mesophyll tissue of the leaves, leaving only the vascular strands and the cuticular tissue or the toughened margins of the leaves. With the intense

TABLE II

List of the commoner Meiofauna found in the
organic horizon at Delamere Forest
(Kendrick and Burges, 1962)

Phylum: Annelida	
Class: Chaetopoda	
Order: Oligochaeta	
Family: Enchytraeidae	
	Fredericia spp.
Phylum: Arthropoda	
Class: Arachnida	
Order: Acarina	
Family: Oribatidae	
	Adoristes ovatus
	Carabodes minusculus
	Ceratoppia bipilis
	Chamobates incisus
	Odontocepheus elongatus
	Oppia unicarinata
	Pelops tardus
	Platynothrus peltifer
	Thyriosoma lanceolata
	Immature Oribatei
Subphylum: Insecta	
Class: Apterygota	
Order: Collembola	
Family: Entomobryidae	
	Orchesella cincta
	Lepidocyrtus sp.
Class: Pterygota	
Subclass: Exopterygota	
Order: Hemiptera	
Family: Aphididae	
	Cinaria pinea
Subclass: Endopterygota	
Order: Diptera	
Family: Cecidomyiidae	
	Cecidomyia baeri

animal activity, the amount of black faecal material increases. Initially, this appears to be mainly due to the activity of mites and collembola and the pellets retain their individual structure for quite long periods, perhaps because of the presence of an outer membrane. However, as the pellets accumulate, the Enchytraeidae become more noticeable and instead of the predominance of discrete pellets, amorphous black material which may well be the excreta of Enchytraeidae becomes much more abundant. At this stage, the residual leaves are usually dark in colour, very soft and fragile. Their final disappearance is associated with the activity of somewhat larger organisms such as millipedes. At the junction of the litter and the mineral soil, there is often a well-marked greasy layer, the H layer of Hesselmann. To the naked eye, this is amorphous and almost black. Under the microscope, it is seen to be a mixture of faecal pellets in all stages of disintegration, fragments of leaf tissue and hyphae and very often the exoskeletons or other chitinized remains of soil animals. Gray and Bell (1963) isolated a number of fungi from the chitinous-rich H layer and showed that some of the most abundant species, *Mortierella parvispora*, *Trichoderma viride* and *Penicillium spinulosum*, have the capacity to break down chitin actively under laboratory conditions. This phase may well represent one of the final stages in the mineralization of both primary and secondary organic materials in the litter. There is considerable evidence to show that some of the highly dispersed amorphous dark-coloured material in the H layer is washed downwards into the upper layers of the mineral soil.

V. CHEMICAL CHANGES DURING THE DECOMPOSITION OF THE LITTER

The chemical changes associated with the breakdown of the litter have been followed only in the most general terms. Most investigators have used a very simple form of analysis in which they have estimated the water-soluble, alcohol-soluble, ether-soluble, presumptive hemicellulose, presumptive cellulose and presumptive lignin fractions. More detailed investigations have been made of the fate of individual mineral constituents and, to a lesser extent, of nitrogenous material. In broad terms, the water soluble components disappear first, followed successively by the alcohol and the ether soluble fractions, then the hemicelluloses, celluloses and lignin fractions. Many of the studies have been somewhat difficult to interpret because the method of analysis used involves hydrolysis with weak acid to remove the hemicelluloses, with strong sulphuric acid to remove cellulose, and the residue has been regarded as lignin plus mineral material. While this is reasonably true in fresh plant material, when any extensive decomposition has occurred a number of other substances which are resistant to strong sulphuric acid are found and these give a falsely high reading for lignin content.

During decomposition, the C/N ratio of the litter undergoes a progressive change. As the decomposition proceeds, carbon dioxide is given off but the nitrogenous material tends to accumulate in the organisms carrying out the decomposition, so that the C/N ratio is progressively reduced. Freshly fallen plant material may have a C/N ratio as low as 20:1 in nitrogen-rich species such as some Leguminosae, whereas in woody tissues or in nitrogen-poor species, the C/N ratio may be of the order of 50:1. In the H layer, the C/N ratio is usually near to 10 or 12:1, which corresponds approximately to that found in micro-organisms. At this stage, the proteins are broken down to amino acids and deamination occurs with the release of ammonia, which appears to be absorbed directly by plant roots under mor conditions.

The behaviour of the mineral fraction of the litter shows a number of interesting features. Sodium is very rapidly removed from the freshly fallen litter and much of the potassium is washed out within a few weeks. The phosphate content also falls rapidly, as does the magnesium content. Part of the calcium seems to be fairly rapidly mobilized, but something like half of it remains quite firmly held in the plant material. Detailed studies on the litter of *Casuarina* (Burges, 1956) demonstrated that the mobilized sodium, once having been released from the tissues, is readily washed through the litter and presumably disappears in the drainage water. On the other hand, the magnesium, phosphate and, to a lesser extent, potassium which are released from the freshly fallen material appear to be trapped in the lower layers of the litter and accumulate in the zone of dense fungal mycelium, where it is held until the mycelium is in turn decomposed or is translocated by the fungus.

Microbial utilization of the sugars, starches and pectins seems to be very rapid and it is difficult to detect any appreciable quantities of these in the litter. Physiological tests on micro-organisms isolated from the litter indicate that practically all the litter species are capable of utilizing these simple substrates. The decomposition of cellulose can again be accomplished by a wide range of species. It is interesting to note that although in any one soil, one may be able to isolate 30 to 40 species of micro-organisms which under laboratory conditions can decompose cellulose rapidly, if cellulose films are added to that soil, only one or two species usually dominate the film. These species are relatively constant for the particular soil. Changing soil conditions even only slightly will often change completely the species which appear to dominate the decomposing cellulose (Griffith and Jones, 1963). The majority of the larger fungi which occur in litter seem to be active decomposers of cellulose and some also of lignin. The one group which characteristically lacks the ability to decompose these substrates is the mycorrhizal fungi (Harl, 1959). Many of the common species of *Collybia*, *Marasmius*, *Tricholoma*, etc., are very active cellulose decomposers.

The decomposition of lignin seems to be carried out primarily by basidiomycetes and a relatively small number of ascomycetes. Our knowledge of the decomposition of lignin is derived almost entirely from a study of the decomposition of wood or sawdust and the fungal species which have been examined in detail are primarily those associated with woody substrates. Although one may perhaps assume that the decomposition of the lignified tissue in vascular strands of leaves forms the same kind of biochemical pattern as the decomposition of wood, this is not necessarily so. In recent years there has been considerable interest in the decomposition of compounds which are not normally regarded as major constituents of the plant tissue, such as chitin, cutin, flavonoids, suberin, etc., because although these particular compounds may comprise only a small percentage of the total material, the absolute amounts of these added to the soil is considerable.

One of the most characteristic features of decomposing litter is the gradual darkening of the tissues and ultimately the formation of the black material grouped under the vague name "humus". Despite the immense amount of work carried out by both chemists and biologists, virtually nothing is known about the process which leads to the formation of humus and not a great deal has been added to our knowledge since Waksman's account of 1936. In pine litter, black material which has many characteristics of humic acids makes its appearance in a relatively early stage of the decomposition of the needles, usually considerably before one can detect any disintegration of the lignin. At the stage where lignin begins to decompose, there is usually a marked increase in the amount of humic acids. It is also apparent that during the microbial decomposition of the litter, many of the fungal species which are present in great abundance have dark pigments either in their hyphal walls or in their spores. As pointed out earlier (p. 9, see also Burges, Hurst and Walkden, 1964) there is good reason for believing that humic acids are essentially complex polymers of phenolic materials and that the phenols concerned may have come from flavonoid material in the plant debris, from the decomposing lignin and perhaps also from microbial syntheses. Even if such a view is correct, there is still no evidence to show whether the flavonoids and the lignin are first broken down to their monomeric units and then re-polymerized, or whether they are incorporated into the complex polymer with only relatively slight degradation or modification.

The biochemical processes involved in the decomposition of the various substrates differ considerably. Readily soluble substances such as the simple sugars and amino acids appear to be absorbed directly and then metabolized within the microbial tissue. Other substances, such as starch and pectins, are broken down by extracellular enzymes which can at times diffuse appreciable distances from the organisms which produce them and hydrolize their substrate. The products of hydrolyses are then available for absorption not only by the organism which caused the initial hydrolysis, but by any other microorganism which may be in the near vicinity. It is interesting to note that most of the species associated with this kind of process in nature have relatively high growth rates and often tend to form relatively dense, short-lived mycelia. Decomposition of cellulose is also brought about by a hydrolytic enzyme system which usually contains two or more components which act differently on the polymer chain. Although the enzyme systems are extra-cellular, they seldom act at any great distance from the micro-organisms which produced them. The production of the cellulase enzymes seems to be very sensitive to environmental conditions and examination of buried films of cellulose suggests that some other factors than the presence of cellulose often become limiting. Availability of nitrogenous materials is the most common factor which seems to influence the rate of cellulose decomposition.

The decomposition of the phenolic polymers, lignin and humic acids is less well understood. As yet, no one has demonstrated any enzyme system capable of decomposing these substrates. Hurst and Burges (1966) have assembled evidence to show that there are many features in common between the processes involved in the breakdown of these two types of substrates. In both substrates, it has been suggested that a critical step in the decomposition is the breakage of the ether-oxygen links in the polymer. The initial stage in the decomposition of humic acid appears to be a reduction of carboxyl groups and it has been suggested that this leads to a weakening of the ether link. In the decomposition of lignin, it is relatively easy to detect a number of intermediate degradation products, of which vanillic acid and syringic acid can most readily be demonstrated. No comparable intermediate products have been obtained in the biological degradation of humic acids but chemical degradation (Burges *et al.*, 1964) reveals the presence of comparable compounds.

Once lignin or humic acid has been degraded to simpler aromatic substances, these would form suitable substrates for a wide range of soil organisms, as has been shown by Henderson (1957). It is highly probable that, in the same way that the physical breakdown of the plant tissue is carried out by a succession of organisms belonging to widely separated taxonomic groups, so the decomposition of a complex substrate such as lignin would involve a succession of micro-organisms, each of which might carry out a relatively small number of biochemical steps.

VI. DECOMPOSITION PROCESSES IN THE MINERAL SOIL

The two major sources of organic matter in the mineral layers of the soil are the death of roots and the bringing down of organic matter from the litter layers. This latter may be due either to the washing down of dissolved or dispersed organic matter, as occurs under mor humus, or by the active transport of relatively undecomposed debris by soil animals, as occurs in mull soils.

The processes of decomposition of root tissues are in many ways similar to those which have been described for the decomposition of material in the litter. There are, however, a number of well-marked differences. First, the moisture conditions in the soil fluctuate less than in the litter and second, roots usually carry a very much more extensive surface flora and are subject to continued exploration by neighbouring micro-organisms. As a root ages, the outer tissues decrease in physiological importance and this is associated with a decrease in the resistance of the tissue and a consequential invasion by weak parasites and saprophytes. Although the micro-organisms involved differ taxonomically from those which occur in the litter, the decomposition appears to follow the same kind of pattern that has already been described. In soils which are reasonably porous there is usually quite extensive animal activity, which again plays an important part in the decomposition processes, although one does not meet the marked successional and seasonal pattern which appears to be so characteristic of mor litter. Where aeration is impeded, either by fine texture or by waterlogging, the normal processes of decomposition are inhibited. Not only does the plant material accumulate but so also does the structural material of micro-organisms and particularly fungal hyphae.

It has already been pointed out that in the litter layer, years are often involved in the decomposition of leaf and stem fragments on the surface. The duration of some of the organic fractions in the mineral soil may, however, be very considerably longer than this. Paul *et al.* (1964) have extracted humic acid fractions from some of the prairie soils in North America and on the basis of ^{14}C-dating work have estimated that the humic acids had what they termed a "mean residence" period of about 1,000 years. In a podzol under *Pinus* in Sweden, Tamm and Östlund (1960) found that the mean residence period for the humic acids in the B horizon was about 400 years. In contrast to this, the B horizon humic acid of podzols under the East Anglian heaths had ^{14}C-ages ranging between 1,580 and 2,860 years (Perrin *et al.*, 1964).

REFERENCES

Bray, J. R. and Gorham, E. (1964). *Adv. ecol. Res.*, 2, 101–152.
Burges, A. (1956). *Proc. 6th Int. Congr. Soil. Sci. Paris II*, 741–745.
Burges, A., Hurst, H. M. and Walkden, B. (1964). *Geochim. cosmochim. Acta*, 28, 1547–1554.
Carlisle, A., Brown, A. H. F. and White, E. J. (1966a). *J. Ecol.* 54.
Carlisle, A., Brown, A. H. F. and White, E. J. (1966b). *J. Ecol.* 54, 87–98.
Frankland, J. C. (1966). *J. Ecol.* 54, 41–64.
Gray, T. R. G. and Bell, T. F. (1963). *In* "Soil organisms" (J. Doeksen and J. van der Drift, eds.), pp. 222–230. North Holland Publ. Co., Amsterdam.
Griffith, E. and Jones, D. (1963). *Trans. Br. mycol. Soc.* 46, 285–294.
Handley, W. R. C. (1954). *Bull. For. Commun., London*, No. 23, H.M.S.O.
Harley, J. L. (1959). "The Biology of Mycorrhiza." Leonard Hill Books, London.
Henderson, M. E. K. (1957). *J. gen. Microbiol.* 16, 686–695.
Hurst, M. H. and Burges, A. (1966). "Lignin and Humic Acids" (in press).
Kendrick, W. B. (1959). *Can. J. Bot.* 37, 907–912.
Kendrick, W. B. and Burges, A. (1962). *Nova Hedwigia*, 4, 313–342.
Paul, E. A., Campbell, C.A., Rennie, D. A. and McCallum, K. D. (1964). in the reports of the Inter. Soil Sci. Congress, Bucharest 1964. *Chem. Comm.*
Perrin, R. M. S., Willis, E. H. and Hodge, C. A. H. (1964). Nature, *Lond.* 202, 165.
Stenlid, G. (1958). *Encycl. Pl. Physiol.* 4, 615–637.
Tamm, C. O. and Ostlünd, H. G. (1960). Nature, *Lond.* 185, 706.
Webster, J. (1956). *J. Ecol.* 44, 517–544.
Webster, J. (1957). *J. Ecol.* 45, 1–30.

Chapter 17

Soil Micro-Organisms and Plant Protection Chemicals

N. WALKER

Rothamsted Experimental Station
Harpenden, Herts., England

I. INTRODUCTION

During the last 20 or 30 years, tremendous advances have been made in the development and use of synthetic organic substances for controlling various pests, diseases and weeds. Consequently, an ever-increasing quantity and variety of potent, synthetic compounds find their way into soil. Many of these compounds are highly specific poisons to insect or other pests, or they are herbicides against different species of weeds, but the specificity is not complete and secondary effects on desirable plants or organisms can be caused. The toxicity and persistence of these compounds in soil, therefore, may raise serious problems. The fate of such substances needs careful study if harmful consequences to plants, animals and humans are to be avoided. Much attention has already been given to this subject and there are numerous reviews dealing with different aspects of the interactions between soil micro-organisms and pesticides and other chemicals (see, e.g., Audus, 1960; Bollen, 1961; Martin and Pratt, 1958; Eno, 1958; Fletcher, 1960; Freed and Montgomery, 1963; Martin, 1963; Newman and Downing, 1958).

Two general lines of inquiry are of interest and concern to the soil microbiologist: first, the effects of unusual synthetic chemicals on agriculturally useful soil micro-organisms; and, second, the part played by micro-organisms in detoxifying and decomposing such chemicals. Many of these modern compounds are very potent and a few pounds per acre are often sufficient to achieve an acceptable control of weeds or insect pests. Such amounts, for example of the substituted phenoxyacetic acid herbicides, have no harmful effects on the majority of soil micro-organisms; indeed, there is little evidence that any of the widely used herbicides and pesticides have any lasting deleterious action on the soil microflora (Martin and Pratt, 1958; Eno, 1958; Newman and Downing, 1958). The most harmful substances seem to be various fungicides and fumigants (e.g. chloropicrin, formaldehyde, aliphatic halogen compounds) which can have a partial sterilizing effect; but, even with these, the soil becomes recolonized in course of time and eventually the ecological balance is restored. This aspect, therefore, will not be considered here.

The part played by soil micro-organisms in degrading residual toxic chemicals is more relevant as it is a vital factor in maintaining soils in a useful and fertile condition. A more detailed consideration of this role forms the subject of this chapter. The discovery of the so-called hormone herbicides, 2,4-dichlorophenoxyacetic acid and related compounds, was a crucial one in the modern phase of using highly selective substances for plant protection and pest control; moreover, these compounds were among the first to be found susceptible to bacterial decomposition in the soil. Thus, it is not surprising that more work has been done on the investigation of the microbiological decomposition of herbicides than of other plant protection chemicals.

Some knowledge of the bacterial metabolism of aromatic substances, which has been particularly useful in later investigations of the biological degradation of synthetic herbicides, existed before the discovery of these herbicides. The utilization of such unlikely nutrient sources as hydrocarbons and other aromatic compounds by bacteria has received increasing study during the last 30 years (see reviews by Happold, 1950; Zobell, 1946, 1950; Evans, 1956; Fuhs, 1961; Treccani, 1962). Work by Söhngen, Tausson, Fowler and a few others before 1930 demonstrated that there existed bacteria capable of deriving their carbon and energy from aliphatic hydrocarbons, aromatic hydrocarbons and related substances such as phenol. Since then, much work has been done on the metabolic pathways involved in the bacterial dissimilation of these substances. Benzoic acid and phenol oxidation in soil bacteria were studied by Evans (1947), who used mainly a *Vibrio* sp., isolated from a sewage filter bed by Happold and Key in 1932. Evans found that both phenol and benzoic acid were oxidized to catechol which then underwent ring fission. Later, Kilby (1951) isolated β-oxoadipic acid as a product appearing after ring fission, and Evans and Smith (1951) recognized that the first product formed from catechol was *cis-cis*-muconic acid, which may be oxidized enzymatically to β-oxoadipic acid by way of two isomeric, unsaturated lactones. Succinic and acetic acids were later products in the dissimilation. Details of the metabolic pathways of various hydroxy-benzoic acids, benzene, naphthalene, phenanthrene, anthracene, chloro- and methyl-naphthalenes are given in the reviews already mentioned, especially those by Evans, Fuhs and Treccani. Similarly the oxidative metabolism of aliphatic hydrocarbons, from methane to the higher, longer chain liquid paraffins, by various microbial species has been studied and some of the intermediate steps in their dissimilation elucidated. Much of this information has provided a useful background of knowledge to similar studies on the microbial decomposition of plant protection chemicals, especially herbicides, as several of these are also benzene derivatives.

A. ELECTIVE OR ENRICHMENT CULTURE

There is a close analogy between the development of an enrichment culture of micro-organisms and the ecological changes in microflora that take place in soil when some unusual substance is added, so that some discussion of this technique is necessary. It is not yet fully understood how a microbial population, capable of metabolizing some foreign, apparently stable, chemical that may even be very toxic to most other higher organisms, can develop in soil or other substrate. Various stages in the process can be recognized, but the ultimate mechanism is still unknown by which a given bacterium acquires the necessary, modified, enzymic constitution that enables it to derive its energy and carbon requirements for growth from the unusual substance. Nevertheless, once a micro-organism has become so adapted, either because of a gene-controlled mutation or by some enzyme alteration (induced or adapted enzyme formation) and, provided that other conditions for growth such as nutrient supply, pH, aeration, moisture, etc., are favourable, then a population of adapted organisms can develop. Depending on the supply of the foreign chemical, this adapted population may become the dominating part of the microbial population in the soil, because it has the advantage of a nutrient supply denied to other organisms not able to use this substrate.

The idea of treating soil as though it were a mammalian tissue and perfusing it with various solutions, as is done by physiologists when studying metabolic processes, was developed by Quastel (1946) and led to the use of soil percolators (e.g. Lees and Quastel, 1944). Audus (1949, 1960) studied the kinetics of the disappearance of 2,4-dichlorophenoxyacetic acid (2,4-D) in a soil percolator and distinguished three phases in the process: first, a fairly rapid adsorption of a small fraction of the 2,4-D; then a long period (15–16 days) in which 2,4-D concentration remained unchanged; and, third, a rapid progressive decline in 2,4-D concentration, coinciding with the logarithmic growth of bacteria able to decompose it. Subsequent additions of 2,4-D were metabolized at a similar rate, without any delay. The long lag at first was necessary for adapted bacteria to form and multiply; the subsequent growth of the population then existing mainly depended on the nutrient supply (2,4-D, in this case). Later, Audus (1950) isolated a strain of *Bacterium globiforme* which grew with 2,4-D as its only carbon source.

In principle, of course, there is nothing new in selective culture of a particular microbial species or group from a mixed population by providing either a particular nutrient or specialized conditions; it was a method much used by

Beijerinck and van Iterson. Merely incubating a mixture of wet soil and a small quantity of the specific substrate, with suitable aeration, is also often satisfactory. The concentration of the substrate is important, as many compounds are toxic at high concentration, e.g. more than 0·1% phenol is bactericidal to many organisms, but some bacteria can grow vigorously in 0·05% phenol solution. The type of micro-organism encouraged is also affected by the pH, temperature and air supply: conditions that normally govern microbial growth.

Examples of the microbiological decomposition in soil and in culture of selected herbicides and other plant protection chemicals will be given further on. In several instances, micro-organisms responsible for the degradation of particular chemicals have been isolated in pure culture and investigations made of the pathway by which these substances are dissimilated.

The disappearance or degradation of other chemicals has been found to occur under conditions that favour microbial growth or is prevented by agents or conditions, e.g. enzyme inhibitors, antiseptics, sterilization by heat, etc., that prevent microbiological activity, thus providing circumstantial evidence that the decomposition is microbiological. Proof of the microbial nature of the decomposition is best obtained by the isolation and identification of the responsible organisms.

II. MICROBIOLOGICAL DECOMPOSITION OF HERBICIDES

A. PHENOXYACETIC ACID DERIVATIVES

The compounds, 2,4-dichlorophenoxyacetic acid (2,4-D), 2-methyl-4-chlorophenoxyacetic acid (MCPA) and 2,4,5-trichlorophenoxyacetic acid (2,4,5-T) are now used in thousands of tons annually to control dicotyledonous weeds. As already stated, Audus (1949) was the first to study in detail the kinetics of the biological detoxication of these substances in soil. Nutman, Thornton and Quastel (1944) had reported that 2,4-D was decomposed in soil. Audus identified a *Bacterium globiforme* strain that grew with 2,4-D as its sole carbon source and caused the decomposition of 2,4-D when it was inoculated into soil in a percolator. He also found that the bacterial population developed in a soil percolator in response to 2,4-D would decompose both 2,4-D and MCPA but not 2,4,5-T, whereas the population developed in response to MCPA would decompose 2,4,5-T also. Several workers have isolated other species of soil bacteria which can decompose 2,4-D or MCPA and use these compounds as energy and carbon sources. The metabolic pathway by which different bacteria dissimilate these compounds has also been investigated and there seems to be differences in metabolism by different bacterial species. Evans and his co-workers obtained evidence of the following pathway in a 2,4-D-decomposing Pseudomonad:

2,4-D → 2,4-Dichlorophenol → 3,5-Dichlorocatechol → α-Dichloro-*cis-cis*-muconate → α-Chloro-γ-carboxymethylene- Δ$^\alpha$-butenolide → α-Chloro-maleylacetate.

There seems general agreement that 2,4-dichlorophenol is a stage in the dissimilation of 2,4-D (see Rogoff and Reid, 1956; Walker and Newman, 1956; Steenson and Walker, 1957) by various bacteria. Steenson and Walker found that neither 6-hydroxy-2,4-D nor 3,5-dichlorocatechol was oxidized by a 2,4-D-decomposing *Achromobacter* strain and suggested 4-chlorocatechol as the next metabolic intermediate; but it is likely that there are metabolic differences between species. Ultimately, all the carbon of 2,4-D is liberated as carbon dioxide and the chlorine in the ionic form. MCPA is degraded by bacteria in a fairly analogous manner in which an early intermediate appears to be the corresponding 5-chloro-2-cresol. Gaunt and Evans (1961) isolated the lactonic acid α-methyl-γ-carboxymethylene-Δ^{α}-butenolide and detected 5-chloro-2-cresol and a small amount of 6-hydroxy-4-chloro-2-methyl-phenoxyacetic acid in cultures of a MCPA-decomposing soil bacterium. They suggested the following pathway of degradation for MCPA:

MCPA $\rightarrow$ 6-Hydroxy-MCPA $\rightarrow$ 5-Chloro-3-methylcatechol $\rightarrow$ α-Methyl-γ-chloromuconic acid $\rightarrow$ α-Methyl-γ-carboxymethylene-Δ^{α}-butenolide $\rightarrow$ α-Methyl-maleylacetic acid $\rightarrow$ Smaller molecules.

Although there are differences in the way 2,4-D and MCPA are metabolized by different bacterial species, several species of soil bacteria can convert these herbicides completely to carbon dioxide, water and chloride ions, and so completely detoxify them in soil.

2,4,5-T is a much more resistant compound and its metabolism in bacteria has not yet been worked out because of the difficulty of isolating such organisms in pure culture.

B. OTHER PHENOXYALKYLCARBOXYLIC ACID DERIVATIVES

Herbicidal activities more specific than that of 2,4-D are found in compounds that are not themselves very phytotoxic but are converted either by soil micro-organisms or by plants into highly phytotoxic substances. For example, 2,4-dichlorophenoxyethyl sulphate is used to control weeds in deep-rooted crops because it is hydrolysed in wet soil to 2,4-dichlorophenoxy-ethanol which, in turn, is oxidized by soil bacteria to the phytotoxic 2,4-D.

Homologues of 2,4-D, for example, γ-(2,4-dichlorophenoxy)-butyric acid, that are degraded in certain plant species to the phytotoxic 2,4-D, were introduced by R. L. Wain and co-workers to control susceptible weeds among crop plants, that do not convert the compound to 2,4-D and so are unaffected by them. Such chlorophenoxyalkyl carboxylic acid herbicides are susceptible to microbiological decomposition in soil. Webley, Duff and Farmer (1958) showed that some soil *Nocardia* species oxidized a number of ω-aryloxy-n-alkyl carboxylic acids by a β-oxidation mechanism; for example, γ-(2-methyl-4-chlorophenoxy)-butyric acid (MCPB) and γ-(2,4-dichloro-phenoxy)-butyric acid (2,4-DB) were converted slowly to the corresponding β-hydroxy-acid. In contrast, Macrae, Alexander and Rovira (1963) reported the decomposition of 2,4-DB by a *Flavobacterium* species in which oxidation, involving fission of the ether linkage, occurred and gave rise to 2,4-dichloro-phenol, butyric and crotonic acids as primary degradation products which subsequently were further metabolized. Once again, therefore, there are different metabolic pathways in different microbial species for the same initial substrate. Alexander and Aleem (1961) studied also the effect of chemical structure on the decomposition of aromatic herbicides by micro-organisms and concluded that in a halogenated phenoxyalkyl carboxylic acid, the presence of a meta-substituted halogen makes the compound very resistant to decomposition. ω-Substituted phenoxyalkyl carboxylic acids are readily degraded but the decomposition of an α-substituted phenoxyalkyl carboxylic acid is influenced both by the presence of a meta-halogen and the length of the aliphatic chain, decomposition being rapid for acetate and caproate but not for propionate and valerate.

C. CHLORO-SUBSTITUTED ALIPHATIC ACIDS

Several workers have studied the persistence and decomposition of substances of this group including trichloroacetic acid and sodium α,α-dichloropropionate (dalapon) by a range of soil organisms. Jensen (1957) described three groups of soil bacteria capable of decomposing various chloro-aliphatic acids. Some Pseudomonads decomposed monochloroacetic, monochloropropionic and monobromoacetic acids but had little effect on di- or trichloroacetic acid. A group of bacteria, possibly belonging to the genus *Agrobacterium*, decomposed α,α-dichloropropionic acid and dichloroacetic acid but did not attack mono- and trichloroacetic acids. A third type of bacteria decomposed trichloroacetic acid in media containing a little vitamin B_{12}. Jensen (1960) showed that the ability of bacteria to release chloride from these halogeno-aliphatic acids was caused by inducible enzymes which he termed "dehalogenases." Some fungi, including *Trichoderma viride*, were also found to decompose some of these acids (Jensen, 1959).

Acetate- and propionate-utilizing bacteria from soil or from the rumen of sheep were found by Hirsch and Stellmach-Helwig (1961) to have little ability to decompose α,α-dichloropropionic or trichloroacetic acid compared with bacteria from soil enrichments in which these acids had been decomposed.

Hirsch and Alexander (1960) isolated from soil several *Pseudomonas* and *Nocardia* strains that could decompose the herbicides α,α-dichloropropionic acid and trichloroacetic acid; similar results have been reported by other workers. Bromo-acetate, bromo-propionate and even iodo-acetate were decomposed by some of these micro-organisms but fluoroacetate was not. *Pseudomonas* and *Agrobacterium* strains able to decompose α,α-dichloropropionic acid were also isolated by Magee and Colmer (1959).

D. SUBSTITUTED PHENYLCARBAMATES AND PHENYLUREA COMPOUNDS

The herbicide, *iso*-propyl-N-phenylcarbamate (IPC) is not very persistent in soils because of its relatively high vapour pressure; however, it is also subject to microbiological decomposition (Freed and Montgomery, 1963). The chloro derivative, iso-propyl-N-(3-chlorophenyl)-carbamate (CIPC) is much more resistant to microbiological attack. The metabolism of these compounds by suitable micro-organisms has not yet been investigated in detail.

Although the substituted urea herbicides, monuron 3-(4-chlorophenyl)-1,1-dimethylurea and diuron 3-(3,4-dichlorophenyl)-1,1-dimethylurea are very persistent in soil (e.g. only 10% of a dose of 2 p.p.m. monuron was lost in 90 days), Hill, McGahen, Baker, Finnerty and Bingeman (1955) concluded that microbial decomposition was a main cause of the loss of monuron from soil. Geissbühler, Haselbach, Aebi and Ebner (1963) showed that N'-(4-chlorophenoxy)-phenyl-NN-dimethylurea suffered a 25–35% loss in humus soil in 8 weeks and it was degraded by bacterial suspensions from this soil to N'-(4-chlorophenoxy)-phenyl-N-methylurea, N'-(4-chlorophenoxy)-phenylurea, N'-(4-chlorophenoxy)-aniline and at least two other substances.

E. TRIAZINE HERBICIDES

Simazine (2-chloro-4,6-bis-ethylamino-s-triazine) and atrazine (2-chloro-4-ethylamino-6-iso-propylamino-s-triazine) are the two most widely used substances of this class; they are very persistent in soil, simazine more so than atrazine, partly because of their very slight solubility in water. Freed found that the maize plant can metabolize these compounds to the corresponding hydroxy derivatives with elimination of the chlorine atom (unpublished work). The metabolism of simazine in treated plants has practical significance in causing the disappearance of at least part of the simazine applied to soil. A crop of maize, therefore, seems the best crop to use for shortening the residual activity of this type of herbicide (Gysin and Knüsli, 1960).

Burschel (1961) found that simazine decomposes in soil by a first order reaction; the same proportion of the initial dose was found after a given time irrespective of the size of the dose. The decomposition was greatly affected by temperature and the amount of humus present, both effects being consistent with the activity of micro-organisms.

French workers, Guillemat, Charpentier, Tardieux and Pochon (1960) obtained evidence that species of fungi can use simazine as a nitrogen source; the degradation of simazine was dependent on the amount of available carbon in the medium. Ragab and McCollum (1961) showed that C^{14}-labelled simazine was degraded both by plants and soil micro-organisms; in the latter case, the labelled simazine was decomposed in non-sterile soil but not in sterilized soil. Talbert and Fletchall (1964) also showed that the inactivation of simazine and atrazine at 2 lb/acre in the field was most rapid when conditions were favourable for the growth of soil micro-organisms.

F. MISCELLANEOUS HERBICIDES

Amitrole (3-amino-1,2,4-triazole) is not very persistent in soil and can be decomposed by micro-organisms, although the rate of decomposition may vary according to the different populations and activities of the micro-organisms involved (Ashton, 1963). Likewise, endothal (di-sodium 3,6-endoxo-hexahydro-phthalate) is readily decomposed by microbes and, when used as an aquatic herbicide, its persistence depends on the amount of silt or plant debris present (Hiltibran, 1962).

Ammonium sulphamate is a fairly stable compound, but Jensen (1963) isolated two strains of a bacterium and some strains of *Aureobasidium pullulans* that used it as a nitrogen source, although they grew slowly.

Gundersen and Jensen (1956) obtained a strain of *Corynebacterium simplex* from soil enrichment cultures containing 4,6-dinitro-*o*-cresol (DNOC); the bacterium could use this herbicide as its source of both nitrogen and carbon. The dissimilation of DNOC resulted in the fission of the nitro group para to the hydroxyl in the form of nitrite ions. 4-Nitro-, 2,4-dinitro- and 2,4,6-trinitro-phenols were also decomposed but not 4,6-dinitro-*o*-butylphenol, which therefore would be a more persistent herbicide.

Douros and Reid (1956) isolated strains of *Pseudomonas aeruginosa* and *Ps. putida* which decomposed 2,4-dinitro-*o*-*sec*-butylphenol and grew with this compound as the sole carbon source.

III. MICROBIOLOGICAL DECOMPOSITION OF PESTICIDES

A. INSECTICIDES

Many of the modern insecticides are very insoluble in water and, partly on this account, are strikingly resistant to microbial attack. There is some evidence that a few of these substances are affected by soil micro-organisms. For example, Jones (1956), who studied the behaviour of DDT, chlordane, benzene hexachloride, dieldrin, aldrin, endrin and methoxychlor and some other compounds in 3 types of soil, found that after 3 years about half of the DDT and benzene hexachloride and 10% of the chlordane had disappeared. He concluded that DDT and benzene hexachloride can be broken down very slowly by microbial action. Lichtenstein and Schulz (1960) obtained evidence that micro-organisms might cause the oxidation of aldrin to dieldrin (i.e. the epoxide of aldrin) in soils, but they concluded that these insecticides were removed from the soil mainly by volatilization (see Harris and Lichtenstein, 1961). On the other hand, Jönsson and Fåhraeus (1960) isolated some bacterial strains from soil which grew fairly well in liquid medium in which aldrin was the only carbon source, indicating that these bacteria were able to decompose aldrin to some extent although the chlorinated ring was not attacked. Thus, a slow and incomplete biological decomposition of aldrin seems possible.

B. FUMIGANTS AND FUNGICIDES

Little work has been done on the biological decomposition of fungicides and fumigants but there are suggestions that some may be susceptible to slow microbial breakdown. Richardson (1954) obtained evidence of the micro-biological decomposition of the fungicide, thiram (*bis*-(dimethylthiocarba-moyl)-disulphide) and Spanis *et al.* (1962) showed that "Semesan" (2-chloro-4-(hydroxymercuri)-phenol) was inactivated by *Aspergillus* and *Penicillium* species.

Fumigants like carbon disulphide, formaldehyde, chloropicrin or methyl bromide can partially sterilize soil; they reduce numbers of micro-organisms temporarily and the new population of micro-organisms sometimes differs from the original although a normal one is eventually restored. The study of interactions between micro-organisms and these substances is, therefore, more complicated. Fungi are more susceptible than bacteria to substances like methyl bromide, although there are resistant species of both fungi and bacteria.

Hansen and Nex (1953) found a very slow decomposition of ethylene dibromide took place in soil stored at 16–17°; 91% of the amount added was decomposed in 172 days in a neutral loam containing 6·4% organic matter. Decomposition was very much slower in more acid soils.

Wensley (1953) made a detailed study of the bactericidal and fungicidal effects of methyl bromide, ethylene dibromide and a mixture containing 50% of dichloropropene. Methyl bromide was the most toxic to fungi, bacteria and actinomyces, ethylene dibromide the least toxic, although it was superior to methyl bromide as a nematicide. Adsorption on soil reduced the fungicidal and bactericidal activity of ethylene dibromide.

IV. CONCLUSION

The above incomplete survey of the available information (up to 1964) on the effects of micro-organisms in detoxifying plant protection chemicals illustrates the relevance of microbiological studies to this problem. Understanding of these effects is still fragmentary; only a few bacterial species have been studied and even fewer fungi. Interactions in soil are complex and metabolic pathways often differ in different micro-organisms. At present little if anything is known of the possible role of other small organisms such as algae, protozoa, the host of other microbial species, microscopic soil fauna, etc., in the disposal of chemicals added to soil. Compounds that are very persistent or insoluble in water may also be affected by slow chemical reaction with soil constituents and by irradiation by visible and ultra-violet light. These effects complicate micro-biological studies and much more work is clearly desirable.

REFERENCES

Alexander, M. and Alleem, M. I. H. (1961). *J. agric. Fd Chem.* **9**, 44–47.
Ashton, F. M. (1963). *Weeds*, **11**, 167–170.
Audus, L. J. (1949). *Pl. Soil*, **2**, 31–36.
Audus, L. J. (1950). *Nature, Lond.* **166**, 356.
Audus, L. J. (1960). *In* "Herbicides and the soil." (E. K. Woodford and G. R. Sagar, eds.), pp. 1–19. Blackwell, Oxford.

Bollen, W. B. (1961). *A. Rev. Microbiol.* **15**, 69–92.

Burschel, P. (1961). *Weed Res.* **1**, 131–141.

Douros, J. D., Jr., and Reid, J. J. (1956). *Bact. Proc.* 23–24.

Eno, C. F. (1958) *J. agric. Fd Chem.* **6**, 348–351.

Evans, W. C. (1947). *Biochem. J.* **41**, 373–382.

Evans, W. C. and Smith, B. S. W. (1951). *Biochem. J.* **49**, x.

Evans, W. C. (1956). *Rep. Prog. Chem.* **53**, 279–294.

Fletcher, W. W. (1960). *In* "Herbicides and the soil." (E. K. Woodford and G. R. Sagar, eds.), pp. 20–62. Blackwell, Oxford.

Freed, V. H. and Montgomery, M. L. (1963). *Res. Rev.* **3**, 1–18.

Fuhs, G. W. (1961). *Arch. Mikrobiol.* **39**, 374–422.

Garrett, S. D. (1956). "The Biology of root-infecting fungi." Cambridge University Press, London.

Gaunt, J. K. and Evans, W. C. (1961). *Biochem. J.* **79**, 25P.

Geissbühler, H., Haselbach, C., Aebi, H. and Ebner, L. (1963). *Weed. Res.* **3**, 277–297.

Guillemat, J., Charpentier, M., Tardieux, P. and Pochon, J. (1960). *Annls. Épiphy.* **11**, 261–290.

Gundersen, K. and Jensen, H. L. (1956). *Acta Agric. scand.* **6**, 100–114.

Gysin, H. and Knusli, E. (1960). *Adv. Pest Control Res.* **3**, 289–358.

Hansen, W. J. and Nex, R. W. (1953). *Soil Sci.* **76**, 209–214.

Happold, F. C. (1950). *Biochem. Soc. Symp.* **5**, 85–96.

Harris, C. R. and Lichtenstein, E. P. (1961). *J. econ. Ent.* **54**, 1038.

Hill, G. D., McGahen, J. W., Baker, H. M., Finnerty, D. W. and Bingeman, C. W. (1955). *Agron. J.* **47**, 93–104.

Hiltibran, R. C. (1962). *Weeds*, **10**, 17–19.

Hirsch, P. and Alexander, M. (1960). *Can. J. Microbiol.* **6**, 241–249.

Hirsch, P. and Stellmach-Helwig, R. (1961). *Zentbl. Bakt. ParasitKde* (Abt. II) **114**, 683–686.

Jensen, H. L. (1957). *Can. J. Microbiol.* **3**, 151–164.

Jensen, H. L. (1959). *Acta Agric. scand.* **9**, 421–434.

Jensen, H. L. (1960). *Acta Agric. scand.* **10**, 83–103.

Jensen, H. L. (1963). *J. appl. Bact.* **26**, 253–261.

Jones, L. W. (1956). *Bull. Utah agric. Exp. Stn*, 390, 1–17.

Jönsson, A. and Fåhraeus, G. (1960). *K. Lantbr. Högsk. Annl.* **26**, 323–332.

Kilby, B. A. (1951). *Biochem. J.* **49**, 671–676.

Lees, H. and Quastel, J. H. (1944). *Chem. Ind.* 238–239.

Lichstenstein, E. P. and Schultz, K. R. (1960). *J. econ. Ent.* **53**, 192–197.

Macrae, I. C., Alexander, M. and Rovira, A. D. (1963). *J. gen. Microbiol.* **32**, 69–76.

Magee, L. A. and Colmer, A. R. (1959). *Can. J. Microbiol.* **5**, 255–260.

Martin, J. P. (1963). *Res. Rev.* **4**, 96–129.

Martin, J. P., Helmkamp, G. K. and Ervin, J. O. (1956). *Proc. Soil Sci. Soc. Am.* **20**, 209–212.

Martin, J. P. and Pratt, P. F. (1958). *J. agric. Fd Chem.* **6**, 345–348.

Newman, A. S. and Downing, C. R. (1958). *J. agric. Fd Chem.* **6**, 352–353.

Nutman, P. S., Thornton, H. G. and Quastel, J. H. (1945). *Nature, Lond.* **155**, 498.

Quastel, J. H. (1946). Lecture on Soil Metabolism, Royal Institute of Chemistry, London.

Ragab, M. T. and McCollum. (1961). *Weeds*, **9**, 72–84.

Richardson, L. T. (1954). *Can. J. Bot.* **32**, 335–346.
Rogoff, M. H. and Reid, J. J. (1956). *J. Bact.* **71**, 303–307.
Spanis, W. C., Munnecke, D. E. and Solberg, R. A. (1962). *Phytopathology*, **52**, 455–462.
Steenson, T. I. and Walker, N. (1957). *J. gen. Microbiol.* **16**, 146–155.
Talbert, R. E. and Fletchall, O. H. (1964). *Weeds*, **12**, 33–37.
Treccani, V. (1962). *In* "Progress in Industrial Microbiology," vol. 4, pp. 1–33. Heywood, London.
Walker, R. L. and Newman, A. S. (1956). *Appl. Microbiol.* **4**, 201–206.
Webley, D. M., Duff, R. B. and Farmer, V. C. (1958). *J. gen. Microbiol.* **18**, 733–746.
Wensley, R. N. (1953). *Can. J. Bot.* **31**, 277–308.
Zobell, C. E. (1946). *Bact. Rev.* **10**, 1–49.
Zobell, C. E. (1950). *Adv. Enzymol.* **10**, 443–486.

Author Index

Numbers in italics refer to the pages on which references are listed in bibliographies at the end of each article.

A

Abd-el-Malek, Y., 123, *124*
Abraham, C. H., 442, *446*
Adam, K. M. G., 171, 173, *189*
Addison, M. A., 151, *190*
Adolph, E. F., 173, *189*
Aebi, H., 499, *502*
Agnihothrudu, V., 178, *189*, 443, *445*, 452, *473*
Agrell, I., 398, 399, 400, 402, 403, 404, *409*
Aichberger, R., von, 313, *318*
Ainsworth, C. C., 68, *102*, 140, *142*
Ajello, L., 69, 94, *102*, *106*
Alacevic, M., 114, *124*
Aldrich, D. G., 438, *447*
Alexander, F. E. S., 25, *47*, 54, *102*
Alexander, M., 17, 19, 42, *47*, 63, 100, *106*, *107*, 117, *125* 440, *447*, 497, 498, *501*, *502*
Alexopoulos, J., 118, *125*
Alikhanian, S. L., 113, 114, *124*
Alleem, M. I. H., 498, *501*
Allen, M. B., 135, 136, 137, *142*
Allen, M. W., 199, *210*
Allen, O. N., 436, *446*
Allison, F. E., 455, *473*
Ameniya, M., 29, *48*
Amici, A. M., 117, *126*
Anand, N., 168, 180, 181, 182, *194*
Andersen, A. L., 60, *102*
Anderson, D. A., 83, *106*
Anderson, D. L., 114, *124*
Anderson, E. J., 63, *102*
Andrassy, I., 208, *210*
Andrewartha, H. G., 241, *256*
Angrist, A. A., 117, *126*
Anscombe, F. J., 180, *189*
Anstett, M. A., 318, *318*
Anwar, A. A., 442, *445*
Apinis, A., 121, *124*

B

Apinis, A. E., 65. *102*
Arai, T., 113, *124*
Archangels'kii, M. P., 297, *318*
Arias, R. O., 423, 424, *431*
Aristovskaya, T. V., 150, 164, *189*
Ark, P. A., 459, *473*
Armiger, W. H., 455, *473*
Arutyuryan, R. Sh., 183, *193*
Ashton, F. M., 500, *501*
Atkins, W. R. G., 422, *431*
Atkinson, R. G., 458, *473*
Audus, L. J., 493, 495, 496, *501*
Austermann, R. J., 94, *106*
Avel, M., 272, *318*
Avery, R. J., 111, *124*
Avetisyan, N. A., 183, *193*
Aytoun, R. S. C., 86, *102*

B

Bachrach, E., 424, *431*
Backer, C. A., 142, *142*
Backus, E. J., 114, 116, *127*
Backus, M. P., 65, *109*
Badura, L., 65, *106*
Baer, J. G., 184, *189*
Bailey, D. L., 472, *477*
Baker, E. W., 379, *393*
Baker, H. M., 499, *502*
Baker, K. F., 63, 71, 73, 89, *102*, *104*, *108*, *110*, 443, *445*
Baker, R., 64, *106*
Bakhtin, P. U., 293, *319*
Balaam, L. N., 142, *146*
Bald, J. G., 73, *108*
Baldacci, E., 114, 116, *124*
Ball, D. F., 286, *322*
Balloni, W., 130, *143*
Balogh, J., 390, *393*
Balows, A., 94, *106*
Bamberg, R. H., 439, *445*
Banage, W. B., 207, 208, *210*

505

Subject Index

A

Acari (Mites), 363
  and decomposition processes, 391
  biological activity, 389
  detritus-feeding, 392, 393
  distribution, 367
  distribution patterns, 371
  diurnal movements, 371
  feeding habits, 375, 377
  feeding rate, 387
  in litter, 371
  life forms of, 372
  metabolism, 388, 392
  parasitic, 379
  respiration rates, 390
  seasonal fluctuations of, 373
  seasonal movements, 371
  taxonomy of, 364
  vertical distribution, 370
Achromobacter, 45
Actinomycetaceae, 112
Actinomycetes, 111
  effect on Protozoa, 183
  nitrogen fixation by, 121
  pigments of, 118
  spores, 116
  thermophilic, 120
Actinophages, 114
Actinoplanaceae, 112
Aeration of soil, 28
Affinity index, 454
Aggregation centres (Enchytraeidae), 245
Agrobacterium, 45, 46
Aldrin, 500
Algae, 129
  abundance of, 131
  as food for Astigmata, 382
  as food for Protozoa, 184
  interactions with other soil organisms, 139

Algae—*contd*
  nutrition of, 135
  of rice fields, 136
Algal cells, number in soil, 130
Alginates, degradation of, 121
Amino acids, 6
Amitrol, 499
Amoebae
  cysts of, 167
  inter-relationship with bacteria, 166
Anabiosis (Nematodes), 203
Anaerobic bacilli, distribution, 30
Antibiotic index, 130
Antibiotics, 39, 435
  from root tissues, 463
  in soil, 100, 436
  in unsteralized soil, 436
  production, 120, 123, 440, 470
  volatile, 438
Arthrobacter, 42, 43, 44, 47
Arthropoda, 323
  aggregated distribution, 326
  effect of cultivation on, 329
  fauna of mull and mor, 323
  fauna of tropical soils, 327
  horizontal distribution, 326
  in surface litter, 328
  population, 330
  succession in carrion, 349
  vertical distribution, 326, 328
Aschiza, 356
Astigmata, feeding habits, 382
Atrazine, 499
Autochthonous bacteria, 35, 42
  flora, 42
Autotrophs, 42
Axenic culture (Nematodes), 200
Azotobacter, 16, 28, 31, 45, 46
  effect of algae on, 139
  in the root region, 455

524